D1072189

Mathematics for daily living

Harry Lewis

McCormick-Mathers Publishing Company
Cincinnati, Ohio 45202

McCORMICK-MATHERS PUBLISHING COMPANY
New York • Cincinnati

Manufactured in the United States of America

5 7 9 10 8 6

ABOUT THE AUTHOR

DR. LEWIS has relied heavily on his many years of experience as a mathematics educator in writing this textbook. As both a teacher and a department chairman, he has taught mathematics on all grade levels and all ability levels to students in junior and senior high schools. He has also taught methods courses in mathematics at New York University and prepared graduate students for the actuarial examinations given by the Actuarial Society of America. Dr. Lewis is also the author of a consumer mathematics textbook and three textbooks on business mathematics. He has authored many articles on the teaching of mathematics and has been a contributor to one of the yearbooks of the National Council of Teachers of Mathematics. Dr. Lewis, formerly chairman of the mathematics department at East Side High School, Newark, New Jersey, and principal of Arts High School in that city, is now a professor in the secondary education department at Jersey City State College, where he is teaching methods courses in mathematics. In addition, he is supervising mathematics student teachers during their internship period.

PHOTO CREDITS

Page x—*Metropolitan Transportation Authority, State of New York;* page 6—*City of New York, Department of Traffic;* Page 27—*City of New York, Transportation Administration;* Page 39—*City of New York, Transportation Administration;* Page 48—*City of New York, Transportation Administration;* Page 55—*Port of New York Authority;* Page 60—*United Air Lines;* Page 79—*Bay Area Rapid Transit District;* Page 85—*TWA;* Page 98—*Information Canada Phototheque;* Page 106—*A&P Co.;* Page 144—*National Film Board of Canada;* Page 178—*U.S. Internal Revenue Service;* Page 206—*Chase Manhattan Bank;* Page 222—*Chase Manhattan Bank;* Page 224—*Photo Courtesy of the Bowery Savings Bank;* Page 246—*Chase Manhattan Bank;* Page 276—*Chase Manhattan Bank;* Page 285—*Photo Courtesy of R. C. A.;* Page 302—*New York Stock Exchange;* Page 308—*New York Stock Exchange;* Page 348—*Merrill, Lynch, Pierce, Fenner & Smith, Inc.;* Page 354—*U.S. Department of Housing and Urban Development;* Page 372—*Honeywell, Inc.;* Page 354—*U.S. Departmentment of Housing and Urban Development;* Page 372—*Honeywell, Inc.;* Page 388—*A.T.&T.;* Page 398—*U.S. Department of Commerce, Bureau of the Census;* Page 428—*U.S. Department of Housing and Urban Development;* Page 438—*American Airlines;* Page 454—*U.S. Department of Housing and Urban Development;* Page 470—*U.S. Department of Housing and Urban Development;* Page 476—*Equitable Life Assurance Society of the United States.*

PREFACE

Since the first edition of *Mathematics for Daily Living* appeared five years ago, there has been a dramatic change in the attitude of educators toward the teaching of consumer mathematics. No longer is their primary concern whether or not to teach consumer mathematics but at what grade level, and for how long a period, it should be taught. In this five-year period, the value of presenting consumer mathematics in secondary schools has ceased to be a subject of dispute.

Mathematics teachers and their students—when given the option—are turning their backs on general mathematics and reaching for a subject area they hope will prove to be more interesting, more understandable, and more relevant in terms of both the students' current needs and their anticipated future needs: they are reaching for a consumer-oriented mathematics. In fact, the "turned-off" general mathematics student does show a greater enthusiasm for learning when, for example, he is determining what it will cost him to buy a used car than when he is faced with the solution of linear equations. It has long been an established fact that a student will be far more receptive to learning under conditions where he himself can perceive the value of that learning.

With regard to the question of how much time should be allotted to the teaching of consumer mathematics, opinions vary widely. In some schools, two full years—formerly devoted to general mathematics—have been set aside for the teaching of consumer mathematics, while in others, only a one-semester course is given. It is my experience that the one-semester course is designed only for those students who have had a three-year program of college-preparatory mathematics.

The Second Edition

The widespread acceptance of the first edition of *Mathematics for Daily Living* is very gratifying. It is my sincere belief that those changes which have been made in this second edition will further enhance the proven value of the text as a teaching aid. Just what are these changes? Of course, the most important change is the complete updating of all material to reflect the changes which have occurred in both the economy and social structure of the United States in the intervening years.

New and important topics have been introduced while topics which are no longer relevant have been dropped. The passage of the "Truth-in-Lending" law, which requires the lender to notify the borrower of the annual rate of interest on a loan, has made obsolete the need to compute the rate of interest charged on an installment loan. Hence, the formula for finding the approximate rate of interest on an installment purchase or small loan, as well as all the material pertaining to this formula, no longer appears in the text. On the other hand, material pertaining to the cost of a credit-loan card and of utilizing a check-cashing service has been added. Also, the inevitability of the changeover to the metric system necessitated the introduction of the use of some fundamental metric units.

An attempt was made to provide the second edition of *Mathematics for Daily Living* with a more attractive, easier-to-read format. The deletion of the chapter on statistics and the condensation of some of the more extended narrative materials made possible the "opening up" of the book. Many interesting and informative photographs have been included in this new edition. Whereas we have lost little or nothing by condensing the reading matter, we believe we have gained a great deal by making the book more attractive to the student.

With deep humility we wish to thank the many, many teachers who have accepted the first edition of this textbook into their classroom. We are quite certain their students will find this edition even more rewarding.

Suggestions for Using the Text

Although certain chapters are tied together—such as Chapters 1 and 2, Chapters 6 and 7, and Chapters 8, 9, and 10—with a minimum of caution the topics in this text can be taught in almost any order that the teacher prefers. It is suggested, however, that the teacher develop entire chapters rather than skip from units in one chapter to units in another. An effort has been made to explore each and every topic presented as fully as possible—keeping in mind the age and grade level of these students—rather than to give token exposure to a multitude of unrelated ideas. Being exposed to a few topics in depth will tend to have greater meaning for the student than a fleeting glimpse of far more topics than he can possibly assimilate.

Acknowledgements

There are many people to whom I am indebted for the information contained in this book. In particular, I wish to thank Mr. Stanley Andrews for his help and advice in the writing of the material related to insurance.

TABLE OF CONTENTS

504
CAREY TRANSPORTATION, INC.

CHAPTER 1

AUTOMOBILE OWNERSHIP

There are very few things that people look forward to as much as having their own car. No matter whether one is 17 or 70, the excitement of kicking the tires, slamming the doors, or just sitting behind the wheel never seems to fade. Considering the great interest there is in this topic, it would seem wise that our course begin with a study of car ownership.

Unit 1: Owning a Car

Before buying a car there are a few facts you should know. The first of these is how much money you will need. Chances are that you probably do not have enough money to pay cash for a car. However, no dealer will even discuss a sale, except of a very, very low-priced car unless he is sure of a down payment.

NEW-CAR MONTHLY PAYMENT TABLE

	18 Months—14.56%		24 Months—14.71%		30 Months—14.83%		36 Months—14.96%	
Unpaid Balance	Amount Per Month	Total Life-Insurance Premium	Amount Per Month	Total Life-Insurance Premium	Amount Per Month	Total Life-Insurance Premium	Amount Per Month	Total Life-Insurance Premium
$ 20	$ 1.24	$ .14	$ .97	$ .19	$ .80	$ .24	$ .69	$ .30
40	2.48	.28	1.93	.38	1.60	.48	1.39	.59
60	3.73	.42	2.90	.57	2.41	.72	2.08	.88
80	4.97	.56	3.87	.76	3.21	.96	2.77	1.17
1,000	62.09	7.08	48.35	9.47	40.10	12.00	34.65	14.68
1,100	68.30	7.78	53.18	10.42	44.11	13.20	38.11	16.14
1,200	74.51	8.49	58.02	11.36	48.12	14.40	41.57	17.61
1,300	80.72	9.20	62.85	12.31	52.13	15.60	45.04	19.07
1,400	86.92	9.90	67.69	13.26	56.14	16.80	48.50	20.54
1,500	93.13	10.61	72.52	14.20	60.15	18.00	51.97	22.01
1,600	99.34	11.32	77.36	15.15	64.15	19.20	55.43	23.48
1,700	105.55	12.03	82.19	16.10	68.16	20.40	58.90	24.94
1,800	111.76	12.73	87.03	17.04	72.17	21.60	62.36	26.41
1,900	117.97	13.44	91.86	17.99	76.18	22.80	65.83	27.88
2,000	124.18	14.15	96.70	18.94	80.19	24.00	69.29	29.35
2,100	130.39	14.86	101.53	19.88	84.20	25.20	72.76	30.81
2,200	136.60	15.56	106.37	20.83	88.21	26.40	76.22	32.28
2,300	142.81	16.27	111.20	21.78	92.22	27.60	79.69	33.75
2,400	149.01	16.98	116.04	22.72	96.23	28.80	83.15	35.21
2,500	155.22	17.68	120.87	23.67	100.24	30.00	86.61	36.68
2,600	161.43	18.39	125.71	24.62	104.25	31.20	90.08	38.15
2,700	167.64	19.10	130.54	25.56	108.26	32.40	93.54	39.61
2,800	173.85	19.81	135.38	26.51	112.27	33.60	97.01	41.08
2,900	180.06	20.51	140.21	27.46	116.28	34.80	100.47	42.55
3,000	186.27	21.22	145.05	28.40	120.29	36.00	103.94	44.02

The down payment can be made in cash, or in the form of another car that is being traded in for the purchase of a newer model. This simply means that the dealer is willing to give you a certain amount of money for your old car. You, in turn, then return the money to him in order to reduce the total amount you owe him. Take a specific example. Suppose you decide to buy a new car which costs $2,846. The trade-in value you are being granted on your old car is $326. The amount that remains to be paid is:

$$\$2{,}846 - \$326 = \$2{,}520$$

Once the decision is made as to how much is still due after the down payment, you have two choices open. Either you can borrow the money directly from the automobile agency, or, if you prefer, you can go to your own bank and borrow the money there. In any event, whichever choice you make, the method for computing the cost is the same. In both cases, reference is made to one of two tables similar to those on pages 2 and 4. The first of these tables is used when the loan involves the purchase of a new car, while the second pertains to a loan on a used car. You will see in the exercises that follow that the cost of borrowing money to buy a used car is a good deal greater than the cost of a loan for a new car. Can you explain why this should be so?

ILLUSTRATION 1: George Newsome borrowed $2,100 to purchase a new car. He agreed to pay this debt back monthly over a 2-year period. How much did this loan cost him?

EXPLANATION: Since the loan was on a new car, you refer to the New-Car Monthly Payment Table. To find the monthly payment, run your finger down the Unpaid-Balance column until you reach the numeral 2,100. Then place the edge of a piece of paper on the row containing 2,100. Follow this across until you come to the two columns that pertain to the 24-month payment plan. Why do you stop there? The two numerals you are looking at are $101.53 and $19.88. The first of these, as indicated by the heading, represents the amount of each monthly payment, while the second is the total cost of the life insurance that you are urged to buy. By multiplying 24 by $101.53, you determine the total amount paid back over the 2-year period. This amount includes not only the charge for borrowing the money but also the cost of the life insurance. In this illustration, the product turns out to be $2,436.72. Subtracting $19.88 from $2,436.72 leaves a difference of $2,416.84, which is actually the total amount paid on the $2,100 loan. Hence, after you subtract $2,100 from $2,416.84, the remainder of $316.84 is the cost of the loan, or the amount of money Mr. Newsome paid the bank in addition to the $2,100 he borrowed.

USED-CAR MONTHLY PAYMENT TABLE

	12 Months—27.23%		18 Months—27.68%		24 Months—27.85%		30 Months—27.98%	
Unpaid Balance	Amount Per Month	Total Life-Insurance Premium	Amount Per Month	Total Life-Insurance Premium	Amount Per Month	Total Life-Insurance Premium	Amount Per Month	Total Life-Insurance Premium
$ 20	$ 1.92	$ .10	$ 1.37	$ .15	$ 1.10	$ .21	$ .93	$ .27
40	3.85	.20	2.75	.30	2.19	.42	1.87	.54
60	5.77	.30	4.12	.45	3.29	.63	2.80	.81
80	7.69	.40	5.49	.61	4.38	.84	3.74	1.09
500	48.06	2.50	34.34	3.85	27.41	5.28	23.36	6.84
600	57.68	3.00	41.20	4.62	32.89	6.33	28.03	8.21
700	67.29	3.50	48.07	5.39	38.37	7.39	32.70	9.57
800	76.90	4.00	54.94	6.16	43.85	8.45	37.37	10.94
900	86.52	4.50	61.81	6.93	49.33	9.50	42.04	12.31
1,000	96.13	5.00	68.67	7.70	54.81	10.56	46.71	13.68
1,100	105.74	5.49	75.54	8.47	60.29	11.61	51.38	15.05
1,200	115.36	5.99	82.41	9.24	65.77	12.67	56.05	16.41
1,300	124.97	6.49	89.28	10.01	71.26	13.72	60.73	17.78
1,400	134.58	6.99	96.14	10.78	76.74	14.78	65.40	19.15
1,500	144.19	7.49	103.01	11.55	82.22	15.84	70.07	20.52

SOLUTION:

Monthly payment = \$101.53
Total of monthly payments = 24 × \$101.53
= \$2,436.72
Total returned on debt alone = \$2,436.72 − \$19.88
= \$2,416.84
Cost of loan = \$2,416.84 − \$2,100
= \$316.84

In the explanation, reference is made to the fact that you are urged to take out life insurance when borrowing money for the purchase of a car. Actually, many lending agencies refuse to lend money unless you insure yourself. This is protection for them because, in the event of your death before the debt is completely paid back, the lending agency can recover the unpaid balance of the debt from the insurance company.

ILLUSTRATION 2: On reaching 19, Erica Sanford bought a used car as a birthday present for herself. She made a down payment of \$460 on the total cost of \$1,200, and the rest she agreed to pay off over a period of 30 months.

a. What was the total amount she paid back over the 30 months?
b. What was the total life-insurance premium she had to pay?

SOLUTION:

Since a used car is involved, you must use the Used-Car Monthly Payment Table.

(a) Amount of loan = \$1,200 − \$460 = \$740

Amount per month on \$700 =	\$32.70
+ Amount per month on \$ 40 =	1.87
Amount per month on \$740 =	\$34.57

Total paid over 30-month period = 30 × \$34.57 = \$1,037.10

(b)

Total life-insurance premium for \$700 =	\$9.57
+ Total life-insurance premium for \$ 40 =	.54
Total life-insurance premium for \$740 =	\$10.11

EXPLANATION: After making the down payment of \$460, Erica still had \$740 to pay. Notice that the numeral "740" does not appear in the "Unpaid-Balance" column of the table. Hence, to determine the monthly payment on \$740, you have to add the payment on \$700 to the payment on \$40. The first payment is \$32.70, while the second is \$1.87, making a total payment of \$34.57. Similarly, to answer Part (b), it is necessary to add the total life-insurance premium on \$700 to the premium on \$40. The total of these (\$9.57 and \$.54) is \$10.11.

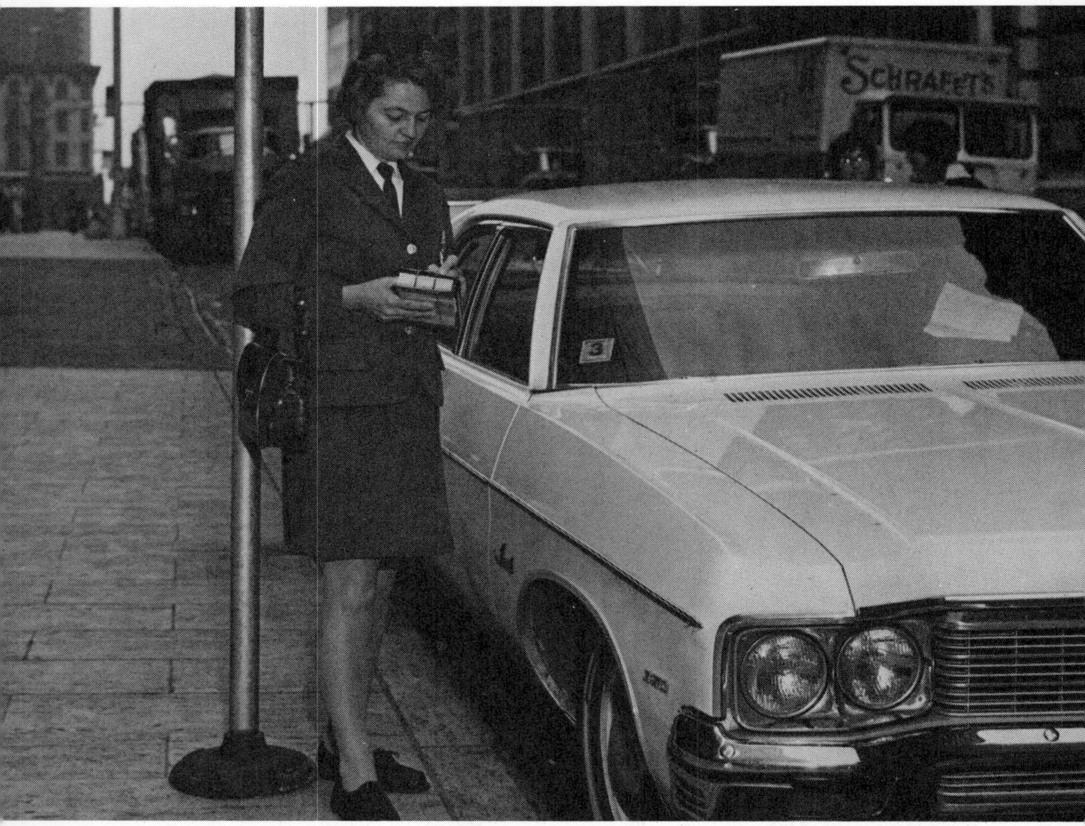

Fines for parking violations remain one of the hidden costs of automobile ownership. In some cities, illegal parking on heavily-traveled streets can cost as much as $75.

Before leaving these two tables it should be called to your attention that the annual interest rates on these car loans appear in the headings of each of the tables. The person who lends you the money for the car must not only write that interest rate in the contract you sign but he must also tell you that rate orally. This is required by a recent federal law called the "Truth-in-Lending Law." Notice that the used-car rate is almost double the new-car rate.

EXERCISES A

Do you recall how to do the computation in the following exercises? If not, you will probably want to refer to the pages indicated for additional help.

1. Arrange the following numerals in columns and add. (See page 482.)

a. 4.68 + 3.76 = ________
b. 5.92 + 6.05 + 2.21 = ________
c. 12.52 + 26.37 + 18.43 + 36.80 = ________
d. 2.17 + 14.85 + 6.02 + 53.11 = ________
e. 58.74 + 9.06 + .54 + 136.52 = ________
f. 142 + 52.77 + 2 + .06 + 5.95 = ________

2. Arrange the following numerals in columns and subtract. (See page 489.)

a. 58 − 23 = ________
b. 164 − 31 = ________
c. 89 − 86 = ________
d. 154 − 72 = ________
e. 281 − 16 = ________
f. 307 − 54 = ________
g. 300 − 96 = ________
h. 2.95 − .42 = ________
i. 26.47 − 2.13 = ________
j. 5.39 − .06 = ________
k. 4.29 − .57 = ________
l. 8.73 − .27 = ________
m. 7.08 − .12 = ________
n. 200 − 5.82 = ________

3. Arrange the following numerals in columns and multiply. (See page 498.)

a. 14 × 8 = ________
b. 23 × 5 = ________
c. 16 × 7 = ________
d. 45 × 4 = ________
e. 58 × 2 = ________
f. 91 × 6 = ________
g. 87 × 3 = ________
h. 64 × 9 = ________
i. 12 × 24 = ________
j. 51 × 13 = ________
k. 73 × 30 = ________
l. 46 × 25 = ________
m. 60 × 19 = ________
n. 87 × 46 = ________
o. 38 × 54 = ________
p. 29 × 82 = ________

4. Arrange the following numerals in columns and multiply. (See page 498.)

a. 2.21 × 3 = ________
b. 3.45 × 4 = ________
c. 4.07 × 5 = ________
d. 6.38 × 6 = ________
e. 17.26 × 7 = ________
f. 23.85 × 8 = ________
g. 31.06 × 9 = ________
h. 40.02 × 2 = ________
i. 3.42 × 12 = ________
j. 15.04 × 30 = ________
k. 86.53 × 24 = ________
l. 103.42 × 18 = ________
m. 90.04 × 36 = ________
n. 78.82 × 28 = ________
o. 117.65 × 62 = ________
p. 100.29 × 81 = ________

B

1. Find the monthly payment and the total life-insurance premium on each of the following loans. Use the New-Car Monthly Payment Table on page 2.

	Unpaid Balance	Period Of Debt	Monthly Payment	Total Life-Insurance Premium
a.	$1,500	18 months	$________	$________
b.	2,500	24 months	________	________
c.	1,400	36 months	________	________

	Unpaid Balance	Period Of Debt	Monthly Payment	Total Life-Insurance Premium
d.	3,000	30 months	$______	$______
e.	1,200	24 months	______	______
f.	60	30 months	______	______
g.	2,700	18 months	______	______
h.	1,600	36 months	______	______

2. Find the monthly payment and the total life-insurance premium on each of the following loans. Use the Used-Car Monthly Payment Table on page 4.

	Unpaid Balance	Period Of Debt	Monthly Payment	Total Life-Insurance Premium
a.	$ 20	12 months	$______	$______
b.	500	24 months	______	______
c.	1,000	18 months	______	______
d.	80	30 months	______	______
e.	800	24 months	______	______
f.	1,300	12 months	______	______
g.	60	30 months	______	______
h.	600	18 months	______	______

3. Determine the monthly payment on each of the following unpaid balances. Use the New-Car Monthly Payment Table.

	Unpaid Balance	Period Of Debt	Monthly Payment		Unpaid Balance	Period Of Debt	Monthly Payment
a.	$1,560	18 months	$______	d.	1,280	30 months	$______
b.	2,520	24 months	______	e.	1,760	18 months	______
c.	3,040	36 months	______	f.	2,920	24 months	______

4. Determine the total life-insurance premium on each of the following unpaid balances. Use the Used-Car Monthly Payment Table.

	Unpaid Balance	Period Of Debt	Total Life-Insurance Premium		Unpaid Balance	Period Of Debt	Total Life-Insurance Premium
a.	$ 540	12 months	$______	d.	760	24 months	$______
b.	960	30 months	______	e.	1,320	12 months	______
c.	1,560	18 months	______	f.	1,080	30 months	______

5. Find the total repaid, including the life-insurance premium, on each of the following new-car loans.

	Loan	Period Of Debt	Total Repaid		Loan	Period Of Debt	Total Repaid
a.	$1,000	30 months	$______	c.	2,300	24 months	$______
b.	1,500	30 months	______	d.	2,700	36 months	______

	Loan	Period Of Debt	Total Repaid		Loan	Period Of Debt	Total Repaid
e.	1,400	18 months	$______	h.	3,020	24 months	$______
f.	2,560	30 months	______	i.	1,280	36 months	______
g.	1,540	24 months	______	j.	2,640	18 months	______

6. Find the total repaid, including the life-insurance premium, on each of the following used-car loans.

	Loan	Period Of Debt	Total Repaid		Loan	Period Of Debt	Total Repaid
a.	$ 500	30 months	$______	d.	580	30 months	$______
b.	800	12 months	______	e.	820	24 months	______
c.	1,400	18 months	______	f.	1,540	12 months	______

7. How much more will be repaid than was originally borrowed on each of the following new-car loans?

	Loan	Period Of Debt	Total Repaid	Total Life-Insurance Premium	Total Paid On Debt	Cost Of Loan
a.	$1,000	24 months	$______	$______	$______	$______
b.	2,000	30 months	______	______	______	______
c.	3,000	36 months	______	______	______	______
d.	1,200	30 months	______	______	______	______
e.	2,100	18 months	______	______	______	______
f.	2,800	24 months	______	______	______	______
g.	2,220	30 months	______	______	______	______
h.	1,780	24 months	______	______	______	______

8. How much more will be repaid than was originally borrowed on each of the following used-car loans?

	Loan	Period Of Debt	Total Repaid	Total Life-Insurance Premium	Total Paid On Debt	Cost Of Loan
a.	$ 500	30 months	$______	$______	$______	$______
b.	1,400	12 months	______	______	______	______
c.	1,000	18 months	______	______	______	______
d.	640	30 months	______	______	______	______
e.	520	24 months	______	______	______	______

C

1. Janis Cleary purchased a new car valued at $2,746 by making a down payment of $546. She borrowed the remainder from the automobile dealer who used the New-Car Monthly Payment Table for finding the terms of the loan.

a. How much money did Janis have to borrow? ________
b. If she agrees to repay the money over a 36-month period, including the life-insurance premium, what will be the total amount repaid? ________
c. If she agrees to repay the money over an 18-month period, including the life-insurance premium, what will be the total amount repaid? ________
d. How much more will it cost Janis if she repays the debt over a 36-month period rather than over an 18-month period? ________

2. When Mr. Gilbert purchased his car, he made a down payment of $758.46 on the $2,158.46 that was the cost of the car. Mr. Gilbert agreed to pay off the balance in monthly installments over a two-year period.

a. How large was the unpaid balance? ________
b. If the New-Car Monthly Payment Table is used for computing the cost of the loan, how much will Mr. Gilbert have to repay? In computing the total repayment, include the cost of the life insurance. ________
c. If the Used-Car Monthly Payment Table is used for computing the cost of the loan, how much will Mr. Gilbert have to repay? In computing the total repayment, include the cost of the life insurance. ________
d. How much more will it cost Mr. Gilbert to borrow the money he needs if the car he purchases is a used car rather than a new car? ________

3. Find the monthly payment and the total life-insurance premium on each of the following unpaid balances. Use the New-Car Monthly Payment Table.

	Unpaid Balance	Period Of Loan	Monthly Payment	Total Life-Insurance Premium
a.	$4,000	18 months	$________	$________
b.	3,600	24 months	________	________
c.	5,400	36 months	________	________

4. Find the total amount that will be repaid on a loan of $2,000 for a period of 12 months. The total payment is to include the life-insurance premium. Use the Used-Car Monthly Payment Table to solve this problem. ________

Unit 2: Automobile Insurance

In addition to the monthly payments that have to be made on the car you buy, you will be faced with the expense of purchasing automobile insurance. There are a number of states that require you to have this insurance before you are allowed to drive your car.

Section 1: Bodily-Injury and Property-Damage Insurance

Of the four types of insurance that can be purchased for protection in driving a car, two cover you in the event you damage someone else's property, or inflict injury on some person other than a member of your own family. These are the two that the state department of motor vehicles wants you to have. It is concerned as to whether you have enough insurance to pay for the damage you might inflict on other people or their property. The two varieties of insurance that cover these situations are explained below.

Property-Damage Insurance: In this type of insurance, you protect yourself from suffering any financial loss in the event you damage someone's property. This property can include such things as a car, a house, a lawn, a bicycle, shrubbery, a storefront; in fact, just about anything. The amount of the damage for which the insurance company will pay depends on how much you insured yourself for. The amount can be as little as $5,000, or as much as $50,000. The most common policy, however, is for $10,000. This means that the insurance company will pay up to $10,000 for damage that you might have caused. Any amount over that, you, yourself, will have to pay. Thus, if the cost of the damage amounts to $14,000, the insurance company will pay $10,000, while you will have to pay the remaining $4,000. On the other hand, if you have purchased a $25,000 property-damage policy, then the insurance company will pay the entire $14,000, and you will pay nothing.

Bodily-Injury Insurance: By buying this type of insurance you protect yourself from any financial loss in the event you injure anyone during an automobile accident in which you are at fault. These policies are so written that they cover two different possibilities. As an example, the basic bodily-injury policy is called the 15/30 policy. In this plan your insurance company will pay any *one* person up to $15,000 for injuries you may have caused that person during an accident. Also, should more than one person be injured as a result of this same accident, then the company will pay no more than $30,000 to be distributed among all of them no matter how many people were involved.

For instance, imagine that during an accident in which you are at fault, four people are injured. One of the injured persons sues you to collect for the damages he has suffered and is granted $18,000 by court action. The remaining three are granted amounts of $5,000, $3,000, and $2,000, respectively. In making payment, the insurance company will give only $15,000 to the person who was granted $18,000 and you will have to pay the balance of $3,000. Since the total of the damages to the remaining three people when added to the $15,000 comes to less than $30,000, the company will pay the full amount to these three and you will have to pay them nothing.

To determine the cost of purchasing either bodily-injury or property-damage insurance, it is necessary to refer to four different tables. The first of these is a Basic Cost Table, part of which is shown here:

SEMIANNUAL BASIC COST FOR BODILY-INJURY AND PROPERTY-DAMAGE INSURANCE

	Territory					
	01	02	05	06	25	26
B.I.	$40.70	$38.50	$33.10	$23.40	$18.80	$15.90
P.D.	$17.60	$15.80	$14.70	$13.30	$11.40	$ 9.80
No-Fault Insurance	$ 4.80	$ 5.60	$ 4.00	$ 3.20	$ 2.60	$ 2.20

Notice that the cost of the insurance depends on the territory in which you live. Each state is divided into a great many of these territories—only six of which appear here. The greater the history of accidents in a territory, the greater the cost of the insurance. Chances are that the 01 territory is a busy city area, while the 26 territory is a sparcely settled country area.

The last line of the table above refers to a type of insurance that is a legal requirement in some states. The law is basically the same in the various states that require no-fault automobile insurance although the amount of money involved varies somewhat. As an illustration, if you are involved in an automobile accident where the extent of the bodily injury to yourself comes to *$200 or less*, then you simply send the medical bills to *your* insurance company, which must pay your bills. It does not matter whether the accident was caused by you or by the person driving the other car; in either event your insurance company must pay your medical bills if they total $200 or less. However, unless your medical bills amount to more than $200, you do not have the right to sue the other driver on the grounds that his carelessness caused you pain and suffering. The $200-limit mentioned here happens to be the limit in effect in one state; in another, the limit is $250; while in still another, the limit is $500.

In the states that have a "no-fault insurance" law, the basic cost shown on the last line of the table is automatically added to the cost of the bodily-injury and property-damage insurance.

The next three tables are called factor tables. The term "factor" is used here to mean a number by which the basic premium is multiplied in order to obtain the actual cost of the insurance. For instance, in the following table, note that the cost of a 25/50 bodily-injury policy is found by multiplying the basic-cost premium by 1.41. Similarly, a $25,000 property-damage policy will cost 1.08 times the premium shown in the Basic Cost Table. Notice that the greater the protection (coverage) you buy, the greater the factor that must be multiplied by the basic cost.

COVERAGE-LIMIT FACTOR TABLE

Bodily Injury

Limit	15/30	25/50	50/100	100/300
Factor	1.00	1.41	1.55	1.71

PROPERTY DAMAGE

Limit	$5,000	$10,000	$25,000	$50,000	$100,000
Factor	1.00	1.05	1.08	1.13	1.18

The second factor table, which is shown below, assigns a factor to you depending on the number of points you have accumulated over the three-year period prior to purchasing the insurance. For each accident you have had during this time, you are assigned a point. And if you have had no accidents, then you are rewarded by having a factor (.85) that is less than 1. This means that the cost of the insurance for you may be less than the premiums shown in the Basic-Cost Table.

Points are assigned not only for accidents, but also for certain motor vehicle law violations. For example, three points are assigned to persons convicted of driving while intoxicated, or driving when their licenses have been suspended. Notice that a person who has accumulated at least 4 points in a three-year period will have to pay 2½ times the basic cost. If you have just received your license, you will be considered to have no points.

DRIVING-RECORD FACTOR

(Three-Year Period)

Number of Points	0	1	2	3	4
Factor	.85	1.05	1.50	2.00	2.50

AGE-FACTOR TABLE

YOUTHFUL OPERATOR

SEX AND MARITAL STATUS	Driver Training	AGE	PLEASURE USE	WORK LESS THAN 10	WORK 10 OR MORE	BUSINESS USE	FARM USE
			Factor	Factor	Factor	Factor	Factor
UNMARRIED FEMALE	NO	17*	1.55	1.65	1.95	2.05	1.30
		18	1.40	1.50	1.80	1.90	1.15
		19	1.25	1.35	1.65	1.75	1.00
		20	1.10	1.20	1.50	1.60	.85
	YES	17*	1.40	1.50	1.80	1.90	1.15
		18	1.25	1.35	1.65	1.75	1.00
		19	1.15	1.25	1.55	1.65	.90
		20	1.05	1.15	1.45	1.55	.80
MARRIED MALE	NO	17*	1.80	1.90	2.20	2.30	1.55
		18	1.70	1.80	2.10	2.20	1.45
		19	1.60	1.70	2.00	2.10	1.35
		20	1.50	1.60	1.90	2.00	1.25
	YES	17*	1.60	1.70	2.00	2.10	1.35
		18	1.55	1.65	1.95	2.05	1.30
		19	1.50	1.60	1.90	2.00	1.25
		20	1.45	1.55	1.85	1.95	1.20
	N/A	21	1.40	1.50	1.80	1.90	1.15
		22	1.30	1.40	1.70	1.80	1.05
		23	1.20	1.30	1.60	1.70	.95
		24	1.10	1.20	1.50	1.60	.85
UNMARRIED MALE (NOT OWNER OR PRINCIPAL OPERATOR)	NO	17*	2.30	2.40	2.70	2.80	2.05
		18	2.10	2.20	2.50	2.60	1.85
		19	1.90	2.00	2.30	2.40	1.65
		20	1.70	1.80	2.10	2.20	1.45
	YES	17*	2.05	2.15	2.45	2.55	1.80
		18	1.90	2.00	2.30	2.40	1.65
		19	1.75	1.85	2.15	2.25	1.50
		20	1.60	1.70	2.00	2.10	1.35
	N/A	21	1.55	1.65	1.95	2.05	1.30
		22	1.40	1.50	1.80	1.90	1.15
		23	1.25	1.35	1.65	1.75	1.00
		24	1.10	1.20	1.50	1.60	.85
UNMARRIED MALE (OWNER OR PRINCIPAL OPERATOR)	NO	17*	3.30	3.40	3.70	3.80	3.05
		18	3.10	3.20	3.50	3.60	2.85
		19	2.90	3.00	3.30	3.40	2.65
		20	2.70	2.80	3.10	3.20	2.45
	YES	17*	2.70	2.80	3.10	3.20	2.45
		18	2.65	2.75	3.05	3.15	2.40
		19	2.60	2.70	3.00	3.10	2.35
		20	2.55	2.65	2.95	3.05	2.30
	N/A	21	2.50	2.60	2.90	3.00	2.25
		22	2.30	2.40	2.70	2.80	2.05
		23	2.10	2.20	2.50	2.60	1.85
		24	1.90	2.00	2.30	2.40	1.65
		25	1.70	1.80	2.10	2.20	1.45
		26	1.50	1.60	1.90	2.00	1.25
		27	1.35	1.45	1.75	1.85	1.10
		28	1.20	1.30	1.60	1.70	.95
		29	1.10	1.20	1.50	1.60	.85

N/A = Not Applicable *Age 17 or less

AGE-FACTOR TABLE

(Continued)

NO YOUTHFUL OPERATOR

SEX AND MARITAL STATUS	PLEASURE USE	WORK LESS THAN 10	WORK 10 OR MORE	BUSINESS USE	FARM USE
	Factor	Factor	Factor	Factor	Factor
One or More Operators 65 or Over	1.00	1.10	1.40	1.50	.75
One Operator, Female 30-64	.90	1.00	1.30	1.40	.65
All Other	1.00	1.10	1.40	1.50	.75

The last of the factor tables takes into consideration your age. At one time, insurance companies charged everyone the same amount of money and took into consideration only the area in which the person lived. So numerous were the complaints about this that studies were made to determine at what age levels the greatest number of accidents occurred. It was found that the unmarried young man under the age of 21 was the most reckless driver on the road. The factors are now set up whereby he will have to pay the most for his insurance. As the table above indicates, the older you become, the less will be the cost of your automobile insurance. In fact, once a certain age is reached, sex and marital status no longer raise the price of your insurance above the basic cost.

There is another interesting and important point that shouldn't be overlooked. If the school you attend happens to have a behind-the-wheel driver-training course and you were lucky enough to have taken it, then you are granted a discount on the cost of the insurance. For example, an unmarried male of age 17 who owns a car used for pleasure-driving only will be assigned a factor of only 2.70 rather than 3.30 if he has completed a driver-education course. In some territories, depending on the total coverage being purchased, this might mean a savings of anywhere from $50 to $100 a year.

The following illustrations should help clear up any questions about the application of the four tables discussed above. Three of the tables are needed for finding the factors, while the fourth is needed for determining the basic cost.

ILLUSTRATION 1: Emily Greenwood, who is not married and is just 20 years of age, has just purchased a 50/100 bodily-injury insurance policy. She had had no driver-training course while in high school. In addition, last year she was involved in one accident. What was the total factor used in computing the cost of her policy if she uses the car for pleasure-driving only?

EXPLANATION: The total factor consists of three parts:

1. the coverage-limit factor
2. the driving-record factor
3. the age factor

Each of the three factor tables has to be examined in order to determine what each individual factor will be. Thus, for the limits of 50/100, you find that the factor from the Coverage-Limit Factor Table is 1.55. Similarly, the driving-record factor for one accident is found to be 1.05, while the age factor for an unmarried female of age 20 who has not had a driver-training course is 1.10. The total factor is the sum of these three factors.

SOLUTION:

	Coverage-limit factor	= 1.55
	Driving-record factor	= 1.05
+	Age factor	= 1.10
	Total factor	= 3.70

ILLUSTRATION 2: Edwin Murray is 23 years of age and lives in an area that is designated as a "25" territory. He had no record of accidents when he purchased a $25,000 property-damage policy. What did this policy cost him semiannually if he is married and uses his car for business? There is no no-fault law in Edwin's state.

SOLUTION:

	Coverage-limit factor	= 1.08
	Driving-record factor	= .85
+	Age factor	= 1.70
	Total factor	= 3.63

Basic cost for property-damage insurance = $11.40

Total cost = 3.63 × $11.40
= $41.38, or $41

EXPLANATION: The total factor is determined as in Illustration 1. By examining the table on page 12, you find the basic cost of property damage insurance in a "25" territory to be $11.40 for a half year period. The actual cost for the half-year, however, is the product of the basic cost and the total factor. This product is $41.38. The cost of automobile insurance, though, is always rounded off to the nearest dollar.

Hence, in this illustration, the premium will be $41. Had Edwin purchased both property-damage and bodily-injury insurance, then the cost of each would have been rounded off to the nearest dollar before adding to find the total cost of the automobile insurance.

EXERCISES

A

Do you recall how to determine the answer in each of the following exercises? If not, you will probably want to refer to the pages indicated for help.

1. Round off each of the following amounts to the nearest dollar (pages 525–526).

a. $46.27 ________	c. $12.02 ________	e. $9.50 ________
b. $54.75 ________	d. $46.51 ________	f. $ .67 ________

2. Round off each of the following amounts to the nearest dime (pages 526–527).

a. $12.61 ________	c. $85.35 ________	e. $7.96 ________
b. $23.27 ________	d. $32.03 ________	f. $9.98 ________

B

1. What is the coverage factor on each of the following insurance policies?

	Type Of Insurance	Coverage Limit	Factor
a.	Bodily Injury	25/50	________
b.	Bodily Injury	100/300	________
c.	Bodily Injury	15/30	________
d.	Property Damage	$25,000	________
e.	Property Damage	$10,000	________
f.	Property Damage	$50,000	________

2. What is the driving-record factor for persons who have the following number of points?

a. Number of points: 2 ________
b. Number of points: 0 ________

In the exercises which follow, if a person uses his car for work and drives more than 10 miles this will be indicated by the symbol "10+"; if he uses his car for work and drives less than 10 miles, this will be indicated by the symbol "10–". Do not include no-fault insurance in any exercise in group B.

3. What is the age factor for each of the following drivers?

	Sex	Age	Married	Driver Training	Car Owner	Use	Factor
a.	Female	26	—	—	—	Pleasure	
b.	Male	34	—	—	—	Pleasure	
c.	Male	26	Yes	—	—	10+	
d.	Male	22	No	—	No	Farm	
e.	Female	20	Yes	—	—	Business	
f.	Female	19	No	Yes	—	10–	
g.	Male	24	Yes	—	—	Pleasure	
h.	Male	21	No	—	No	10–	
i.	Male	17	No	No	Yes	Farm	
j.	Female	18	No	No	—	10+	
k.	Male	29	No	—	Yes	Pleasure	
l.	Male	45	—	—	—	Business	
m.	Male	19	No	No	No	10–	
n.	Male	24	Yes	—	—	10+	

4. Find the total factor in the purchase of each of the following bodily-injury insurance policies.

	Coverage Limits	Points	Sex	Age	Married	Driver Training	Car Owner	Use	Total Factor
a.	15/30	0	M	32	—	—	—	Pleasure	
b.	25/50	1	F	23	—	—	—	10–	
c.	50/100	2	M	21	No	—	No	Farm	
d.	15/30	4	M	24	Yes	—	Yes	10+	
e.	25/50	3	F	19	No	Yes	—	Business	
f.	100/300	1	M	20	No	No	Yes	Pleasure	

5. Find the total factor in the purchase of each of the following property-damage insurance policies.

	Coverage Limits	Points	Sex	Age	Married	Driver Training	Car Owner	Use	Total Factor
a.	$ 5,000	1	M	28	Yes	—	—	Pleasure	
b.	25,000	3	F	37	—	—	—	Business	
c.	10,000	0	M	22	Yes	—	—	10–	
d.	50,000	2	M	20	No	Yes	Yes	10+	

6. Find the cost of each of the following bodily-injury insurance policies.

	Coverage Limits	Territory	Points	Sex	Age	Married	Driver Training	Car Owner	Use	Total Factor	Total Cost
a.	15/30	01	0	M	46	—	—	—	Pleasure		
b.	25/50	05	1	M	27	Yes	—	—	Business		
c.	50/100	26	3	F	20	Yes	—	—	10+		
d.	100/300	02	2	M	63	—	—	—	Pleasure		
e.	15/30	25	4	M	21	No	—	Yes	10–		
f.	25/50	06	3	F	19	No	No	—	Business		

7. Find the cost of each of the following property-damage insurance policies.

	Coverage Limits	Territory	Points	Sex	Age	Married	Driver Training	Car Owner	Use	Total Factor	Total Cost
a.	$ 5,000	02	1	M	28	Yes	—	—	10–	______	______
b.	50,000	26	0	F	23	—	—	—	10+	______	______
c.	10,000	01	2	M	22	No	—	No	Pleasure	______	______
d.	25,000	05	4	M	19	No	Yes	No	Farm	______	______

C

1. Roger Baker was in an automobile accident in which his car damaged property to the extent of $11,500. Roger had $5,000 property-damage insurance coverage.
   a. How much of the damage was paid for by the insurance company? ______
   b. How much of the cost of the damage did Roger have to pay? ______
   c. If Roger had been covered by a $10,000 property-damage policy, how much of the cost of the damage would he himself have had to pay? ______
   d. If Roger had been covered by a $25,000 property-damage policy, how much of the cost of the damage would he himself have had to pay? ______
2. Dorothy Lomb injured three people in an automobile accident in which she was at fault. Her automobile-insurance coverage included a 25/50 bodily-injury liability policy.
   a. If only one of the injured persons claimed any damage and that claim was $14,000, how much of this amount would the insurance company pay? Assume that the courts upheld this claim. ______
   b. If the claim of the injured person in Part (a) had been $30,000, how much of this would the insurance company pay? ______
   c. If the three injured persons each claimed $10,000 and were granted this by court action, what is the total amount that the insurance company would have to pay? ______
   d. If the three injured persons had been granted $20,000 each, what is the total amount the insurance company would have to pay? ______
   e. If one of the three injured persons had been granted $35,000, while the remaining two were granted $5,000 each, what is the total amount that the insurance company would have to pay in settlement? ______

f. If one of the three injured persons had been granted $35,000 while the remaining two were granted $20,000 each, what is the total amount the insurance company would have to pay? ________

3. Peter Ryan, who lives in an "06" territory, recently purchased a new car. He immediately covered himself with a 50/100 bodily-injury liability policy. He has no points against his record. Peter is 17 years old and is not married. He uses the car for pleasure-driving only and lives in a state that has a no-fault insurance law.
   a. How much would this policy have cost him if he had completed a driver-training course? ________
   b. How much would this policy have cost him if he had not completed a driver-training course? ________
   c. How much would Peter have saved by taking a driver-training course? ________
4. When Sarah Channing purchased her car she also purchased a $25,000 property-damage and 100/300 bodily-injury insurance policy. She lives in an area designated as a "26" territory. Sarah is 43 years old and has had just one accident during the past three years. She drives to and from her place of work, which is less than 10 miles from her home.
   a. How much does she have to pay for this coverage? ________
   b. How much would Sarah have had to pay if she lived in an "01" territory? ________
   c. How much does Sarah save by being a resident of a "26" territory rather than an "01" territory? ________

Section 2: Collision and Comprehensive Insurance

It has been stated that there are four varieties of automobile insurance that you can purchase to protect yourself from any financial loss. The two that you have already examined—bodily-injury and property-damage insurance—afford you coverage against any damage or injury you might inflict upon someone else, or someone else's property. Now you are going to investigate the type of insurance you can buy that will cover you against the cost of damage to your own car.

Collision Insurance: Usually, the complete name for this coverage is given as collision, or upset, insurance, and its very name implies in exactly what way you are protected. Should your car be damaged in any way as a result of an accident with another car, or by having a blowout and perhaps overturning, or by skidding into a tree, or by any one of a number of similar mishaps, then the insurance company will pay you for the cost of all or some of the damage to your car. The amount it will pay you, however, will depend on the type of policy you have purchased. To illustrate, if you have purchased a $100-deductible collision policy, then the insurance company will pay for that part of the damage to your car that exceeds $100. Thus, if the extent of the damage is $160 you will have to pay the first $100 while the remaining $60 will be paid by the company. Had the damage been $275, you would still pay only $100 for the repair, but now the insurance company would have to pay $175.

Collision insurance can be purchased for other deductible amounts, such as $200-deductible, $250-deductible, and even larger amounts.

Comprehensive Insurance: This variety of insurance protects you against practically any type of damage done to your car other than through collision or upset. In fact, you are even covered in the event your car is dented by objects falling from an airplane, or for any other equally unlikely event. However, most people purchase this policy for the fire and theft clauses that are contained in it. That is, if your car is either destroyed by fire, or stolen and never recovered, the insurance company will pay you the value of the car at that time. In the event that the fire does not completely destroy the car, then the company will pay the total cost for repairing it. Similarly, if the car is stolen and found some two weeks thereafter, the coverage will frequently be such that your transportation for these few weeks will be paid for, as well as any damage done to the car.

A comprehensive policy also contains a feature called the *malicious-damage clause*. Under this clause, you are protected from financial loss should some person throw a brick through the rear window of your car, slash the canvas top of your convertible, damage your radio antenna, scratch their initials on the door, or do any one of a number of similar things.

The cost of the comprehensive and collision insurance is computed in much the same way as the property-damage and bodily-injury costs were found. However, as can be seen in the table on page 22, in addition to considering the territory in which the car is garaged, both the make and the age of the car are taken into account in determining the premium on such a policy. Although the table here shows only three different makes of car, actual insurance tables have as many as fifty or sixty. Not only would a car such as a Buick be listed, but also each and every model of the Buick would have its own premium.

SEMIANNUAL BASIC COST FOR COLLISION AND COMPREHENSIVE INSURANCE

		Territory					
Car Make: A		01	02	05	06	25	26
Age: 0–12 months	Comprehensive	$ 13	$11	$ 8	$ 7	$ 6	$ 5
	$100-Deductible	41	34	25	23	22	21
	$250-Deductible	25	20	15	14	13	13
Age: 13–36 months	Comprehensive	12	10	8	7	6	5
	$100-Deductible	36	30	22	21	20	18
	$250-Deductible	22	18	13	13	12	11
Age: 37 months and over	Comprehensive	8	7	6	5	4	3
	$100-Deductible	32	26	19	18	17	15
	$250-Deductible	19	16	11	11	10	9
Car Make: B							
Age: 0–12 months	Comprehensive	18	16	12	10	9	7
	$100-Deductible	72	60	43	40	39	36
	$250-Deductible	43	36	26	24	23	22
Age: 13–36 months	Comprehensive	16	13	11	8	7	6
	$100-Deductible	63	52	38	35	34	32
	$250-Deductible	38	31	23	21	20	19
Age: 37 months and over	Comprehensive	12	10	8	6	5	4
	$100-Deductible	54	44	33	30	29	27
	$250-Deductible	32	26	20	18	17	16
Car Make: C							
Age: 0–12 months	Comprehensive	37	31	23	19	17	14
	$100-Deductible	111	91	67	62	59	57
	$250-Deductible	67	55	40	37	35	34
Age: 13–36 months	Comprehensive	32	26	19	16	15	12
	$100-Deductible	97	80	59	54	52	49
	$250-Deductible	58	48	35	32	31	29
Age: 37 months and over	Comprehensive	23	18	14	12	11	8
	$100-Deductible	83	69	50	46	44	43
	$250-Deductible	50	41	30	28	26	26

ILLUSTRATION: Joanna Farnsworth has just purchased a new car of Make B which she insured under a $250-deductible collision-insurance policy. During the previous three years Joanna had one accident. She is 26 years old and unmarried. She lives in a "25" territory and uses the car for business. How much will this insurance cost her?

SOLUTION:

	Driving-record factor	= 1.05
+	Age factor	= 1.50
	Total factor	= 2.55

Basic cost for $250-deductible = $23

Semiannual premium = 2.55 × $23

= $58.65, or $59

EXPLANATION: The driving-record factor and the age factor are found as before. To determine the basic cost of the $250-deductible collision policy, examine that part of the table pertaining to the "B"-make cars. Since the car is new it will fall into the age group "0–12 months." Running your finger across the "$250-deductible" row in this group, you come to the column headed by the numeral "25," the territory in which Joanna lives. Your finger is pointing to the numeral "$23," which represents the semiannual basic cost for a $250-deductible collision-insurance policy on a new "B"-make car garaged in a "25" territory. The solution is completed by finding the product of the total factor, 2.55, and the basic cost, $23.

EXERCISES A

1. In each of the following situations the owner's car is covered by the collision insurance indicated. How much will the insurance company have to pay for the damages to his car?

	Type of Collision-Insurance Policy	Extent of Damage	
a.	$100-Deductible	$ 80	$________
b.	$100-Deductible	250	________
c.	$200-Deductible	940	________
d.	$100-Deductible	100	________
e.	$250-Deductible	75	________
f.	$250-Deductible	375	________
g.	$200-Deductible	850	________
h.	$250-Deductible	850	________

2. Find the semiannual basic cost of each of the following comprehensive-insurance policies.

	Age In Months	Car Make	Territory	Basic Cost
a.	5	A	02	$______
b.	14	A	05	______
c.	36	B	26	______
d.	25	B	01	______
e.	12	C	25	______
f.	42	C	06	______

3. Find the semiannual basic cost of each of the following $100-deductible collision-insurance policies.

	Age In Months	Car Make	Territory	Basic Cost
a.	17	A	01	$______
b.	39	B	25	______
c.	4	A	05	______
d.	0	C	26	______
e.	37	A	02	______
f.	24	B	06	______

4. Find the semiannual basic cost of each of the following $250-deductible collision-insurance policies.

	Age In Months	Car Make	Territory	Basic Cost
a.	42	C	26	$______
b.	0	B	05	______
c.	14	B	01	______
d.	36	A	25	______
e.	12	C	02	______
f.	37	A	05	______

5. Find the cost of each of the following comprehensive-insurance policies.

	Car Make	Age In Months	Territory	Points	Sex	Age	Married	Driver Training	Car Owner	Use	Total Cost
a.	A	0	02	0	M	37	—	—	—	Pleasure	$______
b.	B	16	25	0	F	25	—	—	—	10+	______
c.	A	21	06	1	M	22	Yes	—	—	10–	______
d.	C	32	01	3	M	20	No	Yes	No	Farm	______
e.	A	38	26	0	M	17	No	No	No	Pleasure	______
f.	B	10	05	1	F	19	No	Yes	—	Business	______

6. Find the cost of each of the following $100-deductible collision-insurance policies.

	Car Make	Age In Months	Terri-tory	Points	Sex	Age	Married	Driver Training	Car Owner	Use	Total Cost
a.	B	13	26	2	F	28	—	—	—	10–	$______
b.	C	30	05	0	M	65	—	—	—	Pleasure	______
c.	A	0	01	0	F	20	Yes	—	—	Business	______
d.	C	16	06	1	M	18	No	No	Yes	10+	______

7. Find the cost of each of the following $250-deductible collision-insurance policies.

	Car Make	Age In Months	Terri-tory	Points	Sex	Age	Married	Driver Training	Car Owner	Use	Total Cost
a.	C	12	01	1	M	19	No	Yes	Yes	Pleasure	$______
b.	B	45	05	2	M	20	Yes	Yes	—	10–	______
c.	A	1	26	3	M	25	Yes	—	—	Business	______
d.	B	26	02	1	F	18	No	Yes	—	10+	______

B

1. Bruce Williams, who is married, purchased a new "C"-make car on his twenty-seventh birthday. Bruce lives in an area designated as an "05" territory and he had no accidents during the previous three years. He uses his car for pleasure-driving only.
   a. How much will he have to pay for a $100-deductible collision-insurance policy? ________
   b. How much will he have to pay for a $250-deductible collision-insurance policy? ________
   c. How much more will a $100-deductible policy cost him than a $250-deductible policy? ________
2. On Alice's eighteenth birthday her parents gave her a used "B"-make car that was 27 months old. Alice had had a driver-education course in school and had never had an accident. She is not married and lives at home with her parents in a "25" territory. The car was immediately insured under a comprehensive policy. She is the only person who uses the car and she uses it only for pleasure-driving.
   a. If Alice's father had kept the ownership of the car in his own name, what would the insurance have cost? ________
   b. If Alice's father had had the ownership of the car turned over to Alice, what would the insurance have cost? ________
   c. How much would have been saved had Alice's father kept the ownership of the car in his own name? ________

3. When Mr. Rothman, who is 48 years old, purchased his new "C"-make car he immediately insured it. He bought $100-deductible collision insurance, comprehensive insurance, 100/300 bodily-injury insurance, and $25,000 property-damage insurance. He had had two accidents during the preceding three years and, during this time, he lived in an "02" territory. He uses the car to drive 17 miles to work each day.
   a. What was the total cost of this coverage? ________
   b. How much would the insurance have cost Mr. Rothman if he had had no accidents during the preceding three years? ________
   c. How much would Mr. Rothman have saved on his insurance cost if he had had no accidents? ________

Unit 3: Operating Costs

The expenses you have been examining up to this point have nothing at all to do with the actual driving of the car. These are the costs that you have to pay before you are even allowed to drive your car.

The obvious expenses of operating a car are the cost of gasoline, of oil, and of tires. The not-so-obvious ones that occur less frequently are the cost of battery replacement, the changes in brake lining, the alignment of the front wheels, and the need for new spark plugs, new points, and so on as the car gets older and older. Also buried in the costs are the federal and state taxes that have to be paid on many of these purchases.

ILLUSTRATION 1: Carlos Alvarez uses his car to drive to and from school and for pleasure-driving on weekends. He finds that during an average week he will use approximately 12 gallons of gasoline. How much can Carlos save each week by buying a grade of gasoline at 46.9¢ per gallon rather than one that would cost him 52.9¢?

SOLUTION:

$$\text{Saving on each gallon} = 52.9¢ - 46.9¢$$
$$= 6¢$$
$$\text{Saving on 12 gallons} = 12 \times 6¢$$
$$= 72¢$$

EXPLANATION: The saving on each gallon is found by subtracting the price per gallon of the cheaper gasoline from the price per gallon of the more expensive gasoline. The difference turns out to be 6¢. Since Carlos purchases 12 gallons each week, his total saving is 12 times 6¢, or 72¢.

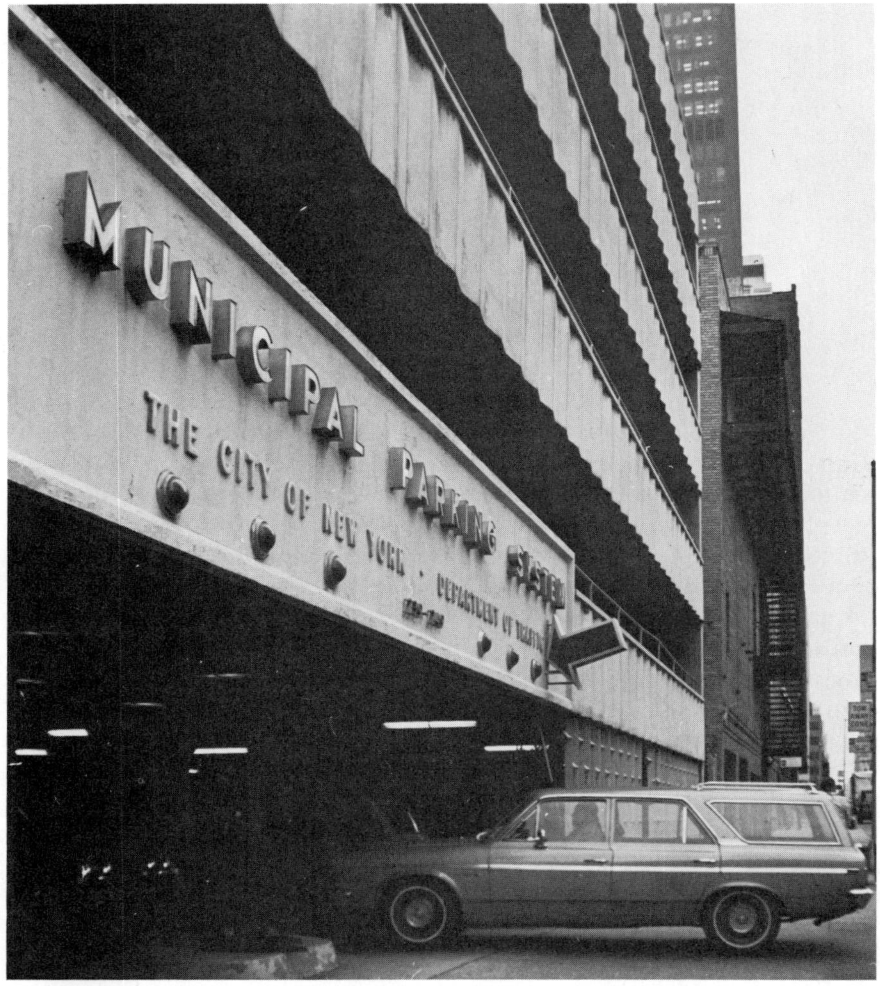

Traffic congestion in city streets is eased by multi-story parking garages. Motorists can pay every day they use the lot, or purchase a monthly ticket at a discount.

ILLUSTRATION 2: Kim Riker drove her car 15,000 miles last year. She found that she averaged 20 miles to a gallon of gasoline. In addition, she had to add a quart of oil to the oil supply every 500 miles.

a. If Kim paid 53.9¢ per gallon of gasoline, what was the total amount that she spent on gasoline during the year?
b. If the oil that Kim used in her car cost 85¢ per quart, what was the total amount she spent on oil during the year?
c. How much did Kim spend for both gasoline and oil during the year?

SOLUTION:

(a) Number of gallons of gasoline purchased = 15,000 ÷ 20
= 750

Cost of each gallon of gasoline = 53.9¢ or \$.539
Cost of 750 gallons of gasoline = 750 × \$.539
= \$404.25

(b) Number of quarts of oil purchased = 15,000 ÷ 500
= 30

Cost of each quart of oil = 85¢ or \$.85
Cost of 30 quarts of oil = 30 × \$.85
= \$25.50

(c) Total cost of both gasoline and oil = \$404.25 + \$25.50
= \$429.75

EXPLANATION: For each 20 miles, the car used 1 gallon of gasoline. Hence, had the car been driven 40 miles, it would have used 2 gallons; had it been driven 60 miles, it would have used 3 gallons of gasoline. Thus, the number of gallons of gasoline can be found by dividing the total distance traveled by the number of miles the car can travel on each gallon of gasoline. In this illustration, the number of gallons purchased was 750. Multiplying the 750 by the cost per gallon (53.9¢) gave the total spent on gasoline (\$404.25). Before finding the product of 750 and 53.9¢ it was necessary to rewrite the 53.9 cents in terms of dollars. The cost of oil for the year was computed in exactly the same manner as the cost of gasoline.

EXERCISES A

Do you recall how to find the answer in each of the following exercises? If not, you will probably want to refer to the pages indicated for help.

1. Round off each of the following numbers to the nearest whole number (pages 525–526).

a. 46.2 ____ e. 50.63 ____ i. 9.9 ____
b. 59.1 ____ f. 58.47 ____ j. 29.7 ____
c. 93.7 ____ g. 73.49 ____ k. 99.6 ____
d. 81.0 ____ h. 85.51 ____ l. 109.8 ____

2. Round off each of the following amounts to the nearest cent (pages 526–527).

a. \$2.462 ____ d. \$6.857 ____ g. \$12.789 ____
b. \$5.501 ____ e. \$7.496 ____ h. \$36.583 ____
c. \$3.314 ____ f. \$4.028 ____ i. \$43.007 ____

3. Determine the quotient in each of the following exercises. Each answer will be a whole number (pages 508–509).

a. 782 ÷ 34 = ______	j. 4,891 ÷ 67 = ______
b. 675 ÷ 27 = ______	k. 3,034 ÷ 82 = ______
c. 630 ÷ 45 = ______	l. 6,734 ÷ 91 = ______
d. 992 ÷ 62 = ______	m. 20,150 ÷ 650 = ______
e. 276 ÷ 12 = ______	n. 14,850 ÷ 450 = ______
f. 495 ÷ 15 = ______	o. 20,250 ÷ 750 = ______
g. 2,520 ÷ 56 = ______	p. 13,975 ÷ 325 = ______
h. 1,908 ÷ 36 = ______	q. 17,500 ÷ 625 = ______
i. 1,800 ÷ 75 = ______	r. 37,200 ÷ 775 = ______

4. Determine the quotient to the nearest whole number in each of the following exercises (pages 508–509).

a. 83 ÷ 25 = ______	h. 224 ÷ 29 = ______
b. 176 ÷ 34 = ______	i. 412 ÷ 74 = ______
c. 182 ÷ 42 = ______	j. 566 ÷ 86 = ______
d. 337 ÷ 64 = ______	k. 518 ÷ 43 = ______
e. 325 ÷ 53 = ______	l. 573 ÷ 24 = ______
f. 252 ÷ 37 = ______	m. 999 ÷ 51 = ______
g. 305 ÷ 66 = ______	n. 3,462 ÷ 75 = ______

B

1. The federal tax on gasoline is 4¢ per gallon. How much tax is paid on each of the following purchases of gasoline?

	Number Of Gallons	Tax		Number Of Gallons	Tax		Number Of Gallons	Tax
a.	8	$______	e.	65	$______	i.	6.5	$______
b.	12	______	f.	82	______	j.	8.5	______
c.	15	______	g.	154	______	k.	17.5	______
d.	18	______	h.	295	______	l.	49.5	______

2. The state tax per gallon of gasoline varies from state to state. The federal tax is 4¢ per gallon. In the following exercises, find the total tax paid on each of the purchases shown.

	Number Of Gallons	State Tax Per Gallon	State Tax	Federal Tax	Total Tax
a.	7	10¢	______¢	______¢	______¢
b.	9	7¢	______¢	______¢	______¢
c.	14	8¢	______¢	______¢	______¢
d.	25	9¢	______¢	______¢	______¢
e.	64	7¢	______¢	______¢	______¢
f.	58	8.5¢	______¢	______¢	______¢
g.	76	7.5¢	______¢	______¢	______¢
h.	124	8.5¢	______¢	______¢	______¢
i.	150	6.58¢	______¢	______¢	______¢

3. Find the cost, to the nearest cent, of each of the following purchases of gasoline.

	Number Of Gallons	Price Per Gallon	Exact Cost	Cost To the Nearest Cent
a.	5	45.9¢	$________	$________
b.	4	46.9¢	________	________
c.	8	51.9¢	________	________
d.	12	54.9¢	________	________
e.	18	52.9¢	________	________
f.	75	56.9¢	________	________
g.	86	47.4¢	________	________
h.	94	50.4¢	________	________
i.	4.3	54.3¢	________	________
j.	6.7	51.7¢	________	________
k.	8.2	53.8¢	________	________
l.	12.4	54.6¢	________	________

4. How many gallons of gasoline were used during each of the following trips?

	Distance Traveled	Miles Per Gallon	Number Of Gallons
a.	3,000 miles	15	________
b.	3,500 miles	14	________
c.	2,400 miles	8	________
d.	7,200 miles	25	________
e.	15,400 miles	22	________
f.	4,420 miles	26	________

5. How many quarts of oil were used during each of the following trips?

	Distance Traveled	Miles Per Quart	Number Of Quarts
a.	6,000 miles	500	________
b.	9,000 miles	600	________
c.	12,000 miles	750	________
d.	14,400 miles	450	________
e.	27,000 miles	1,500	________
f.	28,800 miles	1,800	________

6. Over the period of one year, a person purchased the number of gallons of gasoline shown in each of the following exercises. How much would he have saved had he been able to use the cheaper of the two grades of gasoline?

	Number Of Gallons	Cost Per Gallon Of Cheaper Grade	Cost Per Gallon Of More Expensive Grade	Saving Per Gallon	Total Saving
a.	600	47.9¢	52.9¢	$______	$______
b.	800	46.9¢	49.9¢	______	______
c.	750	49.2¢	56.2¢	______	______
d.	1,200	50.9¢	58.9¢	______	______
e.	1,400	51.3¢	61.5¢	______	______
f.	1,050	48.9¢	57.2¢	______	______
g.	970	50.6¢	59.1¢	______	______
h.	1,450	53.4¢	61.3¢	______	______

7. What was the cost of the gasoline consumed on each of the following trips?

	Distance Traveled	Miles Per Gallon	Number Of Gallons Consumed	Cost Per Gallon	Total Cost
a.	6,000 miles	10	______	57.6¢	$______
b.	9,000 miles	15	______	51.9¢	______
c.	8,400 miles	12	______	48.9¢	______
d.	7,840 miles	14	______	50.6¢	______
e.	8,260 miles	28	______	53.4¢	______
f.	10,080 miles	16	______	51.8¢	______

8. Gasoline was purchased for each of the following cars in liters while the distance was recorded in kilometers. How many liters of gas were used during each of the following trips?

	Distance Traveled	Kilometers Per Liter	Number of Liters
a.	5,400 kilometers	5	______
b.	7,820 kilometers	4	______
c.	8,680 kilometers	7	______
d.	19,500 kilometers	6	______
e.	9,750 kilometers	6.5	______

9. Gasoline was purchased for each of the following cars in liters while the distance was recorded in kilometers. What was the cost of gasoline consumed on each of the following trips?

	Distance Traveled	Kilometers Per Liter	Number of Liters	Cost per Liter	Total Cost
a.	6,000 kilometers	5	______	14.1¢	$______
b.	15,000 kilometers	6	______	14.3¢	______
c.	7,200 kilometers	7.5	______	14.7¢	______
d.	15,500 kilometers	6.2	______	14.9¢	______
e.	17,280 kilometers	5.4	______	13.9¢	______

C

1. The first summer after Eva Garrett purchased her new car she took a 12,000-mile trip around the country. She found that she was purchasing gas at an average price of 54.9¢ per gallon.
   a. How many gallons did she purchase if her car averaged 20 miles per gallon? ________
   b. How much did she spend for gasoline? ________
   c. How many gallons of gasoline would she have purchased if her car had averaged 12 miles per gallon? ________
   d. How much would she have spent for gasoline had her car averaged 12 miles per gallon of gasoline? ________
   e. How much was she able to save since her car averaged 20 miles per gallon of gasoline rather than 12 miles per gallon? ________
2. Gene Bradley is a salesman for Soft Tread Shoes, Inc. He drives his car approximately 45,000 miles each year on business. Gene finds that his car averages 15 miles for each gallon of gasoline and 750 miles for each quart of oil.
   a. If the average price per gallon of gasoline that he purchases is 53.9¢ what is the total amount that he spends on gasoline during the year? ________
   b. If the average price per quart of oil that he purchases is 87¢, what is the total amount that he spends on oil during the year? ________
   c. What is the total amount that he spends on both gasoline and oil during the year? ________
3. In operating his car, Jim Butler uses 25 quarts of oil a year.
   a. If he purchased the oil at a gasoline station, he would have to pay 95¢ a quart. How much would he have to pay for the oil over the period of the year under these conditions? ________
   b. If he purchased the oil in 4-quart containers at an auto-parts store, each can would cost him $2.00. How much would he have to pay for the oil under these conditions? ________
   c. How much would he save each year if he purchased the oil in 4-quart cans at an auto-parts store? ________

Unit 4: Traveling by Road Map

Many people look forward to owning a car so that they can use it for traveling. In view of this the large gasoline companies have prepared road maps that they distribute at no charge to help you get about the country. No matter which company prepares the road maps, they are all read in much the same manner. The *legend* is usually in the lower right-hand corner. This is simply a description of what the different

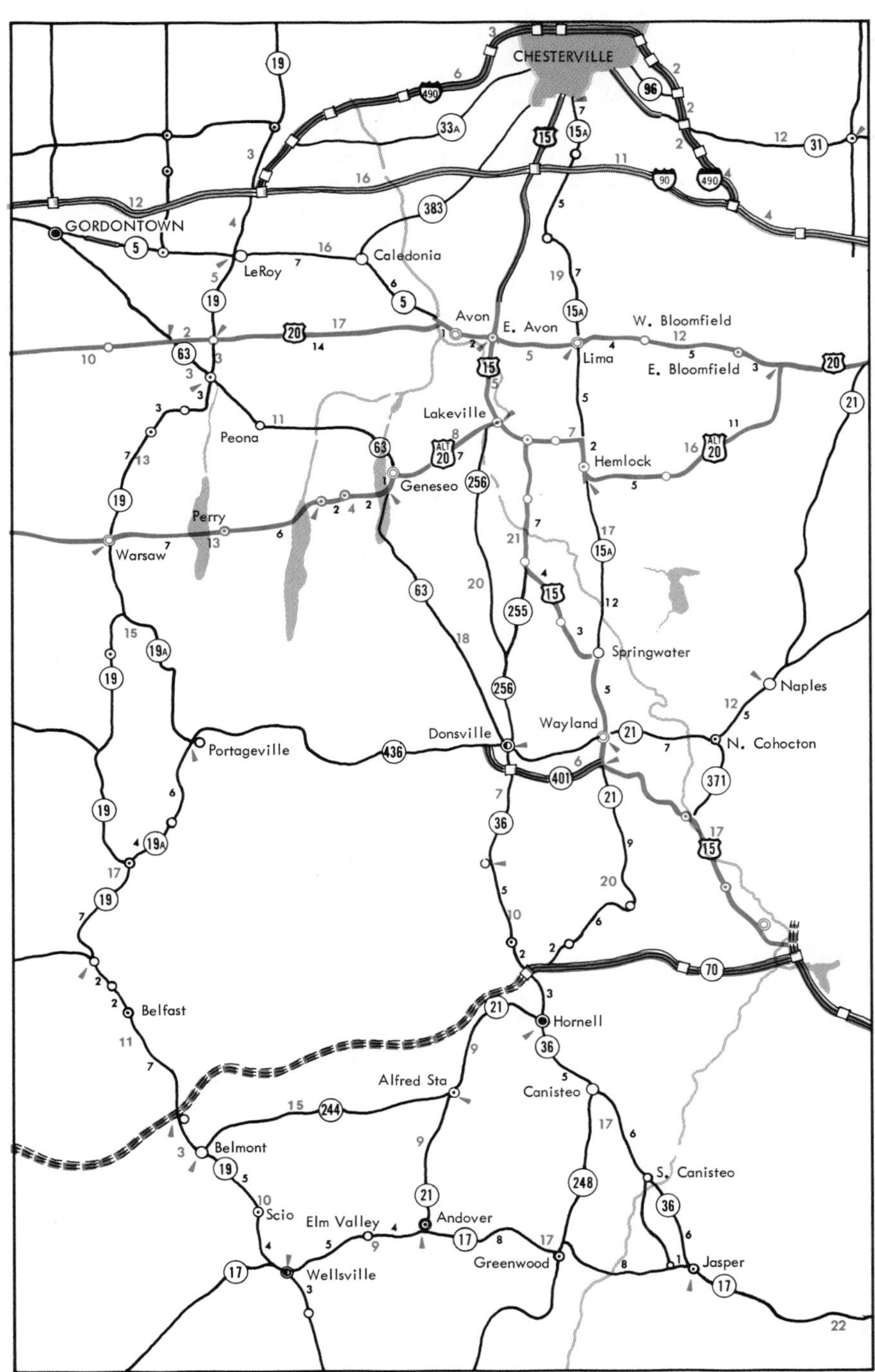
CHESTERVILLE
GORDONTOWN
LeRoy
Caledonia
Avon
E. Avon
W. Bloomfield
Lima
E. Bloomfield
Lakeville
Peona
Geneseo
Hemlock
Perry
Warsaw
Springwater
Naples
Wayland
Donsville
Portageville
N. Cohocton
Belfast
Hornell
Alfred Sta
Canisteo
Belmont
S. Canisteo
Scio
Elm Valley
Andover
Greenwood
Jasper
Wellsville

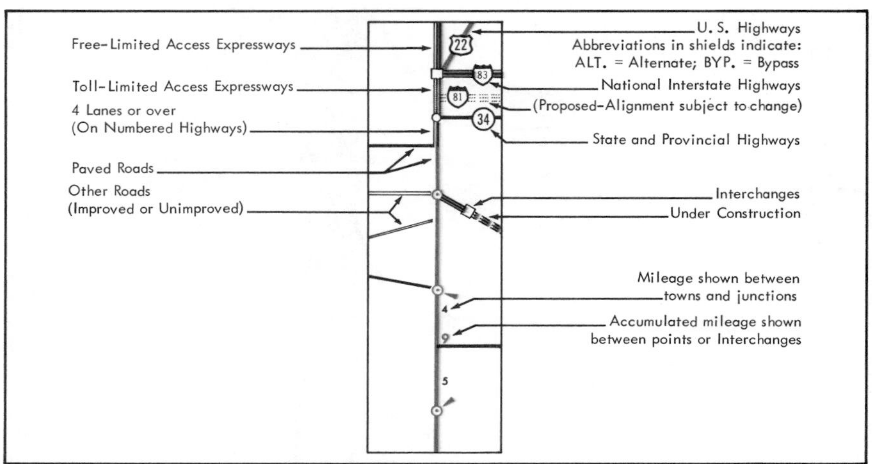

colored and/or dotted lines represent, how to find the distance between towns, a scale of miles, and whatever else the mapmaker thinks is important to know in order to read the map.

In the section of the map legend shown above, notice that the distance between two red arrowheads on a road is indicated by a red numeral between the arrowheads. Similarly, the distance between two towns, or between a town and a road junction, is shown by a smaller black numeral. For instance, at the very bottom of the map you will find Route 17. At Wellsville there is a red arrowhead and at Andover there is another red arrowhead. The relatively large red numeral 9 that appears between the arrowheads indicates the distance between these two towns. Notice also the black numeral 5 on this same stretch of highway. This numeral tells the number of miles from Wellsville to Elm Valley.

To the right of Greenwood along this same Route 17 you will find the small black numeral 8. That is the number of miles from Greenwood to the road junction that is one mile to the left of Jasper.

Quite often when you set out on a trip you would like to have some idea of where you might be stopping that evening. But knowing in the morning just where you are going to be that evening means knowing just how far you expect to travel that day. To determine this requires a little arithmetic. Consider the situation in which you drive your car at approximately 40 miles per hour. In 2 hours you will have traveled 80 miles; in 3 hours, 120 miles. Thus, to determine the distance traveled, you need merely multiply the average speed at which the car is traveling by the number of hours it is driven. A car averaging 55 miles an hour for 6 hours will travel 330 miles during this period of time. In this situation, the 330 is simply the product of 55 and 6. You can generalize what you have just learned by expressing this by the following formula:

$$D = R \times T$$

where

D represents the distance traveled
R represents the average hourly rate
T represents the number of hours traveled

ILLUSTRATION: On the first day of his trip to the West, Charles McCabe drove his car at an average rate of 60 miles per hour for a period of 7 hours. He stopped twice during the day to buy gas at 52.9¢ per gallon.

a. How far did Charles travel that day?
b. If his car averages 13 miles to the gallon of gasoline, determine, to the nearest gallon, how many gallons his car used that day.
c. What was the approximate cost of the gasoline consumed that day?

SOLUTION:

(a) $D = R \times T$
$= 60 \times 7$
$= 420$ miles

(b) Number of gallons consumed $= 420 \div 13$
$= 32.3$, or 32 gallons

(c) Cost of gasoline $= 32 \times 52.9¢$
$= 32 \times \$.529$
$= \$16.928$ or $\$16.93$

EXPLANATION: Determining the distance traveled in Part (a) is simply a matter of applying the distance formula. The product of the rate, or number of miles per hour, and the number of hours equals the 420 miles, which is the distance traveled. The more interesting feature is the solution to Part (b). Notice that the number of gallons is rounded off to the nearest gallon. This is usually done by most travelers, for when they say that their car averages 13 miles to the gallon of gasoline, they're not quite sure of this number. It may be 13.2 miles, or 13.3 miles, or 12.9, or 12.5, and they probably have rounded the number off to the nearest mile. Hence, to say that a car had used exactly 32.3 gallons of gas is inaccurate. Therefore, when the number of gallons is found, it seems that it would be wise to round the answer off to the nearest gallon. The answer is only approximate at best. Computing the answer to Part (c) needs no explanation, for you did quite a few of these problems in Unit 3.

EXERCISES

A

Use the map on page 33 when answering the questions in this set of problems.

1. Each of the following highways passes through Chesterville. Which of them is a United States highway and which a state highway?

a. 15 ________	c. 33A ________	e. 383 ________
b. 31 ________	d. 96 ________	f. 15A ________

2. How far is it between the following towns?
   a. From Belmont to Alfred Station along highway 244. ________
   b. From Wellsville to Belmont along highway 19. ________
   c. From Wayland to Naples along highway 21. ________
   d. From East Avon to Lima along highway 20. ________
   e. From Canisteo to South Canisteo along highway 36. ________
   f. From Le Roy to Caledonia along highway 5. ________
   g. From Geneseo to Lakeville along alternate highway 20. ________

3. How far is it between the following points?
   a. From Hemlock to highway 20 along alternate highway 20. ________
   b. From Warsaw to Le Roy along highway 19. ________
   c. From Lima to Chesterville along highway 15A. ________
   d. From Avon to East Bloomfield along highway 20. ________
   e. From Belfast to Portageville along highways 19 and 19A. ________

4. Gloria Tremarco drove from her home in Wellsville to her friend's home in Alfred Station.
   a. If she used routes 17 and 21, how far did she travel? ________
   b. If she used routes 19 and 244, how far did she travel? ________
   c. How many miles less would she travel if she uses routes 17 and 21? ________

B

1. What is the distance traveled by an automobile under each of the following sets of conditions?

Rate	Number Of Hours	Distance In Miles	Rate	Number Of Hours	Distance In Miles
a. 40 mph*	5	________	c. 45 mph	2	________
b. 50 mph	3	________	d. 65 mph	4	________

*"mph" is the abbreviation for "miles per hour."

	Rate	Number Of Hours	Distance In Miles		Rate	Number Of Hours	Distance In Miles
e.	35 mph	7	________	h.	40 mph	$2\frac{1}{2}$	________
f.	47 mph	6	________	i.	60 mph	$4\frac{1}{2}$	________
g.	56 mph	9	________	j.	48 mph	$5\frac{1}{2}$	________

2. How many gallons of gasoline were used during each of the following trips? Find your answer to the nearest gallon.

	Distance Traveled	Miles Per Gallon	Number Of Gallons
a.	4,000 miles	9	________
b.	7,500 miles	11	________
c.	9,600 miles	8	________
d.	8,500 miles	13	________
e.	21,900 miles	15	________
f.	26,500 miles	24	________
g.	32,400 miles	19	________
h.	27,800 miles	28	________

3. How many gallons of gasoline were used during each of the following trips? Find your answer to the nearest gallon.

	Rate At Which Car Traveled	Number Of Hours	Distance In Miles	Miles Per Gallon	Number Of Gallons
a.	30 mph	5	________	8	________
b.	40 mph	4	________	15	________
c.	50 mph	7	________	12	________
d.	45 mph	9	________	25	________
e.	55 mph	6	________	14	________
f.	52 mph	$2\frac{1}{2}$	________	9	________
g.	46 mph	$4\frac{1}{2}$	________	16	________
h.	38 mph	$5\frac{1}{2}$	________	23	________

4. The cars below have speedometers which register the speed in kilometers per hour (kph). What is the distance traveled by each car under the conditions given below?

	Rate	Number of Hours	Distance in Kilometers
a.	65 kph	4	________
b.	72 kph	3	________
c.	83 kph	6	________
d.	90 kph	2	________
e.	64 kph	$8\frac{1}{2}$	________

5. Gasoline was purchased for each of the following cars in liters while the speed was recorded in kilometers per hour. How many liters of gasoline were used during each of the following trips?

Rate	Number of Hours	Distance in Kilometers	Kilometers Per Liter	Number of Liters
a. 50 kph	3	______	6	______
b. 70 kph	4	______	7	______
c. 80 kph	7	______	5	______
d. 44 kph	6	______	6.6	______
e. 75 kph	9	______	5.4	______

C

1. Last summer, Mr. and Mrs. Norris took a trip around the country. During a period of 8 weeks, they traveled 13,200 miles. They kept an accurate record of the gas they purchased and they found that their car averaged 14 miles to a gallon of gasoline.
   a. How many gallons of gasoline did they buy on the trip? Find your answer to the nearest gallon. ______
   b. If the average cost of the gasoline they purchased was 51.4¢ per gallon, what was the total cost of gasoline? ______
2. On the third day of his trip, Roland Green put in a full $9\frac{1}{2}$ hours of driving on throughways. He averaged 52 miles per hour.
   a. How far did Roland travel that day? ______
   b. If his car averages 18 miles to the gallon of gasoline, how many gallons did the car consume that day? Find your answer to the nearest gallon. ______
   c. If gas cost him 48.9¢ per gallon, what was the total cost of gasoline for that day? ______
3. The Carters purchased a trailer which they towed around behind their car during their 6-week summer vacation. They found that they traveled about 5 hours each day at the average rate of 35 miles per hour.
   a. How far did they travel during the 6-week period? ______
   b. With the trailer attached, the car averaged only 7 miles to the gallon of gasoline. How many gallons of gas did they purchase on the trip? ______
   c. If the trailer were not attached, the car would have averaged 12 miles to the gallon of gasoline. How many gallons of gas would the Carters have purchased if they did not have the trailer? Find your answer to the nearest gallon. ______
   d. The average cost of gasoline was 54.7¢ per gallon. How much would the Carters have saved on the cost of gasoline if they had not been towing a trailer? ______

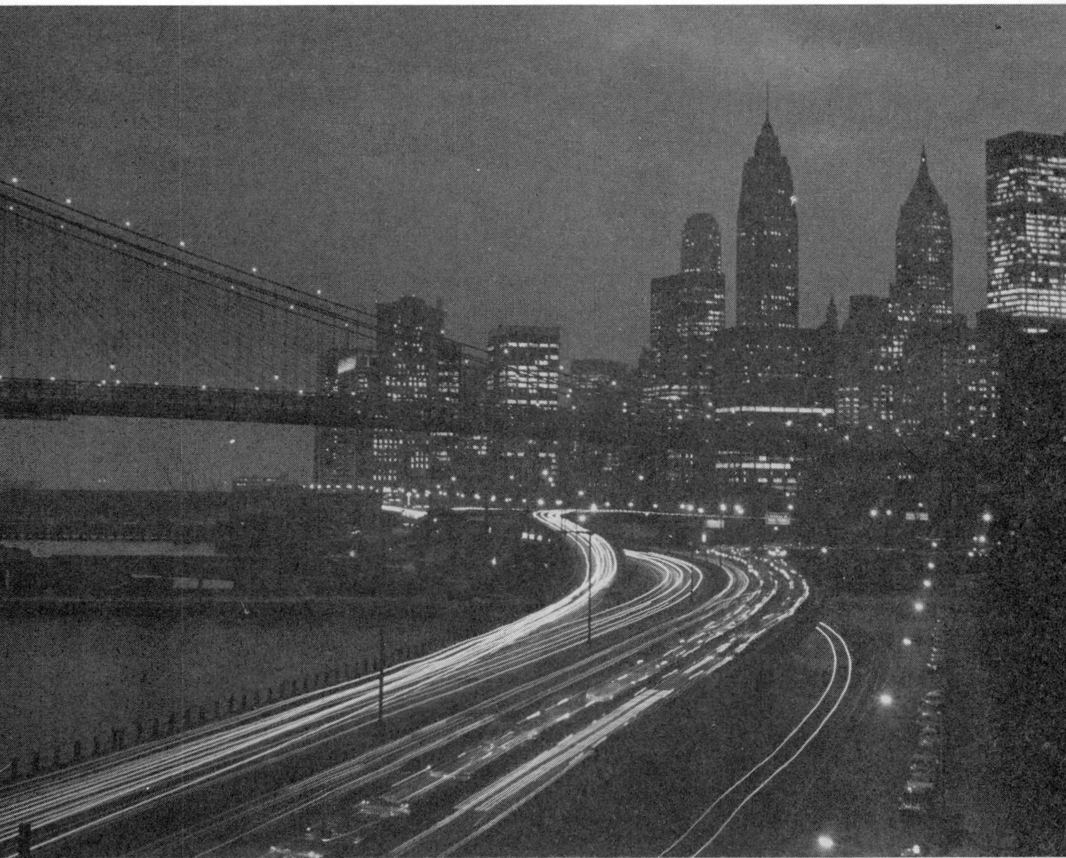

Bridges, tunnels, and elevated six- to eight-lane highways give today's driver easy access to the central business and entertainment areas of America's major cities.

Unit 5: Determining Average Speed

People who travel long distances are not only interested in how far they have traveled but also in what their average speed was, or, in other words, how much distance was covered for each hour traveled. For instance, if you traveled 60 miles over a period of 2 hours, then your average speed, also called average *rate,* was 30 miles per hour. However, if it took you 10 hours to travel those 60 miles, then your average rate was only 6 miles per hour.

In the first situation the average speed was found by dividing the total distance traveled, or 60 miles, by the time it took to travel this distance, which was 2 hours. In the second situation we again divided the distance traveled by the number of hours to find the average speed of 6 miles per hour. Thus, in general we can say,

Average Speed = Distance traveled ÷ Time

Writing this statement as a formula, it becomes,

$$R = D \div T$$

This is usually read as "Rate equals distance divided by time." It can be recognized as simply another form of the "Distance Formula" we learned earlier. (See page 35.)

ILLUSTRATION 1: Susan Bromberg traveled 6½ hours last Sunday. When she checked the odometer (distance indicator) of her car, she found that she had covered 310 miles. To the nearest mile, at what average speed was she traveling?

SOLUTION:

$$\begin{aligned} R &= D \div T \\ &= 310 \div 6\tfrac{1}{2} \\ &= 310 \div 6.5 \\ &= 47.7 \text{ mph, or } 48 \text{ mph} \end{aligned}$$

EXPLANATION: After replacing the Distance and Time in the formula by 310 and 6½, the problem becomes a simple division exercise. Notice, however, that the mixed number 6½ was changed to the decimal 6.5. Usually, it is a great deal easier to divide by a decimal than it is to divide by a mixed number.

While you are examining the speed at which you drive a car, it might be a good idea to spend a little time on this topic. The remark you hear about being able to "stop on a dime" is, of course, foolish. If you're traveling at 60 miles an hour, in the time it takes to get your foot off the gas pedal and onto the brake pedal, the car will have traveled 66 feet! This is before you even have a chance to apply the brakes! You will travel another 180 feet while you are doing this. Altogether, from the moment you start to react until the moment the car comes to a complete stop, you will have traveled at least 246 feet. This is longer than most city blocks, many of which are only a little more than 200 feet long.

The figures given above are based on ideal conditions. That is, they assume that the driver is alert and not drowsy from hours of driving; or has not turned his head to talk to someone in the back seat. Also, these figures are based on perfect road conditions—no ice, no snow, no oil slick, and no rain. Finally, they take for granted that the car's brakes are in good condition.

The time that it takes to react to the need for braking a car is called the *reaction time*. This is the time needed to remove your foot from the gas pedal and place it on the brake pedal. Studies have shown that it takes the normal person about 3/4 of a second before he realizes that disaster is facing him. By using the distance formula, you could show that a car traveling at 10 miles per hour would travel 11 feet in this time. Another way of stating this is that for each mile per hour of speed that a car is traveling, it will travel just a little more than 1 foot during the reaction time of the driver.

ILLUSTRATION 2: If a car is traveling at 55 miles per hour, approximately what distance will the car cover during the reaction time of the driver?

SOLUTION:

Speed of car = 55 mph

Approximate distance traveled during reaction time = 55 feet

EXPLANATION: For each mile per hour of speed, the car will travel approximately 1 foot during the reaction time. Since the car is traveling at 55 miles per hour, the reaction distance is approximately 55 feet.

The distance needed to bring a car to a complete stop once you have your foot on the brake pedal is a little more difficult to compute than the reaction distance. By making a careful check of a great many drivers in action, one study has shown that the braking distance can be found by using the following formula:

$$\text{Braking Distance} = (1/10 \times \text{Speed})^2 \times 5$$

Whenever a small 2 is placed above, and to the right of, a number, it means that this number should be multiplied by itself. Thus, 5^2 means 5×5; 8^2 means 8×8; 26^2 means 26×26, and so forth.

ILLUSTRATION 3: A car is traveling at the rate of 60 miles per hour. What braking distance will the driver need in order to bring the car to a complete halt?

SOLUTION:

$$\begin{aligned} \text{Braking Distance} &= (1/10 \times \text{Speed})^2 \times 5 \\ &= (1/10 \times 60)^2 \times 5 \\ &= (6)^2 \times 5 \\ &= 36 \times 5 \\ &= 180 \text{ feet} \end{aligned}$$

EXPLANATION: After replacing the Speed with 60, the formula calls for finding 1/10 of 60, which is 6. Now you multiply 6 by itself and get a product of 36. The computation is then completed by multiplying 36 by 5, which equals 180. The 180 is the number of feet it will take a car traveling at 60 mph to stop, once the driver's foot is on the brake pedal.

Incidentally, the expression 6^2 is read as "6 squared." Had it been 4^2, it would have been read as "4 squared." How would you read 7^2? 9^2? 27^2? 3.5^2? What is the value of 7^2? of 9^2?

ILLUSTRATION 4: Rodney Kent is driving his car at 45 miles an hour. Approximately how far will the car travel from the moment he realizes that he must apply his brakes until the moment the car comes to rest?

SOLUTION:

Speed of car = 45 mph
Approximate reaction distance = 45 feet

$$\begin{aligned}\text{Braking Distance} &= (1/10 \times 45)^2 \times 5\\ &= (4.5)^2 \times 5\\ &= 20.25 \times 5\\ &= 101.25 \text{ feet, or } 101 \text{ feet}\end{aligned}$$

$$\begin{aligned}\text{Total stopping distance} &= 45 \text{ feet} + 101 \text{ feet}\\ &= 146 \text{ feet}\end{aligned}$$

EXPLANATION: The reaction distance was found as in Illustration 2, while the braking distance was found as in Illustration 3. The total stopping distance is merely the sum of these two distances.

EXERCISES A

Do you recall how to find the answer in each of the following exercises? If not, you will probably want to refer to the pages indicated for help.

1. Change each of the following mixed numbers to a decimal (page 507).

a. $6\frac{1}{2}$ ______	e. $9\frac{1}{2}$ ______
b. $7\frac{1}{4}$ ______	f. $7\frac{2}{5}$ ______
c. $8\frac{1}{5}$ ______	g. $7\frac{3}{10}$ ______
d. $5\frac{3}{4}$ ______	h. $4\frac{1}{4}$ ______

2. Find the quotient in each of the following exercises (pages 508–509).

a. 217 ÷ 6.2 ____________ e. 247 ÷ 9.5 ____________
b. 126 ÷ 8.4 ____________ f. 693 ÷ 12.6 ____________
c. 162 ÷ 4.5 ____________ g. 3,384 ÷ 14.4 ____________
d. 507 ÷ 7.8 ____________ h. 5,969 ÷ 23.5 ____________

3. Find the quotient in each of the following exercises. Before dividing, change each divisor to a decimal (pages 508–509).

a. 279 ÷ $5\frac{1}{2}$ ____________ d. 957 ÷ $8\frac{1}{4}$ ____________
b. 540 ÷ $7\frac{1}{2}$ ____________ e. 1,700 ÷ $6\frac{1}{4}$ ____________
c. 798 ÷ $9\frac{1}{2}$ ____________ f. 1,786 ÷ $4\frac{3}{4}$ ____________

4. Find the quotient to the nearest whole number in each of the following exercises. Before dividing, change each divisor to a decimal (pages 508–509).

a. 247 ÷ $3\frac{1}{2}$ ____________ d. 526 ÷ $9\frac{3}{4}$ ____________
b. 325 ÷ $5\frac{1}{2}$ ____________ e. 475 ÷ $8\frac{1}{4}$ ____________
c. 481 ÷ $9\frac{1}{2}$ ____________ f. 583 ÷ $10\frac{1}{2}$ ____________

B

1. What is the approximate reaction distance needed to stop a car that is traveling at each of the following speeds?

a. 60 mph ____________ d. 85 mph ____________
b. 40 mph ____________ e. 72 mph ____________
c. 35 mph ____________ f. 63 mph ____________

2. What is the average speed at which each of the following cars is traveling? Find your answer to the nearest mile.

	Distance Traveled	Time Spent In Traveling	Average Speed
a.	342 miles	7 hours	____________ mph
b.	295 miles	6 hours	____________ mph
c.	473 miles	8 hours	____________ mph
d.	539 miles	10 hours	____________ mph
e.	184 miles	$2\frac{1}{2}$ hours	____________ mph
f.	197 miles	$3\frac{1}{2}$ hours	____________ mph
g.	356 miles	$6\frac{1}{2}$ hours	____________ mph
h.	471 miles	$8\frac{1}{2}$ hours	____________ mph

3. What is the average speed at which each of the following cars is traveling? The odometer (distance indicator) registers the distance traveled in kilometers.

	Distance Traveled	Time Spent In Traveling	Average Speed
a.	335 kilometers	5 hours	______ kph
b.	595 kilometers	7 hours	______ kph
c.	294 kilometers	6 hours	______ kph
d.	405 kilometers	$7\frac{1}{2}$ hours	______ kph
e.	162 kilometers	$4\frac{1}{2}$ hours	______ kph
f.	221 kilometers	$6\frac{1}{2}$ hours	______ kph

4. What braking distance will a car travel if it is moving at each of the following speeds? Round off each answer to the nearest whole number.

Speed	Braking Distance	Speed	Braking Distance
a. 40 mph	______ ft.	f. 35 mph	______ ft.
b. 50 mph	______ ft.	g. 65 mph	______ ft.
c. 80 mph	______ ft.	h. 25 mph	______ ft.
d. 20 mph	______ ft.	i. 42 mph	______ ft.
e. 90 mph	______ ft.	j. 76 mph	______ ft.

5. Ten cars are traveling at the speeds indicated below. What is the total distance each car will travel from the moment the driver realizes that he must apply the brakes until the moment the car stops? Round off each answer to the nearest whole number.

Speed	Reaction Distance	Braking Distance	Total Distance
a. 10 mph	______ ft.	______ ft.	______ ft.
b. 30 mph	______ ft.	______ ft.	______ ft.
c. 70 mph	______ ft.	______ ft.	______ ft.
d. 25 mph	______ ft.	______ ft.	______ ft.
e. 55 mph	______ ft.	______ ft.	______ ft.
f. 85 mph	______ ft.	______ ft.	______ ft.
g. 32 mph	______ ft.	______ ft.	______ ft.
h. 18 mph	______ ft.	______ ft.	______ ft.
i. 27 mph	______ ft.	______ ft.	______ ft.
j. 63 mph	______ ft.	______ ft.	______ ft.

C

1. On Wednesday of the first week of their trip, the Archers took 9 hours to travel 378 miles. The following day they drove for $5\frac{1}{2}$ hours and covered 293 miles. At what average speed were they traveling during the two-day period? ______

2. On a wet road, the reaction time of the driver is the same as on a dry road. However, the braking distance is twice as great. A car is traveling on a wet road at the rate of 52 miles per hour.
   a. What is the reaction distance? ________
   b. What is the braking distance? ________
   c. What is the total distance a driver will need to stop a car that is traveling at 52 miles per hour on a wet road? ________
3. Joseph Gomez is traveling at the rate of 41 miles per hour.
   a. What is the total distance he will need to stop the car if he is traveling on a dry road? ________
   b. What is the total distance he will need to stop the car if he is traveling on a wet road? ________
   c. How much more distance is needed if the road is wet than if it is dry? ________
4. How much more distance is needed to stop a car on a dry road if it is traveling at 60 miles per hour than if it is traveling at 30 miles per hour? ________
5. Phyllis Trent is driving her car on a clear day at the rate of 60 miles per hour. She rounds a bend in the road and spots an accident pileup 200 feet ahead. Assuming she has good brakes, will she be able to stop in time? ________________________

Unit 6: Paying for Traveling Costs

There are two principal ways in which people when traveling can solve their money worries. One of these is to obtain a credit card from a gasoline company. With one of these cards, it is possible to buy gas, oil, and even tires all over the country, at gasoline stations belonging to this company without using any money. In recent years, most gasoline companies have made arrangements with motel chains whereby the cost of lodging at any of the motels in that particular chain can be charged against the gasoline credit card. There is no charge to obtain the card, or to use the card. In this way, you can travel for a relatively long time with very little money.

Two credit card forms are shown on page 46. They are pretty much alike. The one at the top is the form used as a receipt after buying gas, while the one below it is the receipt for motel lodging. Both of these forms are mailed to the credit office of the gasoline company. The company, in turn, pays both the owner of the gasoline station and the motel keeper. Then you are billed for these two items, as well as any others that you may have charged during the monthly period.

CREDIT CARD NUMBER 675 000 316 9

PRINT CUSTOMER NAME AND ADDRESS JOHN Q PUBLIC

Merchandise listed hereon received.

CUSTOMER'S SIGNATURE

X John Q. Public

DEALER IN PHILLIPS 66 PRODUCTS

TUNNEL RD 66
ASHEVLE NC RR BI

DELIVERY DATE 7 3 7-

CUSTOMER'S ORDER NO.

COMMODITY	GALS.	PRICE	AMOUNT	
Phillips Gasoline Sixty-Six ☐ Flite-Fuel ☐	8	33 9/10	2	71
Motor Oil				
632930	TOTAL		2	71

VEHICLE OR LICENSE NO XZY 123

STATE N. J YEAR 7-

APPLICABLE FEDERAL STATE AND LOCAL TAXES INCLUDED IN PRICE AND AMOUNT.

DELIVERY TICKET PHILLIPS 66

FORM 834

0 1 2 3 4 5 6 7 8 9

24 25 26 27 28 29 30 31 32 33 34 35 36 37 38 39 40 41 42 43 44 45 46 47 48 49 50 51

NUMBER 675 000 316 9

NAME JOHN Q PUBLIC

ESTABLISHMENT NUMBER, NAME & CITY

QUALITY CTS MOTEL REDMON
243 212 271 7 ASHEVILLE
732 050 212 3 N.C.

DATE 7 3 7-

ESTABLISHMENT AND CARDHOLDER REPRESENT THAT THIS CHARGE IS GENUINE, HAVING BEEN MADE AND SIGNED FOR AS INDICATED.

SIGN HERE ▶ John Q. Public

CARDHOLDER'S SIGNATURE

VERIFICATION NUMBER

REMIT ONLY TO
PHILLIPS PETROLEUM COMPANY
P O BOX 73
KANSAS CITY, MISSOURI 64141

FORM 834-Q 6-69

PHILLIPS 66

RECORD OF CHARGE

AMOUNT		ITEM
		MDSE AND/OR SERVICES
16	00	ROOMS
	48	TAX
		TIP
		MISC
16	48	TOTAL CHARGE

CUSTOMER COPY

ILLUSTRATION 1: The distance from Louisville, Kentucky, to Miami, Florida, is 1,126 miles. When William Sanford made the trip between the two cities, he drove only 6 hours each day at the average speed of 45 miles per hour. He charged the cost of lodging and gas against his credit card.

a. How many hours did William drive the car during the trip?
b. If William started early on the morning of the first day he traveled, how many nights of lodging did he have to pay for before arriving at Miami?
c. If he paid \$14 plus 5% tax for each night of lodging, what were the total motel costs while on the road?

SOLUTION:

(a) Number of hours = 1,126 ÷ 45
= 25.0 hours, or 25 hours

(b) Number of days on the road = 25 ÷ 6
= 4.2

Number of nights of lodging = 4

(c) Cost of 4 nights lodging without tax = 4 × \$14
= \$56

Tax on cost of lodging = \$56 × 5%
= \$56 × .05
= \$2.80

Total motel costs = \$56 + \$2.80
= \$58.80

EXPLANATION: To justify the use of division to find the answer to Part (a), consider the case of a person who was able to walk at the rate of 3 miles per hour. How long did it take him to walk 6 miles? How long did it take him to walk 21 miles? To find the answer of 2 hours in the first case, you had to divide the 6 by 3, while in the second case, you had to divide 21 by 3 to get the answer of 7 hours. In each situation, it was necessary to divide the distance the person traveled by the speed at which he traveled to determine the number of hours that it took him to cover the distance. In general, the formula can be stated as follows:

$$T = D \div R$$
(Time = Distance ÷ Rate)

This formula is just another form of the distance formula. When finding the answer to Part (a), you simply apply the same procedure as with the man walking at the rate of 3 miles per hour. Now, however, the numbers are somewhat larger.

In computing the answer to Part (b), you use the fact that Mr. Sanford's driving time is 25 hours. Since he drives only 6 hours each day, it will take him slightly more than 4 days to reach Miami. This means that he will have to seek lodging for 4 nights, and, on the 5th day, he will be on the road only a few hours before he reaches Miami.

For Part (c), you have to perform multiplication where one of the numbers is a percent number. It is not possible to multiply by a num-

Keeping traffic flowing smoothly is a major objective of every large city. Architects work with city planners and traffic-control experts in the construction of elaborate highway approaches which contain complex but nevertheless efficient patterns.

ber that is expressed in its percent form. Change the percent form to the decimal form before multiplying.

ILLUSTRATION 2: William's car in Illustration 1 averaged 14 miles to the gallon of gasoline.

a. How many gallons of gasoline did he have to buy on the trip? Find your answer to the nearest gallon.
b. If William purchased gas at 51.4¢ per gallon, what was the total cost of gas that was charged against his credit card?
c. What was the total bill sent to him by the gasoline company whose credit card he held? Consider both motel charges and gasoline charges.

SOLUTION:

(a) Number of gallons purchased $= 1126 \div 14$
$= 80.4$ gallons, or 80 gallons

(b) Cost of gasoline $= 80 \times \$.514$
$= \$41.12$

(c) Total bill $= \$58.80 + \$41.12$
$= \$99.92$

EXPLANATION: Parts (a) and (b) are done in exactly the same manner as the problems in the earlier units. The answer to Part (c) is found simply by adding the cost of the lodging found in Illustration 1 to the cost of the gasoline found in Part (b) of this problem.

The second method a traveler can use to protect his money is traveler's checks. They can be bought at almost any bank. American Express, First National City Bank of New York, and other companies sell them. For these two, the cost is exactly the same—10¢ for each \$10 worth of checks. They can be purchased in amounts of \$10, \$20, \$50, or \$100.

All companies have designed checks that are pretty much the same. There are two places on the face of the check where you have to sign your name. At the time of purchase, you sign in one of these places in the presence of the bank teller. Then, when you have to cash a check, you again sign for the person to whom you are giving the check. In this way, the two signatures can be matched to check whether the same person signed them.

In the event that the checks are lost or stolen, you simply report the theft to the company from which you bought them. New checks will be issued immediately.

ILLUSTRATION 3: Before Edwina Battle set out on her trip, she bought \$850 worth of traveler's checks. How much did she have to pay for these checks?

SOLUTION:

Cost of each \$10 worth of traveler's checks = \$.10
Number of \$10 amounts in \$850 = 850 ÷ 10
= 85
Cost of \$850 worth of traveler's checks = 85 × \$.10
= \$8.50

EXPLANATION: Since the cost of traveler's checks is based on each \$10 amount bought, it is necessary to find the number of \$10 amounts in \$850. To do this, divide 850 by 10 for a quotient of 85. Notice that the fastest way to divide a whole number ending in zeros by 10 is simply to cross off the end zero. To find the cost for 85 \$10-amounts, at a cost of 10¢ for each \$10 amount, simply multiply 85 by 10¢. Why was the 10¢ written in the form \$.10?

ILLUSTRATION 4: Edwina gave the waiter at the restaurant a \$20 traveler's check in payment for her lunch. The total cost of the meal was \$2.80. She also tipped the waiter 15% of the bill. How much change from the \$20-check did she keep?

SOLUTION:

Amount of tip = \$2.80 × 15%
= \$2.80 × .15
= \$.42
Total amount spent = \$2.80 + \$.42
= \$3.22
Change received from \$20 check = \$20.00 − \$3.22
= \$16.78

EXPLANATION: Before multiplying \$2.80 by 15%, it is necessary to change the percent numeral to a decimal numeral. How is this done? After adding the cost of the meal to the amount of the tip, the total of \$3.22 is subtracted from \$20.

EXERCISES A

Do you recall how to find the answer in each of the following exercises? If not, you will probably want to refer to the pages indicated for help.

1. Change each of the following percent numerals to its equivalent decimal form (pages 514–516).

a. 35% ________	e. 4% ________
b. 45% ________	f. 7% ________
c. 16.2% ________	g. $3\frac{1}{2}$% ________
d. 58.3% ________	h. $5\frac{1}{2}$% ________

2. Find the product in each of the following exercises (pages 519–521).

a. 20 × 15% ______	e. 137 × 5% ______
b. 65 × 24% ______	f. 251 × 8% ______
c. 36 × 12% ______	g. 40 × 2½% ______
d. 125 × 36% ______	h. 56 × 3½% ______

3. Find the product in each of the following exercises. Round off each product to the nearest cent (pages 526–527).

a. $6.84 × 13% ______	d. $29.67 × 5.6% ______
b. $5.92 × 24% ______	e. $23.75 × 5½% ______
c. $14.82 × 3.2% ______	f. $49.23 × 8½% ______

B

1. Find the state sales tax that had to be paid on each of the following motel bills.

	Motel Bill	State Sales Tax Rate	Sales Tax		Motel Bill	State Sales Tax Rate	Sales Tax
a.	$14.00	5%	$______	f.	$12.50	6%	$______
b.	17.00	6%	______	g.	9.50	7%	______
c.	26.00	7%	______	h.	38.50	6.2%	______
d.	54.00	4%	______	i.	21.75	4½%	______
e.	14.50	6%	______	j.	53.25	6½%	______

2. An average tip given to a waiter is 15% of the cost of the meal. How much will the waiter receive as his tip for serving meals where the costs are as follows?

	Cost of Meal	Waiter's Tip		Cost of Meal	Waiter's Tip
a.	$ 4.00	$______	e.	$ 2.50	$______
b.	6.00	______	f.	5.70	______
c.	22.00	______	g.	12.30	______
d.	35.00	______	h.	26.85	______

3. How much will a person have to pay when purchasing traveler's checks for each of the following amounts?

	Total Value Of Traveler's Checks	Cost		Total Value Of Traveler's Checks	Cost
a.	$ 80	$______	e.	$ 250	$______
b.	200	______	f.	780	______
c.	700	______	g.	4,500	______
d.	1,200	______	h.	1,450	______

4. How much change will a person receive after paying each of the following bills with traveler's checks?

	Amount Of Bill	Size Of Traveler's Check	Change
a.	$ 7.50	$ 10	$______
b.	6.95	10	______
c.	8.50	20	______
d.	12.45	20	______
e.	3.25	20	______
f.	16.50	50	______
g.	37.25	50	______
h.	29.30	100	______
i.	59.95	100	______
j.	64.19	100	______

5. How much change from each of the traveler's checks indicated will a person receive after having paid for the cost of the meal and tipped the waiter 15% of that cost?

	Cost Of Meal	Waiter's Tip	Total Cost	Size Of Traveler's Check	Change
a.	$ 3.00	$______	$______	$10	$______
b.	5.00	______	______	10	______
c.	4.50	______	______	10	______
d.	2.70	______	______	10	______
e.	12.50	______	______	20	______
f.	17.50	______	______	50	______
g.	26.40	______	______	50	______
h.	37.60	______	______	50	______

6. In each of the following exercises, a person spent the number of nights indicated at a motel. What will his total bill be for his stay at the motel? Include state tax.

	Cost Per Night	Number Of Nights	Total Motel Charge	State Tax Rate	State Tax	Total Charge, Including Tax
a.	$ 9.00	2	$______	4%	$______	$______
b.	12.00	4	______	5%	______	______
c.	16.00	5	______	6%	______	______
d.	10.50	2	______	7%	______	______
e.	12.50	6	______	6%	______	______
f.	16.50	10	______	6.2%	______	______
g.	18.50	8	______	$4\frac{1}{2}$%	______	______
h.	14.50	14	______	$6\frac{1}{2}$%	______	______

7. To the nearest hour, how many hours will it take to drive the distance shown in each of the following exercises?

	Total Distance Traveled	Average Rate	Number Of Hours
a.	240 miles	40 mph	________
b.	370 miles	50 mph	________
c.	420 miles	60 mph	________
d.	870 miles	50 mph	________
e.	625 miles	55 mph	________
f.	942 miles	55 mph	________
g.	673 miles	45 mph	________
h.	1,342 miles	47 mph	________
i.	1,075 miles	35 mph	________
j.	2,480 miles	53 mph	________

8. If a person travels the number of hours per day shown below, how many days will it take him to make the trip? Find your answer to the nearest day. Round off the number of hours needed to make the trip to the nearest hour.

	Total Trip Distance	Average Rate	Number Of Hours	Traveling Hours Each Day	Number Of Days
a.	940 miles	40 mph	________	4	________
b.	867 miles	30 mph	________	5	________
c.	1,250 miles	50 mph	________	5	________
d.	2,375 miles	52 mph	________	8	________
e.	3,295 miles	55 mph	________	7	________
f.	3,850 miles	48 mph	________	9	________

C

1. Janice Evans purchased 3 \$100 traveler's checks, 8 \$50 checks, 10 \$20 checks, and 20 \$10 checks. What was the total cost of these checks? ________

2. Vivian Spellman and her family stayed 10 days at the shore in a motel at a cost of \$21.50 per day. The state sales tax rate where they spent the vacation is 6%. In traveling to the motel and returning to their home, they had to purchase gas four times at a cost of \$7.25, \$6.90, \$6.35, and \$8.65. If both their motel and gasoline expenses were charged against their gasoline credit card, for what amount did the gasoline company bill them at the end of the month?

____

3. Bill Spivak used his car to travel from his home in Omaha, Nebraska, to the home of a friend in San Francisco, California—a distance of 1,725 miles. He planned to drive his car at an average rate of 50 miles per hour.

a. How many hours should he plan on driving? Find your answer to the nearest hour. ________

b. If he starts driving early in the morning and drives for eight hours each day, how many days will he be traveling? Find your answer to the nearest day. ______

c. If he averages $16.50 per night as the cost for motel rooms and $11.75 per day for food, what will be the total cost for just these two expenses for the trip? In computing your answer, include the cost of food for the last day, but not the motel cost. Why? ______

Unit 7: Depreciation on a Car

Possibly the greatest expense connected with owning a car does not involve the use of the car at all. By merely buying a car and keeping it in a garage until the day you sell it costs quite a lot of money. Although you may never use the car, the value of the car decreases each year. Automobile manufacturers produce new models, and so the older ones are less in demand by buyers. Hence, the price of an older car decreases in spite of the fact that the car may be in excellent condition.

The decrease in the value of a car over a period of years is called the *depreciation* on the car. Thus, a car that had an original value of $4,000 and is worth only $1,000 at present is said to have *depreciated* $3,000 in value. To a small extent, the value of a car depends upon the condition the car is in, but its value is judged largely on how old the car is.

The greatest depreciation on a car occurs during the first year. In fact, if you buy a car from a dealer at 10:00 in the morning and sell it back to him at 11:00 that same morning, you would probably have to take a loss of several hundred dollars. A car for which you paid $5,400 one year will be worth only $3,200 the next—a loss of $2,200. However, the following year its value may be only $1,300. During the second year it will have depreciated only $900 as against the $2,200 of the first year. By the time this car is six years old, it will be worth only $700. This is a drop in value of $4,700 over a six-year period, and yet, the car may have been driven very little. Within a year or two afterward, its value will be about $100. This is pretty much what its junk value will be. From that point on, it will retain that value until it is discarded.

Although depreciation varies from year to year, with the greatest depreciation occurring the first year, followed by smaller depreciation each succeeding year, car owners like to consider yearly depreciation as remaining the same. First they determine how much the car has decreased in value by subtracting the trade-in value from the

During morning rush hour on the New Jersey Turnpike, express buses to New York are permitted to use one of the lanes on the opposite side of the road.

amount they paid for the car. The total depreciation is then divided by the number of years they have owned the car. This technique of averaging is much the same as if you were finding your average weekly weight loss over a period of time. That is, if you lost 12 pounds in 4 weeks, you would say that, on the average, you had lost 3 pounds each week. Yet, usually, the greatest weight loss occurs the first week. After that first week, the amount lost is much less. In general,

Average Annual Depreciation =
Total Depreciation ÷ Number of Years

ILLUSTRATION: Mr. Elliott purchased a car for \$3,600. Five years later, when purchasing a newer model, he received \$600 as the trade-in value for the car. What was the average annual depreciation on the car?

SOLUTION:

Total Depreciation = \$3,600 − \$600
= \$3,000
Average Annual Depreciation = Total Depreciation ÷ Number of Years
= \$3,000 ÷ 5
= \$600

EXPLANATION: Finding the average annual depreciation depends upon knowing the total depreciation over the five-year period. To determine this total depreciation, subtract the trade-in value of the car from its original value. Then divide the total depreciation of \$3,000 by the 5 years that Mr. Elliott owned the car. You then obtain an average annual depreciation of \$600.

EXERCISES A

1. Find the average annual depreciation on each of the following cars. Find your answer to the nearest dollar.

	Total Depreciation	Number Of Years	Average Annual Depreciation
a.	\$1,400	2	\$________
b.	1,800	3	________
c.	2,300	4	________
d.	3,100	5	________
e.	1,750	3	________
f.	2,045	4	________
g.	2,726	5	________
h.	3,518	6	________

2. Find the average annual depreciation on each of the following cars. Find your answer to the nearest dollar.

	Value When New	Trade-in Value	Total Depreciation	Number Of Years	Average Annual Depreciation
a.	\$3,400	\$1,600	\$________	4	\$________
b.	1,800	400	________	5	________
c.	5,200	800	________	5	________
d.	4,700	2,375	________	3	________
e.	3,914	1,250	________	4	________
f.	2,827	425	________	6	________
g.	6,748	575	________	8	________
h.	2,436	50	________	9	________

B

1. Judy Bailey paid $3,128, plus a 6% state sales tax, when she purchased her new car. Three years later she sold the car for $1,465.
   a. How large was the sales tax that Judy had to pay? ________
   b. What was the total amount, including the tax, that she had to pay for the car? ________
   c. What was the total depreciation on the car? ________
   d. What was the average annual depreciation on the car? Find your answer to the nearest dollar. ________
2. Alex Desmond purchased a new car for $3,650. If he trades in the car at the end of 3 years, he will receive $1,250 for it. However, if he keeps it for 5 years, its trade-in value will be $650.
   a. What is the average annual depreciation over the three-year period? ________
   b. What is the average annual depreciation over the five-year period? ________
   c. How much greater is the average annual depreciation over the three-year period than over the five-year period? ________

Unit 8: Chapter Review and Test

In solving some of the following problems, you will have to refer to the tables in this chapter.

1. Find the total amount repaid, including the life-insurance premium, on each of the following new-car loans.

	Loan	Period Of Debt	Total Repaid
a.	$2,000	18 months	$________
b.	2,600	30 months	________
c.	1,560	24 months	________
d.	2,840	36 months	________

2. In the purchase of automobile insurance, what age factor will be used for the following driver?

Sex	Age	Married	Driver Training	Car Owner	Use	Age Factor
Female	19	No	Yes	–	Pleasure	________

3. Find the cost of a 50/100 bodily-injury insurance policy to the purchaser. Use the following information.

Points	Sex	Age	Married	Territory	Use	Total Cost
2	Male	26	Yes	05	Business	________

4. Tom Willard was at fault in an automobile accident. As a result of court action, the driver of the other car was granted $30,000 for the injuries he suffered. If Tom carried a 25/50 bodily-injury insurance policy, how much did the insurance company pay the injured party? ________
5. When Joe Fry applied his brakes on an icy road, his car slid into a tree. The extent of damage to the car came to $135. How much of the cost of repairing the car did the insurance company pay if Joe has purchased a $100-deductible collision-insurance policy? ________
6. What is the cost of 10.6 gallons of gasoline at 52.9¢ per gallon? Find your answer to the nearest penny. ________
7. a. How many gallons of gasoline were used on a trip of 12,500 miles if the car averaged 14 miles to the gallon of gasoline? Find your answer to the nearest gallon. ________
   b. How much did the driver of this car have to pay for gasoline if the average price per gallon was 55.4¢? Find your answer to the nearest penny. ________
8. According to the road map on page 33 how far is it from Springwater to Lima along state highway 15A? ________
9. How far will a car travel in 8 hours if it is moving at an average speed of 55 miles per hour? ________
10. During a trip, Cheryl Bell's total driving time was 54 hours. She found that she had averaged 50 miles per hour.
   a. How many miles did Cheryl travel? ________
   b. If the car averaged 12 miles to the gallon of gasoline, determine, to the nearest mile, how many gallons were consumed. ________
   c. If the average price of gasoline was 52.7¢ per gallon, what was the total cost of the gasoline consumed? ________
11. At what average speed would a car be traveling if it covered a distance of 342 miles in 8 hours? Find your answer to the nearest mile. ________
12. A car is traveling at the rate of 70 miles per hour.
   a. What is the approximate reaction distance at this speed? ________
   b. What is the approximate braking distance at this speed? ________
   c. How far will the car travel before coming to a complete stop after the driver has seen the need to apply his brakes? ________
13. What is the cost of $350 worth of traveler's checks? ________
14. Jim Clemens and his wife stayed at a motel for a period of 5 nights at a cost of $17.50 per night.

a. What was the cost of lodging for the 5 nights? ________

b. If the state tax rate was 4%, how much tax did Jim Clemens have to pay? ________

c. What was the total bill for these 5 nights? ________

15. After keeping her car for three years, Ruth Adkins sold it for $1,850. She had paid $3,475 for the car.

a. What was the total depreciation on the car? ________

b. What was the average annual depreciation on the car? Compute your answer to the nearest dollar. ________

SAN FRANCISCO INTERNATIONAL AIRPORT
UNITED
UNITED
24
23

CHAPTER 2

COMMERCIAL TRANSPORTATION

There are a great number of people who prefer not to own a car. If you happen to live in a large city, owning a car can be quite a problem. All too often there are no garages in your neighborhood. And if there are, the rents are very high. The daily battle for parking space, plus the high cost of automobile insurance, forces many people to sell their cars and take to taxis, buses, or subways. In this chapter you will take a look at traveling by commercial transportation.

Unit 1: Renting a Car

The cost of renting a car varies from city to city, depending on the demand for rented cars in a particular area. Some rental agencies claim they are less expensive than others. On the whole, though, the charges of all agencies in the same area usually are pretty much the same. When a difference in price exists, it's likely that you are either getting a cheaper car, or an older car, or that the service is not quite so good. Often you will find that the cheaper rates include a hidden cost that is overlooked. For instance, with the larger rental agencies which have outlets throughout the country, it is possible to rent a car in one city and drop it off in another. Smaller companies do not offer this service; the car must be returned to the place from which it was rented.

The table below shows the daily and weekly charges for two car-rental systems. The first of these agencies is among the largest in the world, while the second advertises itself as a low-budget agency. At first glance, it would appear that the rates of Company B are a great deal lower than those of Company A. However, the lower rates do not include the cost of gas, while the higher ones do. Also, Company A

COMPANY A RENTAL RATES

(Rental does not include gas)

	DAILY Monday through Thursday	DAILY Friday through Sunday
Economy Car	\$8.59 + 13¢ per mile	\$15 + 13¢ per mile
Compact Car	\$11.99 + 13¢ per mile	\$16 + 13¢ per mile

(Rental includes gas)

	DAILY	WEEKLY
Standard	\$19 + 19¢ per mile	\$95 + 19¢ per mile
Station Wagon	\$21 + 21¢ per mile	\$105 + 21¢ per mile
Premium	\$22 + 22¢ per mile	\$110 + 22¢ per mile
Luxury	\$25 + 25¢ per mile	\$125 + 25¢ per mile

COMPANY B RENTAL RATES
(Rental does not include gas)

	DAILY	WEEKLY
Sub-compact	\$8 + 8¢ per mile	\$52 + 8¢ per mile
Compact	\$9 + 9¢ per mile	\$55 + 9¢ per mile
Personal-Size	\$10 + 10¢ per mile	\$60 + 10¢ per mile
Full-Size	\$11 + 11¢ per mile	\$65 + 11¢ per mile
Station Wagon	\$13 + 13¢ per mile	\$75 + 13¢ per mile
Van (Passenger)	\$16 + 16¢ per mile	\$85 + 16¢ per mile

provides an air-conditioner with the car at no extra charge, while Company B increases the charge by \$2.00 per day and 2¢ per mile when this equipment is included. Notice, though, that in order to compete with Company B, Company A is also offering rental rates that do not include the cost of gas.

ILLUSTRATION 1: Fred Morrell rented a station wagon from Company A for a single day. If he drove the car 90 miles, what was the rental charge?

SOLUTION:

Base charge for the day = \$21
Cost per mile = 21¢, or \$.21
Cost for 90 miles = 90 × \$.21
= \$18.90
Total cost for the day = \$21 + \$18.90
= \$39.90

EXPLANATION: In addition to the \$21 base charge on a station wagon, Fred had to pay 21¢ for each mile he drove the car. Since he covered 90 miles during the day, his additional charge was 90 times 21¢, or \$18.90. By adding the base charge to the mileage cost, the total cost is found to be \$39.90.

ILLUSTRATION 2: Suppose Fred Morrell of the previous illustration rented a station wagon from Company B rather than from Company A.

a. What was the total cost in rental alone?
b. If the station wagon averaged 9 miles to a gallon of gasoline, how many gallons of gasoline did Fred use that day?
c. If the price of the gasoline was 54.9¢ per gallon, how much did Fred have to pay for the gasoline purchased?
d. What was the total cost for using the car that day?
e. How much would Fred have saved by renting the car from Company B rather than from Company A?

SOLUTION:

(a) Base charge for the day = \$13
Cost per mile = 13¢, or \$.13
Cost for 90 miles = 90 × \$.13
= \$11.70
Total cost for rental = \$13 + \$11.70
= \$24.70

(b) Number of gallons of gasoline used = 90 ÷ 9
= 10

(c) Cost of gasoline = $10 \times \$.549$
= $\$5.49$

(d) Cost for use of car = $\$24.70 + \$5.49$
= $\$30.19$

(e) Saving on Company B car over Company A car = $\$39.90 - \$30.19$
= $\$9.71$

EXPLANATION: The rental rates charged by Company B do not include the cost of gasoline. Therefore, in Part (b), it is necessary to determine how many gallons had been used. By knowing the number of gallons used, it is possible to determine the cost of the gasoline. The combined rental of $24.70 added to the $5.49 paid for gasoline comes to $30.19. This amount is still $9.71 less than the charge of $39.90 made by Company A.

EXERCISES A

1. Find the cost of renting each of the cars below for a day. Use the rate table for Company A.

Type of Car	Base Rate	Number Of Miles	Cost Per Mile	Mileage Cost	Total Cost
a. Standard	$_____	20	$_____	$_____	$_____
b. Premium	_____	40	_____	_____	_____
c. Station Wagon	_____	50	_____	_____	_____
d. Luxury	_____	30	_____	_____	_____
e. Standard	_____	75	_____	_____	_____
f. Luxury	_____	93	_____	_____	_____

2. Find the cost of renting each of the cars below for a week. Use the rate table for Company A.

Type of Car	Base Rate	Number Of Miles	Cost Per Mile	Mileage Cost	Total Cost
a. Luxury	$_____	200	$_____	$_____	$_____
b. Station Wagon	_____	300	_____	_____	_____
c. Standard	_____	500	_____	_____	_____
d. Premium	_____	850	_____	_____	_____
e. Standard	_____	743	_____	_____	_____

3. Find the cost of renting each of the cars below for a day. Do not include the cost of gasoline. Use the rate table for Company B.

Type of Car	Base Rate	Number Of Miles	Cost Per Mile	Mileage Cost	Total Cost
a. Station Wagon	$_____	35	$_____	$_____	$_____
b. Full-Size	_____	67	_____	_____	_____
c. Compact	_____	92	_____	_____	_____

4. Find the total cost of renting each of the cars below for a week. The cost of gasoline is to be included at the price shown. Round off the cost of gasoline to the nearest cent. Use the rate table for Company B.

	Type of Car	Base Rate	Number Of Miles	Cost Per Mile	Mileage Cost	Number Of Gallons	Cost Per Gallon	Gasoline Cost	Total Cost
a.	Sub-compact	$____	300	$____	$____	25	46.9¢	$____	$____
b.	Compact	____	500	____	____	23	52.9¢	____	____
c.	Full-Size	____	275	____	____	28	48.7¢	____	____
d.	Personal-Size	____	934	____	____	86	49.4¢	____	____
e.	Station Wagon	____	1,258	____	____	94	53.2¢	____	____

5. A person rented a compact car from Company B for the number of days shown below. Find the cost of this rental. Include gasoline.

	Number Of Days	Total Base Cost	Number Of Miles	Mileage Cost	Miles Per Gallon	Number Of Gallons	Cost Per Gallon	Gasoline Cost	Total Cost
a.	2	$____	150	$____	15	____	52.1¢	$____	$____
b.	3	____	70	____	14	____	50.9¢	____	____
c.	4	____	156	____	12	____	47.6¢	____	____
d.	5	____	338	____	13	____	48.9¢	____	____

B

1. Sheila Hagel rented an economy car from Company A and drove it 75 miles.
   a. If she had rented the car on Tuesday, what would the rental cost have been? ________
   b. If she had rented the car on Saturday, what would the rental cost have been? ________
   c. How much could she have saved by renting the car on Tuesday rather than on Saturday? ________
2. Company A advertises a special 7-day rate of $99 on the rental of a compact car. For this special rate there is no additional charge for each mile the car is driven. Malcolm Culver took advantage of this offer and drove the car 800 miles during the week.
   a. If he had rented the car from Company B, including the mileage charge, what would the cost for the week have been? ________
   b. How much did he save by renting the car from Company A at this special rate? ________
3. Michael Fernandez rented a compact car on a Friday and drove it 175 miles.
   a. If he had rented the car from Company A, what would the total cost have been? ________

b. If he had rented the car from Company B, what would the total cost have been? ________

c. How much would he have saved by renting the car from Company B rather than from Company A? ________

Unit 2: Traveling by Bus

PART 1

When you travel around the city by bus, you usually simply go out to the corner and, within a reasonable time, a bus comes along to pick

Route Number 114

WEEKDAYS

TO NEWARK

BUTLER Bus Station	POMPTON LAKES Bus Station	MOUNTAIN VIEW Center	SINGAC Four Corners	LITTLE FALLS Main & Center Sts.	CEDAR GROVE Bowden Road	MONTCLAIR D.L. & W. Station	BLOOMFIELD Bloomfield Center	NEWARK P.R.R. Station
—	5.32	5.39	5.44	5.47	5.54	6.05	6.10	6.29
—	—	6.05	6.10	6.13	6.20	6.31	6.36	6.55
—	6.10	6.30	6.35	—	—	6.48	6.53	7.13
—	—	—	6.35	6.38	6.47	7.01	7.07	7.34
—	—	6.52	6.57	7.00	7.09	7.23	7.29	7.51
6.20	6.40	7.00	7.05	—	—	7.23	7.29	7.49
—	—	—	7.12	7.15	7.24	7.38	7.44	8.04
—	—	7.20	7.25	7.28	7.37	7.51	7.57	8.17
—	7.03	7.25	7.30	—	—	7.48	7.54	8.14
—	—	7.35	7.40	7.43	7.52	8.06	8.12	8.32
—	—	—	8.00	8.03	8.12	8.26	8.32	8.59
7.30	7.50	8.12	8.17	8.20	8.29	8.43	8.49	9.09
8.10	8.25	8.47	8.52	8.55	9.04	9.17	9.22	9.42
—	9.00	9.22	9.27	9.30	9.39	9.52	9.57	10.17
—	10.00	10.22	10.27	10.30	10.39	10.52	10.57	11.17
—	11.00	11.22	11.27	11.30	11.39	11.52	11.57	**12.17**
11.40	**12.00**	**12.22**	**12.27**	**12.30**	**12.39**	**12.52**	**12.57**	**1.17**
—	**1.00**	**1.22**	**1.27**	**1.30**	**1.39**	**1.52**	**1.57**	**2.17**
—	**1.55**	**2.17**	**2.22**	**2.25**	**2.34**	**2.47**	**2.52**	**3.12**
—	—	—	—	**2.54**	**3.03**	**3.16**	**3.22**	**3.49**
2.50	**3.10**	**3.32**	**3.37**	**3.40**	**3.49**	**4.02**	**4.08**	**4.35**
—	—	—	—	**4.10**	**4.19**	**4.32**	**4.38**	**5.05**
—	**4.20**	**4.42**	**4.47**	**4.50**	**4.59**	**5.12**	**5.18**	**5.45**
—	—	—	—	**5.00**	**5.09**	**5.22**	—	—
4.30	**5.15**	**5.35**	**5.40**	**5.43**	**5.49**	**6.00**	**6.04**	**6.23**
—	**6.45**	**7.05**	**7.10**	**7.13**	**7.19**	**7.30**	**7.34**	**7.53**
8.13	**8.25**	**8.45**	**8.50**	**8.53**	**8.59**	**9.10**	**9.14**	**9.33**
—	—	—	—	12.00	12.06	12.17	—	—

you up. Although it frequently does not appear that way, all means of public transportation, including buses, must travel on certain approved time schedules.

Most bus schedules look much like the one shown here. Notice that the table is headed by the word "weekdays." This implies that different schedules are followed on Saturdays, Sundays, and holidays.

The half-table on page 66 gives the time schedule for buses traveling to Newark from such starting points as Butler, Pompton Lakes, and Mountain View. The half-table below shows the time schedule for buses traveling in the opposite direction, that is, starting out from Newark and traveling to Mountain View, Pompton Lakes, etc., and ending up in Butler.

Route Number 114

WEEKDAYS

TO BUTLER								
NEWARK P.R.R. Station	BLOOMFIELD Bloomfield Center	MONTCLAIR D.L. & W. Station	CEDAR GROVE Bowden Road	LITTLE FALLS Main & Center Sts.	SINGAC Four Corners	MOUNTAIN VIEW Center	POMPTON LAKES Bus Station	BUTLER Bus Station
6.20	—	—	—	7.05	—	—	—	—
6.35	6.56	7.00	7.11	7.18	7.21	7.26	7.55	8.07
6.59	7.23	7.28	7.42	7.50	7.53	7.58	8.19	—
7.30	7.54	7.59	8.13	8.21	8.24	8.29	8.50	—
8.00	8.24	8.29	8.43	8.51	—	—	—	—
8.30	8.54	8.59	9.13	9.21	9.24	9.29	9.50	—
9.30	9.54	9.59	10.13	10.21	10.24	10.29	10.50	11.29
10.25	10.49	10.54	11.08	11.16	11.19	11.24	11.45	—
11.25	11.49	11.54	**12.08**	**12.16**	**12.19**	**12.24**	**12.45**	—
12.25	**12.49**	**12.54**	**1.08**	**1.16**	**1.19**	**1.24**	**1.45**	**2.17**
1.25	**1.49**	**1.54**	**2.08**	**2.16**	**2.19**	**2.24**	**2.45**	—
2.25	**2.49**	**2.54**	**3.08**	**3.16**	**3.19**	**3.24**	**3.45**	**4.19**
2.57	**3.26**	**3.32**	**3.46**	**3.55**	—	—	—	—
3.25	**3.54**	**4.00**	**4.15**	**4.24**	**4.27**	**4.32**	**4.53**	**5.14**
4.00	**4.29**	**4.35**	**4.49**	**4.58**	—	—	—	—
4.15	**4.41**	**4.47**	**5.01**	**5.10**	**5.13**	**5.18**	**5.39**	**5.59**
4.33	**4.59**	**5.05**	**5.19**	**5.28**	**5.31**	**5.36**	—	—
4.45	**5.11**	**5.17**	**5.31**	**5.40**	**5.43**	**5.48**	—	—
4.50	**5.16**	**5.22**	—	—	**5.39**	**5.44**	**6.05**	—
5.00	**5.26**	**5.32**	**5.46**	**5.55**	**5.58**	**6.03**	—	—
5.15	**5.41**	**5.47**	**6.01**	**6.10**	**6.13**	**6.18**	—	—
5.20	**5.46**	**5.52**	—	—	**6.09**	**6.14**	**6.35**	—
5.40	**6.08**	**6.13**	**6.27**	**6.36**	**6.39**	**6.44**	—	—
6.00	**6.23**	**6.29**	**6.41**	**6.49**	**6.52**	**6.57**	**7.18**	—
6.35	**6.54**	**6.58**	**7.08**	**7.13**	**7.16**	**7.21**	**7.41**	**7.53**
8.05	**8.24**	**8.28**	**8.38**	**8.43**	**8.46**	**8.51**	**9.11**	**9.23**
9.35	**9.54**	**9.58**	**10.08**	**10.13**	**10.16**	**10.21**	**10.41**	—
11.13	**11.32**	**11.36**	**11.46**	**11.51**	—	—	—	—
12.25	12.44	12.48	12.58	1.03	1.06	1.10	—	—

ILLUSTRATION 1: At what time does the bus that leaves Butler at 7:30 A.M. arrive in Newark?

SOLUTION:

Time of leaving Butler = 7:30 A.M.
Time of arrival in Newark = 9:09 A.M.

EXPLANATION: The numbers in lightface type in the table indicate the time between 12:00 midnight and 12:00 noon. Those numbers in the dark, or boldface, type indicate the time of day between 12:00 noon and 12:00 midnight. The former hours are usually indicated by the letters "A.M." and the latter by the letters "P.M." In solving this problem, run your finger down the column headed by Butler until you come to the numeral 7.30. This numeral is but a short way of writing 7:30 A.M. All the numerals in this column represent the various hours at which buses leave Butler for Newark. There are only 7 numerals in this column. This implies that there are only 7 trips that buses on Route Number 114 make from Butler to Newark each day. After placing the edge of a piece of paper along the row containing the numeral 7.30, run your finger along the row until it comes to the column headed by Newark. The numeral 9.09, at which your finger comes to rest, represents the time at which the 7:30 A.M. Butler bus arrives in Newark.

ILLUSTRATION 2: How long does it take the bus that leaves Butler at 7:30 A.M. to make the trip to Newark?

SOLUTION:

Time of leaving Butler = 7:30, or 7 hours and 30 minutes
Time of arrival in Newark = 9:09, or 9 hours and 9 minutes
Traveling time = 9 hours and 9 minutes − 7 hours and 30 minutes
= 8 hours and 69 minutes − 7 hours and 30 minutes
= 1 hour and 39 minutes

EXPLANATION: In finding the number of hours from 7:30 to 9:09, it is necessary to subtract the first number from the second. To do this, you must think of 7:30 in terms of its actual meaning of 7 hours and 30 minutes past midnight. Similarly, 9:09 means 9 hours and 9 minutes past midnight. At this point it is best that the subtraction problem be rewritten vertically, for in that arrangement it is far easier both to understand and to complete.

9 hours and 9 minutes
− 7 hours and 30 minutes

Since it is impossible to subtract 30 minutes from 9 minutes, you have to rewrite the 9 hours as 8 hours and 1 hour. The purpose of doing this is to change the 1 hour into 60 minutes. Then, by combining this with the 9 minutes, you end up with a number from which 30 minutes can be subtracted. Thus:

9 hours and 9 minutes = 8 hours and 1 hour and 9 minutes
= 8 hours and 60 minutes and 9 minutes
= 8 hours and 69 minutes

With this information, it is possible to complete the solution.

$$\begin{array}{r} \text{8 hours and 69 minutes} \\ -\ \text{7 hours and 30 minutes} \\ \hline \text{1 hour and 39 minutes} \end{array}$$

ILLUSTRATION 3: How long does it take the 12:25 P.M. bus out of Newark to make the trip to Butler?

SOLUTION:

Time of leaving Newark = 12:25
Time of arrival in Butler = 2:17 P.M., or 14:17
Traveling time = 14 hours 17 minutes − 12 hours 25 minutes
= 13 hours 77 minutes − 12 hours 25 minutes
= 1 hour 52 minutes

EXPLANATION: In order to understand the computation in the solution above, it is necessary to realize that a time such as 1:00 P.M. is much later than a time of 8:00 A.M. of the same day. In fact, it is 5 hours later. The simplest way of finding the time lapse of 5 hours is to consider midnight as being the 0 hour of any day. Under this consideration, 8:00 A.M. would be 8 hours after the 0 hour of the day, and, in the same way, 1:00 P.M. would be 13 hours after the 0 hour. Then, by subtracting the 8 hours from the 13 hours, you find that the time elapsed from 8:00 A.M. to 1:00 P.M. is 5 hours. Actually, by using this method of writing time, it is not necessary to write A.M. or P.M. after the hour. When a person said that the time is 8:20, everyone would know that this implied that it is 8 hours and 20 minutes after the 0 hour, which is midnight. Similarly, at 3:40 P.M., it would only be necessary to say that the time is 15:40 and omit mention of the P.M. Here, again, people would understand that 15 hours and 40 minutes had elapsed since the 0 hour. Hence, changing from P.M. time as you know it to be to time recorded by this method, can be done simply by adding 12 to the number of hours (unless the time happens to be between 12:00 noon and 1:00 P.M.).

Now to return to the solution in Illustration 3. Notice that the time of 2:17 P.M. was rewritten as 14:17. This change was made in order to be able to subtract the 12 hours and 25 minutes from the 14 hours and 17 minutes.

EXERCISES A

1. When you consider midnight as the 0 hour of the day, how would you rewrite each of the following hours without using the letters A.M. or P.M.?

	Time Normal Recording	Time New Recording		Time Normal Recording	Time New Recording
a.	2:00 A.M.	________	i.	4:00 P.M.	________
b.	5:00 A.M.	________	j.	3:00 P.M.	________
c.	3:30 A.M.	________	k.	1:20 P.M.	________
d.	9:45 A.M.	________	l.	2:15 P.M.	________
e.	10:30 A.M.	________	m.	8:40 P.M.	________
f.	11:20 A.M.	________	n.	10:15 P.M.	________
g.	12:01 A.M.	________	o.	12:20 P.M.	________
h.	12:57 A.M.	________	p.	12:20 A.M.	________

2. Rewrite the following hours and minutes in terms of the number of hours and minutes indicated. The first exercise is completed for you.

a. 5 hr. 20 min. = 4 hr. ___80___ min.
b. 7 hr. 20 min. = 6 hr. ________ min.
c. 6 hr. 0 min. = 5 hr. ________ min.
d. 10 hr. 15 min. = 9 hr. ________ min.
e. 4 hr. 5 min. = 3 hr. ________ min.
f. 11 hr. 23 min. = 10 hr. ________ min.
g. 17 hr. 0 min. = 16 hr. ________ min.
h. 15 hr. 36 min. = 14 hr. ________ min.
i. 14 hr. 12 min. = 13 hr. ________ min.
j. 22 hr. 3 min. = 21 hr. ________ min.
k. 21 hr. 9 min. = 20 hr. ________ min.
l. 17 hr. 1 min. = 16 hr. ________ min.

3. Find the difference in each of the following exercises.

a.	7 hr. 25 min. − 4 hr. 12 min.	e.	21 hr. 55 min. − 9 hr. 38 min.
b.	5 hr. 47 min. − 2 hr. 24 min.	f.	12 hr. 24 min. − 7 hr. 16 min.
c.	18 hr. 31 min. − 12 hr. 19 min.	g.	8 hr. − 5 hr. 20 min.
d.	22 hr. 43 min. − 17 hr. 27 min.	h.	15 hr. − 13 hr. 35 min.

i. 17 hr. 10 min. − 10 hr. 50 min.

j. 14 hr. 5 min. − 12 hr. 20 min.

k. 23 hr. 21 min. − 20 hr. 25 min.

l. 14 hr. 7 min. − 12 hr. 53 min.

4. Find the elapsed time in each of the following exercises.

	From	To	Elapsed Time		From	To	Elapsed Time
a.	1:10 A.M.	1:50 A.M.	________	h.	10:00 A.M.	2:00 P.M.	________
b.	2:15 A.M.	2:40 A.M.	________	i.	11:00 A.M.	5:00 P.M.	________
c.	3:12 P.M.	4:20 P.M.	________	j.	10:20 A.M.	1:30 P.M.	________
d.	10:15 P.M.	11:48 P.M.	________	k.	9:05 A.M.	3:20 P.M.	________
e.	5:40 P.M.	6:10 P.M.	________	l.	7:45 A.M.	2:30 P.M.	________
f.	9:30 P.M.	11:20 P.M.	________	m.	5:37 A.M.	7:10 P.M.	________
g.	2:53 A.M.	9:05 A.M.	________	n.	6:52 A.M.	9:07 P.M.	________

B

For this set of exercises, use the bus schedule on pages 66–67.

1. At what time will the buses that leave Butler at the hour indicated arrive at each of the locations indicated?

	Hour Of Leaving	Location	Hour Of Arrival
a.	6:20 A.M.	Singac	________
b.	7:30 A.M.	Montclair	________
c.	8:10 A.M.	Bloomfield	________
d.	11:40 A.M.	Newark	________
e.	2:50 P.M.	Mountain View	________
f.	4:30 P.M.	Little Falls	________

2. At what time will the buses that leave Newark at the hour indicated arrive at each of the locations indicated?

	Hour Of Leaving	Location	Hour Of Arrival
a.	7:30 A.M.	Bloomfield	________
b.	10:25 A.M.	Little Falls	________
c.	8:00 A.M.	Cedar Grove	________
d.	5:20 P.M.	Singac	________
e.	8:05 P.M.	Pompton Lakes	________
f.	11:25 A.M.	Mountain View	________

3. How long does it take the buses that leave Pompton Lakes for Newark at the hour indicated to reach each of the locations indicated?

	Hour Of Leaving	Location	Hour Of Arrival	Time Spent Traveling
a.	9:00 A.M.	Bloomfield	________	________
b.	10:00 A.M.	Newark	________	________

	Hour Of Leaving	Location	Hour Of Arrival	Time Spent Traveling
c.	7:03 A.M.	Montclair	________	________
d.	7:50 A.M.	Cedar Grove	________	________
e.	1:55 P.M.	Newark	________	________
f.	3:10 P.M.	Montclair	________	________
g.	12:00 P.M.	Newark	________	________

4. How long does it take the buses that leave Newark at the hour indicated to reach each of the locations indicated?

	Hour Of Leaving	Location	Hour Of Arrival	Time Spent Traveling
a.	8:00 A.M.	Little Falls	________	________
b.	9:30 A.M.	Pompton Lakes	________	________
c.	1:25 P.M.	Singac	________	________
d.	4:33 P.M.	Cedar Grove	________	________
e.	9:30 A.M.	Butler	________	________
f.	11:25 A.M.	Pompton Lakes	________	________
g.	12:25 P.M.	Singac	________	________

C

For the following questions, use the bus schedule on pages 66–67.

1. Consider the bus that leaves Butler at 6:20 A.M.

a. How many stops will it make after leaving Butler? ________

b. At what places that Route Number 114 bus normally stops will it not stop on this trip? ________

c. Mr. Grant has to walk for approximately 10 minutes from the time he gets off the bus until the time he reaches the place where he works. He has to be at work at 9:00 A.M. in Montclair. Can he take the 7:30 bus out of Butler, or must he take the 6:20 bus? ________

2. George Peabody works in Newark but lives in Butler.

a. If he misses the 4:15 bus out of Newark when going home in the afternoon, until what hour will he have to wait before the next bus leaves for Butler? ________

b. How long is this waiting time? ________

3. Consider the schedule for the buses leaving Newark for Montclair.

a. How long does it take the bus that leaves Newark at 6:35 in the morning to make this trip? ________

b. How long does it take the bus that leaves Newark at 4:45 in the afternoon to make this trip? ________

c. How much longer does it take the afternoon bus to make the trip than the morning bus? ________

d. Why should the trip take more time in the afternoon than it takes in the morning? ________

PART 2

The time schedules for buses traveling long distances between states are somewhat more difficult to read than the one you have just examined. The schedule shown below is for Route Number 65A of an

NEW YORK—BALTIMORE—WASHINGTON

Trip Numbers 65A		7051	9	2029	117	2033	7121	173	2057	2037	2053	115	2039
New York, NY Port Authority Term.	Lv	12 01	2 00	3 30	5 30	7 45	8 30	9 30	10 30	10 45	**12 30**	**1 30**	**1 45**
Jersey City, NJ	Lv	↓				8 10		↓		11 10		↓	↓
Newark, NJ	Lv	12 35				8 30		10 05		11 30		**2 05**	**2 20**
Bellmawr, NJ						10 00				↓			↓
Wilmington, DE	Lv			↓		10 50				**1 45**			**4 35**
State Road, DE	Ar	2 45		5 50		11 05				**2 00**			**4 50**
State Road, DE	Lv	2 45	NON-STOP	6 05	NON-STOP	11 15	NON-STOP		NON-STOP	**2 10**	NON-STOP	NON-STOP	**5 00**
Elkton Jct., MD				6 25		11 35				**2 30**			**5 20**
Northeast Jct., MD		↓		6 30		11 40		↓		**2 35**			**5 25**
Perryville, MD		3 20		6 40		11 50		**12 50**		**2 45**			**5 35**
Aberdeen, MD		3 30		6 50		**12 01**		**1 00**		**2 55**			**5 45**
Edgewood Road, MD		↓	↓	7 00	↓	**12 10**	↓	↓	↓	**3 05**	↓	↓	**5 55**
Baltimore, MD	Ar	4 15	5 30	7 45	9 05	**12 50**	11 59	**1 45**	**2 00**	**3 55**	**4 00**	**5 30**	**6 40**
Baltimore, MD	Lv	4 20	5 35	7 50	9 10	**12 55**		**1 50**		**4 00**			**6 45**
Washington, DC	Ar	5 15	6 30	8 45	10 05	**1 50**		**2 45**		**5 00**			**7 40**

interstate bus company. The numbers that appear across the top line (7051, 9, 2029, 117, and so on) are the trip numbers on this route. For instance, Trip Number 7051 will leave the Port Authority terminal in New York City at 12:01 in the morning and arrive in Newark at 12:35. It will then continue until its next stop at State Road, Delaware. After making three more stops—at Perryville, Aberdeen, and Baltimore—it will arrive at Washington, D.C., at 5:15 in the morning. Notice that this table is read by going down the column, while the bus schedule on pages 66–67 is read by going across the row.

Whenever the time of day is shown in a bus schedule it means that the bus makes a stop at that place at that hour. Thus, Trip Number 115 leaves New York at 1:30 in the afternoon, stops in Newark at 2:05, and makes no other stops until it reaches Baltimore at 5:30. Incidentally, the numbers in dark type and the numbers in light type have exactly the same meaning as they had on the bus schedule on pages 66–67. In fact, all time schedules, whether they be bus, train, or plane, use the same notation to distinguish between P.M. and A.M. times.

ILLUSTRATION 1: Trip Number 117 makes only two stops between New York and Washington, while Trip Number 2033 stops at every point along the route. How much longer does Trip Number 2033 take in making the journey than Trip Number 117?

SOLUTION:

Trip Number 117
Time of leaving New York = 5:30
Time of arrival at Washington = 10:05
Traveling time = 10 hr. 5 min. − 5 hr. 30 min.
= 9 hr. 65 min. − 5 hr. 30 min.
= 4 hr. 35 min.

Trip Number 2033
Time of leaving New York = 7:45
Time of arrival in Washington = 1:50 P.M., or 13:50
Traveling time = 13 hr. 50 min. − 7 hr. 45 min.
= 6 hr. 5 min.

Extra time needed for Trip Number 2033 = 6 hr. 5 min. − 4 hr. 35 min.
= 5 hr. 65 min.
− 4 hr. 35 min.
= 1 hr. 30 min.

EXPLANATION: To find the traveling time for Trip Number 117, it is necessary to change 10 hours 5 minutes to 9 hours 65 minutes. How is this done? In writing the time of arrival at Washington for Trip Number 2033, you must rewrite 1:50 P.M. as 13:50. How does this help you find the traveling time?

It is impossible for an interstate bus company to publish a rate table showing the cost of transportation along all its routes. The airlines and trains can do this, as we shall soon see. However, buses stop at so many different places in traveling between cities that all the rates cannot be shown in a single table, for there are too many. Also, different trips between the same two cities will sometimes follow different routes. This, too, affects any rate table the company might want to publish.

It is interesting to note that the rates of all buses traveling between different states are determined by an agency of the federal government called the Interstate Commerce Commission. Hence, two different companies running buses over the same route between two cities must charge exactly the same rate. Since they cannot attract customers by lowering their rates, they try to attract them by offering better service. The fares in the following table are those charged between a few selected cities.

To encourage travelers to use its buses both in going to their destinations and in returning home, bus companies offer a discount rate on the purchase of a round-trip ticket. A person who purchases one of these tickets pays approximately 5% less than twice the one-way fare.

ONE-WAY BUS FARES BETWEEN SELECTED CITIES

	Atlanta	Chicago	Denver	Los Angeles	San Francisco	Seattle	Washington, D.C.
New York	$37.95	$42.20	$73.40	$106.60	$106.60	$98.85	$12.35
San Antonio	42.95	48.85	43.45	59.40	70.50	85.30	65.30
Seattle	84.60	66.85	51.70	44.80	33.80	–	92.70
Denver	61.55	38.50	–	48.75	48.75	51.70	64.45

ILLUSTRATION 2: How much will Beverly Odom pay for a round-trip bus ticket between Seattle and San Francisco?

SOLUTION:

One-way fare = $33.80

Round-trip fare without discount = 2 × $33.80
= $67.60

Approximate discount on round-trip fare = 5% × $67.60
= .05 × $67.60
= $3.38

Approximate round-trip fare = $67.60 – $3.38
= $64.22

EXPLANATION: If there were no discount on the round-trip fare, then Beverly would have to pay twice the one-way fare of $33.80, or $67.60. However, the bus company offers a discount of approximately 5%. The percent numeral 5% has to be changed to its equivalent decimal form, .05, before the product of 5% and $67.60 can be found. Subtracting the discount from twice the one-way cost gives the round-trip fare of $64.22.

EXERCISES

A

Do you recall how to find the answer in each of the following exercises? If not, you will probably want to refer to the pages indicated for help.

1. Change each of the following percent numerals to its equivalent decimal numeral form (pages 514–515).

a. 20% ______	d. 2% ______	g. 4.5% ______
b. 35% ______	e. 5% ______	h. 5.2% ______
c. 42% ______	f. 7% ______	i. 6.7% ______

2. Find the product to the nearest penny in each of the following exercises (pages 519–521).

a. 10% × $62.00 = ______	f. 10% × $75.15 = ______
b. 10% × $45.50 = ______	g. 5% × $123.25 = ______
c. 20% × $56.30 = ______	h. 20% × $156.45 = ______
d. 25% × $87.40 = ______	i. 30% × $187.75 = ______
e. 35% × $93.20 = ______	j. 10% × $193.95 = ______

B

1. At what time will each of the following trips arrive in Wilmington, Delaware?

a. Trip Number 2033 ______	c. Trip Number 2039 ______
b. Trip Number 2037 ______	

2. Find the time spent on each of the following bus trips.

	Trip Number	From	To	Leaving Time	Arrival Time	Length Of Time
a.	7051	Baltimore	Washington, D.C.	______	______	______
b.	2039	New York	Baltimore	______	______	______
c.	2037	Wilmington	Baltimore	______	______	______
d.	117	New York	Washington, D.C.	______	______	______
e.	115	Newark	Baltimore	______	______	______
f.	2033	Jersey City	Aberdeen	______	______	______

	Trip Number	From	To	Leaving Time	Arrival Time	Length Of Time
g.	7051	New York	Washington, D.C.	________	________	________
h.	2033	Wilmington	Washington, D.C.	________	________	________
i.	2037	Newark	Washington, D.C.	________	________	________
j.	2057	New York	Baltimore	________	________	________
k.	2033	New York	Baltimore	________	________	________

3. Find the cost of each of the following one-way trips. Use the table on page 75.

	From	To	Cost
a.	San Antonio	Denver	$________
b.	Seattle	Washington, D.C.	________
c.	New York	San Francisco	________
d.	Denver	Seattle	________
e.	Seattle	Los Angeles	________
f.	Atlanta	San Antonio	________
g.	Los Angeles	New York	________

4. Find the approximate round-trip bus fare in each of the following exercises. Use the table on page 75.

	From	To	One-Way Fare	Two-Way Fare	Discount	Round-Trip Fare
a.	San Antonio	Los Angeles	$______	$______	$______	$______
b.	Denver	Chicago	______	______	______	______
c.	New York	Atlanta	______	______	______	______
d.	Seattle	San Francisco	______	______	______	______
e.	Denver	Washington, D.C.	______	______	______	______
f.	Chicago	New York	______	______	______	______

5. At what average speed would the buses have to travel in order to cover the distances shown in each of the following exercises? Find your answer to the nearest mile. (See Chapter 1, page 40.)

	Traveling Time	Distance Traveled	Average Speed
a.	2.5 hours	125 miles	________ mph
b.	4.5 hours	243 miles	________ mph
c.	6.5 hours	299 miles	________ mph
d.	3 hr. 30 min.	190 miles	________ mph
e.	7 hr. 30 min.	395 miles	________ mph
f.	5 hr. 30 min.	265 miles	________ mph

6. Determine the average speed to the nearest mile at which the buses have to travel in order to keep on schedule. Use the bus schedule on page 73.

	Trip Number	From	To	Distance Between Cities	Traveling Time	Average Speed
a.	2037	Newark	Washington, D.C.	218 mi.	________	________ mph
b.	9	New York	Washington, D.C.	224 mi.	________	________ mph
c.	2053	New York	Baltimore	188 mi.	________	________ mph

C

1. James Nazario is planning to take the bus from Newark, N.J., to Aberdeen, Md.
   a. How much time will it take the bus on Trip Number 2033? ________
   b. How much time will it take the bus on Trip Number 7051? ________
   c. How much more time will James spend on the "2033" trip? ________
2. How much more time will it take to travel between New York and Baltimore by bus on Trip Number 2037 than on Trip Number 173? ________
3. Use the bus schedule on page 73 to answer each of the following questions.
   a. How long does it take the bus on Trip Number 2033 to make the trip from New York to Newark? ________
   b. How long does it take the bus on Trip Number 173 to make the trip from New York to Newark? ________
   c. Why should more time be needed for Trip Number 2033? ________

Unit 3: Traveling by Railroad

Train schedules are read in much the same way as bus schedules. The following schedule, however, contains an additional feature that needs examining. The hours on the left side of the table are read in the usual manner, that is, by starting at the top of the table and working your way down. Thus, Trip Number 17 leaves New York at 11:00 A.M., pulls into Newark at 11:16 A.M., and then goes on to Trenton, arriving there at 12:00 noon.

Read Down				Read Up		
17	37	29		42	48	18
11 00	**2 00**	**7 30**	Lv New York, Penna Sta. . . . . Ar	8 00	**12 20**	**8 55**
11 16	**2 16**	**7 46**	Newark	7 43	**12 05**	**8 40**
12 00	**2 59**	**8 29**	Trenton	6 56	11 20	**7 55**
12 27	**3 26**	**8 57**	North Philadelphia	6 25	10 52	**7 27**
12 36	**3 35**	**9 06**	Philadelphia, 30th St. Sta.	6 12	10 43	**7 17**
1 06	**4 04**	**9 39**	Wilmington	5 35	10 14	**6 48**
2 08	**5 05**	**10 40**	Baltimore, Penna Sta.	4 32	9 10	**5 45**
2 50	**5 45**	**11 20**	Ar Washington, D.C. Lv	3 50	8 30	**5 00**

The numbers on the right side of the table, however, are read in the reverse direction, that is, by starting at the bottom and working your way up to the top of the table. For instance, Trip Number 42 leaves Washington, D.C., at 3:50 A.M. and arrives in Baltimore at 4:32 A.M. From Baltimore it goes to Wilmington, arriving there at 5:35 A.M. It then makes a number of other stops along the way until it arrives in New York at 8:00 A.M.

ILLUSTRATION 1: How long does it take Trip Number 48 to travel from Baltimore to Newark?

SOLUTION:

Time of leaving Baltimore = 9:10 A.M.
Time of leaving Newark = 12:05 P.M.
Traveling time = 12 hrs. 5 min. − 9 hrs. 10 min.
= 11 hrs. 65 min. − 9 hrs. 10 min.
= 2 hrs. 55 min.

EXPLANATION: This solution differs from the earlier ones only in that it is necessary for you to read the table from bottom to top. Note first that the train leaves Baltimore at 9:10 A.M. Then, by running your finger up the column for Trip Number 48, you discover that it arrives in Newark at 12:05 P.M. The solution is then completed in exactly the same manner as in the earlier problems of finding the number of hours between two numerals in a time schedule.

The quiet, computerized Bay Area Rapid Transit system (BART), one of America's newest rail lines, accepts passengers at the Lake Merritt station in Oakland, California.

Trains that carry people from suburban areas to a city offer their passengers the opportunity to save quite a bit of money on the purchase of *commutation* tickets. Although different railroad companies may have different plans, the usual commutation ticket is either of the weekly variety, or the monthly variety. With the former, a passenger usually has 12 one-way trips he can make during a particular week and for this he pays a flat fee. With the monthly commutation ticket, the passenger may make as many trips as he wants to make during the month. In both cases, the cost is a good deal less than the total cost of the individual trips, or the round-trip fares, over the same period.

1-Day Round Trip, One-Way, and Commutation Fares

	Between New York (Pennsylvania Station) and			
Subject to Change	1-Day Round Trip	One-Way	Monthly Commutation	Weekly Commutation
Newark	–	$0.70	$24.35	$ 6.80
Elizabeth	$1.70	1.15	35.05	9.70
Rahway	2.10	1.44	46.15	12.90
Avenel	2.30	1.60	48.20	13.45
Edgar	2.30	1.60	48.65	13.55
Woodbridge	2.30	1.60	48.65	13.55
Perth Amboy	2.50	1.75	49.30	13.70
South Amboy	2.70	1.85	50.10	14.00
Matawan	3.10	2.13	52.65	14.80
Hazlet	3.30	2.29	52.70	14.80
Middletown	3.50	2.40	54.05	15.05
Red Bank	4.00	2.65	54.20	15.15
Little Silver	4.25	2.80	54.95	15.30
Monmouth Park	–	2.95	–	–
Long Branch	4.70	3.10	55.65	15.50
Elberon	4.70	3.10	56.15	15.70
Allenhurst	5.00	3.25	56.40	15.75
No. Asbury Park	5.05	3.40	56.40	15.75
Asbury Park	5.05	3.40	56.50	15.75
Bradley Beach	5.05	3.40	56.65	15.80
Avon	5.25	3.50	56.70	15.80
Belmar	5.25	3.50	56.80	15.90
Spring Lake	5.50	3.65	57.05	15.95
Sea Girt	5.50	3.65	57.20	15.95
Manasquan	5.75	3.80	57.25	16.00
Point Pleasant Beach	5.75	3.80	57.50	16.10
Bay Head Junction	6.00	3.95	57.60	16.10

ILLUSTRATION 2: Mr. Kerner lives in Avon and is employed in New York. He works 22 days during an average business month. How much can he save by purchasing a monthly commutation ticket rather than one-way tickets?

SOLUTION:

Cost of monthly commutation ticket = \$56.70
Cost of one-way trip = \$3.50
Number of one-way trips in one day = 2
Number of one-way trips in 22 days = 22 × 2
= 44
Cost of 44 one-way trips = 44 × \$3.50
= \$154
Saving = \$154 − \$56.70
= \$97.30

EXPLANATION: To find the cost of the monthly commutation ticket from New York to Avon, run your finger down the first column until it reaches the word "Avon." After placing the edge of a piece of paper beneath this word, run your finger along the paper's edge until it comes to the column headed by the words "Monthly Commutation." The numeral your finger will be pointing to is "\$56.70"—the cost of the monthly commutation ticket between New York and Avon.

You may have wondered why the person in Illustration 2 did not buy 1 round-trip ticket each day rather than 2 one-way tickets. Buying a round-trip ticket instead of 2 one-way tickets, however, is not always possible. Frequently, the railroad will insist that round-trip tickets be used only between the hours of 9:30 in the morning and 4:30 in the afternoon. The 1-day round-trip ticket is designed to attract the non-commuter into using the train to the city rather than a car.

EXERCISES A

1. Determine the time at which each of the following trains pulls into the station indicated. Use the schedule on page 78.

	Trip Number	Station	Time
a.	17	North Philadelphia	________
b.	37	Wilmington	________
c.	17	Baltimore	________
d.	29	Washington	________

2. Determine the time at which each of the following trains pulls into the station indicated. Use the schedule on page 78.

	Trip Number	Station	Time
a.	42	Trenton	________
b.	48	Wilmington	________
c.	48	Newark	________
d.	18	Philadelphia	________

3. Find the time spent on each of the following train trips.

	Trip Number	From	To	Leaving Time	Arrival Time	Length Of Time
a.	37	New York	Wilmington	________	________	________
b.	37	Trenton	Baltimore	________	________	________
c.	29	North Philadelphia	Washington	________	________	________
d.	17	Newark	Wilmington	________	________	________
e.	42	Washington	New York	________	________	________
f.	42	Baltimore	Newark	________	________	________
g.	18	Wilmington	North Philadelphia	________	________	________
h.	42	Philadelphia	Trenton	________	________	________
i.	48	Philadelphia	Newark	________	________	________
j.	48	Baltimore	New York	________	________	________

4. Find the cost of a one-way ticket between New York and each of the following stations. Use the table on page 80.

a. Newark	________	d. Red Bank	________
b. Edgar	________	e. Allenhurst	________
c. Hazlet	________	f. Sea Girt	________

5. Find the cost of the weekly commutation ticket between New York and each of the following stations. Use the table on page 80.

a. Avenel	________	d. Bradley Beach	________
b. South Amboy	________	e. Belmar	________
c. Long Branch	________	f. Point Pleasant Beach	________

6. How much will a person save by purchasing a 1-day round-trip ticket rather than 2 one-way tickets between New York and each of the following stations?

Station	1-Day Round Trip	One Way	Two Times One Way	Saving
a. Red Bank	$________	$________	$________	$________
b. Woodbridge	________	________	________	________
c. Sea Girt	________	________	________	________
d. Middletown	________	________	________	________
e. Elberon	________	________	________	________

7. How much will a person save by purchasing a weekly commutation ticket rather than 5 round-trip tickets for the week in traveling between New York and each of the following stations?

Station	Weekly Commutation	1-Day Round Trip	Five 1-Day Round Trips	Saving Or Loss
a. Elizabeth	$________	$________	$________	$________
b. Perth Amboy	________	________	________	________
c. Little Silver	________	________	________	________
d. Spring Lake	________	________	________	________
e. Rahway	________	________	________	________

8. Over the period of one year, a commuter will purchase either 50 weekly commutation tickets, or 12 monthly commutation tickets. How much can commuters save by buying the monthly tickets if they travel between New York and each of the following stations?

Station	Weekly Commutation	50 Weekly Commutations	Monthly Commutation	12 Monthly Commutations	Saving
a. Newark	$________	$________	$________	$________	$________
b. Hazlet	________	________	________	________	________
c. Bradley Beach	________	________	________	________	________
d. Allenhurst	________	________	________	________	________
e. Belmar	________	________	________	________	________

B

1. The distance from Baltimore to Newark is 176 miles. The train on Trip Number 48 leaves Baltimore on time, but arrives in Newark 5 minutes late.

a. At what time did the train arrive in Newark? ________

b. How long did the trip take? ________

c. At what average speed, to the nearest mile, did the train have to travel in making this trip? ________

2. Steve Evans is planning to take the trip from New York to Washington. He is thinking of leaving sometime in the early afternoon.

a. If he takes Train Trip Number 37, how long will this trip take him? Use the train schedule on page 78. ________

b. If he takes Bus Trip Number 2039, how long will this trip take him? Use the bus schedule on page 73. ________

c. How much time can he save by taking the train instead of the bus? ________

3. Steve Evans of Problem 2 decided he would also compare the cost of traveling by bus against the cost of traveling by train.

a. Find the cost of a one-way bus ticket between New York and Washington. Use the table on page 75. ________

b. If the cheapest one-way train fare between New York and Washington is $14.50, how much can Steve save by traveling by bus? ________

c. The railroad offers no discount on a round-trip ticket to Washington. The bus company offers a 5% discount rate off twice the one-way fare on this trip. How much would Steve save by purchasing a round-trip bus ticket instead of 2 one-way train tickets? ________

Unit 4: Traveling by Air

PART 1

Each airline publishes a booklet in which it lists alphabetically the various cities from which its flights originate. The table on page 86 is a section of a flight timetable used by an airline for the city of Los Angeles. Included in this table are some of the cities to which planes are flown from Los Angeles by this company.

Perhaps the best way of clarifying the information shown in the table is to interpret each of the items on the first line of the very first flight from Los Angeles to Chicago.

1. The numerals "8:45a" and "2:25p" indicate that the plane will leave Los Angeles at 8:45 in the morning and arrive in Chicago at 2:25 in the afternoon. As usual, the lightface and boldface type refer to A.M. and P.M. time, respectively.
2. The letter "O" to the right of 2:25p indicates that the plane will land at O'Hare airport in Chicago.
3. The numeral "318" is the *flight number*. It is similar to the trip number on a bus schedule.
4. The words "Non-Stop" imply that the plane will make no stops on its flight from Los Angeles to Chicago. Notice that further along in that column there is a flight that will stop off at Dallas on its way to Chicago.
5. The numeral "707" indicates the type of plane that will be flown on the trip.
6. The very last word, "daily," implies that this flight is made every day of the week.

Just below the top line in the "Chicago" section of the table, these symbols appear.

F \$172.00 Y \$132.00 K \$119.00 FN \$132.00 YN \$106.00

The letters "F," "Y," and "K" indicate the type of service that is available to passengers:

F (First-Class Service): Special meals are provided and there is no charge for cocktails. The seats are wider and there is much more

Nearly 300 passengers can be carried on one of these "jumbo jets." These planes have great appeal because they are so much more spacious and luxurious than smaller planes.

leg room between the seats than in the other services. Also, there are fewer passengers for each steward or stewardess.

Y (Coach Service): Meals are served at no cost but there is a charge for cocktails.

K (Economy Service): The service is much the same as in the coach service except that the passengers are offered only a beverage rather than a meal.

The letters "FN" and "YN" refer to *first class night flights* and *coach night flights*, respectively. The cost of the night flights is a great deal lower than that of the day flights. However, special, reduced night rates are not available for every night flight. As an illustration, notice that flight 196 to Chicago is a night flight and yet a person can not buy a ticket at the night rates. This is indicated by the fact that a small star does not appear after the flight number, 196. However, on flight number 262 out of Los Angeles to Chicago, there is a star to the right of the flight number, implying that night rates are available for this flight.

Notice, too, that the 12:40 A.M. flight out of Los Angeles to Chicago has two flight numbers, 262 and 206. The first flight, number 262, takes the passengers to Dallas. At Dallas the passengers leave this plane and pick up flight 206, which will take them on to Chicago. Now, if you will look at the "Dallas" section of this table, you will discover that this same flight 262 is listed there on the last line. This is the flight that a person would take if he wanted to go from Los Angeles to Dallas at 12:40 in the morning. He would arrive in Dallas at 5:17 A.M. From this point, if he wanted to go to Chicago, he would pick up flight number 206, as stated earlier.

FROM LOS ANGELES (PDT)

Leave	Arrive	Flight	Stops or Connecting City	Meals	Equipment	Operates
		F$172.00 Y$132.00 K$119.00 FN$132.00 YN$106.00				
TO: CHICAGO (CDT)						
				Airports M - Midway O- O'Hare		
8:45a	**2:25p** O	318	NON-STOP		707	Daily
10:00a	**3:38p** O	184	NON-STOP		D10	Daily
12:00p	**5:43p** O	194	NON-STOP		707	Daily
3:30p	**9:10p** O	192	NON-STOP		707	Daily
12:20a	5:55a O	196	NON-STOP		707	Daily
12:40a	8:56a O	262/206★	Dallas		D10/727	Ex Su
12:40a	8:56a O	262/206★	Dallas		D10/707	Su
12:40a	9:52a O	262/238★	Dallas		D10/727	Daily
		F$181.00 Y$139.00 FN$139.00 YN$111.00				
TO: CINCINNATI (EDT)						
7:40a	**3:52p**	200/342	Dallas		707/707	Sa
7:40a	**3:52p**	200/342	Dallas		707/727	Ex Sa
8:30a	**5:25p**	250/514	Memphis		727/727	Daily
12:00p	**7:40p**	390	One-Stop		727	Daily
1:00p	**9:13p**	20/394	Dallas		707/727	Daily
12:40a	9:10a	262/612★	Dallas		D10/707	Daily
					F$195.00 Y$150.00	
TO: CLEVELAND (EDT)						
9:15a	**4:19p**	74	NON-STOP		707	Daily
12:45p	**7:45p**	72	NON-STOP		707	Daily
11:00p	6:00a	36	NON-STOP		707	Daily
					F$188.00 Y$145.00	
TO: COLUMBUS, Ohio (EDT)						
7:40a	**4:48p**	200/424	Dallas		707/727	Daily
1:00p	**10:26p**	20/120	Dallas		707/727	Daily
TO: DALLAS FT WORTH (CDT)			F$128.00 Y$99.00 FN$99.00 YN$78.00			
					Airport D - Dallas	
7:40a	**12:22p** D	200	NON-STOP		707	Daily
10:00a	**2:40p** D	122	NON-STOP		727	Daily
1:00p	**5:40p** D	20	NON-STOP		707	Daily
2:30p	**7:10p** D	324	NON-STOP		727	Daily
3:45p	**8:25p** D	78	NON-STOP		707	Sa
5:10p	**9:50p** D	306	NON-STOP		727	Daily
9:30p	2:04a D	314★	NON-STOP		727	Daily
10:35p	3:12a D	378★	NON-STOP		707	Daily
12:40a	5:17a D	262★	NON-STOP		D10	Daily

★ Nightcoach Fares, FN, YN

FROM LOS ANGELES (PDT) (Cont'd)

Leave	Arrive	Flight	Stops or Connecting City	Meals	Equipment	Operates
			F$174.00 Y$134.00 FN$134.00 YN$107.00			
TO: LOUISVILLE (EDT)						
7:40a	**3:40p**	200/424	Dallas		707/727	Daily
8:30a	**4:17p**	250	One-Stop		727	Daily
1:00p	**9:03p**	20	One-Stop		707	Daily
12:40a	10:29a	262/344★	Dallas		D10/727	Daily
			F$156.00 Y$121.00			
TO: MEMPHIS (CDT)						
8:30a	**1:45p**	250	NON-STOP		727	Daily
10:00a	**5:27p**	122	Two-Stop		727	Daily
1:35p	**6:50p**	528	NON-STOP		727	Daily
5:10p	**11:33p**	306/264	Dallas		727/727	Daily
12:40a	7:58a	262/180	Dallas		D10/727	Daily
			F$229.00 Y$176.00 FN$176.00 YN$141.00			
TO: NEW YORK NEWARK (EDT)						
			Airports E - Newark J - Kennedy L - LaGuardia			
8:45a	**4:39p** J	2	NON-STOP		747	Daily
8:45a	**5:44p** E	318/220	Chicago		707/707	Daily
9:00a	**5:53p** L	68/418	Detroit		D10/727	Ex Sa
11:00a	**6:47p** E	8	NON-STOP		707	Daily
12:00p	**9:10p** L	390/146	St Louis		727/727	Daily
1:00p	**8:52p** J	32	NON-STOP		747	Daily
4:30p	12:23a J	4	NON-STOP		707	Ex Sa
10:30p	6:20a J	10	NON-STOP		707	Daily
10:35p	8:03a L	378/428★	Dallas		707/727	Daily
12:20a	9:43a E	196/358	Chicago		707/707	Daily
12:20a	9:50a L	196/246	Chicago		707/727	Daily
12:40a	11:13a E	262/84★	Dallas		D10/707	Daily
			F$123.00 Y$94.00 FN$94.00 YN$76.00			
TO: OKLAHOMA CITY (CDT)			Via Dallas F$128.00 Y$99.00 FN$99.00 YN$78.00			
9:25a	**1:57p**	382	NON-STOP		707	Daily
12:40p	**5:10p**	178	NON-STOP		707	Daily
2:30p	**8:58p**	324/69	Dallas		727/707	Daily
5:10p	**11:05p**	306	One-Stop		727	Daily
12:40a	7:40a	262/238★	Dallas		D10/727	Daily

★ Nightcoach Fares, FN, YN

Similarly, a person flying from Los Angeles to Cincinnati at 12:40 A.M. would take this very same flight 262 (see the "Cincinnati" section of the table) and leave the plane in Dallas. At that point he would pick up flight 612, which would take him on to Cincinnati.

The number of dollars that is written immediately to the right of the flight-service code shows the cost of a one-way ticket for that flight. In the case of the flights from Los Angeles to Chicago, the cost of a first-class flight is $172, while the coach fare is only $132. There is no discount offered on round-trip tickets.

The prices listed in the table already include the federal tax of 8% on the airline's original charge for these flights. The amount of federal tax, or 8% of the original price, comes to just about 7.4% of the amount the traveler must pay for a ticket.

ILLUSTRATION 1: Anna Caruso took flight number 250 out of Los Angeles to Memphis. She traveled in the coach section of the plane.

a. What was the cost of this flight?
b. Approximately how much federal tax was included in the price of Anna's ticket?

EXPLANATION: To find the cost of the flight it is necessary to examine the "Memphis" section of the table. To the right of the letter "Y"—representing coach service—is the numeral "$121.00"; this is the cost of Anna's flight. The approximate amount of federal tax is determined by computing 7.4% of that amount.

SOLUTION:

(a) Coach service fare = $121

(b) Approximate federal tax = 7.4% × $121
= .074 × $121
= $8.95

The computation needed to determine the time spent in traveling by bus or train was relatively simple. However, a plane will frequently cross a number of *time zones* when flying from one part of the country to another. The United States is divided into four different time zones and whenever we pass from one zone to another we either gain an hour in time or lose an hour in time.

Pacific	Mountain	Central	Eastern
7 P.M.	8 P.M.	9 P.M.	10 P.M.

When it is 10:00 in the evening in the Eastern time zone, it is only 9:00 in the evening in the Central time zone, and but 7:00 in the evening in the Pacific time zone. Therefore, if a person were to travel from New York to Los Angeles, he would have to turn his watch *back an hour* three times for each of the three times he crossed a time-zone line. Similarly, were he traveling in the reverse direction, he would have to set his watch *ahead* three hours to account for the three time-zone lines he crossed.

ILLUSTRATION 2: How long was Anna's flight in Illustration 1?

EXPLANATION: The letters "PDT" next to the words "Los Angeles" in the heading of the table signify "Pacific Daylight Time," while the letters "CDT" next to the word "Memphis" signify "Central Daylight Time." Hence, Anna left Los Angeles at 8:30 A.M. Pacific time and arrived in Memphis at 1:45 P.M. Central time. Had Anna *not* reset her watch while traveling, when she landed in Memphis it would have read 11:45 A.M. rather than 1:45 P.M., since Pacific time is 2 hours behind Central time. Hence, Anna was in flight only from 8:30 A.M. *Pacific* time until 11:45 A.M. *Pacific* time. Therefore, the computation can be completed as in the past.

SOLUTION:

Time in flight = 11:45 A.M. − 8:30 A.M.
= 11 hr. 45 min. − 8 hr. 30 min.
= 3 hr. 15 min.

A simple device useful in computing time in flight is to consider the traveler as not having reset his watch while in flight. Then ask yourself just what time the traveler's watch would read at the moment he arrived at his destination. By examining the time-zone diagram on page 88 you would know whether to subtract or add one hour, two hours, or three hours to the time of arrival as shown in the flight table.

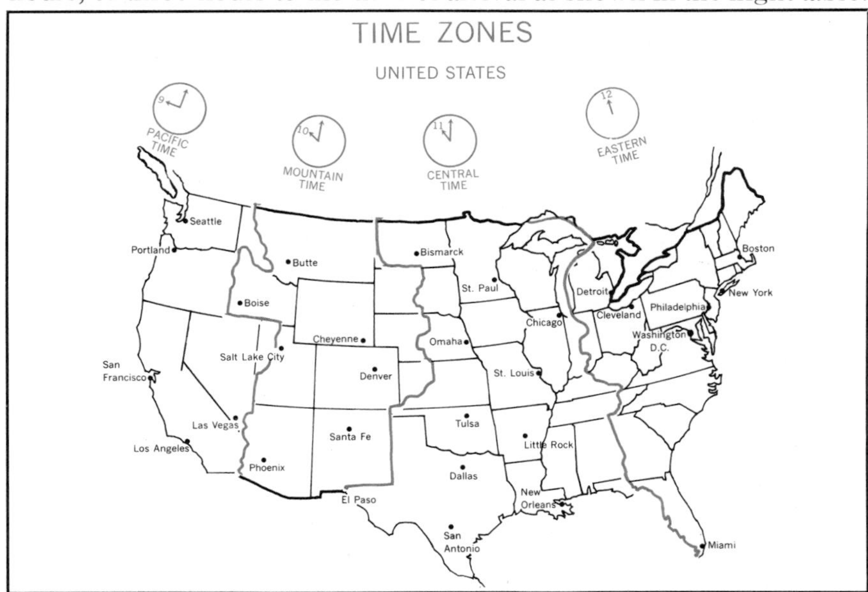

ILLUSTRATION 3: How long will it take flight number 250 out of Los Angeles to reach Louisville?

EXPLANATION: The flight will arrive in Louisville at 4:17 P.M. Eastern time. If a passenger did not reset his watch after leaving Los Angeles, it would read 3 hours earlier than 4:17 P.M.; that is, his watch would read 1:17 P.M. The problem is now completed in the usual manner.

SOLUTION:

$$\begin{aligned}\text{Time in flight} &= 1{:}17 \text{ P.M.} - 8{:}30 \text{ A.M.}\\ &= 13 \text{ hr. } 17 \text{ min.} - 8 \text{ hr. } 30 \text{ min.}\\ &= 12 \text{ hr. } 77 \text{ min.} - 8 \text{ hr. } 30 \text{ min.}\\ &= 4 \text{ hr. } 47 \text{ min.}\end{aligned}$$

EXERCISES A

1. Each of the following travelers does not change the setting of his watch while in flight. What time will *his* watch read at the time of arrival after traveling between the time zones shown?

	Zone Traveling From	Zone Traveling To	Arrival Time	Watch Time
a.	Pacific	Central	5:45p	________
b.	Pacific	Eastern	7:25p	________
c.	Pacific	Mountain	2:30a	________
d.	Pacific	Eastern	9:30p	________
e.	Mountain	Central	6:40a	________
f.	Mountain	Eastern	9:43a	________
g.	Central	Eastern	8:53p	________
h.	Pacific	Central	1:10p	________
i.	Pacific	Eastern	2:04p	________

2. Each of the following travelers does not change the setting of his watch while in flight. What time will *his* watch read at the time of arrival after traveling between the time zones shown?

	Zone Traveling From	Zone Traveling To	Arrival Time	Watch Time
a.	Eastern	Central	2:35p	________
b.	Eastern	Pacific	4:27p	________
c.	Eastern	Mountain	5:54a	________
d.	Central	Pacific	2:15a	________
e.	Central	Mountain	10:36p	________
f.	Mountain	Pacific	6:42a	________
g.	Eastern	Pacific	11:25a	________
h.	Eastern	Mountain	12:14a	________
i.	Central	Pacific	11:53a	________

3. At what time will the following flights out of Los Angeles arrive at their destination?

	Flight Number	City of Arrival	Time of Arrival
a.	184	Chicago	________
b.	72	Cleveland	________
c.	20	Louisville	________
d.	528	Memphis	________
e.	306	Oklahoma City	________

4. A traveler wants to leave Los Angeles at approximately the time indicated. Which flight should he take?

	Approx. Time of Leaving	Destination	Flight Number
a.	10:00 A.M.	Chicago	________
b.	7:30 A.M.	Columbus	________
c.	1:30 P.M.	Memphis	________
d.	5:00 P.M.	Dallas	________
e.	9:30 A.M.	Oklahoma City	________

5. How many hours will it take each of the following flights out of Los Angeles to reach its destination?

	Flight Number	Destination	Leave	Arrive	Time in Flight
a.	192	Chicago	________	________	________
b.	20	Louisville	________	________	________
c.	200	Dallas	________	________	________
d.	20/120	Columbus	________	________	________
e.	74	Cleveland	________	________	________
f.	8	New York	________	________	________
g.	196	Chicago	________	________	________
h.	72	Cleveland	________	________	________

6. Find the one-way fare from Los Angeles to each of the cities indicated.

	Destination	Flight Service	Fare
a.	Chicago	First Class	$________
b.	Columbus	Coach	________
c.	Cincinnati	Night First Class	________
d.	Memphis	Coach	________
e.	New York	Night Coach	________
f.	Chicago	Economy	________

7. What is the approximate federal tax that a traveler will have to pay on each of the following flights out of Los Angeles?

	Destination	Flight Service	Fare	Approx. Federal Tax
a.	Louisville	First Class	$______	$______
b.	Columbus	Coach	______	______
c.	Cleveland	Coach	______	______
d.	Cincinnati	Night Coach	______	______
e.	Newark	Night First Class	______	______
f.	Dallas	Coach	______	______

B

1. John Vaughn bought a first-class ticket for a flight from Los Angeles to Oklahoma City.
  a. If the plane stops off at Dallas, what will the cost be? ______
  b. If the flight is non-stop, what will the cost be? ______
  c. How much can John save by traveling non-stop? ______

2. A traveler takes the 5:10 P.M. flight out of Los Angeles for Memphis.
  a. What will be the number of the flight that leaves Los Angeles? ______
  b. At what city will the plane make a stop? ______
  c. What will be the number of the flight the traveler will take to go from that city to Memphis? ______
  d. At what time will the traveler land in the stop-over city? ______

3. A traveler flies from Los Angeles to Oklahoma City.
  a. If he leaves on the 12:40 A.M. flight, how long will it take him? ______
  b. If he leaves on the 2:30 P.M. flight, how long will it take him? ______
  c. How much traveling time can he save by taking the earlier flight? ______

4. How much money can a person save by going night first class from Los Angeles to Chicago rather than day first class? ______

PART 2

Although the chances of being killed in an airplane accident are very small, many people buy flight insurance before setting out on a trip. This insurance can be obtained at a vending machine where for only $2.50 it is possible to purchase as much as $100,000 worth of flight insurance. Quite apparently, if a company is willing to charge so little for so much coverage, it must feel that there is little risk of an air accident occuring.

RATE SCHEDULE

Premium	Principal Sum	
	One-way Trip	Round Trip
$ .50	$ 20,000	$15,000
.75	30,000	22,500
1.00	40,000	30,000
1.25	50,000	37,500
1.50	60,000	45,000
1.75	70,000	52,500
2.00	80,000	60,000
2.25	90,000	67,500
2.50	100,000	75,000

The insurance rates shown above are typical of those charged for flight trip-insurance. The *principal sum* is the amount of money given to your *beneficiaries*. These are the people you name in the policy to receive the insurance in the event an accident should befall the plane and you are killed. If you are not killed in the accident, there is still a possibility of collecting either part, or all, of the principal sum. This will depend on how badly you are injured.

Nature of Injury	Amount of Benefit
Loss of life, or both feet, or both hands, or both eyes	The principal sum
Loss of one hand and one foot	The principal sum
Loss of one hand and one eye, or one foot and one eye	The principal sum
Loss of one foot, or one hand	One half of the principal sum
Loss of one eye	One fourth of the principal sum

ILLUSTRATION 1: At the start of a one-way air trip, Sam Traymore purchased $1 worth of insurance. The plane made a forced landing, during which one of Sam's eyes was so badly injured that he lost the sight of it. How much did Sam receive from the insurance company to compensate him for this loss?

SOLUTION:

Principal sum for a $1 premium on a one-way trip = $40,000
Coverage for loss of one eye = $\frac{1}{4} \times \$40{,}000$
$= \$10{,}000$

EXPLANATION: According to the rate schedule, a premium of $1 will purchase $40,000 worth of insurance on a one-way trip. The loss of one eye entitles Sam to one fourth of this insurance, or $10,000.

Travelers can not only insure themselves against any injury that might occur to them as a result of an accident, but they can also insure their baggage and personal effects against damage, loss, or theft. The section of the rate table shown here is similar to others offering this insurance coverage.

BAGGAGE AND PERSONAL EFFECTS INSURANCE

	Amount of Insurance							
	$300	$400	$500	$600	$700	$800	$900	$1,000
Term Days	Premiums							
1–3	$2.00	$2.50	$3.00	$3.50	$3.75	$4.25	$ 4.50	$ 5.00
4–5	2.75	3.50	4.25	4.75	5.50	6.00	6.50	7.00
6–7	3.50	4.25	5.00	6.00	7.00	7.75	8.50	9.25
8–10	4.00	5.25	6.25	7.50	8.75	9.75	10.75	11.75

This company will not insure baggage and personal effects for more than $2,000. Should a person want insurance for an amount between $1,000 and $2,000, the cost will be the premium for $1,000 plus one-half the premium for the amount over $1,000.

ILLUSTRATION 2: What is the cost of $1,700 worth of baggage and personal effects insurance for a period of 9 days?

EXPLANATION: The 9-day period falls in the "8–10"-day group. In view of this, you run your finger along the "8–10"-day row until you come to the cost of $1,000 worth of insurance. To this must be added one-half the cost of $700 worth of insurance. In finding half of $8.75, it is necessary to round off the answer to the next highest penny. The total cost of the insurance is the sum of the $1,000 premium and half the $700 premium.

SOLUTION:

Cost of $1,000 insurance = $11.75
One-half the cost of $700 insurance = ½ × $8.75
= $4.38
Total cost of $1,700 insurance = $11.75 + $4.38
= $16.13

EXERCISES

1. In each of the following exercises, what is the amount of the principal sum of flight insurance that can be purchased?

	Premium	Type of Trip	Principal Sum
a.	$ .75	One-way	$____
b.	1.50	Round	____
c.	2.00	One-way	____
d.	2.50	Round	____

2. Each of the people in the following exercises was traveling by air. How much did either they, or their beneficiaries, receive as a result of an accident if they had purchased flight insurance for the premiums listed?

	Premium	Type Of Trip	Principal Sum	Extent Of Injury	Insurance Received
a.	$1.00	Round	$____	Death	$____
b.	1.75	One-way	____	Death	____
c.	2.50	One-way	____	Loss of one hand	____
d.	1.50	Round	____	Loss of one foot	____
e.	1.25	Round	____	Loss of one hand	____
f.	.50	Round	____	Loss of one eye	____
g.	2.25	Round	____	Loss of one eye	____

3. Find the cost of the baggage and personal-effects insurance in each of the following exercises.

	Amount Of Insurance	Term In Days	Premium		Amount Of Insurance	Term In Days	Premium
a.	$300	4	$____	d.	$1,000	1	$____
b.	700	3	____	e.	400	7	____
c.	900	6	____	f.	800	10	____

4. Find the cost of baggage and personal-effects insurance in each of the following exercises.

	Amount Of Insurance	Term In Days	Premium On $1,000	Premium On Excess	½ Premium On Excess	Total Cost
a.	$1,300	1	$____	$____	$____	$____
b.	1,500	3	____	____	____	____
c.	1,800	9	____	____	____	____
d.	1,700	6	____	____	____	____
e.	1,400	5	____	____	____	____

Unit 5: Chapter Review and Test

In doing the computation for many of the following problems, it will be necessary for you to refer to the tables in this chapter.

1. Find the cost of renting each of the following cars for a Tuesday. Use the rate table on page 62 for Company A.

Type Of Car	Base Rate	Number Of Miles	Cost Per Mile	Mileage Cost	Total Cost
a. Standard	$________	60	$________	$________	$________
b. Luxury	________	87	________	________	________

2. Harold Amant rented a compact car for one week from Company B, whose rate table appears on page 62. He drove the car 420 miles during this period.
   a. How much did he pay the company for the rental of the car alone? ________
   b. How much did he pay the company in mileage cost? ________
   c. If the car averaged 21 miles to the gallon of gasoline, how many gallons of gasoline did he have to buy? ________
   d. If the average cost of each gallon of gasoline was 58.9¢, what did he have to pay for gasoline during the week? ________
   e. What was the total cost to Harold for renting the car that week? ________

3. The time in each of the following exercises is given in terms of normal recording. Rewrite them without using the letters A.M. or P.M.

	Time Normal Recording	Time New Recording		Time Normal Recording	Time New Recording
a.	3:00 A.M.	________	d.	2:00 P.M.	________
b.	7:20 A.M.	________	e.	5:30 P.M.	________
c.	9:12 A.M.	________	f.	9:43 P.M.	________

4. Nine hours and 15 minutes can be written as 8 hours and how many minutes? ________
5. Find the time that has elapsed in each of the following exercises.

From	To	Time Elapsed	From	To	Time Elapsed
a. 4:20 A.M.	6:35 A.M.	________	c. 8:30 A.M.	1:40 P.M.	________
b. 2:45 P.M.	8:12 P.M.	________	d. 10:58 A.M.	5:23 P.M.	________

6. Determine the time it will take the bus that leaves Butler at 2:50 P.M. to arrive in Newark. Use the bus schedule on page 66. ________

7. A person takes bus Trip Number 2037 out of Jersey City for Washington. How long will this trip take him? Use the bus schedule on page 73. ________

8. What is the approximate cost of a round-trip bus ticket between Washington and San Antonio? Use the bus-rate table on page 75. ________

9. How long will it take the train that leaves Baltimore at 9:10 in the morning to arrive in Trenton? Use the schedule on page 78. ________

10. Determine how much a person would save by purchasing a 1-day round-trip ticket from Bellmar to New York instead of 2 one-way tickets. Use the rate table on page 80. ________

11. Mr. Richards commutes each day from his home in Elberon to his place of employment in New York. His working week is from Monday through Friday. How much can he save each week by purchasing a weekly commutation ticket instead of one-way tickets? Use the table on page 80. ________

12. A traveler flies from a city in the Eastern time zone to a city in the Pacific time zone. If he does not change the setting of his watch while in flight, what time will his watch read when he lands if the time at the airport of arrival is 6:25 P.M.? ________

13. How much money can a person save on a one-way trip from Los Angeles to Columbus if he travels coach rather than first class? Use the table on page 86. ________

14. What is the time in flight for flight number 122 out of Los Angeles to Dallas? Use the table on page 86. ________

15. Approximately how much federal tax will a person have to pay on a first class night flight out of Los Angeles to New York? Use the table on page 87. ________

16. How much flight insurance can be purchased for $2.25 on a one-way trip? ________

17. As a result of an accident on a round-trip business flight from Chicago to Houston, Mr. Gregory lost one hand. If he had purchased $2.00 worth of flight insurance before making the trip, how much compensation would he have received from the insurance company? ________

18. What is the cost of $800 worth of baggage and personal-effects insurance for a period of 7 days? Use the table on page 94. ________

M and A

CHAPTER 3

PURCHASING CONSUMER GOODS

People begin to develop shopping habits very early in life. Perhaps as a child you would buy that 10¢ bar of candy at the corner store rather than walking another block or so to another store where it was sold for 7¢. It is seemingly trivial incidents like this that help create a pattern of thinking that is carried into adult life. The 3¢ saved on candy at age eight may lead to the $15-saving on a tape recorder at age seventeen and perhaps to the $175-saving on a car at age twenty-one.

Unfortunately, most people do not shop wisely. With just a little effort—and a little training—everyone can not only change their poor shopping habits but save a good deal of money each year. The purpose of this chapter is to take a look at a few of the things that might be considered before making a purchase.

Unit 1: Shopping at a Supermarket

PART 1

The average shopper does not go from supermarket to supermarket before making a purchase. Frequently, markets will run weekly specials in which they drop prices drastically on some items in order to attract customers. Unless a shopper starts out with list in hand of the best buys taken from advertisements of several supermarkets in the area, a great deal of both time and energy can be wasted trying to track down bargains.

It is possible, though, to save money by shopping wisely and yet do all the shopping in the same store. The purchase of a cheaper can of coffee does not necessarily mean the purchase of a poorer quality coffee. Preferring one brand of coffee, or any other item, over another brand often is merely a matter of personal taste.

As a shopper you have much to gain by taking a closer look at that large economy-size package, whether it contains cornflakes or laundry detergent. All too often you may find that the top quarter of the super giant-size box contains nothing but air.

By law the weight of the contents of every can, box, or bottle must appear on the label. Interpreting these measures, though, may create a problem. For instance, various items are measured in terms of *ounces*, and yet the "ounces" of one item may be quite different than the "ounces" of another item. Thus, with laundry detergent, 1 pound is equivalent to 16 *ounces* in what is called *avoirdupois* measure. This is the manner in which *dry* material is measured. However, in buying an item such as vegetable juice, you will again run across the "ounce," except that this time it is a unit of *liquid* measure.

There are only a few different measures that appear on the labels of practically all items sold in a supermarket. Five of these are pounds, gallons, quarts, pints, and ounces. The relationships between these units are shown below:

AVOIRDUPOIS MEASURE

1 pound (lb.)	=	16 ounces (oz.)

LIQUID MEASURE

1 gallon (gal.)	=	4 quarts (qt.)
1 quart	=	2 pints (pt.)
1 quart	=	32 ounces (oz.)

ILLUSTRATION 1: How many ounces are there in 1 quart, 14 ounces?

EXPLANATION: According to the table of liquid measure, there are 32 ounces in a quart. Hence, by changing the 1 quart to 32 ounces and adding these to the 14 ounces, you can find the total number of ounces in 1 quart, 14 ounces.

SOLUTION:

1 quart, 14 ounces = 32 ounces + 14 ounces
= 46 ounces

ILLUSTRATION 2: A 1-pound, 9-ounce jar of applesauce can be purchased for 39 cents. What is the cost of each ounce of applesauce to the nearest tenth of a cent?

EXPLANATION: Since each pound is equivalent to 16 ounces, then the number of ounces in 1 pound, 9 ounces is 25. Hence, 25 ounces of applesauce cost 39 cents and, therefore, 1 ounce would be 1/25 of 39 cents. To find 1/25 of a number means to divide that number by 25.

SOLUTION:

Total weight = 1 lb. + 9 oz.
= 16 oz. + 9 oz.
= 25 oz.
Cost of 25 oz. = 39¢
Cost of 1 oz. = 39¢ ÷ 25
= 1.56¢, or 1.6¢

ILLUSTRATION 3: Desmond James purchased three cans of kernel corn for 70¢. How much would he have paid had he purchased only one can?

EXPLANATION: As in the previous illustration, if 3 cans cost 70¢ then 1 can would cost $1/3$ that amount. Finding $1/3$ of 70¢ involves dividing 70¢ by 3. However, dividing 70¢ by 3 gives a quotient of $23\frac{1}{3}$¢. It is not possible to give the dealer one third of a penny. Even though a mixed number involving one third as its fractional part is normally rounded off by dropping the one third, this is never done in the purchase of food. No matter how small the fraction of a penny may be in computing the cost of one can, the cost is always rounded off to the next higher cent. Thus, $14\frac{1}{4}$¢ will be rounded off to 15¢; $29\frac{1}{8}$¢ will be rounded off to 30¢; and the same for any other fraction of a cent.

SOLUTION:

Cost of 3 cans = 70¢
Cost of 1 can = 70¢ ÷ 3
= $23\frac{1}{3}$¢, or 24¢

So far we have dealt with only five different units of measure that are found on the labels of items in the supermarket. There are, though, four additional units of measure that often appear in parentheses immediately beside the more familiar units. Two of these units are the *liter* and *milliliter*. They are used when measuring liquids. The relationship between them is,

1,000 milliliters (ml) = 1 liter (l)

The other pair of units, the gram and kilogram, are used for measuring weight. The relationship between these two units is,

1,000 grams (g) = 1 kilogram (kg)

Chances are that you will be seeing more and more of these units over the next few years. When the United States officially adopts the "metric system," it will be largely in terms of the four units listed above that food will be purchased at the supermarket.

Perhaps the best way of making a connection between the traditional units and the new ones is to remember that,

A liter is just slightly larger than a quart.

A kilogram is just slightly larger than two pounds.

Quite apparently, then, the milliliter must be very small indeed. Since it is one thousandth of a liter, it must also be approximately one thousandth the size of a quart. This is far, far smaller than even a thimbleful of liquid.

Similarly, a gram must be a very small weight. As one thousandth of a kilogram, it is about one thousandth of a two-pound weight.

ILLUSTRATION 4: A 1.36-liter can of orange drink costs 39¢. To the nearest tenth of a cent, what is the cost of 1 liter of the drink?

EXPLANATION: The only difference between this illustration and Illustration 2 is that the unit of measure in this situation is the "liter" while in the earlier one, it is the "ounce." The cost per liter is found in the same manner as the cost per ounce, that is, by dividing the total cost by the number of liters.

SOLUTION:

Cost of 1.36 liters = 39¢
Cost of 1 liter = 39¢ ÷ 1.36
= 28.68¢, or 28.7¢

EXERCISES

A

Do you recall how to do the division in the following exercises? If not, you will probably want to refer to pages 508–509 for help. Determine the quotient correct to the nearest tenth of a cent.

1. 56¢ ÷ 9 = ________
2. 47¢ ÷ 5 = ________
3. 24¢ ÷ 7 = ________
4. 78¢ ÷ 8 = ________
5. 52¢ ÷ 6 = ________
6. 84¢ ÷ 3 = ________
7. 103¢ ÷ 9 = ________
8. 114¢ ÷ 7 = ________
9. 146¢ ÷ 8 = ________
10. 159¢ ÷ 6 = ________
11. 56¢ ÷ 17 = ________
12. 95¢ ÷ 26 = ________
13. 107¢ ÷ 35 = ________
14. 126¢ ÷ 46 = ________

B

1. Each of the following is expressed in terms of dollars. Rewrite them in terms of cents.

a. $1.25 ________
b. $2.56 ________
c. $1.87 ________
d. $4.06 ________
e. $2.09 ________
f. $7.62 ________
g. $1 ________
h. $2 ________
i. $5 ________

2. Write each of the following measures in terms of ounces only.

a. 2 lb. ________
b. 5 lb. ________
c. 9 lb. ________
d. 1 lb. 3 oz. ________
e. 2 lb. 10 oz. ________
f. 4 lb. 1 oz. ________
g. 5 lb. 14 oz. ________
h. 9 lb. 7 oz. ________

3. Write each of the following measures in terms of pints only.

a. 3 qt. ________
b. 7 qt. ________
c. 2 qt. 1 pt. ________
d. 7 qt. 1 pt. ________
e. 15 qt. 1 pt. ________
f. 27 qt. 1 pt. ________

4. Write each of the following measures in terms of quarts only.

a. 4 gal. ________
b. 8 gal. ________
c. 10 gal. ________
d. 1 gal. 1 qt. ________
e. 2 gal. 3 qt. ________
f. 5 gal. 2 qt. ________
g. $\frac{1}{2}$ gal. ________
h. $2\frac{1}{2}$ gal. ________

5. Write each of the following measures in terms of ounces only.

a. 1 qt. ________
b. 3 qt. ________
c. 8 qt. ________
d. 2 qt. 5 oz. ________
e. 5 qt. 14 oz. ________
f. 9 qt. 6 oz. ________
g. 1 pt. ________
h. 3 pt. ________

6. What is the cost of each ounce of food in the following purchases? Find your answer to the nearest tenth of a cent.

	Total Cost	Number Of Ounces	Cost Per Ounce		Total Cost	Number Of Ounces	Cost Per Ounce
a.	59¢	8	______¢	e.	$1.62	14	______¢
b.	37¢	6	______¢	f.	$1.97	26	______¢
c.	49¢	5	______¢	g.	$2.05	37	______¢
d.	76¢	9	______¢	h.	$3.19	18	______¢

7. What is the cost of each kilogram of food in the following purchases? Find your answer to the nearest tenth of a cent.

	Total Cost	Number of Kilograms	Cost per Kilogram		Total Cost	Number of Kilograms	Cost per Kilogram
a.	48¢	2	______¢	e.	28¢	.5	______¢
b.	64¢	4	______¢	f.	48¢	.32	______¢
c.	87¢	3	______¢	g.	70¢	.28	______¢
d.	91¢	5	______¢	h.	75¢	.75	______¢

8. What is the cost of each ounce of food in each of the following purchases? Find your answer to the nearest tenth of a cent.

	Total Cost	Weight Of Purchase	Number Of Ounces	Cost Per Ounce
a.	67¢	1 lb.	______	______¢
b.	84¢	2 lb.	______	______¢
c.	95¢	1 lb. 5 oz.	______	______¢
d.	$1.37	2 lb. 7 oz.	______	______¢
e.	$2.95	3 lb. 12 oz.	______	______¢
f.	$3.06	2 lb. 14 oz.	______	______¢

9. What is the cost of each liter of food in each of the following purchases?

	Total Cost	Number of Liters	Cost per Liter		Total Cost	Number of Liters	Cost per Liter
a.	68¢	2	______¢	e.	42¢	1.2	______¢
b.	96¢	3	______¢	f.	81¢	1.8	______¢
c.	$1.24	4	______¢	g.	65¢	2.5	______¢
d.	$1.98	6	______¢	h.	$3.06	3.6	______¢

10. What is the cost of each ounce of food in the following purchases? Find your answer to the nearest tenth of a cent.

	Total Cost	Measure Of Contents	Number Of Ounces	Cost Per Ounce
a.	54¢	1 qt.	______	______¢
b.	76¢	2 qt.	______	______¢
c.	87¢	2 qt. 3 oz.	______	______¢

	Total Cost	Measure Of Contents	Number Of Ounces	Cost Per Ounce
d.	$1.21	1 qt. 5 oz.	________	________¢
e.	$2.17	2 qt. 18 oz.	________	________¢
f.	$4.95	4 qt. 25 oz.	________	________¢

11. Prices in supermarkets are stamped on cans as 2/47¢, or 5/83¢, and so on. These prices are read as 2 cans for 47¢, or 5 cans for 83¢. How much will a person have to pay on the purchase of one can of each of the following items if they are marked as shown?

	Marking On Can	Cost Per Can		Marking On Can	Cost Per Can
a.	2/15¢	________¢	g.	4/62¢	________¢
b.	2/37¢	________¢	h.	5/87¢	________¢
c.	2/95¢	________¢	i.	5/96¢	________¢
d.	3/16¢	________¢	j.	2/$1.15	________¢
e.	3/95¢	________¢	k.	3/$1.96	________¢
f.	4/85¢	________¢	l.	5/$2.16	________¢

B

1. Frozen orange juice can be purchased at 5 cans for $1.06. How much would a person save by buying 5 cans at one time rather than 5 separate cans on 5 separate occasions? ________

2. How many ounces are there in 3 gallons, 2 quarts of a liquid? ________

3. Peanut butter can be purchased in a 1-pound, 2-ounce jar at 67¢, or in a 1-pound, 12-ounce jar at 89¢.

a. How much will a person have to pay per ounce if he purchases the smaller jar of peanut butter? Find your answer to the nearest tenth of a penny. ________

b. How much will a person have to pay per ounce if he purchases the larger jar of peanut butter? Find your answer to the nearest tenth of a penny. ________

c. How much can a person save on each ounce of peanut butter by purchasing the larger jar instead of the smaller jar? Find your answer to the nearest tenth of a penny. ________

4. A certain brand of floor wax can be purchased in a 1-pint, 11-ounce container for 53¢, or in a larger container of 1 quart, 14 ounces at 85¢.

a. How much will a person have to pay per ounce if he purchases the smaller container of floor wax? Find your answer to the nearest tenth of a penny. ________

b. How much will a person have to pay per ounce if he purchases

Finding best buys while shopping is still confusing. Consumers have to pay attention to quality, package size, and how much one item costs when they are all marked 3/25¢.

the larger container of floor wax? Find your answer to the nearest tenth of a penny. ________

c. How much can a person save on each ounce of floor wax by purchasing the larger container instead of the smaller one? Find your answer to the nearest tenth of a penny. ________

PART 2

A good deal of the difficulty in trying to shop wisely in a supermarket comes from a combination of the way items are marked for sale and the peculiar sizes in which they are packaged. Thus, a certain brand of applesauce can be purchased in one of two sizes. In the 8-ounce container, the cost is 29¢ for 2 jars, while in the 15-ounce container, the cost is 67 cents for 3 jars. All too often the larger size is not the more economical buy, so larger size alone can not always be used as a guide.

In spite of the odd pricing design, there is a way in which it is possible to compare the costs of two different size containers of the same item. In order to try to eliminate the confusion created by the food companies, a number of states have passed a "unit pricing" law. This law requires merchants to provide every item with a label, either right on the container or on the shelf edge, showing the price per ounce, or price per gram, or price per quart, or, in general, the price per whatever unit of measure used on the item itself. By reading the unit price the shopper can immediately determine whether the "large economy size" is really any less expensive than the smaller container. Of course, finding the unit price of an item is nothing more than what you learned to do in Part 1 of this unit.

At this time your concern will be with determining which of two sizes or brands of an item will cost you less money to buy. The computation involves just another step or two beyond what you have already been doing. The illustrations below will help clarify this.

ILLUSTRATION 1: A 9-ounce jar of beets can be purchased for 21¢. At the same unit price, what would be the cost of a 15-ounce jar of these beets?

EXPLANATION: Just as in the exercises in Part 1, the first objective is to determine the cost per ounce. In this situation that cost turns out to be 2.3¢. Knowing that the price of 1 ounce is 2.3¢, to find the cost of 15 ounces you need simply multiply that number by 15.

SOLUTION:

$$\begin{aligned}\text{Cost of 9 ounces} &= 21¢\\ \text{Cost of 1 ounce} &= 21¢ \div 9\\ &= 2.3¢\\ \text{Cost of 15 ounces} &= 15 \times 2.3¢\\ &= 34.5¢\text{, or } 35¢\end{aligned}$$

EXPLANATION (continued): Notice that the cost per ounce is rounded off to the nearest tenth of a cent. For most purchases at the supermarket this will not affect the final cost by more than a penny or two.

ILLUSTRATION 2: A 24-ounce can of vegetable juice costs 36¢, while a 1-quart, 14-ounce can of the same brand costs 54¢. Which is the better buy?

EXPLANATION: The computation here is identical to that of Illustration 1 with but one additional step. As before, it is first necessary to determine the cost of the larger can of vegetable juice if it had been sold at the same unit price as the smaller can. Once that is done, a comparison can be made between that price and the 54¢ that is the actual price of the larger can.

SOLUTION:

Cost of 24 ounces = 36¢
Cost of 1 ounce = 1.5¢
Number of ounces in 1 quart 14 ounces = 32 + 14
= 46
Cost of 46 ounces = 46 × 1.5¢
= 69¢
Saving by buying larger can = 69¢ − 54¢
= 15¢

EXPLANATION (continued): Thus, the large can of 46 ounces would have cost 69¢ had it been purchased at the same cost per ounce as the small can. Therefore, by paying only 54¢ for the large can, a person can save 15¢

ILLUSTRATION 3: Frozen orange juice can be bought in a 6-ounce can at a cost of 5 cans for $1.06. If purchased in the 12-ounce can, the cost is 3 cans for $1.19. Which is the better buy?

SOLUTION:

Total number of ounces in 5 small cans = 5 × 6 ounces
= 30 ounces
Cost for 30 ounces = 106¢
Cost for 1 ounce = 106¢ ÷ 30
= 3.5¢
Total number of ounces in 3 large cans = 3 × 12 ounces
= 36 ounces
Cost for 36 ounces = 36 × 3.5¢
= 126¢
Saving by buying larger cans = 126¢ − 119¢
= 7¢

EXPLANATION: After determining the total number of ounces under each purchase arrangement, the solution follows the same pattern as in Illustration 2.

EXERCISES A

1. The weight and price of a small can of vegetables are given in each of the following exercises. The weight of a larger can is also given. If the larger can is bought at the same unit price as the smaller one, what is the cost of the larger can? Round off the cost in each case to the next higher penny.

	Weight of Contents of Smaller Can	Cost of Smaller Can	Weight of Contents of Larger Can	Cost per Ounce	Cost of Larger Can
a.	6 oz.	15¢	8 oz.	______¢	______¢
b.	9 oz.	21¢	15 oz.	______¢	______¢
c.	10 oz.	35¢	16 oz.	______¢	______¢
d.	16 oz.	56¢	26 oz.	______¢	______¢
e.	21 oz.	98¢	36 oz.	______¢	______¢
f.	7 oz.	47¢	23 oz.	______¢	______¢
g.	9 oz.	69¢	17 oz.	______¢	______¢
h.	14 oz.	85¢	25 oz.	______¢	______¢
i.	12 oz.	$1.08	16 oz.	______¢	______¢
j.	18 oz.	$1.35	27 oz.	______¢	______¢
k.	1 lb. 2 oz.	63¢	1 lb. 10 oz.	______¢	______¢
l.	1 lb. 5 oz.	49¢	1 lb. 14 oz.	______¢	______¢
m.	2 lb. 3 oz.	$2.55	3 lb. 8 oz.	______¢	______¢
n.	4 lb. 7 oz.	$4.29	6 lb. 1 oz.	______¢	______¢

2. The weight and cost of a small can of vegetables are given in each of the following exercises. The weight and cost of a larger can of the same vegetables are also given. How much more would a person have to pay if he bought the larger can at the same unit price as the smaller one? Round off the cost in each case to the next higher penny.

	Weight of Contents of Smaller Can	Cost of Smaller Can	Weight of Contents of Larger Can	Cost of Larger Can	Saving
a.	5 oz.	21¢	15 oz.	49¢	______¢
b.	4 oz.	30¢	10 oz.	61¢	______¢
c.	8 oz.	60¢	14 oz.	89¢	______¢
d.	14 oz.	91¢	22 oz.	119¢	______¢
e.	10 oz.	85¢	26 oz.	189¢	______¢
f.	15 oz.	95¢	27 oz.	139¢	______¢
g.	16 oz.	84¢	24 oz.	109¢	______¢
h.	9 oz.	$1.08	15 oz.	$1.54	______¢
i.	12 oz.	$1.28	21 oz.	$1.87	______¢
j.	7 oz.	93¢	12 oz.	$1.19	______¢
k.	15 oz.	86¢	23 oz.	$1.12	______¢
l.	12 oz.	$1.34	27 oz.	$2.59	______¢
m.	18 oz.	$1.07	32 oz.	$1.69	______¢
n.	1 lb. 2 oz.	72¢	1 lb. 14 oz.	$1.12	______¢
o.	1 lb. 4 oz.	95¢	2 lb. 4 oz.	$1.50	______¢
p.	2 lb. 1 oz.	$1.54	3 lb. 3 oz.	$1.99	______¢

3. In each of the following exercises, you are to determine which of the two buys is the better. You are to do this by finding what the cost of the second amount would be if it is purchased at the same rate as the first amount.

a. One 8-ounce box of cornflakes for 33¢
or ____________
One 18-ounce box of cornflakes for 58¢

b. One box of 48 tea bags for 61¢
or ____________
One box of 100 tea bags for $1.09

c. Two 9-ounce cans of stewed tomatoes at 43¢
or ____________
One 1-pound can of stewed tomatoes for 35¢

d. Three 12-ounce jars of strawberry jelly for $1.00
or ____________
One 17-ounce jar of strawberry jelly for 59¢

e. Five pounds of potatoes for 80¢
or ____________
Twenty pounds of potatoes for $2.10

f. Two 12-ounce cans of vegetable juice for 41¢
or ____________
One 1-quart, 14-ounce can of vegetable juice for 64¢

g. Two 6-ounce cans of pineapple juice for 23¢
or ____________
One 1-quart, 14-ounce can of pineapple juice for 37¢

h. One 1-pound, 9-ounce jar of applesauce for 44¢
or ____________
Two 15-ounce jars of applesauce for 53¢

i. Two 9-ounce cans of creamed corn for 39¢
or ____________
Two 1-pound, 1-ounce cans of creamed corn for 51¢

j. One 1-pound, 2-ounce jar of peanut butter for 69¢
or ____________
One 1-pound, 12-ounce jar of peanut butter for $1.07

k. One 1-pint, 11-ounce can of floor wax for 83¢
or ____________
One 1-quart, 14-ounce can of floor wax for $1.33

l. Two 1-quart bottles of floor wax for 47¢
or ____________
One 1-gallon bottle of floor wax for 60¢

m. One 1-quart jar of starch for 23¢
or ____________
One ½-gallon jar of starch for 42¢

n. A 6-pack of tomato juice for 56¢ (5½ ounces in each can)
or ____________
Three 1-quart, 14-ounce cans of tomato juice for $1.30

o. A .68-kilogram box of iced tea mix at $1.02
or ____________
A .51-kilogram box of iced tea mix at 88¢

p. One 1.50-liter can of punch for 39¢
or
Two 1.36-liter cans of punch for 77¢ ________

B

1. At a supermarket, two quarts of milk cost 79¢, or a half gallon, 76¢. Alice Bradburn purchases 4 quarts of milk each day except Sunday.
   a. How much will she have to pay for the milk each day if she buys it by the quart? ________
   b. How much will she have to pay for the milk each day if she buys it by the half gallon? ________
   c. How much can she save in a week by buying milk by the half gallon rather than by the quart? ________
   d. How much can she save in one year by buying milk by the half gallon rather than by the quart? ________
2. A box of powdered milk costs $1.05 at a supermarket. With the contents, it is possible to make 8 quarts of whole milk. Whole milk is sold here for 40¢ a quart. The Frost family uses 16 quarts of milk each week.
   a. What is the cost of the family's weekly milk supply if it uses fresh whole milk? ________
   b. What is the cost of the family's weekly milk supply if it uses powdered milk? ________
   c. How much money can the family save each week by buying powdered milk instead of fresh whole milk? ________
   d. How much can the family save in a year by buying powdered milk instead of fresh whole milk? ________

Unit 2: Counting Change

The checker at the supermarket will normally not try to overcharge you, for he has nothing to gain. Any overcharge ends up in the supermarket's bank account, since the checker has to account for every penny he rings up on the cash register. However, checkers sometimes make mistakes. They are not necessarily careless, but price changes are made daily on many, many items, and keeping track of them is almost impossible. Then, too, prices stamped on containers are sometimes so badly blurred that they can easily be misread. Hence, it is a good idea to watch the register when poorly marked items are being rung up. In fact, it's a good idea to remember the prices of a number of items and spot-check to see if they are being charged correctly.

You should take a moment while you are still at the cash register to make certain you receive the correct amount of change. Once you have walked away from the counter, it becomes embarrassing to return with money in hand to point out that you have been short-changed.

The best way to count change is by the additive method. Suppose you hand a cashier a $5 bill for a purchase of $2.36. She would start by giving you 4 cents and saying that $2.36 plus 4¢ is $2.40. To this, she would add 10¢, bringing the total to $2.50. This would be followed by a 50¢ piece so that you would now be up to $3.00. Then you would receive two $1 bills to bring the grand total to $5. Thus, your purchase, plus the change you received, would be equivalent to the $5 you gave the cashier.

Notice that, when counting change, it is not necessary to determine the actual amount of change. This amount could have been found by subtracting $2.36, the cost of the purchase, from $5, given in payment, for a difference of $2.64, your change. The chance of errors occurring in subtraction is much greater than in addition. Hence, it is advisable to add the change to the cost of the purchase until you reach the amount given in payment.

ILLUSTRATION 1: How much change should be returned to a person who gave a $10-bill to pay for a $3.78 purchase?

EXPLANATION: Start with $3.78 and add just enough pennies to bring the total to an amount ending in either 0 or 5. In this case, you add pennies to bring the total to $3.80. Then add the largest valued coins possible to bring the total to the nearest dollar amount. If you used nickels, you would have to have 4 of them to bring the amount to $4.00. However, only 2 dimes will bring you to $4.00. Hence, you use 2 dimes. You next add a $1 bill to bring the total to $5.00. Finally, you add a $5 bill to reach the $10 that was given in payment.

SOLUTION:

Change given in payment of the $3.78 purchase
= 2¢ + 10¢ + 10¢ + $1 + $5

There are times when you have a pocketful of coins and have to pay for a purchase that amounts to $3.07. If you give the cashier a $5-bill, you will receive a $1-bill, plus 93¢, in change. Instead, you could give her $5 and 7¢ in change. By doing this, the change you receive from the cashier will be two $1-bills.

In the event both bills and coins are given in payment of a purchase —unless the payment is the exact amount—it is best immediately to deduct the change given from the amount of the purchase. You then count out the change given you as if the purchase actually cost the smaller amount. Thus, if the cost is \$2.27, and you give the cashier \$5 and 2¢ as payment, you should immediately deduct the 2¢ from the \$2.27 and think of the purchase price as \$2.25 before counting the change. Similarly, if the cost is \$8.55 and you give the cashier \$10 and 5¢, you now think of the cost as \$8.50. You also have to think that you gave only \$10 in payment of the purchase. The extra 5¢ has already been subtracted to lower the price from \$8.55 to \$8.50.

ILLUSTRATION 2: Jim Eddy gave a cashier \$10.03 in payment of a \$6.68 purchase. Use the table below to indicate how much change he should receive.

1¢	5¢	10¢	25¢	50¢	\$1	\$5	\$10

EXPLANATION: Immediately deduct 3¢ from \$6.68 and think of the cost as \$6.65 rather than \$6.68. Also, think of the amount that Mr. Eddy gave the cashier as \$10.00 rather than \$10.03. Hence, adding 10¢ to \$6.65 brings the total to \$6.75. Another quarter will make the total \$7.00 and three \$1 bills will bring the final total to \$10.

SOLUTION:

1¢	5¢	10¢	25¢	50¢	\$1	\$5	\$10
		1	1		3		

EXERCISES

1. Draw a table similar to the following and indicate how much change will be returned if a \$1 bill is given for each of the purchases shown.

Amount Of Purchase	Change				
	1¢	5¢	10¢	25¢	50¢
85¢					
75¢					
67¢					
54¢					
36¢					
28¢					
19¢					
6¢					

2. Draw a table similar to the following and indicate how much change will be returned if a $5-bill is given for each of the purchases shown.

Amount Of Purchase	Change					
	1¢	5¢	10	25¢	50¢	$1
$4.50						
$4.16						
$4.02						
$3.78						
$2.53						
$1.89						
98¢						
59¢						
25¢						

3. Draw a table similar to the following and indicate how much change will be returned if the amount shown is given for each of the purchases listed.

Amount Of Purchase	Payment Made	Change							
		1¢	5¢	10¢	25¢	50¢	$1	$5	$10
62¢	$1.02								
83¢	$1.03								
54¢	$1.04								

Purchase	Payment	Change							
26¢	$1.01								
$1.08	$5.08								
$1.17	$5.02								
$3.25	$5.25								
$2.62	$5.12								
$4.29	$10.04								
$1.57	$10.07								
$1.84	$10.09								

Unit 3: Computing the Discount on a Purchase

PART 1

During the past twenty-five years discount houses have mushroomed all over the country. Originally they were set up to sell name-brand articles such as refrigerators, freezers, radios, television sets, lawn mowers, and other appliances at prices much below what the local hardware store, or the large department store, was charging. At present, they are selling everything from food to pets. By now, it is difficult to tell whether the prices are really lower than those in the department store, or whether they are lower because of the quality of the product. In addition, the city department stores, to compete with the discount houses, have opened branches in large suburban shopping centers. Here they, too, offer daily bargains to attract the shopper.

Part of the confusion about determining how much of a bargain you are really getting arises from something called the manufacturer's list price, or the manufacturer's suggested price. This is the price at which the manufacturer suggests that stores sell his merchandise. Usually, this price is far higher than anyone would want to pay for the article. The merchant is in a position where he can quote the selling price in terms of relatively large discounts being granted from the list price. For instance, if the manufacturer's suggested price on a shirt is $9, the merchant can offer it at $6 and advertise a discount of $3. This makes it appear that you are being granted quite a saving. In reality, the shirt is probably worth only $6 to begin with, and it has been deliberately listed higher than it should have been.

Most reliable stores advertise their products in terms of the list price and the selling price. Hence, there is no question about what the manufacturer says you should pay and what you actually have to pay. Thus, the advertisement might appear as follows:

WINDOW SHADES IN WHITE OR EGGSHELL	
Manufacturer's List Price	**Our Price**
$2.49	$1.79

In this way, you know that you will be saving exactly 70¢ on each shade. There are a large number of merchants, though, who prefer to disguise their true sale prices. Their advertisements might appear as follows:

Sofas Usually Selling
from $145 to $395
NOW
Reduced 30% to 65%

Notice that nowhere does it say just how much you are going to pay for a sofa, nor is it possible to tell whether you will receive the 30% or the 65% on the one you happen to want.

The purpose of this unit is to develop some method to determine whether the discount the merchant says you are receiving is really what you do receive. A discount is simply a reduction in the price of an article from what it had been priced at originally. Thus, in the case of the illustration of the window shades, since the original price was $2.49 and the new price is $1.79, the discount is 70¢.

In the illustration about the sofas, the 30% and 65% are the *discount rates*. As with any other percent values, they indicate the saving for each $100 in the list price of the article, rather than the saving itself. To see how to handle situations where the discount rate is given rather than the discount itself, it would be best to examine the following illustrations.

ILLUSTRATION 1: Phyllis Samuels received a 15% discount on an FM radio that had been priced at $80. What discount did she receive?

EXPLANATION: On page 520 of the appendix, it is pointed out that the word "of" in phrases such as "25% of $90," or "23% of $94," and so on, implies the operation of multiplication between the two numbers. Since in this problem the discount is 15% of the $80, finding this discount involves nothing more than finding the product of 15% and $80. Before this can be done, however, it is necessary to change the numeral 15% from its percent form to its decimal form.

SOLUTION:

$$\begin{aligned} \text{Discount} &= 15\% \text{ of } \$80 \\ &= .15 \times \$80 \\ &= \$12.00 \end{aligned}$$

ILLUSTRATION 2: A desk that regularly sells for \$120 can be bought during a sale at a discount rate of 20%. How much will a buyer have to pay for the desk if he purchases it during the sale?

SOLUTION:

$$\begin{aligned} \text{Discount} &= 20\% \text{ of } \$120 \\ &= .20 \times \$120 \\ &= \$24.00 \\ \text{Selling Price} &= \$120 - \$24 \\ &= \$96 \end{aligned}$$

EXPLANATION: The discount is found in exactly the same way as in Illustration 1. Since the discount represents the amount the selling price was reduced, it is now only a matter of subtracting \$24 from \$120 to find the new selling price of the desk.

A person who says that he had to pay 100% of the original price for an article is simply implying that he had to pay the entire amount at which the article was priced. Hence, if someone is granted a 20% discount off the original price, he will merely pay 20% less than the 100% or but 80% of the original price. Thus, in Illustration 2 the selling price could have been found by determining 80% of the original price of \$120 rather than computing the discount first and then subtracting that amount from \$120. Eighty percent of \$120 turns out to be the \$96 that was found earlier as the selling price.

ILLUSTRATION 3: George Shaw was able to purchase a hammock listed at \$14.99 at a discount rate of 40%. How much did he have to pay for the hammock?

SOLUTION:

$$\begin{aligned} \text{Selling price} &= 100\% \text{ of original price} - 40\% \text{ of original price} \\ &= 60\% \text{ of original price} \\ &= 60\% \text{ of } \$14.99 \\ &= .60 \times \$14.99 \\ &= \$8.9940, \text{ or } \$8.99 \end{aligned}$$

EXPLANATION: Since George received a 40% discount rate off the original price, he had to pay only 60% of the original price. Sixty percent of \$14.99 is \$8.99, which is the price he had to pay.

EXERCISES A

Do you recall how to find the answers in the following exercises? If not, you will want to refer to the pages indicated for help.

1. Change each of the following percent numerals to its equivalent decimal numeral. (See pages 516–517.)

a. 15%	______	d. 7%	______	g. 4.6%	______
b. 28%	______	e. 9%	______	h. 8.7%	______
c. 54%	______	f. 2%	______	i. 9.6%	______

2. Find the value of the following. (See pages 519–520.)

a. 20% of 50 = ______	f. 48% of 78 = ______
b. 16% of 70 = ______	g. 62% of 173 = ______
c. 34% of 120 = ______	h. 53% of 249 = ______
d. 45% of 63 = ______	i. 36% of 856 = ______
e. 27% of 29 = ______	j. 84% of 927 = ______

B

1. Find the discount to the nearest penny on each of the following purchases.

	Original Price	Discount Rate	Discount
a.	$ 30.00	20%	$______
b.	50.00	40%	______
c.	75.00	10%	______
d.	60.00	35%	______
e.	18.00	25%	______
f.	45.00	18%	______
g.	22.50	15%	______
h.	8.75	12%	______
i.	19.75	25%	______
j.	4.99	50%	______
k.	37.85	28%	______
l.	49.95	34%	______
m.	109.85	10%	______
n.	257.50	22%	______

2. Find the discount to the nearest penny on each of the following purchases. After finding the discount, determine how much the buyer will have to pay for each purchase.

	Original Price	Discount Rate	Discount	Selling Price
a.	$ 40.00	30%	$______	$______
b.	20.00	10%	______	______

	Original Price	Discount Rate	Discount	Selling Price
c.	$ 65.00	60%	$______	$______
d.	85.00	45%	______	______
e.	130.00	15%	______	______
f.	145.00	31%	______	______
g.	7.50	14%	______	______
h.	34.50	38%	______	______
i.	156.85	55%	______	______
j.	249.50	16%	______	______

3. Purchasers are granted the following discount rates. What percent of the selling price do they have to pay?

a. 20%	______	e. 15%	______	i. 6%	______
b. 10%	______	f. 25%	______	j. 14%	______
c. 30%	______	g. 45%	______	k. 32%	______
d. 40%	______	h. 50%	______	l. 41%	______

4. Without finding the discount, find the selling price to the nearest penny on each of the following purchases.

	Original Price	Discount Rate	Selling Price
a.	$ 10.00	10%	$______
b.	70.00	20%	______
c.	90.00	40%	______
d.	75.00	30%	______
e.	62.00	35%	______
f.	4.50	25%	______
g.	12.75	60%	______
h.	58.25	55%	______
i.	124.50	15%	______
j.	263.80	45%	______

C

1. A garden umbrella that usually sells for $29.99 is on sale at a discount rate of 35%.

a. What discount is the purchaser being offered? Find your answer to the nearest penny. ______

b. How much will the purchaser have to pay for the umbrella? ______

2. Men's nylon stretch socks that regularly sell for 79¢ a pair can be bought during a sale at three pairs for $1.75.

a. How much would a buyer have to pay if he bought six pairs of socks at the regular price? ______

b. How much would a buyer have to pay if he bought six pairs of socks at the sale price? ______

c. How much could a buyer save by buying six pairs of socks during the sale? ________

3. Men's T-shirts regularly sell 3 for \$4.50. During a spring sale, they are offered 3 for \$2.75. How much can Mario save on the purchase of a half dozen of these T-shirts if he buys them during the sale? ________

4. The usual selling price of men's pure linen initialed handkerchiefs at Mayer's Department Store is \$1.07 each. At the time of its Father's Day sale, the store offered these same handkerchiefs 2 for \$1.19. How much can a person save by buying a dozen of these handkerchiefs during the sale? ________

PART 2

In practically all cases, the rate of discount is expressed in a percent form similar to the numerals used in Part 1 of this unit. There are times, though, when the discount rate is written as a percent numeral that involves a decimal. Thus, the discount rate offered might be 8.5%, or 15.25%, and so forth. These discount rates are treated no differently than the earlier ones examined. Simply move the decimal point two places to the left to change them from their percent form to their equivalent decimal form. Thus, the decimal equivalent for 8.5% is .085 and for 15.25%, .1525.

Sometimes, though, you will find the discount rate expressed in a form such as $12\frac{1}{2}\%$, or $16\frac{1}{4}\%$, and the like. Whenever this happens, it is best to change the fraction immediately to a decimal. In the case of $12\frac{1}{2}\%$, you would rewrite it as 12.5%, while $16\frac{1}{4}\%$ should be written as 16.25%. Except for one case, you will find that the majority of the fractions you will use will be either $\frac{1}{4}$, $\frac{1}{2}$, or $\frac{3}{4}$. In the event their decimal equivalents may have slipped your mind, they are as follows:

$$\frac{1}{4} = .25$$
$$\frac{1}{2} = .50$$
$$\frac{3}{4} = .75$$

ILLUSTRATION 1: Permanent-press, pre-cuffed dress slacks that regularly sell for \$9.95 a pair are dropped $18\frac{1}{2}\%$ in price during a sale. How much will a buyer have to pay for these slacks during the sale?

SOLUTION:

$$\text{Discount} = 18\tfrac{1}{2}\% \text{ of } \$9.95$$
$$= 18.5\% \text{ of } \$9.95$$

$$\begin{aligned}\text{Discount} &= .185 \times \$9.95\\ &= \$1.84075, \text{ or } \$1.84\\ \text{Selling price} &= \$9.95 - \$1.84\\ &= \$8.11\end{aligned}$$

EXPLANATION: After changing the discount rate from the form $18\frac{1}{2}\%$ to 18.5%, it was possible to complete the solution in the same manner as with the problems in Part 1 of this unit.

As mentioned earlier, there is one discount rate involving a fraction that might give you a bit of trouble. This rate is $33\frac{1}{3}\%$. If you try to change the fraction $\frac{1}{3}$ into a decimal as you did with the fractions $\frac{1}{4}$, $\frac{1}{2}$, and $\frac{3}{4}$, you would simply get the repeating decimal $.3333\cdots$. Hence, the best thing to do in the event that the discount rate happens to be $33\frac{1}{3}\%$ is to rewrite this numeral in its equivalent fractional form—$33\frac{1}{3}\% = \frac{1}{3}$.

ILLUSTRATION 2: Emily Parker waited for a sale to buy her vacuum cleaner. The regular price of the cleaner is $64.95. However, she was able to buy it at a saving of $33\frac{1}{3}\%$. How much did she have to pay for the cleaner?

SOLUTION:

$$\begin{aligned}\text{Discount} &= 33\tfrac{1}{3}\% \text{ of } \$64.95\\ &= \tfrac{1}{3} \times \$64.95\\ &= \$21.65\\ \text{Selling price} &= \$64.95 - \$21.65\\ &= \$43.30\end{aligned}$$

EXPLANATION: After changing $33\frac{1}{3}\%$ to the fractional numeral $\frac{1}{3}$, the solution involves nothing more than finding the product of a fraction and a decimal.

Actually, the vacuum cleaner in Illustration 2 could have been advertised at a discount of $\frac{1}{3}$ off the original price. In fact, many merchants prefer to advertise their discount rates in fractions rather than percents.

ILLUSTRATION 3: At a closeout of kitchenware, a service for twelve people that regularly sells for $69.75 is offered at $\frac{2}{3}$ off this price. How much will a buyer have to pay for this set?

SOLUTION:

$$\begin{aligned}\text{Discount} &= \tfrac{2}{3} \times \$69.75\\ &= \$46.50\\ \text{Selling price} &= \$69.75 - \$46.50\\ &= \$23.25\end{aligned}$$

EXERCISES

A

Do you recall how to find the answers in the following exercises? If not, you will want to refer to the pages indicated for help.

1. Change each of the following percent numerals to its equivalent decimal numeral. (See pages 514–516.)

a. 12.5%	______	d. 52.9%	______	g. 9.75%	______
b. 23.7%	______	e. 2.34%	______	h. 12.41%	______
c. 46.1%	______	f. 62.51%	______	i. 59.07%	______

2. Change each of the following percent numerals to its equivalent decimal numeral. (See pages 514–516.)

a. $14\frac{1}{2}$%	______	e. $34\frac{1}{4}$%	______	i. $61\frac{3}{4}$%	______
b. $42\frac{1}{2}$%	______	f. $56\frac{1}{4}$%	______	j. $5\frac{1}{2}$%	______
c. $24\frac{1}{2}$%	______	g. $17\frac{3}{4}$%	______	k. $9\frac{3}{4}$%	______
d. $10\frac{1}{4}$%	______	h. $27\frac{3}{4}$%	______	l. $4\frac{1}{4}$%	______

3. Find the product in each of the following exercises. (See page 519.)

a. 16.5% × 40 = ______	f. 6.25% × 45 = ______
b. 20.5% × 56 = ______	g. 14.25% × 5.8 = ______
c. 41.5% × 37 = ______	h. 43.25% × 1.50 = ______
d. 18.5% × 128 = ______	i. 4.75% × .86 = ______
e. 9.25% × 30 = ______	j. 27.75% × 3.25 = ______

4. Find the product in each of the following exercises. (See page 520.)

a. $12\frac{1}{2}$% × 70 = ______	e. $15\frac{1}{4}$% × 10 = ______
b. $25\frac{1}{2}$% × 92 = ______	f. $2\frac{1}{4}$% × 42.50 = ______
c. $6\frac{1}{2}$% × 1.34 = ______	g. $27\frac{3}{4}$% × 25 = ______
d. $3\frac{1}{2}$% × 2.38 = ______	h. $42\frac{3}{4}$% × 5.70 = ______

5. Find the product to the nearest penny in each of the following exercises. (See page 504.)

a. $\frac{1}{3}$ × \$27 = ______	h. $\frac{1}{3}$ × \$304.11 = ______
b. $\frac{1}{3}$ × \$84 = ______	i. $\frac{1}{3}$ × \$46 = ______
c. $\frac{1}{3}$ × \$126 = ______	j. $\frac{1}{3}$ × \$85 = ______
d. $\frac{1}{3}$ × \$252 = ______	k. $\frac{1}{3}$ × \$92 = ______
e. $\frac{1}{3}$ × \$18.45 = ______	l. $\frac{1}{3}$ × \$116 = ______
f. $\frac{1}{3}$ × \$20.67 = ______	m. $\frac{1}{3}$ × \$4.27 = ______
g. $\frac{1}{3}$ × \$156.18 = ______	n. $\frac{1}{3}$ × \$18.46 = ______

B

1. Buyers were offered a $33\frac{1}{3}$% discount rate on each of the following

purchases. Determine how much they had to pay for each article after first finding the discount to the nearest penny.

Article	Original Price	Discount	Cost to Purchaser
a. Tape Cartridge Player	$ 78.00	$______	$______
b. Portable Car Radio	96.00	______	______
c. Car Speaker Kit	10.95	______	______
d. Car Stereo Tape Player	79.95	______	______
e. Remote Control Switch	16.88	______	______
f. Solid-State Amplifier	32.95	______	______
g. Stereo Receiver	219.95	______	______
h. Matched Stereo System	419.95	______	______

2. How much will a person have to pay for each of the following purchases? First find the discount correct to the nearest penny.

	Original Price	Discount Rate	Discount	Cost
a.	$ 46.00	10.4%	$______	$______
b.	81.00	6.8%	______	______
c.	125.00	7.2%	______	______
d.	12.50	14.5%	______	______
e.	246.75	23.6%	______	______
f.	310.95	34.7%	______	______

3. How much will a person have to pay for each of the following purchases? First find the discount correct to the nearest penny.

	Original Price	Discount Rate	Discount	Cost
a.	$ 55.00	12½%	$______	$______
b.	90.00	30½%	______	______
c.	19.75	5½%	______	______
d.	68.95	23½%	______	______
e.	60.00	8¼%	______	______
f.	75.00	21¼%	______	______
g.	130.50	34¼%	______	______
h.	50.00	6¾%	______	______
i.	82.00	42¾%	______	______
j.	257.20	18¾%	______	______

C

1. When Glenda Daniels purchased her solid-state 3-speed portable stereo tape recorder, she received a discount rate of 22½% on the selling price. What percent of the selling price did she have to pay for the tape recorder? ______
2. A discount of ¼ off the normal price is offered the buyer of a solid state TV set during a sale. What fraction of the normal price w the buyer have to pay for the TV set? ______

3. A ball microphone is placed on sale at a discount rate of 1/5 off the regular price of $13.95.
   a. How much discount will a buyer receive? ________
   b. How much will a buyer have to pay for this microphone if he buys it during the sale? ________
4. The Radio Electronics Shop offers its customers a professional model 4-track stereo tape deck at $249, less a discount of 1/3 of this price. Its competitor, The Stereo Shop, is offering this same deck at $260.50, less 40% of this price.
   a. How much will a buyer have to pay if he purchases the tape deck at The Radio Electronics Shop? ________
   b. How much will a buyer have to pay if he purchases the tape deck at The Stereo Shop? ________
   c. How much can a person save by buying this tape deck in one store rather than the other? ________

Unit 4: Computing the Discount Rate on a Purchase

When you first started looking into discounts and discount rates, you examined an advertisement on the sale of sofas that were originally priced from $145 to $395, but were reduced some 30% to 65%. At the time, there was some thought that perhaps most of the furniture was being sold at prices closer to the 30% discount rate than to the 65% rate. So that there is no question as to which rate you are receiving, you need some method of finding the discount rate when you know the original price and the sale price of the article.

The best place to begin is with the method used for finding the discount. Consider the case where the discount rate is 20% and the original price of the article is $30. To find the discount, you would proceed as follows:

$$\text{Discount} = 20\% \times \$30$$
$$\text{Discount} = .20 \times \$30$$
$$\text{Discount} = \$6$$

This can also be written in the following form:

$$.20 \times \$30 = \$6$$

When you look at this equation, you immediately begin to think in terms of the Product of Two Numbers Principle (see page 518). Recall that this principle states that if the product of two numbers is divided by either of the numbers, the quotient will be the other number. Hence, if you divide $6 by $30, the quotient is .20.

Thus: $.20 = \$6 \div \$30 \qquad (1)$

What does all this mean? If you go back to the wording of the problem, you will see that .20 is the discount rate expressed as a decimal numeral, while $6 is the discount and $30 is the original price of the article. Therefore, if you replace the numerals in equation (1) by the general terms they represent, you come up with the method for finding the discount rate.

$$\text{Discount Rate} = \text{Discount} \div \text{Original Price}$$

ILLUSTRATION 1: A pair of curtains that regularly sells for $14 was sold at a discount of $3. What discount rate was the purchaser receiving? Find your answer to the nearest whole number percent value.

SOLUTION:

$$\begin{aligned} \text{Discount Rate} &= \text{Discount} \div \text{Original Price} \\ &= \$3 \div \$14 \\ &= .214 \\ &= 21.4\%, \text{ or } 21\% \end{aligned}$$

EXPLANATION: The formula developed called for dividing the discount by the original price of the article. In this case, it means dividing $3 by $14. The quotient is found first as the decimal numeral .214, which is then changed to its equivalent percent numeral by moving the decimal point two places to the right. The 21.4 is rounded off to the nearest whole number 21, and hence the discount rate is 21%.

ILLUSTRATION 2: A Yorkshire suit that regularly sells for $85 is priced at $69 during a sale. What discount rate will the purchaser receive when he buys this suit? Find your answer to the nearest whole number percent value.

EXPLANATION: Since the discount-rate formula calls for dividing the discount by the original price, your first task will have to be to find the discount in this problem. Once you know the discount, it is possible to complete the solution as in Illustration 1.

SOLUTION:

$$\begin{aligned} \text{Discount} &= \text{Original Value} - \text{Selling Price} \\ &= \$85 - \$69 \\ &= \$16 \end{aligned}$$

$$\begin{aligned} \text{Discount Rate} &= \text{Discount} \div \text{Original Value} \\ &= \$16 \div \$85 \\ &= .188 \\ &= 18.8\%, \text{ or } 19\% \end{aligned}$$

When you see an article marked \$19.99, you tend to think that the price is around \$19 rather than only one penny away from \$20. Similarly, a stereo speaker selling for \$99.98 appears to be a great deal cheaper than one selling for \$100, and yet there is only a two-cent difference between them. Realizing the way people's minds work, a merchant prices articles a penny or two, or, sometimes, even five pennies, under a round number of dollars. To you, \$17.95 is a better buy than \$18, and \$49.48 has a greater sales appeal than \$50.

The tendency to price merchandise in this manner makes computation of discount rates a little difficult. Hence, it would be best to round the price off to the nearest dollar, or, perhaps, to the nearest half-dollar, before finding the discount rate.

ILLUSTRATION 3: The Burns Brothers Shop is offering, for \$9.98, a can opener that was originally priced at \$12.99. What discount rate will a buyer receive on this purchase?

SOLUTION:

$$\begin{aligned} \text{Original price} &= \$12.99, \text{ or } \$13 \\ \text{Selling price} &= \$9.98, \text{ or } \$10 \\ \text{Discount} &= \$13 - \$10 \\ &= \$3 \\ \text{Discount rate} &= \$3 \div \$13 \\ &= .231 \\ &= 23.1\%, \text{ or } 23\% \end{aligned}$$

EXPLANATION: Both the original price of the can opener and the selling price are rounded off to the nearest dollar. This makes the discount approximately \$3. The solution is then completed in the same manner as in Illustration 2.

EXERCISES A

Do you recall how to find the answer in each of the following exercises? If not, refer to the pages indicated for help.

1. Change each of the following decimal numerals to its equivalent percent numeral. (See page 514.)

a. .35	________	e. .04	________	i. .362	________
b. .62	________	f. .07	________	j. .543	________
c. .41	________	g. .01	________	k. .042	________
d. .17	________	h. .09	________	l. .074	________

2. Write each of the following fractions as a decimal correct to the nearest thousandth. Then rewrite each decimal numeral as a percent numeral correct to the nearest whole number. The first exercise is completed for you. (See page 514.)

	Fraction	Decimal	Percent		Fraction	Decimal	Percent
a.	2/3	.667	67%	g.	17/23	______	______
b.	1/3	______	______	h.	41/74	______	______
c.	2/7	______	______	i.	2.50/6	______	______
d.	3/8	______	______	j.	4.75/9	______	______
e.	5/9	______	______	k.	4.25/12.50	______	______
f.	4/15	______	______	l.	7.40/52.50	______	______

B

1. Determine the discount rate correct to the nearest whole-number percent value in each of the following exercises.

	Original Price	Discount	Discount Rate
a.	$ 5	$ 2	______%
b.	20	5	______%
c.	30	6	______%
d.	40	25	______%
e.	15	10	______%
f.	9	2	______%
g.	8	1	______%
h.	29	4	______%
i.	48	7	______%
j.	125	16	______%
k.	249	40	______%
l.	375	124	______%
m.	495	295	______%
n.	527	227	______%

2. Determine the discount rate correct to the nearest whole-number percent value on each of the following purchases.

Item	Original Price	Sale Price	Discount	Discount Rate
a. Foam Rubber Pillow	$ 9	$ 7	$______	______%
b. Dacron Pillow	6	5	______	______%
c. Serene Pillow	9	8	______	______%
d. Down Pillow	22	18	______	______%
e. Fortrel Suit	55	48	______	______%
f. Sport Coat	40	28	______	______%
g. Topcoat	75	58	______	______%

3. Determine the discount rate correct to the nearest whole-number percent value on each of the following purchases.

Item	Original Price	Sale Price	Discount	Discount Rate
a. Alarm Clock	$ 8.50	$ 4.00	$____	____%
b. Electric Hand Mixer	15.00	8.50	____	____%
c. Electric Frypan	20.00	12.50	____	____%
d. Electric Knife	28.50	14.50	____	____%
e. Toaster	19.75	12.00	____	____%
f. Electric Can Opener	16.75	8.50	____	____%
g. Blender	29.75	19.25	____	____%
h. Hood Dryer	37.25	24.75	____	____%

4. Before determining the discount rate on each of the following purchases, round off both the original and the discount price to the nearest dollar. Find each answer correct to the nearest whole-number percent value.

Item	Original Price	Sale Price	Approximate Discount	Discount Rate
a. 21″ Weekender Bag	$ 14.98	$ 10.99	$____	____%
b. 26″ Pullman Bag	19.99	15.95	____	____%
c. 29″ Pullman Bag	23.95	17.98	____	____%
d. Living-Room Suite	499.95	399.95	____	____%
e. Reclining Chair	154.90	119.98	____	____%
f. Sofa Bed	189.95	168.95	____	____%

C

1. Girls' cotton knit polo shirts that regularly sell from $2.50 to $4.00 are placed on sale at $1.50 each.

a. What discount rate would a purchaser receive if she bought a $2.50 polo shirt at the time of the sale? ________

b. What discount rate would a purchaser receive if she bought a $4.00 polo shirt at the time of the sale? ________

2. A national magazine offered to sell 30 issues to subscribers for $3. The regular subscription rate is $5.77. However, if a person were to buy the 30 issues at a newsstand, he would have to pay $15.

a. What discount rate would a person receive on this special offer over what he would have to pay if he purchased the magazine at a newsstand? ________

b. What discount rate would a person receive on this special offer over what he would have to pay if he purchased the magazine at the regular subscription rate? ________

3. Before finding the discount rate on an article, it usually saves a great deal of time if the regular price and the sale price are rounded off either to the nearest dime, or the nearest quarter. To what amount would you round off each of the following prices?

a. $1.49	________	e. 39¢	________	i. $16.48	________
b. $1.74	________	f. 69¢	________	j. $94.73	________
c. $2.24	________	g. 88¢	________	k. $49.49	________
d. $1.58	________	h. 19¢	________	l. $72.29	________

4. No-iron dungarees that regularly sell for $7.19 can be bought during a sale at $3.74. What discount rate will Ann Perkins receive if she purchases a pair of these dungarees during the sale? Before computing your answer, round off the original selling price and the sale price respectively to the nearest dime and nearest quarter. ________

5. The Bradford Shop regularly sells men's socks for 85¢ a pair. During their 50th anniversary sale, they placed these socks on sale at 3 pairs for $1.75.

a. How much would Tom Baxter have to pay for three pairs of these socks if he bought them when they were not on sale? ________

b. What discount rate would Tom receive if he purchased these socks at the time of the sale? Find your answer to the nearest whole-number percent value. ________

Unit 5: Installment Purchasing

Until now, our discussion has been limited only to the topic of buying the things you need. Paying for them was not discussed. Many people do not have the cash to buy many of the things they need—that is, the relatively large items such as a living-room suite, or a TV set, or a refrigerator, and so on. In fact, one of the first things you talked about at the outset of this course was how to buy an automobile if you didn't have the cash to pay for it.

There are several ways to avoid making immediate payment for merchandise you buy. Probably the most popular of these is the installment purchase. Although each payment may be relatively small, the total is frequently a good deal more than you would have to pay if you paid for the article in one lump sum. Merchants often prefer that the article be bought in this manner for they not only make their normal profit but they also make a profit on the extra it will cost you for paying off the purchase on the installment plan.

ILLUSTRATION 1: A 4-piece living-room suite that regularly sells for $325 can be bought on the installment plan for $20 down and $25 a month for 15 months. How much extra does an installment purchaser have to pay for this suite?

EXPLANATION: On the 15 monthly payments alone, the installment purchaser will be paying back 15 times \$25, or \$375. In addition to this, he made a down payment of \$20. Hence, the total amount he paid for the suite is \$375, plus \$20, or \$395. Since he could have had this same suite for a cash payment of \$325, he paid an extra \$70 for the privilege of paying off the cost over a 15-month period.

Incidentally, this \$70 overpayment is known by a variety of names. Sometimes it is called the installment charge, or carrying charge, while at other times it is referred to as an interest charge.

SOLUTION:

$$\text{Total of monthly installments} = 15 \times \$25 = \$375$$

$$\text{Installment price} = \$20 + \$375 = \$395$$

$$\text{Cash price} = \$325$$

$$\text{Installment charge} = \$395 - \$325 = \$70$$

ILLUSTRATION 2: Walter Bamberg purchased a \$480 refrigerator-freezer combination by making a 10% down payment and paying off the balance over a three-year period in equal monthly payments of \$17.50. How much could Walter have saved had he purchased the refrigerator-freezer for \$480 cash instead of on the installment plan?

SOLUTION:

$$\text{Total of monthly installments} = 36 \times \$17.50 = \$630$$

$$\text{Down payment} = 10\% \times \$480 = .10 \times \$480 = \$48$$

$$\text{Installment price} = \$630 + \$48 = \$678$$

$$\text{Cash price} = \$480$$

$$\text{Installment charge} = \$678 - \$480 = \$198$$

EXPLANATION: In the three-year period there are 36 monthly payments. Since each of the payments is \$17.50, the total for all 36 is 36 times \$17.50, or \$630. Whenever the statement is made in business that a "10% down payment" has to be made, it means that 10% of the cash price is required before the buyer can walk out with the merchandise. In this case, 10% of the cash price is 10% of \$480. Once the down payment is found, the rest of the solution is completed in exactly the same manner as in Illustration 1.

EXERCISES A

1. How large a down payment will have to be made on each of the following installment purchases?

	Cash Price	Percent Of Down Payment Required	Down Payment
a.	$ 250	10%	$______
b.	375	20%	______
c.	450	25%	______
d.	690	15%	______
e.	745	30%	______
f.	495	35%	______
g.	1,240	50%	______

2. How large a down payment—to the nearest penny—will have to be made on each of the following installment purchases?

	Cash Price	Percent Of Down Payment Required	Down Payment
a.	$ 72.50	10%	$______
b.	99.75	20%	______
c.	125.50	5%	______
d.	185.25	25%	______
e.	59.95	10%	______
f.	234.90	40%	______
g.	569.98	30%	______

3. How much will an installment purchaser have to pay under each of the following plans?

	Down Payment	Monthly Payments	Number of Months	Installment Price
a.	$ 50	$20	6	$______
b.	40	25	5	______
c.	75	15	9	______
d.	140	40	12	______
e.	69	18	15	______
f.	56	37	24	______
g.	18	16	36	______

4. How much will an installment purchaser have to pay under each of the following plans?

	Down Payment	Weekly Payments	Number of Weeks	Installment Price
a.	$3.00	$1.00	20	$______
b.	2.95	1.50	30	______
c.	4.50	1.25	52	______
d.	7.95	1.75	40	______

	Down Payment	Weekly Payments	Number of Weeks	Installment Price
e.	$8.25	$2.45	38	$______
f.	5.98	2.65	65	______

5. How much will an installment purchaser have to pay under each of the following plans?

	Down Payment	Monthly Payments	Number of Months	Installment Price
a.	$ 57.50	$15.50	8	$______
b.	69.75	18.75	10	______
c.	49.95	10.25	12	______
d.	120.50	25.50	24	______
e.	134.25	35.50	36	______
f.	129.95	34.50	18	______

6. How much extra will an installment purchaser have to pay when buying an article under each of the following plans?

	Down Payment	Monthly Payments	Number Of Months	Installment Price	Cash Price	Installment Charge
a.	$ 50	$10	5	$______	$ 90	$______
b.	25	5	20	______	95	______
c.	42	16	12	______	210	______
d.	75	23	30	______	605	______
e.	168	35	36	______	1,120	______
f.	212	42	24	______	1,005	______

7. How much extra will an installment purchaser have to pay when buying an article under each of the following plans?

	Down Payment	Monthly Payments	Number Of Months	Installment Price	Cash Price	Installment Charge
a.	$ 10.50	$ 5.00	8	$______	$ 42.00	$______
b.	18.75	6.00	10	______	68.75	______
c.	14.50	4.50	12	______	54.50	______
d.	67.95	10.00	24	______	267.95	______
e.	89.75	15.50	30	______	429.75	______
f.	105.98	36.50	18	______	705.98	______

8. How much extra will an installment purchaser have to pay when buying an article under each of the following plans?

	Cash Price	Down Payment (Rate)	Monthly Payments	Number Of Months	Installment Price	Installment Charge
a.	$200	10%	$15	14	$______	$______
b.	150	20%	22	7	______	______
c.	180	25%	14	12	______	______
d.	175	30%	9	18	______	______
e.	450	15%	18	24	______	______
f.	675	40%	14	36	______	______

B

1. Anna Fernicola could purchase a top-loading washer for $178 in cash. Unfortunately, she did not have the money to do this, so she made arrangements to put down a deposit of $28 and pay off the balance in 15 monthly payments of $12 each. How much extra did Anna have to pay by buying the washer on the installment plan? ________

2. The first thing Joe Brooks did on reaching 18 was to buy a motorcycle for $478.85. Since Joe didn't have the cash to pay, the dealer permitted him to make a down payment of $53.85 and pay off the rest in 30 monthly installments of $19.27 each. How much money could Joe have saved had he had the cash to pay for the motorcycle? ________

3. Joyce Field bought her TV set from a door-to-door salesman by making no down payment, but agreeing to pay him $4.75 each week for a year. Had she taken the time to visit the discount house in her neighborhood, she would have found that this same set could be bought for $139.95 cash. How much money could Joyce have saved had she had the cash and bought the set at a discount house? ________

4. After long hours of pushing his lawn mower, Bob Cramer went out and bought a deluxe riding mower that could double as a snowplow during the winter season. If he had had the cash, the mower would have cost him $729. But he did not, so he arranged to make a 10% down payment and the rest he agreed to pay off monthly over a two-year period. The payments came to $35.15. How much greater is the installment price than the cash price? ________

5. A 120-watt matched solid-state stereo system can be bought for $319.95 cash. If the buyer doesn't have cash, the dealer is willing to arrange an easy-pay plan. This consists of making a down payment of 5% and weekly payments of $4.65 each over a two-year period. How much could a person save when buying this system if he did not take advantage of the easy-pay plan? ________

Unit 6: The Charge Account

The large department stores have deferred-payment plans that are much the same as those used in the monthly installment plans. These plans are called by a variety of names among which the most common are,

The Revolving Charge Account
The Permanent Budget Account
The Convenient Budget Account

The idea behind these accounts, no matter what they are called, is to have the balance, or debt, paid off in monthly payments. A "small" service charge is added to the account each month. Now that the truth-in-lending law has been passed, customers must be informed what the charge is. The rate is 1% or 1½% per month on the unpaid balance, or even 2%, 2½%, or 3%, depending on what other stores in the area are charging and the section of the country in which the store is located.

If you kept your money in a bank, the very highest rate the bank would be permitted to pay you under present law (other than in special accounts) is 5¼% per year. If the service charge happens to be 3% per month, then, on a yearly basis, it would be 36%. This is seven times as much as the rate the bank can pay you. You can see that the revolving charge account was invented less for the convenience of the customer than for the profit of the department store.

At the time you inquire about the possibility of opening a charge account, you are usually asked to fill out a form similar to the one here. It is only after a check is made on how promptly you pay your bills that you are issued a credit card for the charge account.

The application blank on page 135 has an interesting note in the lower-right corner. Notice that you are asked to check whether or not you want to take out credit life insurance with this account. This insurance is the same type you examined at the time you were investigating the purchase of a car. You may remember that if you carried this insurance, in the event that you died before the car was fully paid for, the insurance company would pay off the balance of the debt. Credit insurance on a charge account is exactly the same. Should you die while a balance still remained in the account, this would be cleared up by the insurance company. The very last line of the application states that you have to make a monthly payment of 1/10 of 1% of the unpaid balance for this protection. Here is how some of these accounts operate.

DEPARTMENT STORE A

In this store, you simply tell the credit manager that you would like to have a revolving charge account of $100, $150, $200, $250, or $300. If you choose the $100 account, you will not be permitted to charge merchandise in excess of $100. In addition, each month you must make a payment of at least $10 on your debt. If the amount you owe the store drops below $10, then all you have to pay is whatever this amount happens to be.

ALWAYS USE ZIP CODE

SOURCE CODE | **APPLICATION FOR CHARGE ACCOUNT** **Please Print Clearly** | ACCT. CODE | AUTHORIZED BY | DATE

☐ FLEXIBLE ☐ REGULAR

☐ MR ☐ MRS ☐ MISS | HUSBAND'S 1st NAME | MIDDLE INITIAL | LAST NAME | WIFE'S 1st NAME

HOME ADDRESS | NO. & STREET | APT. NO. | TOWN | STATE | ZIP CODE

HOME PHONE | ☐ RENTS HOW LONG ______ ☐ Roomer C/O ______ | ☐ OWNS HOW LONG ______ HOW LONG ______

USE ONLY IF YOU MOVED IN PAST 3 YRS.

PREVIOUS ADDRESS

HUSBAND'S EMPLOYER (IF SINGLE - YOUR EMPLOYER) | POSITION | HOW LONG

BUSINESS ADDRESS

WIFE'S EMPLOYER | BUSINESS ADDRESS | POSITION | HOW LONG

I HAVE ACCOUNTS AND LOANS WITH

MY BANK IS | BRANCH | ☐ SAVINGS ☐ SPEC. CHECK ☐ REG. CHECK

SUBJECT TO APPLICABLE TERM ON THE REVERSE SIDE OF THIS APPLICATION

I AM OVER 21 ☐ YES ☐ NO CUSTOMER SIGNATURE ▶

INTER | CREDIT FILE | DEPT. NO. | CUSTOMER'S NAME | STORE | SALESPERSON DEPT. NO. SALARY NO.

YES ☐ NO ☐ CREDIT LIFE INSURANCE IS DESIRED. IT IS UNDERSTOOD THAT IN THE EVENT OF APPLICANT'S DEATH, THE CREDIT LIFE INSURANCE WILL PAY OFF THE ACCOUNT BALANCE SHOWN ON THE LATEST BILLING. THE PREMIUM FOR THIS COVERAGE IS AN ADDITIONAL 1/10 OF 1% ASSESSED WITH MONTHLY SERVICE CHARGES.

In the \$150 account, the maximum you can charge is \$150. Now your monthly payment will be at least \$15 unless you manage to bring the debt below \$15. In this event, you will pay only what you owe.

No matter which of these accounts you choose, the "small service charge" is $1\frac{1}{2}\%$ of the unpaid balance carried from the previous month's bill. Incidentally, there is no service charge on any purchases made during the month for which you are being billed.

ILLUSTRATION 1: Joan Clarke has a \$250 charge account at Department Store A. The unpaid balance carried from the previous month's bill is \$195.

a. How large is Joan's monthly payment?
b. How large is the service charge that is added to Joan's account?
c. How much will Joan still owe on her account after she has made the monthly payment?

SOLUTION:

(a) Monthly payment = \$25

(b) Service charge $= 1\frac{1}{2}\% \times \$195$
$= 1.5\% \times \$195$
$= .015 \times \$195$
$= \$2.925$, or \$2.93

(c) Total of account at month's end $= \$195 + \$2.93$
$= \$197.93$

Balance still remaining $= \$197.93 - \$25$
$= \$172.93$

EXPLANATION: Since this is a "\$250 account," the amount of the cash monthly payment has to be \$25. Hence, this is the answer to part (a). For part (b), the service charge is 1½% of the unpaid balance of \$195. In answer to (c), the total debt at the end of the month consists of both the balance that had not been paid, plus the service charge for the month. This comes to \$197.93. After subtracting the \$25 that was paid, you find that Joan still owes this department store \$172.93.

DEPARTMENT STORE B

This department store has set up a payment schedule to this effect.

SCHEDULE OF PAYMENTS

Highest Balance	Monthly Payment	Highest Balance	Monthly Payment
\$ 20 to 100	\$10	\$551 to 600	\$40
101 to 150	12	601 to 650	42
151 to 200	15	651 to 700	45
201 to 250	20	701 to 750	47
251 to 300	25	751 to 800	50
301 to 350	27	801 to 850	52
351 to 400	30	851 to 900	55
401 to 450	32	901 to 950	57
451 to 500	35	951 to 1,000	60
501 to 550	37		

If a person's balance during a particular month happened to be \$317, then the smallest payment he could make would be \$27. However, he can pay off any amount over that he cares to; in fact, he can pay off the entire debt of \$317. What is the least payment that a charge-account customer can make during a month in which his balance is \$637.24?

For the convenience of having a charge account in this store, you would pay a monthly service charge of 1½% on that part of the balance on your debt carried from the previous month's bill that was \$500 or under, and only 1% on that part of the debt over \$500.

ILLUSTRATION 2: Dorian Riker's charge-account balance at Department Store B came to $739 after he paid his bill in February.

a. How large a service charge was made against his account for the month of March?
b. What was the smallest payment Dorian could make in March if there were no charge purchases that month?

SOLUTION:

(a) Service charge on first $500 = $1\frac{1}{2}\% \times \$500$
$= 1.5\% \times \$500$
$= .015 \times \$500$
$= \$7.50$

Balance of debt over $500 = $739 − $500
$= \$239$

Service charge on amount over $500 = $1\% \times \$239$
$= .01 \times \$239$
$= \$2.39$

Total service charge = $7.50 + $2.39
$= \$9.89$

(b) Total March bill = $739 + $9.89
$= \$748.89$

Payment = $47

EXPLANATION: In determining the service charge in Part (a), you separate the computation into two sections. In the first of these, you find the service charge on the first $500 by computing 1½% of this amount. The remainder of the service charge is computed by determining 1% of the balance over the $500 amount. Since the total unpaid balance is $739, the amount over $500 is $239. On $239, 1% is $2.39. Hence, the total service charge is the sum of the two charges of $7.50 and $2.39, or $9.89. In finding the smallest possible payment for March, notice that the total bill of $748.89 falls between $701 and $750. Therefore, according to the "Schedule of Payments," the smallest payment that will be accepted by the store is $47.

DEPARTMENT STORE C

In this case, customers are allowed to charge purchases so long as the total remains under $1,000. Instead of following a schedule of payments, you are told that each month you must make a payment of at least 10% of the bill at the time of payment. You are also granted the option of purchasing credit insurance on your life at a cost of 1/10 of 1% of the unpaid balance carried from the previous month's bill. The monthly service charge here is also based on this unpaid balance, and is 2% of that amount.

ILLUSTRATION 3: After paying her bill in September, the balance in Hazel Jackson's charge account at Department Store C was $237.

a. What service charge will Hazel have to pay in October?
b. How much will have to be added to Hazel's balance to pay for the cost of the credit insurance?
c. What is the smallest payment Hazel can make on her charge account in October if she had no charge purchase in that month?

SOLUTION:

(a) Service charge = 2% × $237
= .02 × $237
= $4.74

(b) Cost of insurance = 1/10 × 1% × $237
= 1/10 × .01 × $237
= .001 × $237
= $.237, or $.24

(c) Total bill for October = $237 + $4.74 + $.24
= $241.98

Minimum payment = 10% × $241.98
= .10 × $241.98
= $24.198, or $24.20

EXPLANATION: The only computation above that might cause a little difficulty is that involving the cost of the insurance in Part (b). To find 1/10 of 1%, it is best to rewrite 1% in its equivalent decimal form of .01. To get 1/10 of this number, simply divide .01 by 10. Thus:

```
     .001
10 ) .010
       10
       --
        0
```

Therefore, 1/10 × 1% × $237 becomes .001 × $237, and this product is $.237. When $.237 is rounded off to the nearest penny, the cost of the insurance turns out to be $.24.

EXERCISES A

If you do not recall how to do the computation in the following exercises, refer to page 514 for help. Write each of the products below as a decimal.

a. 1/10 × 1%	________	d. 1/5 × 1%	________
b. 1/2 × 1%	________	e. 1/8 × 1%	________
c. 1/4 × 1%	________	f. 1/100 × 1%	________

B

1. Use the charge-account plans described for Department Store A on pages 134 - 135 to find the smallest monthly payment on each of the following plans.

a. The $100 plan ________ c. The $150 plan ________
b. The $200 plan ________ d. The $300 plan ________

2. How large will the monthly service charge be on the following charge-account balances under the Department Store A plan?

a. $140 ________ c. $86 ________ e. $254.80 ________
b. $220 ________ d. $132.40 ________ f. $176.47 ________

3. What balance will remain after the smallest monthly payment is made on each of the following charge accounts at Department Store A? No charge purchases were made during the current month.

	Balance From Previous Month	Type Of Account	Service Charge	Monthly Payment	Balance Still Remaining
a.	$ 80	$100	$______	$______	$______
b.	140	150	______	______	______
c.	220	250	______	______	______
d.	260	300	______	______	______
e.	145	200	______	______	______
f.	196	300	______	______	______
g.	234	250	______	______	______
h.	298	300	______	______	______

4. What are the smallest monthly payments that charge-account customers at Department Store B can make if their unpaid bills are as follows? (See page 136.)

a. $157 ________ e. $249.47 ________
b. $234 ________ f. $358.31 ________
c. $469 ________ g. $604.16 ________
d. $723 ________ h. $918.12 ________

5. How large will the monthly service charge be on each of the following charge-account balances at Department Store B?

	Balance From Previous Month	Charge On First $500 Or Less	Charge On Amount Over $500	Total Service Charge
a.	$400	$______	$______	$______
b.	500	______	______	______
c.	800	______	______	______
d.	900	______	______	______

	Balance From Previous Month	Charge On First $500 Or Less	Charge On Amount Over $500	Total Service Charge
e.	$750	$______	$______	$______
f.	840	______	______	______
g.	645	______	______	______
h.	987	______	______	______
i.	712	______	______	______
j.	834	______	______	______

6. What balance will still remain after the smallest monthly payment possible is made on each of the following charge accounts at Department Store B? No charge purchases were made during the current month.

	Balance From Previous Month	Charge On First $500	Charge On Amount Over $500	Total Service Charge	Monthly Payment	Balance
a.	$600	$______	$______	$______	$______	$______
b.	870	______	______	______	______	______
c.	720	______	______	______	______	______
d.	960	______	______	______	______	______
e.	875	______	______	______	______	______

7. What are the smallest monthly payments that charge-account customers at Department Store C can make if their unpaid bills at the time of payment are as follows? (See page 137.)

a. $140	______	e. $237.26	______
b. $630	______	f. $427.18	______
c. $347	______	g. $695.82	______
d. $596	______	h. $874.76	______

8. How large will the monthly service charge be on each of the following charge-account balances at Department Store C?

a. $400	______	e. $685	______
b. $700	______	f. $473	______
c. $540	______	g. $396	______
d. $290	______	h. $478	______

9. The charge-account customers at Department Store C, whose unpaid balances are shown, had chosen to take out credit life insurance. How much did the insurance cost them for this month? (See page 137.)

a. $300	$______	d. $600	$______
b. $800	______	e. $450	______
c. $900	______	f. $570	______

g. $620	$________	l. $487	$________
h. $790	________	m. $312.45	________
i. $623	________	n. $533.82	________
j. $731	________	o. $649.72	________
k. $298	________	p. $158.07	________

10. What balance will remain after the smallest-possible monthly payment is made on each of the following charge accounts in Department Store C? No charge purchases were made during the current month. (See page 137.)

	Balance From Previous Month	Service Charge	Insurance Charge	Total Charge	Total Bill	Monthly Payment	Balance
a.	$200	$____	$____	$____	$____	$____	$____
b.	700	____	____	____	____	____	____
c.	450	____	____	____	____	____	____
d.	680	____	____	____	____	____	____
e.	324	____	____	____	____	____	____

C

1. Two charge-account customers at Department Store A (see pages 134–135) have exactly the same bill of $84.95. However, one has a "$100-account," while the other has a "$250-account." How much less will the first customer's payment be that month than the second customer's if both make the minimum payment? ________

2. Vera Jennings has a charge account at Department Store A (see pages 134–135). During the month of March, her bill was $18.85.

a. If her account is a "$200 account," how much will her minimum payment have to be? ________

b. If her account is a "$300 account," how much will her minimum payment have to be? ________

c. If her account is a "$150 account," how much will her minimum payment have to be? ________

3. After making his May 1 payment, David McLain's "$300-account" at Department Store A showed a balance of $240. He made no charge purchases during May.

a. How large will his minimum payment be on June 1? ________

b. How large will the service charge be for the month of May? ________

c. What is the total amount of merchandise that David will be able to charge during the month of June? ________

Unit 7: Chapter Review and Test

1. Write each of the following measures in terms of ounces only.
   a. 4 pounds ________ b. 3 pounds, 5 ounces ________
2. Write each of the following measures in terms of pints only.
   a. 5 quarts ________ b. 6 quarts, 1 pint ________
3. Write each of the following measures in terms of quarts only.
   a. 6 gallons ________ b. 4 gallons, 3 quarts ________
4. Write each of the following measures in terms of ounces only.
   a. 5 quarts, 7 ounces ________ b. 2 pints, 10 ounces ________
5. A can of creamed corn weighs 1 pound, 1 ounce. The cost of the can is 29¢. What is the cost per ounce of this creamed corn? Compute your answer to the nearest tenth of a penny. ________
6. Peach jelly sells at a supermarket at 3 jars for $1. How much will a customer probably have to pay for 1 jar? ________
7. A 6-ounce box of breakfast flakes sells for 28¢. At the same rate per ounce, how much should a person have to pay for a 9-ounce box of the same flakes? ________
8. An 8-ounce jar of beets costs 19¢. If a person purchased a 20-ounce jar of these same beets, he would have to pay 35¢. How much can a person save by buying the 20-ounce jar rather than by buying 20 ounces of beets at the same rate he paid for the 8-ounce jar?
   ____
9. Mike Jamieson purchased $7.58 worth of food at the supermarket. He gave the checkout clerk a $10 bill in payment. Indicate the change that Mike received. Use a table similar to the one below.

1¢	5¢	10¢	25¢	50¢	$1	$5

10. A television set that regularly sells for $184 was placed on sale at a 25% discount rate.
    a. How much discount did a person receive during the sale?
    ____
    b. How much did a person have to pay for the TV set if he purchased it during the sale? ________
    c. Show how you would find the sale price without first finding the discount. ________
11. During its storewide furniture sale, the Camden Company offered a set of porch furniture at 33⅓% off. If this porch furniture regularly sells for $237, how much will it cost during the sale?
    ____

12. An article that regularly sells for $20 can be purchased during a sale at a discount of $5. What discount rate is a purchaser receiving? ________

13. A $64.95 electric guitar can be purchased during a sale for $49.98. By rounding off each of these prices to the nearest dollar, find the discount rate to the nearest whole-number percent value. ________

14. Bruce Devlin purchased a typewriter that regularly sells for $137. Since he did not have the cash, he was permitted to buy it on the following terms:

$15 down and $8 per month for 18 months

How much could Bruce have saved had he had the cash to pay for the typewriter? ________

15. Richard Parks has a $250 charge account at Department Store A. (See pages 134–135.) After making his monthly payment in March, his account showed a balance of $185.

a. How large was Richard's minimum payment in April? ________

b. How large was the service charge that was added to his account for March? ________

c. How much still remained to be paid after he made his monthly payment in April? He made no charge purchases during the month of March. ________

JOB'S
JOB'S
JOB'S
JOB'S
JOB'S

CHAPTER 4

PERSONAL INCOME

There will be few experiences in your life that will give you more satisfaction than the first money you earn. New worlds will seem to open up before you—a convertible car, a 24-foot speedboat, a trip to Bermuda! It is only after you take a second look at the amount of the check that you settle for another necktie, or another blouse.

The way you receive your earnings depends frequently on the type of position you hold. If you fall into the managerial, or executive, group, you will probably receive an annual salary that is given to you in one of three ways:

1. Monthly
2. Semimonthly, that is, twice a month
3. Biweekly, that is, once every two weeks

If you are not paid in this way, then your earnings may be based on any one, or a combination, of the following methods.

1. Hourly basis
2. Piece-rate basis
3. Commission basis

Since most people will find themselves among the second group, it will be these three methods of computing earnings that will be examined in this chapter.

Unit 1: Earnings Computed on an Hourly Basis

Section 1: Regular Wages and Overtime Wages

The wages of the majority of workers are based on the number of hours that they work. Usually, they earn a certain salary per hour, and their earnings are computed in terms of the total number of hours they work during one week. Frequently, the labor organization that represents the employees of a company will have drawn up a contract with the managers of that company, stating what the hourly rates should be for these employees.

ILLUSTRATION 1: During the past week, Carlos Juárez worked $37\frac{1}{2}$ hours at the rate of \$3.56 per hour. What were his earnings for the week?

SOLUTION:

$$\text{Rate for 1 hour} = \$3.56$$
$$\text{Earnings for } 37\tfrac{1}{2} \text{ hours} = 37\tfrac{1}{2} \times \$3.56 = \$133.50$$

EXPLANATION: There was very little involved in this problem other than finding the product of $37\frac{1}{2}$ and \$3.56. In doing the computation it is best to change $37\frac{1}{2}$ to 37.5 before multiplying.

Most wage contracts include an agreement in them that sets the total number of hours that an employee may work each week. If he works beyond that time, the agreement usually states that he will receive *time and a half* for the overtime work. This simply means that, for each of the overtime hours, his rate of pay will be $1\frac{1}{2}$ times as large as the normal hourly pay rate. Thus, if the normal hourly rate is \$2.00, then, for each hour of overtime work, the employee will receive $1\frac{1}{2}$ times as much as this, or \$3.00.

ILLUSTRATION 2: If the normal hourly wage rate is \$4.47, what will the overtime wage rate be at time and a half?

SOLUTION:

$$\text{Normal hourly wage rate} = \$4.47$$
$$\text{Time-and-a-half rate} = 1\tfrac{1}{2} \times \$4.47 = 1.5 \times \$4.47 = \$6.705$$

EXPLANATION: There are two points of importance in the above solution. Notice that the $1\frac{1}{2}$ was changed to the decimal 1.5 so that the computation would be easier. Also, the overtime pay rate of

\$6.705 was not rounded off to the nearest penny. No rounding off should be done until the total overtime salary is determined.

ILLUSTRATION 3: Mary Sullivan is employed by a company where she is paid time and a half for all work beyond 38 hours per week. If her regular hourly rate is \$3.69, how much will her earnings be during a week in which she worked 45 hours?

SOLUTION:

$$\begin{aligned}
\text{Regular hourly rate} &= \$3.69 \\
\text{Overtime hourly rate} &= 1.5 \times \$3.69 \\
&= \$5.535 \\
\text{Number of hours of overtime} &= 45 - 38 \\
&= 7 \\
\text{Regular salary} &= 38 \times \$3.69 \\
&= \$140.22 \\
\text{Overtime salary} &= 7 \times \$5.535 \\
&= \$38.745, \text{ or } \$38.75 \\
\text{Total salary} &= \$140.22 + \$38.75 \\
&= \$178.97
\end{aligned}$$

EXERCISES A

1. Find the time-and-a-half rate for each of the following regular hourly rates.

	Regular Hourly Rate	Time-and-a-Half Rate		Regular Hourly Rate	Time-and-a-Half Rate
a.	\$3.00	\$______	f.	\$4.64	\$______
b.	5.00	______	g.	3.96	______
c.	3.80	______	h.	3.38	______
d.	3.50	______	i.	3.43	______
e.	3.70	______	j.	3.87	______

2. Determine the earnings of each of the following. None received overtime during the week.

	Hourly Rate	Hours Worked	Earnings		Hourly Rate	Hours Worked	Earnings
a.	\$3.90	40	\$______	g.	\$4.384	39	\$______
b.	3.57	40	______	h.	3.096	40	______
c.	3.85	38	______	i.	4.76	37½	______
d.	4.29	37	______	j.	4.18	38½	______
e.	3.375	40	______	k.	3.83½	36	______
f.	3.845	38	______	l.	3.15½	35	______

3. The regular hourly rate and the number of overtime hours of work are given below. Determine the overtime earnings of each if time and a half is paid for overtime work.

	Hourly Rate	Overtime Rate	Overtime Hours	Overtime Earnings
a.	$4.08	$____	2	$____
b.	3.24	____	3	____
c.	3.88	____	2	____
d.	4.50	____	2	____
e.	3.96	____	4	____
f.	3.75	____	8	____
g.	3.67	____	14	____
h.	4.13	____	11	____
i.	3.72	____	5½	____
j.	5.46	____	7½	____
k.	3.84½	____	6	____
l.	4.06½	____	12	____

4. The maximum number of hours that an employee should work under the regular hourly pay rate is given below. For work beyond this, he receives time-and-a-half pay. Compute the total earnings for the week for each of the following employees.

	Hourly Rate	Overtime Rate	Hours Worked	Maximum For Regular Rate	Regular Earnings	Overtime Hours	Overtime Earnings	Total Earnings
a.	$3.40	$____	42	40	$____	____	$____	$____
b.	4.80	____	48	40	____	____	____	____
c.	3.56	____	45	40	____	____	____	____
d.	4.08	____	41	38	____	____	____	____
e.	5.09	____	43	40	____	____	____	____
f.	4.37	____	40	37	____	____	____	____
g.	4.65	____	37	28	____	____	____	____
h.	4.18	____	41½	39	____	____	____	____
i.	3.10	____	44½	38	____	____	____	____
j.	4.96	____	41½	37	____	____	____	____
k.	3.24	____	43½	38	____	____	____	____
l.	3.88	____	42½	35½	____	____	____	____
m.	5.60	____	40½	37½	____	____	____	____
n.	5.19	____	46½	35½	____	____	____	____

B

1. Each of the following employees is entitled to overtime pay for all the time worked over 7 hours per day. How many regular hours and how many overtime hours will each work during the week?

	Mon.	Tues.	Wed.	Thurs.	Fri.	Regular Hours	Overtime Hours
a.	9	6	5	8	7	______	______
b.	7	7	7	7	9	______	______
c.	7	8	8	8	7	______	______
d.	7	9	7	7	9	______	______
e.	7	10	9	7	8	______	______
f.	6	7	10	7	9	______	______
g.	8	5	4	9	6	______	______
h.	7	8	$7\frac{1}{2}$	7	$7\frac{1}{2}$	______	______
i.	7	$7\frac{1}{2}$	$7\frac{1}{2}$	$7\frac{1}{2}$	$7\frac{1}{2}$	______	______
j.	$8\frac{1}{2}$	$7\frac{1}{2}$	7	7	8	______	______

2. Each of the following employees is entitled to overtime pay for all time worked over 7 hours per day. How much will each earn during the week shown here?

	M	T	W	Th	F	Regular Hours	Overtime Hours	Hourly Rate	Regular Earnings	Overtime Rate	Overtime Earnings	Total Earnings
a.	7	7	7	7	8	______	______	\$3.48	\$______	\$______	\$______	\$______
b.	7	7	7	7	7	______	______	3.96	______	______	______	______
c.	7	6	7	5	7	______	______	4.06	______	______	______	______
d.	9	7	7	9	7	______	______	5.12	______	______	______	______
e.	8	7	7	8	7	______	______	3.86	______	______	______	______
f.	8	8	8	8	8	______	______	4.36	______	______	______	______
g.	9	7	9	8	7	______	______	4.95	______	______	______	______
h.	10	8	7	7	8	______	______	5.03	______	______	______	______

C

1. If Marie Cassela works either Sundays or holidays, she receives double time for each hour of work. This means that she will receive twice as much for each hour of work on those days than she does at her regular hourly rate during the week. Her regular hourly rate is \$4.24 per hour. How much will she receive for a Sunday's work of $6\frac{1}{2}$ hours? ______
2. Mr. Morely works for a firm where the normal work period is $38\frac{1}{2}$ hours per week. He receives time and a half for overtime and double time for Sundays and holidays. His regular rate is \$5.98 per hour.
   a. What will his normal weekly earnings be? ______
   b. What will he earn during a week in which he worked 42 hours? ______
   c. During the week in which he worked the 42 hours, he was also asked to work $5\frac{1}{2}$ hours on Sunday. What were his total earnings for that week? ______
3. Mr. Morely of Problem 2 worked 36 hours during the week of the July 4th holiday. If 5 of the hours of work were on the holiday, what was his total salary for that week? ______

4. Mr. Morley's firm of Problem 2 considers both Thanksgiving Thursday and the Friday that follows it to be holidays. How much will Mr. Morley earn during the week of Thanksgiving, if of the 37 hours he worked, 4 were on Thursday and 7 were on Friday? ________

Section 2: Tardiness Deductions

Employers are as unhappy about tardiness as teachers are. There is a difference, though, and that is that the employer has a way in which to combat this—he simply withholds part of your salary. On the whole, employers will often overlook a tardiness of as much as 15 minutes. When it runs over that, the amount they deduct will depend on the extent of the tardiness. Should tardiness become a habit, the employee may find that he no longer has a job.

A typical scale of wage loss for late arrival at work resembles the following:

MINUTES LATE	LOSS OF SALARY
First 15 minutes	No loss of salary
For each succeeding 10-minute period, or fraction thereof	Quarter of an hour's salary

ILLUSTRATION: Steven Willard clocked in at 8:57 A.M. last Thursday. His workday is supposed to begin at 8:00 A.M. If he earns \$2.86 per hour, how much will be deducted from his salary because of this tardiness?

EXPLANATION: Steven was 57 minutes late on Thursday. For the first 15 of these, there is no loss of salary. This leaves 57 − 15, or 42 minutes to be accounted for. For each 10-minute period, or fraction of a 10-minute period in the 42 minutes, he will lose $1/4$ of an hour's salary. By dividing 10 into 42, you find that there are $4\frac{2}{10}$ 10-minute periods in 42 minutes. Hence, Steven will loss 5 quarter hours of salary. And since 5 times $1/4$ is 1.25, his salary loss will be 1.25 times \$2.86. Incidentally, the phrase "clocked in at 8:57 A.M." means "reported to work at 8:57 A.M." The word "clocked" comes from the fact that an employee usually stamps the clock time on a card when he arrives at work.

SOLUTION:

$$
\begin{aligned}
\text{Number of minutes tardy} &= 57 \\
\text{Number of minutes of salary loss} &= 57 - 15 \\
&= 42 \\
\text{Number of 10-minute periods} &= 42 \div 10 \\
&= 4.2, \text{ or } 5 \\
\text{Number of hours of salary loss} &= 5 \times 1/4 \\
&= 5/4 \\
&= 1.25 \\
\text{Salary loss} &= 1.25 \times \$2.86 \\
&= \$3.575 \\
&= \$3.58
\end{aligned}
$$

EXERCISES A

1. The employees of the Pure Oil Company are supposed to clock in at 8:00 A.M. If they are late, they are docked in salary in accordance with the table on page 150. How many quarter hours of salary will be lost by employees reporting at the following hours?

	Time Of Arrival	Minutes Late	Quarter Hours Of Salary Lost
a.	8:10	______	______
b.	8:14	______	______
c.	8:16	______	______
d.	8:28	______	______
e.	8:33	______	______
f.	8:57	______	______
g.	9:07	______	______
h.	9:25	______	______

2. How much salary will be lost by each of the following employees of the Pure Oil Company of Problem 1 if they clocked in at the hour shown?

	Time Of Arrival	Minutes Late	Quarter Hours Of Salary Lost	Hourly Wage	Salary Loss
a.	8:12	______	______	$3.56	$______
b.	8:18	______	______	3.68	______
c.	8:26	______	______	3.24	______
d.	8:39	______	______	4.96	______
e.	8:42	______	______	4.57	______
f.	8:58	______	______	5.86	______
g.	9:15	______	______	3.40	______
h.	9:26	______	______	5.22	______

B

1. The workday at the Briggs Corporation normally ends at 4:30 in the afternoon. Should an employee work until 5:00, he receives no extra pay for it. However, if he works beyond 5:00 P.M., he will receive 1/4 hour at time-and-a-half pay for each 15 minutes of work, or part thereof, beyond 4:30. Thus, if he works until 4:56, he receives no overtime salary, but if he works until 5:02, he will receive 3/4 of an hour at time-and-a-half salary. How many quarter hours of overtime salary will each of the following employees receive if they clock out at the time shown?

	Time Of Leaving			Time Of Leaving	
a.	4:47	________	d.	5:57	________
b.	5:10	________	e.	4:53	________
c.	5:35	________	f.	6:18	________

2. Virginia Davenport works for the Briggs Corporation of Problem 1 at an hourly rate of $3.08. On Thursday, she worked until 6:25 P.M.
   a. How much overtime pay did she receive for the additional time she worked that day? ________
   b. How much regular salary did she receive for the day if she is employed on an 8-hour day? ________
   c. What were her total earnings for the day? ________
3. The Briggs Corporation of Problem 1 docks employees for tardiness in accordance with the table on page 150. The workday normally begins at 8:00 A.M. On Tuesday of this past week, Peter Marley clocked in at 8:42 A.M. and clocked out at 5:37 P.M. His hourly rate is $3.36.
   a. How much was he docked that day for being tardy? ________
   b. How much were his overtime earnings that day? ________
   c. Since he is employed on an 8-hour day, how much regular salary did he receive for the day? ________
   d. After deducting his loss for tardiness and adding his overtime pay, how much did he earn that day? ________

Unit 2: Earnings Computed on a Piece-Rate Basis

There are a few companies in certain fields that base their employees' wages on the number of articles that an employee produces. Both management and labor agree, in general, that this is not a very good idea. Because a worker will speed up in order to complete as many articles as possible, frequent accidents and inferior workmanship are often the result.

ILLUSTRATION 1: The Marshall Company pays its employees \$3.72 for each article they produce. How much will a person earn during a week in which he was able to complete 47 articles?

SOLUTION:

$$\begin{aligned} \text{Earnings} &= 47 \times \$3.72 \\ &= \$174.84 \end{aligned}$$

EXPLANATION: The computation simply involved multiplying the number of articles produced by the amount received for each article. In the piece-rate wage system, there is no cause for concern with overtime or lateness, for the employee's earnings depend solely on how many articles he turns out.

In recent years, the management and labor of certain companies have agreed on a wage system that represents a combination of the hourly wage rate and the piece-rate method. In this plan, the employee receives a fixed hourly salary for each hour that he works. In addition, if he produces more than a certain number of articles during the week, he will receive a bonus for each such article produced. If he produces less, he loses nothing. Labor is pleased with this, for it knows that each worker will have at least a guaranteed minimum weekly income. Management finds that there are not only fewer accidents, but that greater care is taken in the production of the article.

ILLUSTRATION 2: The Lacombe Corporation pays its employees an hourly wage of \$4.19. In addition, for each article over 125 that the employee produces during a single week, he receives 87¢. How much will Daphne Crane earn during a week in which she works 38 hours and produces 156 articles?

SOLUTION:

$$\begin{aligned} \text{Hourly earnings} &= 38 \times \$4.19 \\ &= \$159.22 \\ \text{Number of articles over 125} &= 156 - 125 \\ &= 31 \\ \text{Piecework earnings} &= 31 \times \$.87 \\ &= \$26.97 \\ \text{Total earnings} &= \$159.22 + \$26.97 \\ &= \$186.19 \end{aligned}$$

EXERCISES A

1. Each of the following employees was paid on a straight piecework basis. The number of articles each produced and the amount he received for each article is shown below. Determine the earnings of each for this week.

	Number Of Articles	Piecework Rate	Earnings
a.	276	62¢	$______
b.	348	47¢	______
c.	395	53¢	______
d.	469	39¢	______
e.	86	$1.84	______
f.	57	$3.06	______
g.	48	$4.19	______
h.	184	$1.15	______

2. All of the following employees worked on an hourly basis. In addition, they received a bonus for each article they produced over a fixed number. Determine the bonus each employee received for the week shown.

	Fixed Number To Be Produced	Actual Number Produced	Bonus Articles	Bonus Per Article	Bonus
a.	100	96	______	42¢	$______
b.	100	117	______	47¢	______
c.	140	162	______	91¢	______
d.	150	159	______	86¢	______
e.	135	157	______	$1.17	______
f.	50	56	______	$3.24	______
g.	65	71	______	$2.76	______
h.	95	121	______	$1.08	______

3. All of the following employees worked on an hourly basis. In addition, they received a bonus for each article produced over a fixed number. Determine the earnings of each employee for the week shown.

	Number Of Hours	Hourly Rate	Regular Pay	Fixed Number To Be Produced	Actual Number Produced	Bonus Articles	Bonus Per Article	Bonus	Total Earnings
a.	40	$3.17	$____	150	140	____	46¢	$____	$____
b.	40	3.95	____	125	117	____	54¢	____	____
c.	40	4.53	____	140	164	____	82¢	____	____
d.	38	5.61	____	130	157	____	95¢	____	____
e.	37	3.86	____	120	168	____	81¢	____	____
f.	42	3.95	____	75	81	____	$1.12	____	____
g.	39	3.58	____	85	107	____	$1.29	____	____
h.	37½	4.98	____	115	139	____	$1.58	____	____

B

1. During the week of June 5, Barbara Faber produced the following number of articles each day.

Monday	Tuesday	Wednesday	Thursday	Friday
85	93	81	86	95

If she receives 52¢ for each article on a straight piecework basis, what were her earnings for the week? ________

2. Hillcrest Electronics pays its employees on a piece-rate basis of 46¢ per article. To discourage careless workmanship, the company deducts 55¢ from the earnings of an employee for each article that is rejected during inspection. How much did Leo Metz receive during a week in which he produced 485 articles, but had 23 of these articles rejected? ________

3. Jerome Hayes works for a firm where he is paid $4.76 per hour. In addition, he is granted a bonus of 18¢ for each article that he produces over 60 each day. What would be his earnings during a week in which he worked 37½ hours and produced the following number of articles daily?

Monday	Tuesday	Wednesday	Thursday	Friday
63	59	57	68	72

____

4. The T and W Company uses the following graduated piecework weekly wage scale.

First 160 articles	75¢ each
Next 25 articles	82¢ each
Next 15 articles	91¢ each
All over 200 articles	$1.05 each

How much will each of the following employees earn during a week in which they produced the number of articles shown?

	Articles Produced	Earnings		Articles Produced	Earnings
a.	150	$________	e.	190	$________
b.	165	________	f.	198	________
c.	180	________	g.	206	________
d.	185	________	h.	215	________

5. Doreen Quinn, who works for the T and W Company of Problem 4, produced an average of 176 articles each week. By carefully analyzing each step of her work, she was able to increase her production by 25%.

a. How much did Doreen earn each week before she made a study of her work? ________

b. By how many articles did Doreen increase her weekly production? ________

c. How much did Doreen earn after changing her methods and increasing her production? ________

d. How much more did Doreen earn each week as a result of this change? ________

Unit 3: Earnings Computed on a Commission Basis

The third method for computing earnings is one in which the employee receives a certain percent of his sales. The people who earn their living in this manner are salespeople. They include the door-to-door sellers of magazines, brushes, vacuum cleaners, encyclopedias; telephone solicitors who try to get you to subscribe to magazines or newspapers; and even the great majority of car salespeople. All of them work on a straight commission basis—that is, their weekly earnings are based on a fixed percent of their total sales.

ILLUSTRATION 1: Harvey Quimby is a salesman for the Atlantic Boat Corporation. His earnings are wholly on a commission basis. How much will he earn during a week in which his sales amounted to \$5,460 and his commission rate is 4%?

SOLUTION:

$$\begin{aligned} \text{Commission} &= \$5{,}460 \times 4\% \\ &= \$5{,}460 \times .04 \\ &= \$218.40 \end{aligned}$$

EXPLANATION: The computation for determining earnings on a commission basis is usually easier if the percent numeral is changed to its equivalent decimal form rather than to a fraction. As you learned earlier, a percent numeral is changed to a decimal numeral by moving the decimal point two places to the left in the percent form.

Just as there exists a wage basis that consists of a combination of the hourly wage system and the piece-rate system, so, too, is there one which combines the hourly wage system with the commission system. Employees who most frequently operate under this program are the salesclerks of large department stores. Not only do they receive an hourly wage but, also, a fixed percent of either their entire sales for the week, or that part of the sales over and above a certain amount.

ILLUSTRATION 2: Jean Merrill works as a saleswoman for the South Shore Department Store at an hourly rate of \$3.15 for a 45-hour week. In addition, she receives $1\frac{1}{2}\%$ of all sales that she makes over \$800 during one week. What are her earnings during a week in which she sells \$2,100 worth of merchandise?

SOLUTION:

$$\begin{aligned}
\text{Hourly earnings} &= 45 \times \$3.15 \\
&= \$141.75 \\
\text{Sales over } \$800 &= \$2{,}100 - \$800 \\
&= \$1{,}300 \\
\text{Commission on sales} &= \$1{,}300 \times 1\tfrac{1}{2}\% \\
&= \$1{,}300 \times .015 \\
&= \$19.50 \\
\text{Total earnings} &= \$141.75 + \$19.50 \\
&= \$161.25
\end{aligned}$$

EXPLANATION: The hourly earnings were found in the usual manner. The \$800 was subtracted from \$2,100, since the woman's commission was based only on that part of her sales in excess of \$800. To simplify the computation, the $1\frac{1}{2}\%$ was changed to the decimal .015 rather than to a fraction.

EXERCISES A

1. All of the following employees work on a straight commission, based on their total sales. How much will each earn during a week in which total sales and commission rate were as shown?

	Total Sales	Commission Rate	Earnings
a.	\$ 800	20%	\$________
b.	500	28%	________
c.	960	22%	________
d.	745	16%	________
e.	873	23%	________
f.	1,376	9%	________
g.	2,007	$6\frac{1}{2}\%$	________
h.	3,925	$8\frac{1}{2}\%$	________
i.	31,000	$5\frac{1}{2}\%$	________
j.	5,400	$16\frac{1}{2}\%$	________

2. All of the following employees worked on an hourly basis. In addition, they received a commission on all their sales above the fixed amount shown. Determine the commission that each received, based on the information here.

	Total Sales For the Week	Commission Based On Sales Above Amount Shown Below	Commission Sales	Commission Rate	Commission
a.	$ 965	$ 800	$______	1%	$______
b.	842	750	______	2%	______
c.	6,254	5,000	______	3%	______
d.	1,686	1,250	______	2½%	______
e.	3,265	1,600	______	1¾%	______

3. All of the following employees worked on an hourly basis. In addition, they received a commission on all their sales above the fixed amount shown. Determine the earnings for the week that each received, based on the information here.

	Number Of Hours	Hourly Rate	Wages	Total Sales For the Week	Commission Based On Sales Above Amount Shown Below	Commission Sales	Commission Rate	Commission	Total Earnings
a.	44	$4.03	$______	$ 692	$ 600	$______	1%	$______	$______
b.	42	3.96	______	847	750	______	3%	______	______
c.	43	4.12	______	1,075	900	______	5%	______	______
d.	41½	4.02	______	1,524	1,200	______	3½%	______	______
e.	38½	3.84	______	1,386	1,000	______	2½%	______	______
f.	40½	5.15	______	1,653	800	______	1½%	______	______

B

1. Kenneth Somers, a real estate agent, works on a straight commission of 7½% of the selling price of the property. He recently sold Mr. Glynn's home for $24,700.
   a. How much commission did Mr. Somers receive? ______
   b. How much of the $24,700 did Mr. Glynn receive? ______
2. Marcia Medina, an insurance broker, receives as her commission 55% of the first year's premium on a life insurance policy and 18% of the annual premium on an automobile insurance policy. How much did she earn during a week in which the first year's premiums on the life insurance that she sold amounted to $346 and the premiums on automobile insurance came to $427? ______
3. One of the authors of a textbook receives 3¼% of the sales of this book. How much did the author receive during a year in which 37,464 copies of the book were sold for $4.10 each? ______
4. The L. R. Meeker Company pays its salespeople a graduated commission, based on the following table:

For the first $800 of sales	12%
For the next $600 of sales	14%
For the next $500 of sales	17%
In excess of $1,900 of sales	18½%

What will be the earnings of each of the following salespeople during a week in which their total sales were the amounts shown below?

Sales	Earnings	Sales	Earnings
a. $ 750	$________	e. $1,342	$________
b. 900	________	f. 1,589	________
c. 1,600	________	g. 1,923	________
d. 2,400	________	h. 2,856	________

Unit 4: Payroll Deductions

Section 1: Income Tax Deductions

PART 1

Unfortunately, the amount of money you earn each week is not the same as the amount of money you receive each week. The federal government, acting through your employer, takes a portion of your weekly earnings. Since the amount deducted is based on how much income you receive, this tax is called an *income tax*.

The income tax law is designed so that everyone does not pay the same amount of tax. Each person's tax is dependent upon two factors:

1. The size of his income.
2. The number of people who depend on him for their support. Each of these people is called a *dependent* or a *withholding allowance*.

Before the tax is computed on your weekly earnings, $14.40 is subtracted from these earnings for each withholding allowance you claim. Thus, if your salary is $175 per week and you are married but have no children, then you are entitled to two allowances—one for yourself and one for your wife or husband. Since $14.40 is deducted for each allowance, the total deduction will be $28.80. Hence, your tax will be computed on what remains after the $28.80 is subtracted from your salary of $175, that is, your tax is computed on only $146.20. This amount is called your *taxable income*. Quite apparently, the more withholding allowances you have, the smaller is the taxable income on which your tax is computed.

To determine the amount of tax to be deducted from your earnings, it is necessary to refer to a table similar to the one on page 160.

TABLE 1. WEEKLY Payroll Period

(a) SINGLE person—including head of household:

If the amount of wages is:		*The amount of income tax to be withheld shall be:*	
Not over $11		0	
Over—	*But not over—*		of excess over—
$11	—$35	14%	—$11
$35	—$73	$3.36 plus 18%	—$35
$73	—$202	$10.20 plus 21%	—$73
$202	—$231	$37.29 plus 23%	—$202
$231	—$269	$43.96 plus 27%	—$231
$269	—$333	$54.22 plus 31%	—$269
$333		$74.06 plus 35%	—$333

(b) MARRIED person—

If the amount of wages is:		*The amount of income tax to be withheld shall be:*	
Not over $11		0	
Over—	*But not over—*		of excess over—
$11	—$39	14%	—$11
$39	—$167	$3.92 plus 16%	—$39
$167	—$207	$24.40 plus 20%	—$167
$207	—$324	$32.40 plus 24%	—$207
$324	—$409	$60.48 plus 28%	—$324
$409	—$486	$84.28 plus 32%	—$409
$486		$108.92 plus 36%	—$486

ILLUSTRATION: Robert Nordland works 39 hours each week at an hourly rate of $4.69. His wife is not employed and they have 3 children. How much is deducted from his salary each week for federal income tax purposes?

SOLUTION:

$$\begin{aligned} \text{Earnings} &= 39 \times \$4.69 \\ &= \$182.91 \end{aligned}$$

$$\begin{aligned} \text{Deductions for 5 allowances} &= 5 \times \$14.40 \\ &= \$72.00 \end{aligned}$$

$$\begin{aligned} \text{Taxable income} &= \$182.91 - \$72.00 \\ &= \$110.91 \end{aligned}$$

$$\begin{aligned} \text{Tax} &= \$3.92 + 16\% \times (\$110.91 - \$39) \\ &= \$3.92 + .16 \times \$71.91 \\ &= \$3.92 + \$11.51 \\ &= \$15.43 \end{aligned}$$

EXPLANATION: The earnings were found in the usual manner. Robert has 5 withholding allowances—himself, his wife, and their 3 children. Since one allowance gives him a deduction of \$14.40, the deduction for the 5 allowances is 5 times as much. The taxable income was found by subtracting the total withholding allowance of \$72 from the total income of \$182.91. To determine the tax itself, look at the lower section of the table on page 160 for that is the section that must be used if the taxpayer is married. Since Robert's taxable wages are \$110.91, which falls between \$39 and \$167, place the edge of a piece of paper along the row in which these two numerals appear. The tax will be \$3.92 plus 16% of that part of the taxable earnings over \$39. The amount over \$39 turns out to be \$71.91. When this is multiplied by 16% the product is \$11.51. Adding this to \$3.92, Robert's weekly federal withholding tax is found to be \$15.43.

When both husband and wife have taxable earnings, they may divide up their total number of withholding allowances any way they wish. Suppose that both Pat and Stanley Lorca work and that they have two children. Then they have a total of four withholding allowances. If Pat takes 3 allowances, then Stanley can only take 1. If Stanley takes 3, then Pat can only take 1 allowance. Or both husband and wife could take 2 allowances each. Finally, either husband or wife could take 4 allowances, in which case the other spouse could take no (0) allowances.

EXERCISES A

1. How large will the deduction be for the withholding allowances claimed by each of the following taxpayers?

	Withholding Allowances	Deduction		Withholding Allowances	Deduction
a.	1	\$________	d.	4	\$________
b.	0	________	e.	7	________
c.	3	________	f.	12	________

2. Any taxpayer who is blind can claim an additional allowance. That is, instead of claiming 1 for himself, he can claim 2. Similarly, a taxpayer can claim 2 for a blind husband or wife. How many allowances can each of the following taxpayers claim?
   a. Mrs. Howland is blind and supports only her son. ________
   b. Mr. Kilburn supports a blind wife and two children. ________
   c. Mr. Bolan is blind and supports a blind wife and one child. ________

3. Any taxpayer who is 65 years old or over can claim an additional withholding allowance. Any taxpayer can claim an additional allowance for a husband or wife who is over 65, too. Thus, if both are over 65, a taxpayer can claim 4 allowances for the two of them. How large will the deduction be for each of the following taxpayers?
   a. Husband over 65, wife under 65, 1 child ________
   b. Husband over 65, wife over 65, 2 children ________
   c. Husband under 65 and blind, wife under 65, 3 children ________
   d. Husband over 65 and blind, wife under 65 ________
   e. Husband and wife both over 65 and both blind ________
4. If the earnings and withholding allowances are as shown, what are the taxable wages of each of the following people?

	Earnings	Withholding Allowances	Deduction	Taxable Wages
a.	$ 90	2	$________	$________
b.	146	4	________	________
c.	172	0	________	________
d.	204.50	3	________	________
e.	214.76	5	________	________
f.	196.12	8	________	________

5. All of the following people are single and their taxable wages are as shown. How much tax will they have to pay weekly?

	Taxable Wages	Weekly Tax
a.	$ 10	$________
b.	18	________
c.	46	________
d.	107	________
e.	124	________
f.	250	________
g.	280	________
h.	350	________
i.	148.16	________
j.	323.48	________

6. All of the following people are married and their taxable wages are as shown. How much tax will they have to pay?

	Taxable Wages	Weekly Tax
a.	$ 18	$________
b.	107	________
c.	194	________
d.	240	________
e.	360	________
f.	455.48	________

7. Compute the weekly tax deduction of each of the following taxpayers.

	Wages	Withholding Allowances	Amount Deducted	Taxable Wages	Married Or Single	Tax
a.	$ 96	2	$________	$________	Married	$________
b.	137	3	________	________	Single	________
c.	182	1	________	________	Married	________
d.	84	1	________	________	Single	________
e.	210	2	________	________	Single	________
f.	245	4	________	________	Single	________
g.	341	5	________	________	Married	________
h.	429.84	6	________	________	Married	________

8. Compute the weekly tax deduction for each of the following taxpayers.

	Hourly Rate	Number Of Hours	Wages	Withholding Allowances	Taxable Wages	Married Or Single	Tax
a.	$3.14	25	$________	0	$________	Single	$________
b.	3.58	37	________	1	________	Single	________
c.	3.12	41	________	3	________	Married	________
d.	4.56	38	________	1	________	Single	________
e.	9.94	41½	________	2	________	Married	________

B

1. Fred Jackson earns $3.98 per hour. During the week of July 17, he worked the following number of hours per day.

Monday	Tuesday	Wednesday	Thursday	Friday
7	8	8	7½	8

Fred has a wife who is blind and one child. How much will be deducted from this week's salary for income tax? ________

2. During the week of May 3, Irene Kraft worked 44 hours at time and a half for all work over 40 hours. Her pay rate is $3.26 per hour. If she is single, but supports both of her parents, for which she receives one allowance for each, how much income tax will be deducted from her salary for this week? ________

3. Frances Midler is a saleswoman for Taylor's, Inc., a department store. She works at an hourly rate of $2.96, plus a 1½% commission on all sales over $500 each week. During the week of April 4, she sold $946 worth of merchandise and worked the following hours:

Monday	Tuesday	Wednesday	Thursday	Friday	Saturday
8	8	6	10	8	4½

If Frances is single and supports only herself, how much was taken from her earnings for the week for income tax? ________

4. Longstreet and Sons pays their employees on a piece-rate basis of \$1.78 for each article produced. During one week, one of their employees, who is 67 years of age and supports a wife who is 68, completed the following number of articles:

Monday	Tuesday	Wednesday	Thursday	Friday
14	17	15	18	21

How much will be deducted from this employee's salary for the week for income tax? ________

5. Harold Reed works at an hourly pay rate of \$3.96, plus time and a half for all work over 8 hours a day. During the week of March 27, he worked the following hours:

Monday	Tuesday	Wednesday	Thursday	Friday
9	8	7	10	8

a. How much overtime pay did he earn for the week? ________
b. How much regular pay did he earn for the week? ________
c. What were his total earnings for the week? ________
d. If Harold were single and claimed 3 allowances, how much would be taken from his salary for income tax? ________
e. If Harold were married and claimed 3 allowances, how much would be taken from his salary for income tax? ________
f. How much would Harold have saved in income tax for that week had he been married rather than single? ________

PART 2

The method for computing withholding tax that was developed in Part 1 requires a great deal of time. In view of this, the Internal Revenue Service has prepared tables similar to the two that appear on pages 165 and 166. With these tables it is possible to tell at a glance just what a person's weekly withholding tax will be.

ILLUSTRATION: Robert Nordland works 39 hours per week at an hourly rate of \$4.69. He and his wife, who is not working, have 3 children. How much is deducted from his salary each week for income tax purposes?

SOLUTION:

$$\text{Earnings} = 39 \times \$4.69$$
$$= \$182.91$$

Number of allowances = 5
Tax from table for married persons = \$15.80

MARRIED Persons—WEEKLY Payroll Period

And the wages are—		And the number of withholding allowances claimed is—										
At least	But less than	0	1	2	3	4	5	6	7	8	9	10 or more
		The amount of income tax to be withheld shall be—										
$100	$105	$14.10	$11.80	$9.50	$7.20	$4.90	$2.80	$.80	$0	$0	$0	$0
105	110	14.90	12.60	10.30	8.00	5.70	3.50	1.50	0	0	0	0
110	115	15.70	13.40	11.10	8.80	6.50	4.20	2.20	.10	0	0	0
115	120	16.50	14.20	11.90	9.60	7.30	5.00	2.90	.80	0	0	0
120	125	17.30	15.00	12.70	10.40	8.10	5.80	3.60	1.50	0	0	0
125	130	18.10	15.80	13.50	11.20	8.90	6.60	4.30	2.20	.20	0	0
130	135	18.90	16.60	14.30	12.00	9.70	7.40	5.10	2.90	.90	0	0
135	140	19.70	17.40	15.10	12.80	10.50	8.20	5.90	3.60	1.60	0	0
140	145	20.50	18.20	15.90	13.60	11.30	9.00	6.70	4.40	2.30	.30	0
145	150	21.30	19.00	16.70	14.40	12.10	9.80	7.50	5.20	3.00	1.00	0
150	160	22.50	20.20	17.90	15.60	13.30	11.00	8.70	6.40	4.10	2.00	0
160	170	24.10	21.80	19.50	17.20	14.90	12.60	10.30	8.00	5.70	3.40	1.40
170	180	26.00	23.40	21.10	18.80	16.50	14.20	11.90	9.60	7.30	5.00	2.80
180	190	28.00	25.20	22.70	20.40	18.10	15.80	13.50	11.20	8.90	6.60	4.30
190	200	30.00	27.20	24.30	22.00	19.70	17.40	15.10	12.80	10.50	8.20	5.90
200	210	32.00	29.20	26.30	23.60	21.30	19.00	16.70	14.40	12.10	9.80	7.50
210	220	34.40	31.20	28.30	25.40	22.90	20.60	18.30	16.00	13.70	11.40	9.10
220	230	36.80	33.30	30.30	27.40	24.50	22.20	19.90	17.60	15.30	13.00	10.70
230	240	39.20	35.70	32.30	29.40	26.50	23.80	21.50	19.20	16.90	14.60	12.30
240	250	41.60	38.10	34.60	31.40	28.50	25.60	23.10	20.80	18.50	16.20	13.90
250	260	44.00	40.50	37.00	33.60	30.50	27.60	24.70	22.40	20.10	17.80	15.50
260	270	46.40	42.90	39.40	36.00	32.50	29.60	26.70	24.00	21.70	19.40	17.10
270	280	48.80	45.30	41.80	38.40	34.90	31.60	28.70	25.80	23.30	21.00	18.70
280	290	51.20	47.70	44.20	40.80	37.30	33.90	30.70	27.80	25.00	22.60	20.30
290	300	53.60	50.10	46.60	43.20	39.70	36.30	32.80	29.80	27.00	24.20	21.90
300	310	56.00	52.50	49.00	45.60	42.10	38.70	35.20	31.80	29.00	26.10	23.50
310	320	58.40	54.90	51.40	48.00	44.50	41.10	37.60	34.10	31.00	28.10	25.20
320	330	60.80	57.30	53.80	50.40	46.90	43.50	40.00	36.50	33.10	30.10	27.20
330	340	63.60	59.70	56.20	52.80	49.30	45.90	42.40	38.90	35.50	32.10	29.20
340	350	66.40	62.40	58.60	55.20	51.70	48.30	44.80	41.30	37.90	34.40	31.20
350	360	69.20	65.20	61.10	57.60	54.10	50.70	47.20	43.70	40.30	36.80	33.40
360	370	72.00	68.00	63.90	60.00	56.50	53.10	49.60	46.10	42.70	39.20	35.80
370	380	74.80	70.80	66.70	62.70	58.90	55.50	52.00	48.50	45.10	41.60	38.20
380	390	77.60	73.60	69.50	65.50	61.50	57.90	54.40	50.90	47.50	44.00	40.60
390	400	80.40	76.40	72.30	68.30	64.30	60.30	56.80	53.30	49.90	46.40	43.00
400	410	83.20	79.20	75.10	71.10	67.10	63.00	59.20	55.70	52.30	48.80	45.40
410	420	86.30	82.00	77.90	73.90	69.90	65.80	61.80	58.10	54.70	51.20	47.80
420	430	89.50	84.80	80.70	76.70	72.70	68.60	64.60	60.50	57.10	53.60	50.20
430	440	92.70	88.00	83.50	79.50	75.50	71.40	67.40	63.30	59.50	56.00	52.60
440	450	95.90	91.20	86.60	82.30	78.30	74.20	70.20	66.10	62.10	58.40	55.00
450	460	99.10	94.40	89.80	85.20	81.10	77.00	73.00	68.90	64.90	60.90	57.40
460	470	102.30	97.60	93.00	88.40	83.90	79.80	75.80	71.70	67.70	63.70	59.80
470	480	105.50	100.80	96.20	91.60	87.00	82.60	78.60	74.50	70.50	66.50	62.40
480	490	108.70	104.00	99.40	94.80	90.20	85.60	81.40	77.30	73.30	69.30	65.20
490	500	112.20	107.20	102.60	98.00	93.40	88.80	84.20	80.10	76.10	72.10	68.00
500	510	115.80	110.60	105.80	101.20	96.60	92.00	87.40	82.90	78.90	74.90	70.80
510	520	119.40	114.20	109.10	104.40	99.80	95.20	90.60	86.00	81.70	77.70	73.60
520	530	123.00	117.80	112.70	107.60	103.00	98.40	93.80	89.20	84.50	80.50	76.40
530	540	126.60	121.40	116.30	111.10	106.20	101.60	97.00	92.40	87.70	83.30	79.20
540	550	130.20	125.00	119.90	114.70	109.50	104.80	100.20	95.60	90.90	86.30	82.00
550	560	133.80	128.60	123.50	118.30	113.10	108.00	103.40	98.80	94.10	89.50	84.90
560	570	137.40	132.20	127.10	121.90	116.70	111.50	106.60	102.00	97.30	92.70	88.10
570	580	141.00	135.80	130.70	125.50	120.30	115.10	109.90	105.20	100.50	95.90	91.30
580	590	144.60	139.40	134.30	129.10	123.90	118.70	113.50	108.40	103.70	99.10	94.50
590	600	148.20	143.00	137.90	132.70	127.50	122.30	117.10	111.90	106.90	102.30	97.70
600	610	151.80	146.60	141.50	136.30	131.10	125.90	120.70	115.50	110.30	105.50	100.90
610	620	155.40	150.20	145.10	139.90	134.70	129.50	124.30	119.10	113.90	108.70	104.10
620	630	159.00	153.80	148.70	143.50	138.30	133.10	127.90	122.70	117.50	112.30	107.30
630	640	162.60	157.40	152.30	147.10	141.90	136.70	131.50	126.30	121.10	115.90	110.70
		36 percent of the excess over $640 plus—										
$640 and over		164.40	159.20	154.10	148.90	143.70	138.50	133.30	128.10	122.90	117.70	112.50

SINGLE Persons—WEEKLY Payroll Period

And the wages are—		And the number of withholding allowances claimed is—										
At least	But less than	0	1	2	3	4	5	6	7	8	9	10 or more
		The amount of income tax to be withheld shall be—										
$80	$82	$12.00	$9.10	$6.50	$3.90	$1.80	$0	$0	$0	$0	$0	$0
82	84	12.40	9.50	6.90	4.30	2.10	0	0	0	0	0	0
84	86	12.80	9.80	7.20	4.60	2.30	.30	0	0	0	0	0
86	88	13.20	10.20	7.60	5.00	2.60	.30	0	0	0	0	0
88	90	13.60	10.60	8.00	5.40	2.90	.90	0	0	0	0	0
90	92	14.10	11.00	8.30	5.70	3.20	1.20	0	0	0	0	0
92	94	14.50	11.40	8.70	6.10	3.50	1.40	0	0	0	0	0
94	96	14.90	11.90	9.00	6.40	3.90	1.70	0	0	0	0	0
96	98	15.30	12.30	9.40	6.80	4.20	2.00	0	0	0	0	0
98	100	15.70	12.70	9.80	7.20	4.60	2.30	.30	0	0	0	0
100	105	16.50	13.40	10.40	7.80	5.20	2.80	.80	0	0	0	0
105	110	17.50	14.50	11.50	8.70	6.10	3.50	1.50	0	0	0	0
110	115	18.60	15.50	12.50	9.60	7.00	4.40	2.20	.10	0	0	0
115	120	19.60	16.60	13.60	10.50	7.90	5.30	2.90	.80	0	0	0
120	125	20.70	17.60	14.60	11.60	8.80	6.20	3.60	1.50	0	0	0
125	130	21.70	18.70	15.70	12.60	9.70	7.10	4.50	2.20	.20	0	0
130	135	22.80	19.70	16.70	13.70	10.70	8.00	5.40	2.90	.90	0	0
135	140	23.80	20.80	17.80	14.70	11.70	8.90	6.30	3.70	1.60	0	0
140	145	24.90	21.80	18.80	15.80	12.80	9.80	7.20	4.60	2.30	.30	0
145	150	25.90	22.90	19.90	16.80	13.80	10.80	8.10	5.50	3.00	1.00	0
150	160	27.50	24.50	21.40	18.40	15.40	12.30	9.50	6.90	4.30	2.00	0
160	170	29.60	26.60	23.50	20.50	17.50	14.40	11.40	8.70	6.10	3.50	1.40
170	180	31.70	28.70	25.60	22.60	19.60	16.50	13.50	10.50	7.90	5.30	2.80
180	190	33.80	30.80	27.70	24.70	21.70	18.60	15.60	12.60	9.70	7.10	4.50
190	200	35.90	32.90	29.80	26.80	23.80	20.70	17.70	14.70	11.70	8.90	6.30
200	210	38.10	35.00	31.90	28.90	25.90	22.80	19.80	16.80	13.80	10.70	8.10
210	220	40.40	37.10	34.00	31.00	28.00	24.90	21.90	18.90	15.90	12.80	9.90
220	230	42.70	39.30	36.10	33.10	30.10	27.00	24.00	21.00	18.00	14.90	11.90
230	240	45.10	41.60	38.30	35.20	32.20	29.10	26.10	23.10	20.10	17.00	14.00
240	250	47.80	43.90	40.60	37.30	34.30	31.20	28.20	25.20	22.20	19.10	16.10
250	260	50.50	46.60	42.90	39.60	36.40	33.30	30.30	27.30	24.30	21.20	18.20
260	270	53.20	49.30	45.40	41.90	38.60	35.40	32.40	29.40	26.40	23.30	20.30
270	280	56.20	52.00	48.10	44.20	40.90	37.60	34.50	31.50	28.50	25.40	22.40
280	290	59.30	54.80	50.80	46.90	43.20	39.90	36.60	33.60	30.60	27.50	24.50
290	300	62.40	57.90	53.50	49.60	45.70	42.20	38.90	35.70	32.70	29.60	26.60
300	310	65.50	61.00	56.50	52.30	48.40	44.60	41.20	37.80	34.80	31.70	28.70
310	320	68.60	64.10	59.60	55.10	51.10	47.30	43.50	40.10	36.90	33.80	30.80
320	330	71.70	67.20	62.70	58.20	53.80	50.00	46.10	42.40	39.10	35.90	32.90
330	340	74.80	70.30	65.80	61.30	56.90	52.70	48.80	44.90	41.40	38.10	35.00
340	350	78.30	73.40	68.90	64.40	60.00	55.50	51.50	47.60	43.70	40.40	37.10
350	360	81.80	76.80	72.00	67.50	63.10	58.60	54.20	50.30	46.40	42.70	39.40
360	370	85.30	80.30	75.30	70.60	66.20	61.70	57.20	53.00	49.10	45.20	41.70
370	380	88.80	83.80	78.80	73.70	69.30	64.80	60.30	55.90	51.80	47.90	44.00
380	390	92.30	87.30	82.30	77.20	72.40	67.90	63.40	59.00	54.50	50.60	46.70
390	400	95.80	90.80	85.80	80.70	75.70	71.00	66.50	62.10	57.60	53.30	49.40
400	410	99.30	94.30	89.30	84.20	79.20	74.10	69.60	65.20	60.70	56.20	52.10
410	420	102.80	97.80	92.80	87.70	82.70	77.60	72.70	68.30	63.80	59.30	54.80
420	430	106.30	101.30	96.30	91.20	86.20	81.10	76.10	71.40	66.90	62.40	57.90
430	440	109.80	104.80	99.80	94.70	89.70	84.60	79.60	74.50	70.00	65.50	61.00
440	450	113.30	108.30	103.30	98.20	93.20	88.10	83.10	78.00	73.10	68.60	64.10
450	460	116.80	111.80	106.80	101.70	96.70	91.60	86.60	81.50	76.50	71.70	67.20
460	470	120.30	115.30	110.30	105.20	100.20	95.10	90.10	85.00	80.00	74.90	70.30
470	480	123.80	118.80	113.80	108.70	103.70	98.60	93.60	88.50	83.50	78.40	73.40
480	490	127.30	122.30	117.30	112.20	107.20	102.10	97.10	92.00	87.00	81.90	76.90
		35 percent of the excess over $490 plus—										
$490 and over		129.10	124.00	119.00	114.00	108.90	103.90	98.80	93.80	88.70	83.70	78.60

EXPLANATION: After finding Robert's salary to be $182.91, refer to the married persons' part of the table, for he is a married man. The easiest way of using this table is to ignore the first column headed by the words "At least." Then, run your finger down the second column titled "But less than" until you come to the first numeral *greater* than the weekly earnings. In this case, the weekly earnings are $182.91 and the first numeral greater than this in that column is 190. Place the edge of a piece of paper along this row and run your finger across to the column headed by the numeral 5, for this is the number of allowances Robert claimed. Your finger will point to $15.80. This is the weekly tax that he will have to pay.

If you glance back at the illustration on page 160, you will discover that the Mr. Nordland in that problem is the same Mr. Nordland as in the one above. This time, however, he seems to be paying $15.80 in income tax rather than the $15.43 found before! No error has been made, for both methods shown for computing the withholding tax give only an approximation of what the weekly tax should be. Once each year the taxpayer must fill out a form showing exactly the amount of tax he must pay on his yearly income. If this amount is less than the total of his weekly deductions, he sends the Internal Revenue Service a bill for his overpayment. If it is more, he sends a check for the difference. Hence, the Internal Revenue Service does not care which method is used for computing the weekly deductions, for it knows that at year's end it will eventually get exactly what the law requires from the taxpayer.

EXERCISES A

The income tax in these problems should be computed through the use of the tables on pages 165 and 166.

1. All of the following persons are single and their weekly earnings are as shown. How much tax will be withheld from their salaries?

	Earnings	Withholding Allowances	Tax
a.	$ 84.58	1	$______
b.	99.23	2	______
c.	163.28	0	______
d.	124.99	3	______
e.	125.01	3	______
f.	314.62	6	______
g.	352.84	2	______
h.	94.00*	1	______
i.	115.00	3	______
j.	280.00	5	______

*Find the first numeral larger than $94 in the "But less than" column.

2. All of the following persons are married and their weekly earnings are as shown. How much tax will be withheld from their salaries?

	Earnings	Withholding Allowances	Tax
a.	$102.43	0	$________
b.	123.57	2	________
c.	154.07	4	________
d.	273.12	5	________
e.	507.16	6	________
f.	130.00	0	________
g.	145.00	2	________
h.	530.00	4	________

3. All of the following persons are single and their weekly earnings are as shown. How much tax will be withheld from their salaries?

	Earnings	Withholding Allowances	Tax
a.	$ 500	0	$________
b.	520	1	________
c.	560	2	________
d.	600	1	________
e.	800	3	________
f.	1,000	5	________

4. All of the following persons are married, and their weekly earnings are as shown. How much tax will be withheld from their salaries?

	Earnings	Withholding Allowances	Tax
a.	$660	0	$________
b.	700	2	________
c.	758	5	________
d.	843.27	8	________

5. Compute the weekly tax withheld for each of the following persons.

	Hourly Rate	Number Of Hours	Earnings	Withholding Allowances	Married Or Single	Tax
a.	$4.07	42	$________	1	Single	$________
b.	3.89	35	________	0	Single	________
c.	4.64	37	________	2	Married	________
d.	2.92	41	________	3	Married	________
e.	3.14	38	________	0	Married	________
f.	3.45	43	________	4	Single	________
g.	4.86	$40\frac{1}{2}$	________	5	Married	________
h.	5.94	$34\frac{1}{2}$	________	6	Married	________

B

1. Robert Reeves has a weekly income of $584.
   a. If he is single and claims 2 allowances, how much will be withheld from his weekly earnings for income tax? ________
   b. If he is married and claims 2 allowances, how much will be withheld from his weekly earnings for income tax? ________
   c. How much less will be withheld if he is married than if he is single? ________
2. Evelyn Reilly earns $4.68 per hour on her job. She works a 38½-hour week with no overtime. Since her husband claims 2 allowances, she claims no allowances. How much will be withheld from her salary over a period of one year for income tax? ________
3. William Grady earns $3.74 per hour on a 38-hour week. He supports a wife and 2 children on his salary.
   a. If the computation for the withholding tax is made by using the table on page 160, how much will be taken from his salary? ________
   b. If the computation for the withholding tax is made by using the table on page 165, how much will be taken from his salary? ________
   c. How much more will be taken from his salary each week if one method of computation is used rather than the other? ________
4. The Frederick Knox Products Corporation pays its employees on a piecework basis according to the following weekly scale:

For the first 35 articles	$3.10 per article
For the next 10 articles	3.45 per article
For the next 15 articles	3.75 per article
For all over 60 articles	4.10 per article

How much will be withheld in income tax for each of the following employees for the week shown below?

	Number Of Articles	Earnings	Withholding Allowances	Married Or Single	Tax
a.	33	$________	1	Single	$________
b.	42	________	0	Married	________
c.	49	________	3	Married	________
d.	67	________	2	Single	________
e.	86	________	4	Married	________

5. Mr. Holmes works for the Frederick Knox Products Corporation of Problem 4. He is 67 years old and blind. His wife is 66 years old and is also blind. During the week of October 17, Mr. Holmes completed 74 articles. How much was withheld for income tax from his salary? ________

Section 2: Social Security

PART 1

The federal government not only deducts a fraction of your weekly earnings for income tax but it also deducts another fraction for *social security.* The social security system acts as an enforced insurance that you must purchase in order to provide an income for you at the time you retire. It also insures you in the event of your death or if you become permanently disabled. The benefits you receive under this insurance program will be examined in Chapter 11. At this point your concern will be with the cost of this insurance to you.

Deductions for social security are made in accordance with the rates in the following table. These rates have changed many times since the social security law was passed. There is no reason to believe that they will remain as shown here through 1985.

Years	Rate
1974–1977	5.85%
1978–1980	6.05%
1981–1985	6.15%

The law provides that deductions must be made from that part of your earnings that is $13,200 or less during one year. Thus, if your earnings are less than $13,200, then 5.85% of your weekly salary will be deducted throughout the entire year. However, if your earnings exceed $13,200, then deductions will be made only until such time as your total earnings reach $13,200. For the remainder of the year nothing is deducted from your salary for social security payments.

One other point of interest—you are not the only one who pays into the fund for your retirement benefits. For each dollar you pay, your employer adds one dollar of his own; the two dollars are held in reserve for you by the government.

ILLUSTRATION 1: The hourly pay rate that Ralph Hopkins receives is $3.95. If he works a 42-hour week, how much is taken from his weekly salary for social security?

SOLUTION:

$$\text{Earnings} = 42 \times \$3.95$$
$$= \$165.90$$
$$\text{Social security deductions} = \$165.90 \times 5.85\%$$
$$= \$165.90 \times .0585$$
$$= \$9.70515, \text{ or } \$9.71$$

EXPLANATION: The social security tax of $9.71 was found by multiplying the weekly wage of $165.90 by the 5.85% rate. Throughout this work you will use the 5.85% rate unless a date later than 1977 is specified.

ILLUSTRATION 2: Joan Mason earns $285.40 each week. Which week of the year will be the last week during which social security deductions will be taken from Joan's salary?

SOLUTION:

Number of weeks during which social security payments will be made = $13,200 ÷ $285.40
= 46.25

Last week in which a payment will be made = 47th

EXPLANATION: If a person earned $13,200 per week, then payments for social security would be made for 1 week only, for in that 1 week he would have reached the $13,200 maximum in his salary on which these payments are made for the entire year. If his earnings were $6,600 per week, then in a period of 2 weeks he would have made all the payments required of him. And if his earnings were $4,400 a week, then it would take 3 weeks. Notice that the number of weeks is found by simply dividing the weekly earnings into $13,200.

In the case of Joan, her weekly earnings of $285.40 is divided into $13,200 to give 46.25. The "46" part of the numeral "46.25" implies that 5.85% of her full salary is deducted for 46 weeks, while the ".25" part implies that 5.85% is taken from only 25/100 of her salary for the 47th week. Hence, the last week during which deductions are taken from her salary for social security is the 47th week.

EXERCISES

1. How much will be deducted from each of the following salaries for social security? None of the employees who received these salaries has earned more than $13,200 prior to this date during the year.

	Weekly Salary	Social Security Tax		Weekly Salary	Social Security Tax
a.	$ 95	$______	f.	$ 94.60	$______
b.	124	______	g.	127.50	______
c.	186	______	h.	146.10	______
d.	237	______	i.	251.90	______
e.	354	______	j.	298.07	______

2. Which week of the year will be the last in which the social security tax will be taken from each of the following weekly salaries?

	Weekly Salary	Last Week of Deductions		Weekly Salary	Last Week of Deductions
a.	$300	________	f.	$275	________
b.	400	________	g.	550	________
c.	600	________	h.	825	________
d.	330	________	i.	309	________
e.	660	________	j.	436	________

3. A person's take-home pay is the actual amount he receives after deductions have been subtracted from his earnings. How much will the take-home pay be for each of the following employees after income tax and social security deductions have been taken from their salaries? Use the income tax tables on pages 165 and 166.

	Weekly Earnings	Withholding Allowances	Income Tax	Social Security	Take-Home Pay
a.	$137	2—Single	$________	$________	$________
b.	158	3—Married	________	________	________
c.	186	1—Single	________	________	________
d.	204	2—Married	________	________	________
e.	261	0—Single	________	________	________
f.	258	3—Married	________	________	________
g.	314	3—Single	________	________	________
h.	384	6—Married	________	________	________
i.	381.90	2—Single	________	________	________
j.	624.10	8—Married	________	________	________

4. Determine the take-home pay for each of the following employees after income tax and social security tax have been deducted. Each receives time and a half for all work over 40 hours per week. Use the income tax tables on pages 165 and 166.

	Hourly Earnings	Number Of Hours	Withholding Allowances	Total Salary	Income Tax	Social Security	Take-Home Pay
a.	$3.10	40	0—Single	$________	$________	$________	$________
b.	2.95	40	1—Single	________	________	________	________
c.	3.90	40	4—Married	________	________	________	________
d.	4.50	38	2—Married	________	________	________	________
e.	5.15	39	0—Married	________	________	________	________
f.	4.67	42	2—Married	________	________	________	________
g.	5.24	44	3—Married	________	________	________	________
h.	4.58	41	4—Married	________	________	________	________
i.	6.37	41½	1—Single	________	________	________	________
j.	5.03	42½	5—Married	________	________	________	________

B

1. If a person earns $210 per week, how much more will be taken from his salary each week for social security in 1978 than in 1977? (Refer to the table on page 170.) ________
2. a. What is the largest annual salary from which social security deductions can be made? ________
   b. What is the largest amount that can be deducted from one person's earnings for social security during 1975? ________
3. Andrew Curran has a monthly income of $595. How much will be deducted from his salary for social security during one year? ________

PART 2

As in the case of the income tax deductions, the Treasury Department provides employers with tables that will tell them the amount to be deducted for social security. Where the income tax table gives only an approximation of the actual withholding tax, the social security table gives the exact amount to be deducted had the wage been multiplied by 5.85%. The table on page 174 is but a small section of the entire social security tax table.

ILLUSTRATION: What will the social security tax be on a weekly wage of $247.67?

SOLUTION:

Social security tax on $247.67 = $14.49

EXPLANATION: As before, run your finger down the "But Less Than" columns until you reach the first wage that is *greater than* $247.67. This will be $247.78. The numeral immediately to the right of $247.78 is the social security tax—$14.49. If you were to multiply $247.67 by the tax rate of 5.85%, the product would be the tax of $14.49 just found in the table.

There are a great many other possible deductions from your earnings in addition to those for social security and income taxes. Included among these are retirement contribution, union dues, hospitalization and medical insurance, and government bonds. These contributions are handled so differently by different companies that it would be difficult to describe any general procedure that might fit all.

SOCIAL SECURITY EMPLOYEE TAX TABLE

5.85 percent employee tax deductions

Wages		Tax to be withheld	Wages		Tax to be withheld	Wages		Tax to be withheld
At least	But less than		At least	But less than		At least	But less than	
$222.14	$222.31	$13.00	$233.25	$233.42	$13.65	$244.36	$244.53	$14.30
222.31	222.48	13.01	233.42	233.59	13.66	244.53	244.71	14.31
222.48	222.65	13.02	233.59	233.77	13.67	244.71	244.88	14.32
222.65	222.83	13.03	233.77	233.94	13.68	244.88	245.05	14.33
222.83	223.00	13.04	233.94	234.11	13.69	245.05	245.22	14.34
223.00	223.17	13.05	234.11	234.28	13.70	245.22	245.39	14.35
223.17	223.34	13.06	234.28	234.45	13.71	245.39	245.56	14.36
223.34	223.51	13.07	234.45	234.62	13.72	245.56	245.73	14.37
223.51	223.68	13.08	234.62	234.79	13.73	245.73	245.90	14.38
223.68	223.85	13.09	234.79	234.96	13.74	245.90	246.07	14.39
223.85	224.02	13.10	234.96	235.13	13.75	246.07	246.24	14.40
224.02	224.19	13.11	235.13	235.30	13.76	246.24	246.42	14.41
224.19	224.36	13.12	235.30	235.48	13.77	246.42	246.59	14.42
224.36	224.53	13.13	235.48	235.65	13.78	246.59	246.76	14.43
224.53	224.71	13.14	235.65	235.82	13.79	246.76	246.93	14.44
224.71	224.88	13.15	235.82	235.99	13.80	246.93	247.10	14.45
224.88	225.05	13.16	235.99	236.16	13.81	247.10	247.27	14.46
225.05	225.22	13.17	236.16	236.33	13.82	247.27	247.44	14.47
225.22	225.39	13.18	236.33	236.50	13.83	247.44	247.61	14.48
225.39	225.56	13.19	236.50	236.67	13.84	247.61	247.78	14.49
225.56	225.73	13.20	236.67	236.84	13.85	247.78	247.95	14.50
225.73	225.90	13.21	236.84	237.01	13.86	247.95	248.12	14.51
225.90	226.07	13.22	237.01	237.18	13.87	248.12	248.30	14.52
226.07	226.24	13.23	237.18	237.36	13.88	248.30	248.47	14.53
226.24	226.42	13.24	237.36	237.53	13.89	248.47	248.64	14.54
226.42	226.59	13.25	237.53	237.70	13.90	248.64	248.81	14.55
226.59	226.76	13.26	237.70	237.87	13.91	248.81	248.98	14.56
226.76	226.93	13.27	237.87	238.04	13.92	248.98	249.15	14.57
226.93	227.10	13.28	238.04	238.21	13.93	249.15	249.32	14.58
227.10	227.27	13.29	238.21	238.38	13.94	249.32	249.49	14.59

• • •

EXERCISES A

1. Determine the social security tax on each of the following weekly salaries. Use the table on page 174. None of the employees who received these salaries has earned more than $13,200 prior to this date during the year.

	Weekly Salary	Social Security Tax		Weekly Salary	Social Security Tax
a.	$223.15	$____	f.	$222.18	$____
b.	226.40	____	g.	244.50	____
c.	234.75	____	h.	224.36	____
d.	237.35	____	i.	236.67	____
e.	247.18	____	j.	245.56	____

2. Determine the take-home pay for each of the following employees after income tax and social security deductions have been taken from their salaries. Use the tables on pages 165, 166, and 174 to compute the social security and income taxes.

	Weekly Earnings	Withholding Allowances	Income Tax	Social Security	Take-Home Pay
a.	$222.85	1—Single	$____	$____	$____
b.	225.25	0—Married	____	____	____
c.	235.20	2—Married	____	____	____
d.	237.60	3—Single	____	____	____
e.	245.51	2—Single	____	____	____
f.	247.38	0—Single	____	____	____
g.	233.35	4—Married	____	____	____
h.	224.02	3—Married	____	____	____
i.	236.50	1—Married	____	____	____
j.	248.47	5—Married	____	____	____

3. Determine the take-home pay for each of the following employees after social security and income taxes have been deducted. Use the tables for social security and income taxes on pages 165, 166, and 174.

	Hourly Rate	M	T	Days W	Th	F	Withholding Allowances	Take-Home Pay
a.	$6.72	7	7	7	7	7	0—Single	$____
b.	6.38	7	8	8	7	7	2—Married	____
c.	5.73	7	7	10	8	7	0—Married	____
d.	6.12	7½	7½	8	8	9	4—Single	____
e.	6.08	7	7½	7½	8	7	4—Married	____
f.	5.39	9	9	9½	9	9½	3—Married	____
g.	6.27	8	8	7½	7½	7	2—Married	____
h.	5.32	7½	7½	8½	9½	9	6—Married	____

4. Determine the take-home pay for each of the following employees after income tax and social security tax have been deducted. Each works on the piece-rate scale shown. Use the tables for social security and income taxes.

	Piece Rate	Number of Articles M	T	W	Th	F	Withholding Allowances	Take-Home Pay
a.	$4.38	9	12	8	14	11	2—Married	$________
b.	$3.86	8	9	14	15	12	1—Single	________
c.	$4.26	7	9	13	12	12	3—Married	________
d.	$1.91	23	29	21	27	29	4—Single	________
e.	72¢	64	60	58	62	65	3—Single	________
f.	84¢	48	53	57	67	56	0—Single	________

B

1. If a person earns $222.75 weekly, what will be the total social security tax that will be taken from his salary during the period of one year? Use the social security table on page 174. ________
2. If a person changes jobs during the year, then both employers will deduct social security tax from his salary until he has earned $13,200 from each. During a period of one year, Edwin Kirby worked for Kirch Furniture Company, earning $9,260, and for Jonathan Green Stores, Inc., earning $6,420. ________
   a. How much social security tax did he pay while an employee of the Kirch Furniture Company? ________
   b. How much social security tax did he pay while an employee of the Jonathan Green Stores, Inc.? ________
   c. What is the maximum amount he should have paid in social security tax for the entire year? (See Problem 2, page 173.)
   d. How much will have to be returned to Edwin by the Treasury Department? ________
3. In addition to social security tax and income tax deductions, each of the following employees has deductions for union dues, hospitalization, and retirement benefits. What is the take-home pay of each? Use the tables for social security and income taxes on pages 165, 166, and 174.

	Earnings	Withholding Allowances	Union Dues	Hospitalization	Retirement Benefits	Take-Home Pay
a.	$223.10	2—Single	$3.24	$1.27	$ .84	$________
b.	234.20	1—Single	2.09	.93	.87	________
c.	245.40	3—Married	1.95	1.36	1.28	________
d.	248.61	5—Married	1.18	1.75	1.94	________
e.	236.50	0—Single	2.83	1.04	2.18	________

Unit 5: Chapter Review and Test

1. What is the time-and-a-half rate if the regular hourly rate is as follows?
a. $3.80 ________ b. $5.04 ________ c. $4.15 ________

2. If a person works 4 hours overtime at time and a half and his regular rate is $3.16, how much does he earn for these 4 hours? ________

3. Silvio Marino normally works a 38-hour week with time and a half for overtime. What will his earnings be during a week in which he works 44 hours at $4.67 per hour? ________

4. Kathy Naylor earns $3.52 per hour. The firm she works for has a lateness penalty that is the same as the rate table on page 150. If Kathy is supposed to report for work at 9:00, but clocks in at 9:47, how much will be deducted from her salary? ________

5. Edyth Cleveland works at the piece-rate basis of $1.47 per article. How much will she earn during the week in which she completes the following number of articles? ________

Monday	Tuesday	Wednesday	Thursday	Friday
15	18	26	23	19

6. Julia Deering works a 41-hour week on a salary of $2.96 per hour, plus a commission of 3½% on everything she sells in excess of $1,250 during the week. What were her earnings for the week of May 12 when she sold $1,958 worth of merchandise? ________

7. a. Compute the income tax deduction for a single person who claimed 1 withholding allowance and earned $158.40 per week. Use the table on page 166. ________

b. Compute the income tax deduction for a married person who claimed 3 withholding allowances and earned $492.75 per week. Use the table on page 165. ________

8. Compute the income tax deduction for Charles Varian who is 69 years of age, blind, and supports a wife who is 66. His weekly earnings are $169.74. Use the table on page 165. ________

9. How much social security tax will be taken from a person's earnings during a week in which his wages are $176.40? ________

10. Determine the social security tax on each of the following weekly salaries. Use the social security tax table on page 174.
a. $236.10 ________ **b.** $247.78 ________ **c.** $233.40 ________

1040

CHAPTER 5

INCOME TAXES

Although part of your salary is withheld each week for income tax payments, you still have to fill out an income tax form once each year by April 15. The weekly deductions are only a rough estimate of the amount you owe the federal government. Hence, the purpose of filing a return, that is, sending the Internal Revenue Service a statement of your income for the year, is to straighten out your account. When you complete the income tax form you may find that more withholding tax than necessary was deducted. When this happens—as it sometimes does—you are entitled to a refund. When you find that the total of your withholding deductions was not quite as large as the tax you owe, you must send a check to the Internal Revenue Service (IRS) covering the difference between what you should pay and what you did pay.

The annual income tax returns that are sent to the IRS are filed on either Form 1040 or Short Form 1040A. The methods for completing both of these forms will be examined in this chapter.

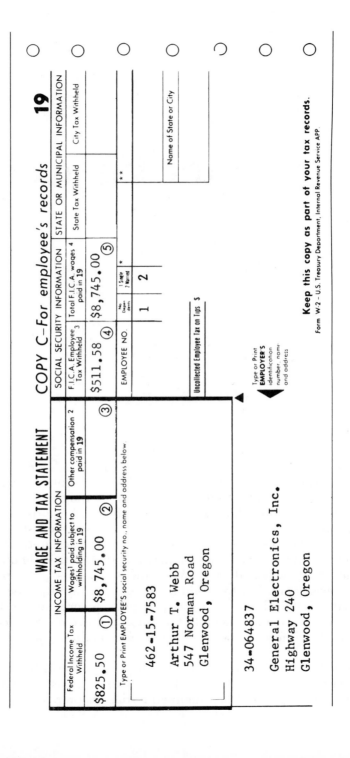

WAGE AND TAX STATEMENT COPY C–*For employee's records* **19**

INCOME TAX INFORMATION			SOCIAL SECURITY INFORMATION		STATE OR MUNICIPAL INFORMATION	
Federal Income Tax Withheld	Wages[1] paid subject to withholding in 19	Other compensation paid in 19 [2]	F.I.C.A. Employee Tax Withheld [3]	Total F.I.C.A. wages paid in 19 [4]	State Tax Withheld	City Tax Withheld
$825.50 ①	$8,745.00 ②	③	$511.58 ④	$8,745.00 ⑤		

Type or Print EMPLOYEE'S social security no., name and address below.

462-15-7583

Arthur T. Webb
547 Norman Road
Glenwood, Oregon

EMPLOYEE NO.	No. Dependents	1 Single 2 Married	*	**
	1	2		

Uncollected Employee Tax on Tips $

Name of State or City

34-064837

General Electronics, Inc.
Highway 240
Glenwood, Oregon

Type or Print EMPLOYER'S identification number, name and address

Keep this copy as part of your tax records.

Form W-2 – U.S. Treasury Department, Internal Revenue Service APP.

Unit 1: Federal Income Tax

Section 1: Short Form 1040A— Computation of Tax by the IRS

Shortly after January 1 of each year, your employer prints four copies of Form W-2, as shown on page 180. One he sends to the IRS so that it will know both the amount of your earnings for the year and how much has been withheld from your pay for both income tax and social security tax. A second copy your employer keeps for his own records, while the remaining two he turns over to you. Of the two that you receive, one is for your records, while the other is attached to the income tax form you send to the District Director of Internal Revenue.

Notice that the form on page 180 is marked "Copy C—For employee's records." This is the form that you keep for yourself. This Form W-2 will be examined in terms of the income of Arthur T. Webb, whose name appears on it.

1. The numeral in the box labeled ① represents the total of all the income tax that was withheld weekly from Mr. Webb's wages during the year.

2. The numeral in box ② is the total of wages paid Mr. Webb for that year by General Electronics, Inc.

3. Since he earned no other money from this company besides that reported in box ②, box ③ was left blank.

4. The letters F.I.C.A. in box ④ are abbreviations for the words Federal Insurance Contributions Act—another name for social security. Hence, the numeral that appears here represents the amount that was deducted from Mr. Webb's wages during the year for the social security tax.

5. In box ⑤, you find the same numeral as in box ②, for Mr. Webb had to pay social security tax on his entire income. Had he earned $14,500 during the year, then this amount would have appeared in the second box, while $13,200 would have appeared in the fifth one. As you may recall, the reason for this is that social security deductions are made only on the first $13,200 of a person's earnings. Since Mr. Webb earned less than $13,200, all of it was subject to the social security tax.

With the information from Form W-2 at his disposal, Mr. Webb was now ready to complete his income tax form. He selected Short Form 1040A (pages 182–183) for it is the simpler of the two forms. A taxpayer can use this form only under these two conditions,

Short Form 1040A U.S. Individual Income Tax Return

Department of the Treasury
Internal Revenue Service

1973

Please print or type

Name (If joint return, give first names and initials of both): Arthur T. and Dorothy
Last name: Webb

Present home address (Number and street, including apartment number, or rural route): 547 Norman Road

City, town or post office, State and ZIP code: Glenwood, Oregon 57064

COUNTY OF RESIDENCE

Your social security number 462 | 15 | 7583

Spouse's social security no. 517 | 21 | 6214

Occupation Yours ▶ Machinist
Spouse's ▶ Housewife

Filing Status—check only one:

1 ☐ Single
2 ☐ Married filing joint return (even if only one had income)
3 ☐ Married filing separately. If spouse is also filing, give spouse's social security number in designated space above and enter full name here ▶ ______
4 ☐ Unmarried Head of Household
5 ☐ Widow(er) with dependent child (Year spouse died ▶ 19....)

Exemptions Regular / 65 or over / Blind

6a Yourself . . ☒ ☐ ☐
b Spouse . . . ☒ ☐ ☐ Enter number of boxes checked ▶ 2
c First names of your dependent children who lived with you Raymond, Sally Enter number ▶ 2
d Number of other dependents (from line 26) . . . ▶
7 Total exemptions claimed . . . . ▶ 4

8 **Presidential Election Campaign Fund.**—Check ☒ if you wish to designate $1 of your taxes for this fund. If joint return, check ☒ if spouse wishes to designate $1. **Note:** *This will not increase your tax or reduce your refund.* **See note on back.**

Attach Copy B of Forms W-2 and Check or Money Order here

9	Wages, salaries, tips, and other employee compensation . . (Attach Forms W-2. If unavailable, attach explanation.)	9	8,745	--
10a	Dividends (See instructions on page 3.) $............, **10b Less exclusion $**........., **Balance ▶**	10c		
11	Interest income	11	127	--
12	Total (add lines 9, 10c, and 11) **(Adjusted Gross Income)**	12	8,872	--

● **If you want IRS to figure your tax, skip the rest of this page and see instructions on page 3.**
● **If line 12 is under $10,000 find tax in Tables 1–12 and enter on line 17. Skip lines 13 through 16.**

13	**If line 12 is $10,000 or more,** enter 15% of line 12 but not more than $2,000 ($1,000 if line 3 checked) .	13		
14	Subtract line 13 from line 12	14		
15	Multiply total number of exemptions claimed on line 7 by $750	15		
16	Taxable income (subtract line 15 from line 14) . . . . **(Figure tax on amount on line 16 using Tax Rate Schedule X, Y, or Z, and enter on line 17.)**	16		

Form 1040A (1973) **Page 2**

17 Tax, check if from: ☐ Tax Tables 1–12 **OR** ☐ Tax Rate Schedule X, Y, or Z . . . **17**

18 Credit for contributions to candidates for public office (see instructions on page 4) **18**

19 Income tax (subtract line 18 from line 17). If less than zero, enter zero **19**

20a Total Federal income tax withheld (attach Forms W–2 to front) . . **20a** 825 | 50

b Excess FICA tax withheld (two or more employers—see instructions on page 4) **b**

c 1973 estimated tax payments (include amount allowed as credit from 1972 return) **c**

21 Total (add lines 20a, b, and c) **21**

22 If line 19 is larger than line 21, enter **BALANCE DUE IRS** Pay in full with return. Write social security number on check or money order and make payable to Internal Revenue Service ▶ **22**

23 If line 21 is larger than line 19, enter amount **OVERPAID** . . . . ▶ **23**

24 Amount of line 23 to be **REFUNDED TO YOU** . . . . ▶ **24**

25 Amount of line 23 to be credited on 1974 estimated tax . . . ▶ **25**

Other Dependents

(a) NAME	(b) Relationship	(c) Months lived in your home. If born or died during year, write B or D.	(d) Did dependent have income of $750 or more?	(e) Amount YOU furnished for dependent's support. If 100% write ALL.	(f) Amount furnished by OTHERS including dependent.
				$	$

26 Total number of dependents listed in column (a). Enter here and on line 6d . . . . ▶

Note: 1972 Presidential Election Campaign Fund Designation.—Check ☐ if you did not designate $1 of your taxes on your 1972 return, but now wish to do so. If joint return, check ☐ if spouse did not designate on 1972 return but now wishes to do so.

Under penalties of perjury, I declare that I have examined this return, including accompanying schedules and statements, and to the best of my knowledge and belief it is true, correct and complete. Declaration of preparer (other than taxpayer) is based on all information of which he has any knowledge.

Sign here

▶ Arthur T. Webb 3/17/ --
Your signature — Date

▶ Dorothy Webb 3/17/--
Spouse's signature (if filing jointly, BOTH must sign even if only one had income)

▶ Preparer's signature (other than taxpayer) — Date

Address (and ZIP Code) — **Preparer's Emp. Ident. or Soc. Sec. No.**

☆ U.S. GOVERNMENT PRINTING OFFICE : 1973—O-500-249 36-2603-697

1. If his income comes from no other sources besides salary, wages, tips, dividends, or interest.
2. If he does not itemize his *deductions*. (This term will be explained later.)

Since Mr. Webb had no income other than the $8,745 he earned at General Electronics and the interest he received on a savings account, he was able to use Form 1040A. Each of the lines of this form will be examined in terms of the information as it applies to Mr. Webb.

Line:

2. After completing the heading, Mr. Webb placed an "X" in the square to the right of the numeral "2." As a married person, Mr. Webb could have chosen to file his own return and have his wife file hers separately—under this condition they would be "married persons filing separately," which is the fill-in for line 3. However, for most married persons, their total tax is usually lower if they include both of their earnings in a single report; that is, they file a "joint" return. By checking one of the squares next to the numerals 1 through 5, the taxpayer notifies the IRS of his marital status.

6a. The term "exemptions" in this section is identical to the term "withholding allowances" that was used at the time you examined the tax the federal government withheld from a person's weekly earnings (see page 159 in Chapter 4). Mr. Webb checked only the first square on line 6a. Were he also age 65 or over and blind, he would have checked the other two squares and received two more exemptions.

6b. He then checked the first square on line 6b, indicating that he claimed but one exemption for his wife; he followed this by writing a "2" as the fill-in for line 6b. The "2" implies that he has claimed 1 exemption for himself and 1 for his wife.

6c. On this line Mr. Webb wrote the names of his two children, whom he also claimed as exemptions, and then he wrote the numeral "2" at the far right.

7. The fill-in for this line is the total number of exemptions claimed—the 2 for himself and his wife and the 2 for his two children, making a total of 4.

8. Mr. Webb checked both squares on this line for he wanted $1 of his taxes, and his wife wanted $1 of her taxes, to be used for a "presidential election fund."

9. The fill-in for line 9 is the total wages shown on the W-2 form.

10c. Since Mr. Webb owned no stock, he had no dividends and therefore nothing to report on this line.

11. Mr. Webb received interest in the amount of $127 from a savings account. This has to be reported as income on line 11.

12. The fill-in here is the total income Mr. Webb had for the year. This number is the sum of lines 9 and 11.

At this point, if Mr. Webb wanted to, he could skip to line 20a, where he would write in the amount of income tax that was withheld from his salary for that year. This number, which is found on the W-2 form, is $825.50. He would then pass over the remaining lines and sign his name at the bottom of the form. Since this is a joint return, he would ask his wife to sign her name also. After attaching the W-2 form, Mr. Webb would then mail the tax return to the IRS where his tax would be computed for him. If he owed the government more money than was withheld from his weekly wages, he would be billed for the extra money. If, on the other hand, he had overpaid the government, the IRS would send him a check for the overpayment.

EXERCISES

Write the fill-ins for lines 1 through 12 and line 20a of Short Form 1040A from the following information.

	Withholding Tax	Wages	Interest	Type of Return
a.	$ 985	$ 7,400	$ 249	Single—1 exemption
b.	$1,501	$ 9,750	$ 752	Single—1 exemption
c.	$2,114	$12,643	$1,247	Single—1 exemption
d.	$1,155	$ 9,856 & $0	$ 957	Joint—Husband and wife
e.	$1,460	$12,824 & $0	$ 623	Joint—Husband, wife, 2 children
f.	$2,110 & $984	$10,947 & $10,423	$2,914	Joint—Husband, wife, 1 child

Section 2: Computation by Taxpayer Using Short Form 1040A and Tax Tables

Let us return to Mr. Webb and examine what would have happened had he decided to compute the tax by himself rather than have the IRS do it for him. Since his income was less than $10,000, he was able to skip lines 13 through 16 and go directly to line 17. There are 12 tables provided by the IRS for finding your tax if your income is under $10,000. The first of these is used by a person who has but one ex-

Table 4 — Returns claiming FOUR exemptions (and not itemizing deductions) (Continued)

If the amount on Form 1040A, line 12, is— At least	But less than	And you are— Single, not head of household	Head of household	* Married filing joint return	Married filing separate return claiming— Low income allowance	%Standard deduction
		Your tax is—				
$6,500	$6,550	$353	$341	$326	$476	$414
6,550	6,600	362	350	334	486	422
6,600	6,650	372	359	342	495	430
6,650	6,700	381	368	350	505	438
6,700	6,750	391	377	358	514	448
6,750	6,800	400	386	366	524	457
6,800	6,850	410	395	374	533	467
6,850	6,900	419	404	382	543	476
6,900	6,950	429	413	390	552	486
6,950	7,000	438	422	398	562	495
7,000	7,050	448	431	406	571	505
7,050	7,100	457	440	414	581	514
7,100	7,150	467	449	422	590	524
7,150	7,200	476	458	430	600	533
7,200	7,250	486	467	438	609	543
7,250	7,300	495	476	446	619	552
7,300	7,350	505	485	454	628	562
7,350	7,400	514	494	463	638	571
7,400	7,450	524	503	471	647	581
7,450	7,500	533	512	480	657	590
7,500	7,550	543	521	488	666	600
7,550	7,600	552	530	497	676	609
7,600	7,650	562	539	505	685	619
7,650	7,700	571	548	514	696	628

If the amount on Form 1040A, line 12, is— At least	But less than	And you are— Single, not head of household	Head of household	* Married filing joint return	Married filing separate return claiming— Low income allowance	%Standard deduction
		Your tax is—				
$7,700	$7,750	$581	$557	$522	$707	$638
7,750	7,800	590	566	531	718	647
7,800	7,850	600	575	539	729	657
7,850	7,900	609	584	548	740	666
7,900	7,950	619	593	556	751	676
7,950	8,000	628	602	565	762	685
8,000	8,050	638	611	573	773	696
8,050	8,100	647	620	582	784	707
8,100	8,150	657	629	590	795	718
8,150	8,200	666	638	599	806	729
8,200	8,250	676	647	607	817	740
8,250	8,300	685	656	616	828	751
8,300	8,350	695	665	625	839	762
8,350	8,400	706	674	634	850	773
8,400	8,450	716	684	644	861	784
8,450	8,500	727	693	653	872	795
8,500	8,550	737	703	663	883	806
8,550	8,600	748	712	672	894	817
8,600	8,650	758	722	682	905	828
8,650	8,700	768	731	691	916	839
8,700	8,750	777	739	699	927	850
8,750	8,800	786	747	707	938	861
8,800	8,850	795	755	715	949	872

If the amount on Form 1040A, line 12, is— At least	But less than	And you are— Single, not head of household	Head of household	* Married filing joint return	Married filing separate return claiming— Low income allowance	%Standard deduction
		Your tax is—				
$8,850	$8,900	$804	$763	$723	$960	$883
8,900	8,950	813	771	731	971	894
8,950	9,000	822	779	739	982	905
9,000	9,050	831	788	748	993	916
9,050	9,100	840	796	756	1,004	927
9,100	9,150	849	804	764	1,015	938
9,150	9,200	858	812	772	1,026	949
9,200	9,250	867	820	780	1,037	960
9,250	9,300	876	828	788	1,048	971
9,300	9,350	885	836	796	1,059	982
9,350	9,400	893	844	804	1,070	993
9,400	9,450	902	852	812	1,081	1,004
9,450	9,500	911	860	820	1,092	1,015
9,500	9,550	920	868	828	1,103	1,026
9,550	9,600	929	876	836	1,114	1,037
9,600	9,650	938	884	844	1,125	1,048
9,650	9,700	947	893	853	1,136	1,059
9,700	9,750	956	901	861	1,149	1,070
9,750	9,800	965	909	869	1,161	1,081
9,800	9,850	974	917	877	1,174	1,092
9,850	9,900	983	925	885	1,186	1,103
9,900	9,950	992	933	893	1,199	1,114
9,950	10,000	1,001	941	901	1,211	1,125

emption; the second, by a person with two exemptions; the third, by one with three exemptions; and similarly for each of the others. Since Mr. Webb had 4 exemptions, he referred to Table 4. Part of this table is shown on page 186. Each of the other tables is identical to this one except that the amount of tax to be paid on the various incomes is different.

As was pointed out when examining both the withholding tax table and the social security tax table, it is best to ignore the column headed by the words "At Least." Run your finger down the "But Less Than" column until you come to the first number *greater than* the "adjusted gross income," which is the income reported on line 12. For Mr. Webb this figure was $8,872. The first number in the "But Less Than" column that is greater than $8,872 is $8,900. After placing the edge of a piece of paper along this row, run your finger across the edge of the paper until you come to the column headed "Married filing joint return." Your finger should be pointing to $723. This is the amount of tax that Mr. Webb owes the government.

Mr. Webb had indicated on line 20a that the tax withheld from his salary, as shown on the W-2 form, had been $825.50. Hence, the IRS has to return to him $102.50, for he had overpaid the tax by that amount of money. Thus, the fill-ins for lines 17 through 24 will be as shown on page 188.

There was no fill-in for line 18 as Mr. Webb made no contribution to any candidate seeking public office. Similarly, there was no fill-in for line 20b since Mr. Webb had had only one job that year and therefore had not paid more than he should have for social security (FICA tax). Line 20c was also left blank, for this line concerns mainly those people who work for themselves. Finally, line 22 is completed only if the taxpayer owes the government money. Thus, had Mr. Webb's withholding tax been only $700 rather than $825.50, then he would have owed the government $23. This amount would have been noted on line 22 and, in addition, Mr. Webb would have had to send a check to the IRS for this amount along with his income tax form. Summarizing,

1. If the taxpayer owes the IRS money, this amount is noted on line 22 and lines 23 and 24 are left blank.
2. If the IRS owes the taxpayer money, this amount is noted on lines 23 and 24 and line 22 is left blank.

Line	Description	Sub-line	Amount	Cents	Line	Amount	Cents
17	Tax, check if from: [x] Tax Tables 1–12 **OR** [ ] Tax Rate Schedule X, Y, or Z . .				17	723	-
18	Credit for contributions to candidates for public office (see instructions on page 4)				18		
19	Income tax (subtract line 18 from line 17). If less than zero, enter zero				19	723	-
20a	Total Federal income tax withheld (attach Forms W–2 to front) . .	20a	825	50			
b	Excess FICA tax withheld (two or more employers—see instructions on page 4)	b					
c	1973 estimated tax payments (include amount allowed as credit from 1972 return)	c					
21	Total (add lines 20a, b, and c)				21	825	50
22	If line 19 is larger than line 21, enter **BALANCE DUE IRS** — Pay in full with return. Write social security number on check or money order and make payable to Internal Revenue Service ▶				22		
23	If line 21 is larger than line 19, enter amount **OVERPAID** . . . . ▶				23	102	50
24	Amount of line 23 to be **REFUNDED TO YOU** . . . . ▶				24	102	50

EXERCISES

1. Each of the following taxpayers claims four exemptions. Determine the income tax that each will have to pay.

	Total Income	Type of Return	Tax
a.	$7,160	Married—joint	$______
b.	8,225	Single—not head of household	______
c.	9,410	Single—head of household	______
d.	7,423	Married—joint	______
e.	8,839	Married—joint	______
f.	9,016	Single—not head of household	______
g.	7,550	Single—head of household	______
h.	8,600	Married—joint	______
i.	9,700	Married—joint	______
j.	7,043	Single—head of household	______

2. Determine the balance due the IRS (line 22), or the overpayment that must be returned to the taxpayer by the IRS (line 23), for each of the following taxpayers. Indicate whether your answer should be written on line 22 or line 23. Each of these taxpayers claimed four exemptions.

	Total Income	Type of Return	Tax	Withholding Tax	Amount On Line 22 or 23
a.	$7,348	Married—joint	$______	$457	$______
b.	8,623	Married—joint	______	629	______
c.	9,417	Single—not head of household	______	930	______
d.	7,624	Single—not head of household	______	690	______
e.	8,546	Single—head of household	______	710	______
f.	9,139	Married—joint	______	785	______
g.	8,650	Married—joint	______	670	______
h.	7,300	Single—head of household	______	480	______
i.	8,100	Single—head of household	______	654	______
j.	8,862	Single—not head of household	______	842	______

3. Write only the fill-ins for lines 9, 11, 12, and 17 through 24 of the 1040A form for each of the following taxpayers. Each of these taxpayers claimed four exemptions.

	Wages	Interest	Type of Return	Withholding Tax
a.	$8,325	$258	Single—head of household	$730
b.	7,958	463	Single—not head of household	702
c.	9,516	152	Married—joint	815
d.	6,724	106	Single—not head of household	425
e.	9,048	651	Married—joint	912
f.	8,139	314	Single—head of household	710

Line	Item	Line	Amount	Cents
12	Total (add lines 9, 10c, and 11) **(Adjusted Gross Income)**	12	12,700	--
	● **If you want IRS to figure your tax, skip the rest of this page and see instructions on page 3.**			
	● **If line 12 is under $10,000 find tax in Tables 1–12 and enter on line 17. Skip lines 13 through 16.**			
13	**If line 12 is $10,000 or more,** enter 15% of line 12 but not more than $2,000 ($1,000 if line 3 checked) .	13	1,905	--
14	Subtract line 13 from line 12	14	10,795	--
15	Multiply total number of exemptions claimed on line 7 by $750	15	3,750	--
16	Taxable income (subtract line 15 from line 14)	16	7,045	--
	(Figure tax on amount on line 16 using Tax Rate Schedule X, Y, or Z, and enter on line 17.)			
17	Tax, check if from: ☐ Tax Tables 1–12 **OR** ☐ Tax Rate Schedule X, Y, or Z . . .	17	1,198	55

Section 3: Computation by Taxpayer Using Short Form 1040A and Tax Rate Schedules

The tax table in Section 2 can be used only if a person's income is less than $10,000. If it is over this amount, then he must fill in lines 13 through 16 of Form 1040A and compute his tax by using one of three tables called *schedules*. A portion of two of these schedules—schedule X and schedule Y—is shown on page 192. Schedule Z, which is used by unmarried persons who are "Heads of Household," is not shown here.

ILLUSTRATION: A married couple with three children file a joint return. Their total income for the year is $12,700. Complete the fill-ins for lines 12 through 17 with this information.

SOLUTION:
See page 190.

EXPLANATION:
12. The fill-in for line 12 is the taxpayer's total income of $12,700.

13. On line 13 the IRS permits the taxpayer to reduce his income by the amount that he has given to charity or for loses through theft, etc. The taxpayer who wants to list all these deductions must use another tax form that will be examined in the next section. If the taxpayer decides not to list these deductions, he will use the 1040A form. In using this form, the IRS automatically allows him 15% of his earnings for the deductions. However, the maximum deduction he can claim on the 1040A form is $2,000. In the event that 15% of his income is greater than $2,000, he is permitted to enter no more than $2,000 on line 13. 15% of $12,700 comes to $1,905.

14. The fill-in for line 14 is the amount that remains after the deduction of $1,905 is subtracted from the income of $12,700.

15. On this line the IRS is granting the taxpayer a $750 reduction from the $10,795 for each exemption the taxpayer claims. For this case there are 5 exemptions—the husband, wife, and three children. Thus, the taxpayer can reduce the amount on which the tax is computed by $3,750.

16. The fill-in here is the actual amount on which the tax is determined. It is the amount that remains after both the 15% deduction and the $750 for each exemption are subtracted from the total income.

17. The taxpayer now examines Schedule Y, for he is a "Married Taxpayer Filing a Joint Return." As usual, he runs his finger down the "But not over" column until he comes to the first number greater than (or the same as) the taxable income on line 16. The first number greater than $7,045 is $8,000. Therefore, he must pay,

SCHEDULE X—Single Taxpayers Not Qualifying for Rates in Schedule Y or Z

If the amount on Form 1040A, line 16, is: / **Enter on Form 1040A, line 17.**

Not over $500....14% of the amount on line 16.

Over—	But not over—		of excess over—
$500	$1,000	$70+15%	$500
$1,000	$1,500	$145+16%	$1,000
$1,500	$2,000	$225+17%	$1,500
$2,000	$4,000	$310+19%	$2,000
$4,000	$6,000	$690+21%	$4,000
$6,000	$8,000	$1,110+24%	$6,000
$8,000	$10,000	$1,590+25%	$8,000
$10,000	$12,000	$2,090+27%	$10,000
$12,000	$14,000	$2,630+29%	$12,000
$14,000	$16,000	$3,210+31%	$14,000
$16,000	$18,000	$3,830+34%	$16,000
$18,000	$20,000	$4,510+36%	$18,000
.	.	.	
$80,000	$90,000	$39,390+68%	$80,000
$90,000	$100,000	$46,190+69%	$90,000
$100,000	....	$53,090+70%	$100,000

SCHEDULE Y—Married Taxpayers and Certain Widows and Widowers

Married Taxpayers Filing Joint Returns and Certain Widows and Widowers

If the amount on Form 1040A, line 16, is: / **Enter on Form 1040A, line 17.**

Not over $1,000....14% of the amount on line 16.

Over—	But not over—		of excess over—
$1,000	$2,000	$140+15%	$1,000
$2,000	$3,000	$290+16%	$2,000
$3,000	$4,000	$450+17%	$3,000
$4,000	$8,000	$620+19%	$4,000
$8,000	$12,000	$1,380+22%	$8,000
$12,000	$16,000	$2,260+25%	$12,000
$16,000	$20,000	$3,260+28%	$16,000
$20,000	$24,000	$4,380+32%	$20,000
$24,000	$28,000	$5,660+36%	$24,000
$28,000	$32,000	$7,100+39%	$28,000
$32,000	$36,000	$8,660+42%	$32,000
$36,000	$40,000	$10,340+45%	$36,000
.	.	.	
$160,000	$180,000	$83,580+68%	$160,000
$180,000	$200,000	$97,180+69%	$180,000
$200,000	....	$110,980+70%	$200,000

Married Taxpayers Filing Separate Returns

If the amount on Form 1040A, line 16, is: / **Enter on Form 1040A, line 17.**

Not over $500....14% of the amount on line 16.

Over—	But not over—		of excess over—
$500	$1,000	$70+15%	$500
$1,000	$1,500	$145+16%	$1,000
$1,500	$2,000	$225+17%	$1,500
$2,000	$4,000	$310+19%	$2,000
$4,000	$6,000	$690+22%	$4,000
$6,000	$8,000	$1,130+25%	$6,000
$8,000	$10,000	$1,630+28%	$8,000
$10,000	$12,000	$2,190+32%	$10,000
$12,000	$14,000	$2,830+36%	$12,000
$14,000	$16,000	$3,550+39%	$14,000
$16,000	$18,000	$4,330+42%	$16,000
$18,000	$20,000	$5,170+45%	$18,000
.	.	.	
$80,000	$90,000	$41,790+68%	$80,000
$90,000	$100,000	$48,590+69%	$90,000
$100,000	....	$55,490+70%	$100,000

$$\$620 + 19\% \text{ of the amount over } \$4{,}000$$

The amount over $4,000 is $3,045 and 19% of $3,045 turns out to be $578.55. Hence,

$$\begin{aligned} \text{Base tax} &= \$620 \\ \text{Tax on excess} &= 19\% \times (\$7{,}045 - \$4{,}000) \\ &= .19 \times \$3{,}045 \\ &= \$578.55 \\ \text{Total tax} &= \$620 + \$578.55 \\ &= \$1{,}198.55 \end{aligned}$$

EXERCISES A

1. What is the tax on the excess *only* in each of the following situations?

	Taxable Income	Percent of Tax on Excess	Tax on Excess
a.	$11,000	25% on excess over $10,000	$______
b.	14,000	32% on excess over $10,000	______
c.	26,000	36% on excess over $24,000	______
d.	35,000	42% on excess over $32,000	______
e.	24,500	40% on excess over $22,000	______
f.	41,300	48% on excess over $40,000	______
g.	63,700	64% on excess over $60,000	______
h.	65,100	55% on excess over $64,000	______

2. What is the tax on each of the following taxable incomes?

	Taxable Income	Tax Computation	Tax
a.	$ 7,000	$1,130 + 25% on excess over $6,000	$______
b.	15,000	$2,260 + 25% on excess over $12,000	______
c.	5,200	$690 + 21% on excess over $4,000	______
d.	17,500	$3,260 + 28% on excess over $16,000	______
e.	21,700	$4,800 + 35% on excess over $20,000	______
f.	29,600	$7,100 + 39% on excess over $28,000	______
g.	20,450	$5,230 + 38% on excess over $20,000	______
h.	69,375	$24,420 + 55% on excess over $64,000	______

3. What is the tax on each of the following taxable incomes? Use the tax rate schedules on page 192.

	Taxable Income	Type of Return	Base Tax	Tax on Excess	Total Tax
a.	$ 7,000	Single	$______	$______	$______
b.	9,000	Married—Joint	______	______	______
c.	9,000	Married—Separate	______	______	______

	Taxable Income	Type of Return	Base Tax	Tax on Excess	Total Tax
d.	$14,000	Married—Joint	$________	$________	$________
e.	8,500	Single	________	________	________
f.	19,200	Married—Joint	________	________	________
g.	17,450	Single	________	________	________
h.	9,625	Single	________	________	________
i.	13,458	Single	________	________	________
j.	21,392	Married—Joint	________	________	________

4. Using the following information and the tax rate schedules X and Y, write *only* the fill-ins for lines 12 through 17 on the 1040A form.

	Adjusted Gross Income	Number of Exemptions	Type of Return
a.	$12,000	3	Married—Joint
b.	11,000	1	Single
c.	14,000	2	Married—Joint
d.	15,000	5	Married—Joint
e.	16,700	3	Single
f.	21,500	4	Married—Joint

B

A taxpayer is single and has a taxable income of $120,000.

1. What tax does he pay on the first $100,000 of his income? ________

2. What tax does he pay on that part of his income above $100,000? ________

3. What is his total tax? ________

4. How much money does the government take from each dollar of his income above $100,000? ________

5. How much money does the government allow this taxpayer to keep for each dollar of his income above $100,000? ________

6. How much tax would he have to pay on this income if he were married and filed a separate return? ________

7. How much less tax does he have to pay as a single person than as a married person filing a separate return? ________

Section 4: Filing Form 1040

Reference was made in the previous section to the deductions that the government allows you to subtract from your total income before computing your tax. You may recall that in computing line 13 of the 1040A form, the IRS automatically grants a taxpayer a deduction of 15% of his income. It was also pointed out that this automatic deduction could never be more than $2,000. However, there are times when a taxpayer's deductions may amount to more than $2,000, or even more than 15% of his earnings. If this is so, then rather than file the short 1040A form, the taxpayer will file the 1040 form. In addition to this, he must also file a form called *Schedule A*, on which he lists, or *itemizes*, all the deductions he is taking.

But just what are these allowable deductions? Below is a sample of some deductions that can be taken and others that can not be.

DEDUCTIONS FOR CONTRIBUTIONS

You can deduct gifts to:	You cannot deduct gifts to:
Churches, including assessments	Relatives, friends, other individuals
Salvation Army, Red Cross, CARE	Foreign organizations
United Funds and Community Chests	Social clubs
Nonprofit schools and hospitals	Labor unions

DEDUCTIONS FOR INTEREST PAYMENTS

You can deduct interest on:	You cannot deduct interest on:
Your personal note to a bank or an individual	A gambling debt or other nonenforceable obligation
A mortgage on your home	

DEDUCTIONS FOR PAYMENT OF TAXES

You can deduct these taxes:	You cannot deduct these taxes:
Real estate taxes	Federal social security taxes
State and local gasoline taxes	Hunting licenses, dog licenses
General sales tax	Auto inspection fees, tags, drivers licenses
State and local income taxes	Water taxes
Personal property taxes	

DEDUCTIONS FOR ACCIDENT OR THEFT LOSSES

You can deduct losses on:	You cannot deduct losses on:
Property such as your home, clothing, or automobile destroyed or damaged by fire	Personal injury to yourself or another person
Property, including cash, which is stolen from you	Accidental loss by you of cash or other personal property
Loss or damage of property by flood, lightning, storm, explosion, or freezing	

Of the deductions listed above, the only one that requires a little care in handling is the one on accident or theft losses. To begin with, you must realize that only those losses that are not covered by insurance are deductible. Thus, if, during an accident, your car was damaged to the extent of $275 and the insurance company paid the entire cost of the repairs, then you could deduct nothing for this loss when itemizing your deductions. However, if you had to pay the $275 yourself, then you still would not be permitted to deduct this entire amount from your income when filing your return. Only that part of the loss over $100 can be deducted. Hence, in this case, you can deduct $175 rather than $275. Had the loss been less than $100, then you would not have been able to make any deduction.

The decision as to whether or not to use Schedule A and the 1040 form when filing a tax return is quite easy to make. It would be best for the taxpayer to itemize his deductions if he falls within any one of the following three groups:

1. Total income over $13,333 (line 12 of Short Form 1040A) and deductions amounting to more than $2,000.
2. Total income between $8,667 and $13,333 and deductions amounting to more than 15% of total income.
3. Total income less than $8,667 and deductions amounting to more than $1,300.

If the taxpayer's earnings and deductions do not fall into one of these groups, then he will pay less tax by either using the table the IRS provides or taking the standard deduction of 15% than by listing his deductions.

ILLUSTRATION 1: Carol Martin's earnings during the past year were $9,647. In itemizing her deductions she found that they included:

North Church	$217	Real estate tax	$654
United Fund	$ 86	State income tax	$136
Red Cross	$ 10	Interest on mortgage	$185

While she was away from home one evening, her apartment was robbed. The loss, which amounted to $394, was not covered by insurance. Should Carol itemize her deductions?

EXPLANATION: When finding the sum of the itemized deductions, begin by subtracting $100 from the theft of $394 worth of valuables, leaving a difference of $294. The sum of this deduction and all the others is $1,582. Since Carol's income falls in "group 2," that is, between $8,667 and $13,333, it is necessary to determine whether or not the total of these deductions is greater than 15% of her income – 15% of Carol's income amounts to $1,447.05. Therefore, as this number is less than $1,582, it is to Carol's advantage to itemize her deductions and use Form 1040.

SOLUTION:

$$\begin{aligned}\text{Deduction for theft} &= \$394 - \$100\\ &= \$294\\ \text{Total of deductions} &= \$294 + \$217 + \$86 + \$10 + \$654 + \$136\\ &\quad + \$185\\ &= \$1{,}582\\ \text{Standard deduction} &= 15\% \times \$9{,}647\\ &= .15 \times \$9{,}647\\ &= \$1{,}447.05\end{aligned}$$

Since the total of the itemized deductions is the greater, Carol should itemize them in filing her income tax form.

Although both the 1040A form and the 1040 form have changed somewhat over the years, and although the amounts allowed for exemptions and for deductions have also changed somewhat over the years, the computation of the tax has always followed the same pattern. After subtracting both the deductions and the allowances for exemptions from the total income, what remains is the *taxable income*, that is, the income on which tax is computed. The tax itself is always found using either a tax table or a tax rate schedule as was shown in the earlier sections.

ILLUSTRATION 2: Compute the tax on a joint return with five exemptions. The total income is $15,470 and the deductions, when itemized, amount to $3,154.

SOLUTION:

1. Total income	$15,470
2. Deductions	− 3,154
Balance	$12,316
3. Exemptions (5 × $750)	− 3,750
4. Taxable income	8,566

5. $$\begin{aligned}\text{Tax} &= \$1{,}380 + 22\% \times (\$8{,}566 - \$8{,}000)\\ &= \$1{,}380 + .22 \times (\$566)\\ &= \$1{,}380 + \$124.52\\ &= \$1{,}504.52\end{aligned}$$

EXPLANATION: The only decision that has to be made in the computation above is whether the deductions should or should not be itemized. Since the income is over $13,333, and the deductions are over $2,000, then the deductions should be itemized. The remaining steps were completed in exactly the same manner as in prior illustrations.

EXERCISES A

1. None of the following losses due to theft was covered by insurance. How much will a taxpayer be permitted to deduct from his income for each of these when filing his tax return?

a. $267	________	c. $49	________
b. $342	________	d. $102	________

2. Determine whether each of the following taxpayers should or should not itemize his deductions. For each exercise, indicate which of the three groups (listed on page 196) you examined when arriving at your answer.

	Total Income	Total of Itemized Deductions	
a.	$15,420	$2,657	________
b.	18,946	3,475	________
c.	7,495	1,562	________
d.	8,346	981	________
e.	16,495	1,769	________
f.	23,472	4,622	________
g.	24,701	1,913	________
h.	9,000	1,420	________
i.	11,000	1,953	________
j.	12,400	1,632	________
k.	9,600	1,274	________
l.	10,524	1,843	________

3. Using the method for computing the tax shown in Illustration 2 on page 197, determine the tax due in each of the following cases.

	Total Income	Total of Itemized Deductions	Exemptions	Type of Return	Tax
a.	$ 8,300	$1,520	1	Single	$________
b.	7,400	1,700	2	Single	________
c.	15,000	2,400	4	Joint	________
d.	16,500	4,500	3	Joint	________
e.	14,000	3,140	5	Joint	________
f.	18,600	2,960	1	Single	________
g.	24,700	5,650	2	Single	________
h.	9,800	1,610	2	Joint	________
i.	10,500	1,748	3	Joint	________
j.	12,900	2,564	1	Single	________

4. After computing the tax as shown in Illustration 2 on page 197, determine the "balance due" or "overpayment" for each of the following taxpayers.

	Total Income	Total of Itemized Deductions	Exemptions	Type of Return	Tax	Income Tax Withheld	Balance Due or Overpayment
a.	$ 7,540	$1,450	2	Single	$______	$ 730	$______
b.	14,500	2,520	4	Joint	______	1,540	______
c.	19,600	4,800	6	Joint	______	1,950	______
d.	23,400	6,700	1	Single	______	3,680	______
e.	10,572	1,640	3	Single	______	1,410	______

B

1. When Henry Stark itemized his deductions he found that they were the following:

Real estate tax	$1,542	Salvation Army	$25
Church	$146	Community Chest	$40
Interest on a loan	$80	Interest on mortgage	$154
State gasoline tax	$47	State income tax	$121

If Henry's total income for the year was $12,647, should he itemize his deductions or use the tax rate schedule? Justify your answer.

____

2. Janine Garrett earned $14,357 last year. In addition, the interest from her savings accounts came to $796. When she itemized her deductions they were as follows:

Church	$650	State gasoline tax	$93
Real estate tax	$1,764	United Fund	$175
State income tax	$423	Interest on mortgage	$794
State sales tax	$158		

If she files a "single" return claiming only herself as an exemption, how much income tax will she have to pay? (Use the outline suggested in Illustration 2 on page 197.) ________

Unit 2: State Income Tax

Computation of state income tax is very much the same as that for federal income tax. For most states the tax is based on the *taxable income*, which is the amount that remains after both exemptions and deductions are subtracted from the taxpayer's total income. This is the same as you found it to be when determining the federal income tax.

There are a few states, though, in which in order to determine the taxable income the taxpayer subtracts *only* the deductions from his total income. However, once he has computed the state tax he is permitted to reduce the tax itself by an amount depending on the number of exemptions he has. The tax rate schedules for several states, including one of this type, namely, Arkansas, are shown on page 201.

ILLUSTRATION 1: How much state income tax will David Thomas have to pay on a taxable income of $12,250 if he lives in Arkansas? Mr. Thomas has a wife and four children.

SOLUTION:

Base tax = $240
Tax on excess = 4.5% × ($12,250 − $9,000)
= .045 × $3,250
= $146.25
Total tax = $240 + $146.25
= $386.25
Reduction for allowances = $35 + 5 × $6
= $35 + $30
= $65
Net tax = $386.25 − $65
= $321.25

EXPLANATION: The total tax is computed in identically the same manner as the federal tax was computed when using the tax rate schedules. In addition to this, however, Mr. Thomas is granted a reduction of $35 for himself and a reduction of $6 for each of his dependents. Hence, the total reduction granted him is $65. Therefore, when this amount is taken from the total tax, he is left with a balance or net tax of $321.25.

ILLUSTRATION 2: If Mr. Thomas had lived in Idaho, how much would his state tax have been?

SOLUTION:

Total exemptions = $1,500 + 5 × $750
= $1,500 + $3,750
= $5,250
Taxable income = $12,250 − $5,250
= $7,000
Base tax = $225
Tax on excess = 7.5% × ($7,000 − $5,000)
= .075 × $2,000
= $150

ARKANSAS

If the taxable income is:
Not over $3,000 . . . . 2% of income

Over	But not Over		Of excess Over
$3,000	$6,000	$60 + 2.5%	$3,000
$6,000	$9,000	$135 + 3.5%	$6,000
$9,000	$15,000	$240 + 4.5%	$9,000
$15,000	$25,000	$510 + 6%	$15,000
$25,000	. . . .	$1,110 + 7%	$25,000

Reduction in tax as follows,
Single: $17.50; Married: $35
Head of household: $35; Each dependent: $6

IDAHO

If the taxable income is:
Not over $1,000 . . . . 2% of income

Over	But not Over		Of excess Over
$1,000	$2,000	$20 + 4%	$1,000
$2,000	$3,000	$60 + 4.5%	$2,000
$3,000	$4,000	$105 + 5.5%	$3,000
$4,000	$5,000	$160 + 6.5%	$4,000
$5,000	. . .	$225 + 7.5%	$5,000

Exemptions as follows:
Single: $750; Married: $1,500
Head of household: $1,500; Each dependent: $750

NORTH CAROLINA

If the taxable income is:
Not over $2,000 . . . . 3% of income

Over	But not Over		Of excess Over
$2,000	$4,000	$60 + 4%	$2,000
$4,000	$6,000	$140 + 5%	$4,000
$6,000	$10,000	$240 + 6%	$6,000
$10,000	. . .	$480 + 7%	$10,000

Exemptions as follows:
Single: $1,000; Married: $2,000
Head of household: $2,000; Each dependent: $600

$$\text{Total tax} = \$225 + \$150$$
$$= \$375$$

EXPLANATION: Notice that in the state of Idaho the state income tax computation involves identically the same procedures as in finding the federal income tax.

EXERCISES A

1. How much North Carolina state income tax will have to be paid in each of the following situations?

	Taxable Income	Base Tax	Tax on Excess	Total Tax
a.	$ 1,000	$______	$______	$______
b.	1,400	______	______	______
c.	2,300	______	______	______
d.	4,700	______	______	______
e.	5,300	______	______	______
f.	6,800	______	______	______
g.	9,370	______	______	______
h.	12,800	______	______	______

2. How much North Carolina state income tax will have to be paid in each of the following situations?

	Total Income	Deductions	Exemptions	Tax
a.	$ 8,700	$3,000	Single	$______
b.	9,300	2,500	Single	______
c.	8,400	2,100	Married, 1 dependent	______
d.	5,750	950	Single	______
e.	10,500	1,800	Head of household, 2 dependents	______
f.	12,600	2,400	Married, 4 dependents	______
g.	18,200	4,700	Single	______
h.	20,300	5,100	Married, 3 dependents	______

3. How much Idaho state income tax will have to be paid in each of the following situations?

	Taxable Income	Base Tax	Tax on Excess	Total Tax
a.	$ 1,600	$______	$______	$______
b.	2,500	______	______	______
c.	3,700	______	______	______
d.	5,200	______	______	______
e.	7,900	______	______	______
f.	10,600	______	______	______
g.	14,520	______	______	______
h.	18,950	______	______	______

4. How much Idaho state income tax will have to be paid in each of the following situations?

	Total Income	Deductions	Exemptions	Tax
a.	$ 7,600	$1,400	Single	$________
b.	8,500	1,700	Single	________
c.	9,800	2,100	Married, 2 dependents	________
d.	11,700	2,400	Head of household, 1 dependent	________
e.	16,420	4,500	Single	________
f.	19,160	5,420	Married, 4 dependents	________

5. How much Arkansas state income tax, *before exemptions*, will have to be paid in each of the following situations?

	Taxable Income	Base Tax	Tax on Excess	Total Tax
a.	$ 2,400	$________	$________	$________
b.	5,700	________	________	________
c.	7,800	________	________	________
d.	11,300	________	________	________
e.	14,550	________	________	________
f.	18,370	________	________	________
g.	27,900	________	________	________

6. How much Arkansas state income tax, *after exemptions*, will have to be paid in each of the following situations?

	Total Income	Deductions	Exemptions	Tax
a.	$ 5,600	$ 460	Single	$________
b.	10,400	2,300	Single	________
c.	9,500	1,700	Married, 1 dependent	________
d.	11,300	2,100	Married, 2 dependents	________
e.	14,800	3,050	Head of household, 1 dependent	________
f.	15,700	2,940	Single	________
g.	21,400	5,680	Married, 3 dependents	________

B

1. a. Two men have exactly the same net income and the same number of dependents, but one is married, while the other is classified as the "head of a household." Will one pay a smaller state income tax than the other if they live in Arkansas? Justify your answer. ________

b. Would there be any difference in their taxes if they lived in North Carolina? ________

2. James Fields is unmarried and has no dependents. His net income last year was $7,314.
   a. If he lived in Idaho how much state income tax did he have to pay? ________
   b. If he lived in North Carolina, how much would his state income tax have been? ________
   c. How much more—or less—would he have had to pay in North Carolina than in Idaho? ________
3. In Arkansas, how much more state income tax would a married man with two dependents have to pay than one with four dependents if they both had exactly the same net income? Assume that the net income of each would require a tax of more than $100. ________
4. How much more—or less—would a single person with no dependents and a net income of $16,000 have to pay in state income tax if he lived in North Carolina rather than in Arkansas? ________

Unit 3: Chapter Review and Test

1. Use the tax table on page 186 to determine the amount of federal income tax the following taxpayers will have to pay. Each of them claimed four exemptions.

	Total Income	Type of Return	Tax
a.	$7,310	Single—not head of household	$________
b.	8,573	Married—joint return	________
c.	9,450	Single—head of household	________

2. Use the tax tables on page 186 to determine the "Balance Due" or the "Overpayment" for the following taxpayer. He claimed four exemptions. ________

Wages	Interest	Type of Return	Withholding Tax
$8,674	$476	Married—Joint	$723

3. What is the tax on the excess *only* in each of the following situations?

	Taxable Income	Percent of Tax on Excess	Tax on Excess
a.	$11,400	27% on excess over $10,000	$________
b.	9,300	22% on excess over $8,000	________

4. What is the tax on the following taxable income?

Taxable Income	Tax Computation	Tax
$14,200	$2,260 + 25% on excess over $12,000	$________

5. What is the federal income tax on each of the following taxable incomes? Use the tax rate schedule on page 192.

	Taxable Income	Type of Return	Base Tax	Tax on Excess	Total Tax
a.	$ 5,000	Single	$________	$________	$________
b.	18,500	Married—joint	________	________	________
c.	13,400	Married—separate	________	________	________

6. How much money can each of the following families claim for exemptions when filing a federal income tax return?

a. Husband (blind, age 37), wife (age 35), children ages 15, 12, and 9. ________

b. Husband (age 69), wife (age 66), dependent child. ________

7. Using the following information and the tax rate schedules on page 192, write only the fill-ins for lines 12 through 17 on the short 1040A form.

Adjusted Gross Income	Number of Exemptions	Type of Return
$10,200	1	Single

____

8. Jane Schilling's car was damaged to the extent of $175 during an automobile accident. She carried no insurance to cover this damage. How much of this loss can she claim as a deduction when filing her federal income tax return? ________

9. A taxpayer has an income of $9,500. When she listed her deductions the total came to $1,540. Explain whether she should or should not itemize these deductions when filing her federal income tax return.

____

10. Using the outline suggested in Illustration 2 on page 197, determine the federal income tax due in the following situation.

Total Income	Total of Itemized Deductions	Exemptions	Type of Return	Tax
$11,600	$2,400	4	Joint	$________

11. The Keeler family lives in Arkansas. It consists of Mr. Keeler, his wife, and three teen-age children. If Mr. Keeler's taxable income last year was $12,750, how much state income tax did he have to pay? ________

SAVINGS

CHAPTER 6

BANKING—THE SAVINGS ACCOUNT

Once a person reaches the point where his earnings provide him with all his needs and he still has money to spare, he begins to consider what he should do with his excess funds. Often as not he will turn to a bank, where his money not only will be safe from loss or theft but also will earn still more money for him. This chapter will deal largely with the way in which this earning takes place.

Unit 1: Completing a Deposit Slip

The deposit slips of most banks or savings and loan associations are pretty much the same as the one shown below. All have one line for "Bills," another line for "Coin," and several lines where checks can be listed separately. At the top of the slip the depositor records his account or book number. The purpose of recording both his name and account number is so that, should the need arise, the bank will have two ways of identifying the person who made the deposit.

The vertical line that separates "Dollars" from "Cents" on the deposit slip is purely a safety device. Banks learned long ago that people

PASS BOOK. No. ______

DEPOSITED TO THE ACCOUNT OF

______
NAME

______
PRESENT ADDRESS

IN

THE SAVINGS INSTITUTION

NEWARK, N.J.

______ 19 __

	DOLLARS	CENTS
BILLS		
COIN		
CHECKS (LIST SEPARATELY)		
TOTAL		

are rather careless in the way they place the decimal points in a column of numerals. To help people write the numerals in the proper position, the line was drawn as a replacement for the decimal point. The numerals to the left of the line record the number of dollars, while those to the right indicate the number of cents. This is common practice on many business forms.

ILLUSTRATION: Philip Demarest deposited 4 ten-dollar bills, 6 five-dollar bills, 8 one-dollar bills, 2 half-dollars, 3 quarters, 7 dimes, one check for $18.62, and another for $146.17. How was the deposit slip filled out?

SOLUTION:

	Dollars	Cents
Bills	78	00
Coin	2	45
Checks	18	62
	146	17
Total	245	24

EXPLANATION: Neither bills nor coins are listed separately. The total of the 4 ten-dollar bills, 6 five-dollar bills, and 8 one-dollar bills came to $78. This numeral was then recorded in the "Dollars" column in line with the word "Bills." Similarly, the total of the coins is $2.45. The $2 appears in the "Dollars" column, while the 45¢ is recorded in the "Cents" column. Checks are listed separately, for if reference has to be made to the deposit slip, it is easy to spot whether the amount of each check was recorded correctly. Finally, the total of the entire deposit—$245.24—appears at the bottom.

EXERCISES A

Complete each of the following deposit slips.

1.

	Dollars	Cents
Bills	45	00
Coin		67
Checks	124	78
Total		

2.

	Dollars	Cents
Bills	93	00
Coin		81
Checks	56	24
Total		

3.

	Dollars	Cents
Bills	59	00
Coin		96
Checks	135	42
	258	17
Total		

4.

	Dollars	Cents
Bills	186	00
Coin	1	85
Checks	39	51
	347	62
Total		

5.

	Dollars	Cents
Bills	285	00
Coin	14	62
Checks	495	25
	106	19
	84	36
Total		

6.

	Dollars	Cents
Bills	547	00
Coin	28	15
Checks	1,246	50
	912	47
	350	25
Total		

B

Draw deposit slips similar to those in Part A, above, and complete them by using the following information.

1. Deposited: 6 ten-dollar bills, 8 five-dollar bills, 4 one-dollar bills, 1 half-dollar, 3 quarters, 4 dimes, 1 check for $46.50. ________
2. Deposited: 3 ten-dollar bills, 12 five-dollar bills, 9 one-dollar bills, 2 half-dollars, 2 quarters, 7 dimes, 4 nickels, 1 check for $126.75, 1 check for $37.50. ________
3. Deposited: 2 twenty-dollar bills, 5 ten-dollar bills, 7 one-dollar bills, 15 quarters, 23 dimes, 8 nickels, 14 pennies, 1 check for $85.72, 1 check for $67.30, 1 check for $140. ________
4. Deposited: 4 twenty-dollar bills, 3 ten-dollar bills, 15 one-dollar bills, 12 half-dollars, 20 quarters, 25 dimes, 15 nickels, 40 pennies, 1 check for $217.20, 1 check for $86.30, 1 check for $109.25. ________
5. Deposited: 8 twenty-dollar bills, 14 ten-dollar bills, 25 five-dollar bills, 20 one-dollar bills, 20 half-dollars, 25 quarters, 50 dimes, 25 nickels, 200 pennies, 1 check for $150, 1 check for $53.40, 1 check for $117.60. ________

Unit 2: The Interest Formula

Section 1: Monthly Periods of Time

Originally money was deposited in a bank mainly for safekeeping. The present-day depositor is much more interested in how much his money will earn for him in a particular bank than in whether that bank is a safe place for his money. In return for leaving his money in a bank, the depositor is paid for its use in terms of the size of his account. The amount he receives is quoted as a percent value, such as, perhaps,

4% or 5% per annum. This simply means that if money is kept on deposit for a period of an entire year, the bank will pay the depositor $4 for each $100, or, if the rate is 5%, then the payment will be $5 for each $100.

The $4 per $100 per year, that is, the 4% per annum, is called the annual rate of interest. Hence, if a person has $200 on deposit, he will receive $4 for each $100, or a total of $8. This $8, called interest, is added to his account automatically at the end of the year. Just as people earn money by working, so, too, does money earn money by working. The bank puts a depositor's money to work by lending it to individuals or companies.

Many banks pay their depositors interest every half year rather than annually. The rate of interest, however, is still advertised on an annual basis where the sign in a bank window says "6% per annum." Thus, if the deposit is $300 and if interest is given once a year, the payment will be $18 at the close of the year. Since interest is paid every half year—semiannually—the amount the depositor receives for the half year is $9. It would seem, then, that finding the half-yearly payment is simply a matter of multiplying the annual interest by 1/2. Similarly, if a bank paid interest every quarter of a year then the quarterly payment would be found by multiplying the annual interest by 1/4. In the situation just examined, where the annual interest is $18 the quarterly amount will be one fourth of this, or $4.50.

Since all interest payments are dependent on the annual interest payment, it would be best to examine how this can be found when the numbers are not quite so simple as those in the previous paragraph. In finding the answer to such questions as, "What is 4% of $128?" you may recall that it is merely necessary to replace the word "of" by the multiplication sign and then determine the product of 4% and $128.

The question you now face appears different from the one above, "What is the annual interest on $128 that is deposited at 4% for a period of one year?" However, when reworded, it turns out to be exactly the same, "What is 4% of $128?" Hence, finding the annual interest reduces itself to computing the product of the amount of money on deposit, called the *principal*, with the annual rate of interest. This is frequently written as:

$$\text{Interest} = \text{Principal} \times \text{Interest Rate}$$

or, in the form of a formula as:

$$I = P \times R$$

ILLUSTRATION 1: Find the interest on $836 for a period of one year if the annual interest rate is 5%.

SOLUTION:

$$\begin{aligned} I &= P \times R \\ &= \$836 \times 5\% \\ &= \$836 \times .05 \\ &= \$41.80 \end{aligned}$$

EXPLANATION: After rewriting 5% as the decimal .05, the product of $836 and .05 is found in the usual way.

In Illustration 1 it was specially noted that the interest rate of 5% was an annual rate. In the world of business, interest rates are always quoted for a period of one year unless otherwise stated. The same will be true in this book.

Had the bank in this illustration paid interest every half year, then one half of the $41.80 would have been the semiannual payment. And if payments were made every quarter of a year, then one fourth of the $41.80 would have been the quarterly interest payment. Rather than first compute the annual interest and then find one half or one quarter of that amount, both steps can be expressed as a single process by writing the interest formula as,

$$I = P \times R \times T$$

where the "T" is either the fraction ½ or ¼, depending on whether the interest is paid semiannually or quarterly. As before, "P times R" represents the annual interest. Furthermore, the "T", or time, can be 1/12 if interest is given monthly. Or the "T" can be 2/12 if interest is given once every two months. And, similarly, the fractions would be 3/12 for once every three months and 4/12 for once every four months.

ILLUSTRATION 2: Find the semiannual interest payment on $1,248 if the interest rate is 4%.

SOLUTION:

$$\begin{aligned} I &= P \times R \times T \\ &= \$1{,}248 \times 4\% \times \text{half-year} \\ &= \$\overset{624}{\cancel{1{,}248}} \times .04 \times \frac{1}{\underset{1}{\cancel{2}}} \\ &= \$24.96 \end{aligned}$$

EXPLANATION: By finding the interest for the half year immediately, it is sometimes possible to simplify the computation by reducing the fractions before multiplying.

ILLUSTRATION 3: Find the quarterly interest payment on $3,420 if the interest rate is $4\frac{3}{4}\%$.

SOLUTION:

$$
\begin{aligned}
I &= P \times R \times T \\
&= \$3{,}420 \times 4\tfrac{3}{4}\% \times \text{quarter} \\
&= \$3{,}420 \times 4.75\% \times \frac{1}{4} \\
&= \overset{855}{\cancel{\$3{,}420}} \times .0475 \times \frac{1}{\underset{1}{\cancel{4}}} \\
&= \$40.6125, \text{ or } \$40.61
\end{aligned}
$$

EXPLANATION: The only part of the solution that might have caused any concern is the renaming of $4\frac{3}{4}\%$ as .0475. It is best to change $4\frac{3}{4}\%$ to the form 4.75% before rewriting it as the decimal .0475 by moving the decimal point two places to the left.

EXERCISES A

If you do not recall how to do the computation in the following exercises, you will probably want to refer to the pages indicated for additional help.

1. Change each of the following percent numerals to its decimal equivalent. (See page 515.)

a. 30%	________	i. 23.4%	________	q. $4\frac{1}{2}\%$	________
b. 10%	________	j. 16.7%	________	r. $5\frac{1}{2}\%$	________
c. 50%	________	k. 5.2%	________	s. $3\frac{1}{2}\%$	________
d. 75%	________	l. 6.4%	________	t. $6\frac{1}{2}\%$	________
e. 5%	________	m. 4.9%	________	u. $8\frac{1}{2}\%$	________
f. 4%	________	n. 7.24%	________	v. $5\frac{1}{4}\%$	________
g. 9%	________	o. 6.87%	________	w. $6\frac{3}{4}\%$	________
h. 6%	________	p. 5.93%	________	x. $7\frac{3}{4}\%$	________

2. Find the product in each of the following exercises. (See page 507.)

a. $20 \times .05 \times \frac{1}{5}$ = ________

b. $60 \times .04 \times \frac{3}{4}$ = ________

c. $10 \times .06 \times \frac{1}{2}$ = ________

d. $500 \times .07 \times \frac{1}{2}$ = ________

e. $800 \times .08 \times \frac{1}{4}$ = ________

f. $900 \times .052 \times \frac{1}{3}$ = ________

g. $1{,}200 \times .065 \times \frac{1}{3}$ = ________
h. $3{,}000 \times .075 \times \frac{1}{6}$ = ________
i. $5{,}400 \times .0825 \times \frac{2}{3}$ = ________

B

1. Find the interest in each of the following exercises. The interest is paid once each year.

	Principal	Interest Rate	Interest		Principal	Interest Rate	Interest
a.	$ 600	5%	$________	i.	$3,400	6.4%	$________
b.	800	4%	________	j.	4,200	7.3%	________
c.	1,200	6%	________	k.	900	4½%	________
d.	5,600	7%	________	l.	1,600	5½%	________
e.	3,250	5%	________	m.	2,800	5¼%	________
f.	6,745	8%	________	n.	3,600	6¼%	________
g.	2,000	4.8%	________	o.	4,800	6¾%	________
h.	5,000	5.6%	________	p.	5,320	7¾%	________

2. Find the semiannual interest in each of the following exercises.

	Principal	Interest Rate	Interest		Principal	Interest Rate	Interest
a.	$ 400	4%	$________	e.	$6,000	4.7%	$________
b.	1,500	5%	________	f.	8,200	5.4%	________
c.	5,400	3%	________	g.	3,200	4½%	________
d.	7,320	4%	________	h.	4,800	5½%	________

3. Find the quarterly interest in each of the following exercises.

	Principal	Interest Rate	Interest		Principal	Interest Rate	Interest
a.	$5,300	4%	$________	e.	$3,200	5.6%	$________
b.	2,200	5%	________	f.	4,000	6.3%	________
c.	6,400	6%	________	g.	2,112	5¼%	________
d.	7,200	7%	________	h.	7,520	6¼%	________

4. If interest is paid for the period of time shown, determine the interest on each of the following deposits.

	Principal	Interest Rate	Period for Which Interest Is Computed	Interest
a.	$9,000	4%	1 month	$________
b.	8,400	5%	1 month	________
c.	6,300	4%	2 months	________
d.	3,900	6%	2 months	________
e.	2,400	4.8%	2 months	________
f.	5,700	6.4%	4 months	________
g.	3,300	4¾%	4 months	________
h.	6,720	6¾%	4 months	________

C

1. Eleanor Rossner had a deposit of $3,675 in a bank that paid 4.87% interest annually.
   a. How much interest did Eleanor receive at the end of the year? (Hint: Rewrite 4.87% as a decimal.) ________
   b. If no deposits or withdrawals were made during the year, how much money did Eleanor have in this account at the close of the year? ________
2. The Greensboro Savings Bank pays interest annually at the rate of 5¼%. George Wells has $5,600 deposited in this bank.
   a. How much interest will George receive at the end of one year? ________
   b. If interest is paid semiannually, how much interest will George receive at the end of one half year? ________
3. Kenneth Stagg has $14,600 on deposit in a bank that pays interest semiannually.
   a. How much interest will he receive at the end of one half year if the interest rate is 7%? ________
   b. How much interest will he receive at the end of one half year if the interest rate is 5%? ________
   c. How much more will he receive at the 7% rate than at the 5% rate? ________
4. How much more interest will a person receive during an interest period in which he has $20,000 on deposit at a bank that pays 7½% interest rather than 5%? Both banks pay interest quarterly. ________

Section 2: Daily Periods of Time

Only rarely does a person have exactly the same amount of money on deposit in a bank for the entire interest period. Therefore, in order to attract business, many banks are now paying interest from the day a person deposits his money until the day he withdraws the money. Also, at the end of every quarter of a year or of every month—depending upon the bank—the interest is added to the depositor's account.

The interest formula that was developed in Section 1 for monthly periods can now be used equally well for the daily periods that are now needed. In the earlier problems it was necessary to determine what fractional part of a year 6 months, or 3 months, or 2 months, and so forth, happened to be. This was done by dividing each of these numbers (of months) by 12, for there are 12 months in a year.

In the present situation it will be necessary to determine what fractional part of a year a specific number of days is, for the bank's interest is computed in terms of *days* rather than months. Where before you divided by 12, now you will have to divide by 365, for there are 365 days in a year (excluding leap years). Thus, the fractional part of a year represented by 25 days is 25/365ths of a year. And, similarly, 40 days is 40/365ths of a year.

ILLUSTRATION: Find the interest on $800 if it is kept in a bank at 5% for a period of 60 days.

SOLUTION:

$$I = P \times R \times T$$
$$= \$800 \times 5\% \times 60/365$$
$$= \$800 \times .05 \times \frac{\overset{12}{\cancel{60}}}{\underset{73}{\cancel{365}}}$$
$$= \frac{\$480}{73}$$
$$= \$6.5753424, \text{ or } \$6.58$$

EXPLANATION: The product of $800 with 5% is the interest for one full year. However, the money had been in the bank for only 60 days. Hence, the depositor is entitled to only 60/365ths of the year's interest. Therefore, the annual interest, represented by ($800 × .05), must still be multiplied by 60/365.

EXERCISES A

Find the interest for the period of time shown for each of the following deposits.

	Principal	Interest Rate	Number of Days	Interest
1.	$1,200	4%	60	$______
2.	1,800	6%	80	______
3.	4,500	5%	40	______
4.	2,300	7%	90	______
5.	1,000	8%	30	______
6.	5,000	6%	35	______
7.	6,000	5.2%	20	______
8.	3,000	6.1%	50	______
9.	4,000	7.4%	25	______

	Principal	Interest Rate	Number of Days	Interest
10.	$8,000	7.6%	45	$______
11.	4,400	5½%	30	______
12.	6,600	6½%	40	______

B

1. Frances Green deposited $756 at a bank that paid interest at a rate of 5% from the day of deposit. If the deposit was made 50 days before interest was given, how much interest did the $756 earn for the period? ______
2. Howard Cramer had $4,000 on deposit at the Regional Savings Bank, which paid interest semiannually at 5%. Ninety days before the end of the interest period, Howard deposited $600 to his account.
   a. How much interest did he receive on the $4,000 for the half year? ______
   b. How much interest did he receive on the $600 for the 90 days? ______
   c. What was the total interest for the period? ______
3. The Cranford National Bank has an interest rate of 4% and interest is paid quarterly. At the beginning of a quarterly period, Mr. Tomkins had $2,600 in his savings account. Sixty days before the end of the period, he deposited $900, and forty days before the end, he deposited $270.
   a. How much interest did he receive on the $2,600? ______
   b. How much interest did he receive on the $900? ______
   c. How much interest did he receive on the $270? ______
   d. What was the total interest that he received for the period? ______

Unit 3: Finding Interest With the Aid of Tables

You may have noticed that in the preceding section you were always told the exact number of days that the money had been in the bank. Normally, though, all that would be known is the date that the money had been deposited and the date when the interest was to be paid. Then, someone would have to determine the number of days from one date to the other. Thus, if the deposit was made on March 17 and interest was to be paid on June 1, before the interest could be computed, an employee of the bank would have to find the number of days from March 17 to June 1. One way of doing this, of course, is to count the days. This method not only takes far too much time, but it offers too many opportunities for making errors. To avoid both of these problems, the following table is usually used.

TIMETABLE

Day of Month	Jan.	Feb.	March	April	May	June	July	Aug.	Sept.	Oct.	Nov.	Dec.
1	1	32	60	91	121	152	182	213	244	274	305	335
2	2	33	61	92	122	153	183	214	245	275	306	336
3	3	34	62	93	123	154	184	215	246	276	307	337
4	4	35	63	94	124	155	185	216	247	277	308	338
5	5	36	64	95	125	156	186	217	248	278	309	339
6	6	37	65	96	126	157	187	218	249	279	310	340
7	7	38	66	97	127	158	188	219	250	280	311	341
8	8	39	67	98	128	159	189	220	251	281	312	342
9	9	40	68	99	129	160	190	221	252	282	313	343
10	10	41	69	100	130	161	191	222	253	283	314	344
11	11	42	70	101	131	162	192	223	254	284	315	345
12	12	43	71	102	132	163	193	224	255	285	316	346
13	13	44	72	103	133	164	194	225	256	286	317	347
14	14	45	73	104	134	165	195	226	257	287	318	348
15	15	46	74	105	135	166	196	227	258	288	319	349
16	16	47	75	106	136	167	197	228	259	289	320	350
17	17	48	76	107	137	168	198	229	260	290	321	351
18	18	49	77	108	138	169	199	230	261	291	322	352
19	19	50	78	109	139	170	200	231	262	292	323	353
20	20	51	79	110	140	171	201	232	263	293	324	354
21	21	52	80	111	141	172	202	233	264	294	325	355
22	22	53	81	112	142	173	203	234	265	295	326	356
23	23	54	82	113	143	174	204	235	266	296	327	357
24	24	55	83	114	144	175	205	236	267	297	328	358
25	25	56	84	115	145	176	206	237	268	298	329	359
26	26	57	85	116	146	177	207	238	269	299	330	360
27	27	58	86	117	147	178	208	239	270	300	331	361
28	28	59	87	118	148	179	209	240	271	301	332	362
29	29		88	119	149	180	210	241	272	302	333	363
30	30		89	120	150	181	211	242	273	303	334	364
31	31		90		151		212	243		304		365

Notice that each of the days of the year is numbered. As an illustration, February 6 is the 37th day of the year, while April 15 is the 105th day of the year. To find that February 6 is the 37th day of the year, simply run your finger down the column headed by the words "Day of Month" until you reach the numeral 6. Place a piece of paper along this row and run your finger along the edge of the paper until it comes to the column headed by "Feb." The numeral your finger will be pointing to is 37. This implies that February 6 is the 37th day of the year.

With this background, finding how many days there are from February 6 to April 15 is a relatively easy matter. You need simply subtract 37 from 105. The difference of 68 is the number of days from the first date to the second.

ILLUSTRATION 1: How many days are there from March 6 to June 1?

SOLUTION:

Day of year represented by March 6: 65
Day of year represented by June 1: 152
Number of days from March 6 to June 1 $= 152 - 65$
$= 87$

SIMPLE INTEREST ON $1
(365-Day Year)
Rates

Days	4%	5%	5.25%	6%	6.5%	7%	7.5%
1	.0001096	.0001370	.0001438	.0001644	.0001781	.0001918	.0002055
2	.0002192	.0002740	.0002877	.0003288	.0003562	.0003836	.0004110
3	.0003288	.0004110	.0004315	.0004932	.0005342	.0005753	.0006164
4	.0004384	.0005479	.0005753	.0006575	.0007123	.0007671	.0008219
5	.0005479	.0006849	.0007192	.0008219	.0008904	.0009589	.0010274
6	.0006575	.0008219	.0008630	.0009863	.0010685	.0011507	.0012329
7	.0007671	.0009589	.0010068	.0011507	.0012466	.0013425	.0014384
8	.0008767	.0010959	.0011507	.0013151	.0014247	.0015342	.0016438
9	.0009863	.0012329	.0012945	.0014795	.0016027	.0017260	.0018493
10	.0010959	.0013699	.0014384	.0016438	.0017808	.0019178	.0020548
11	.0012055	.0015068	.0015822	.0018082	.0019589	.0021096	.0022603
12	.0013151	.0016438	.0017260	.0019726	.0021370	.0023014	.0024658
13	.0014247	.0017808	.0018697	.0021370	.0023151	.0024932	.0026712
14	.0015342	.0019178	.0020137	.0023014	.0024932	.0026849	.0028767
15	.0016438	.0020548	.0021575	.0024658	.0026712	.0028767	.0030822
16	.0017534	.0021918	.0023014	.0026301	.0028493	.0030685	.0032877
17	.0018630	.0023288	.0024452	.0027945	.0030274	.0032603	.0034932
18	.0019726	.0024658	.0025890	.0029589	.0032055	.0034521	.0036986
19	.0020822	.0026027	.0027329	.0031233	.0033836	.0036438	.0039041
20	.0021918	.0027397	.0028767	.0032877	.0035616	.0038356	.0041096
21	.0023014	.0028767	.0030205	.0034521	.0037397	.0040274	.0043151
22	.0024110	.0030137	.0031644	.0036164	.0039178	.0042192	.0045205
23	.0025205	.0031507	.0033082	.0037808	.0040959	.0044110	.0047260
24	.0026301	.0032877	.0034521	.0039452	.0042740	.0046027	.0049315
25	.0027397	.0034247	.0035959	.0041096	.0044521	.0047945	.0051370
26	.0028493	.0035616	.0037397	.0042740	.0046301	.0049863	.0053425
27	.0029589	.0036986	.0038836	.0044384	.0048082	.0051781	.0055479
28	.0030685	.0038356	.0040274	.0046027	.0049863	.0053699	.0057534
29	.0031781	.0039726	.0041712	.0047671	.0051644	.0055616	.0059589
30	.0032877	.0041096	.0043151	.0049315	.0053425	.0057534	.0061644

Deposits to a bank account are rarely made in nice round numbers such as those used in the previous sections. More often the deposits will be in amounts such as \$243.70 or \$1,695.26. Because of this, the difficulty in computation increases many times over what you have been encountering thus far. To simplify the computation, banks will use either computers or tables similar to the one on page 219. This table shows the interest that accumulates on \$1 for periods ranging from 1 day to 30 days at various rates of interest.

ILLUSTRATION 2: A deposit of \$483 was made 27 days before the close of an interest period. How much interest did the depositor receive on the \$483 for that period of time if the annual rate of interest paid by the bank was 5%?

EXPLANATION: The interest on \$1 for 27 days is found in the table at the point where the "27 day" row meets the "5%" column. That interest is \$.0036986. Since this is the interest on \$1, the interest on \$483 will be 483 times as large.

SOLUTION:

Interest on \$1 @ 5% for 27 days = \$.0036986
Interest on \$483 @ 5% for 27 days = 483 × \$.0036986
= \$1.7864238, or \$1.79

ILLUSTRATION 3: Raymond Parks deposited \$560 on April 17 at the Broadway Trust Company, which pays an annual interest rate of 5¼%. If the interest period closed on May 31, how much interest did Raymond receive on this deposit?

SOLUTION:

Day of year represented by April 17: 107
Day of year represented by May 31: 151
Number of days from April 17 to May 31 = 151 − 107
= 44
Interest on \$1 @ 5¼% for 30 days = \$.0043151
Interest on \$1 @ 5¼% for 14 days = \$.0020137
Interest on \$1 @ 5¼% for 44 days = \$.0043151 + \$.0020137
= \$.0063288
Interest on \$560 @ 5¼% for 44 days = 560 × \$.0063288
= \$3.544128, or \$3.54

EXPLANATION: The number of days from April 17 to May 31 (44) is found from the timetable on page 218. The simple interest table, though, does not give the interest for 44 days. To use this table for this purpose it is necessary to add the interest on $1 for 30 days to the interest on $1 for 14 days. This will give the total interest on $1 for the period of 44 days needed in this situation. The computation is then completed in the same manner as in Illustration 2.

EXERCISES A

1. Use the timetable to find the number of days from the first date to the second in each of the following exercises. Both dates occurred during the same year, which was not a leap year.

Period of Time From:	To:	Number Of Days
a. January 6	May 3	________
b. January 17	April 4	________
c. February 13	June 1	________
d. March 15	May 31	________
e. February 23	September 5	________
f. August 12	August 29	________
g. July 2	October 21	________
h. April 17	November 2	________
i. June 12	December 1	________
j. March 19	June 1	________

2. The interest periods of the Guardian National Bank end on June 1 and December 1. Deposits were made on each of the following dates. For how many days during that period did these deposits collect interest?

Date	Number Of Days	Date	Number Of Days
a. February 14	________	e. May 2	________
b. April 7	________	f. September 6	________
c. July 8	________	g. October 14	________
d. August 23	________	h. January 18	________

3. The State Savings Bank issues interest quarterly on February 1, May 1, August 1, and November 1. Deposits were made on each of the following dates. For how many days during the first period did these deposits collect interest?

Date	Number Of Days	Date	Number Of Days
a. January 4	________	f. July 9	________
b. February 17	________	g. September 30	________
c. June 25	________	h. March 1	________
d. April 11	________	i. May 23	________
e. August 28	________	j. October 5	________

4. Use the timetable to find the number of days from the first date to the second date. The second date occurs in the year following the first.

	Period Of Time From:	To:	Number Of Days
a.	December 15	January 12	________
b.	December 3	January 17	________
c.	November 14	January 23	________
d.	November 5	January 31	________
e.	October 17	February 1	________
f.	September 25	February 14	________

B

1. Find the interest on $1 for each set of conditions shown below. Do *not* round off your answers to the nearest cent.

	Number of Days	Rate of Interest	Interest
a.	26	4%	$________
b.	18	4%	________
c.	13	5%	________
d.	27	5¼%	________
e.	8	6%	________
f.	21	7%	________
g.	6	6½%	________
h.	11	7½%	________
i.	23	5¼%	________
j.	20	7%	________

For most people, the first step in opening a savings account is a meeting with one of the bank's financial officers, who explains interest rates and issues a passbook.

2. Find the interest on each of the following deposits under the conditions shown. Round off each answer to the nearest cent.

	Deposit	Number Of Days	Rate of Interest	Interest on $1	Interest on Deposit
a.	$2,000	27	4%	$______	$______
b.	3,000	16	4%	______	______
c.	4,000	25	5%	______	______
d.	5,000	12	4%	______	______
e.	900	16	$5\frac{1}{4}$%	______	______
f.	750	21	6%	______	______
g.	4,300	14	5%	______	______
h.	1,200	29	$6\frac{1}{2}$%	______	______
i.	840	19	7%	______	______
j.	685	11	$5\frac{1}{4}$%	______	______

3. Find the interest on $1 under the following conditions. Do *not* round off your answers to the nearest cent.

	Number Of Days	Rate of Interest	Interest
a.	40	4%	$______
b.	50	5%	______
c.	60	6%	______
d.	35	7%	______
e.	45	5%	______
f.	42	$5\frac{1}{4}$%	______
g.	57	4%	______
h.	36	$6\frac{1}{2}$%	______

4. Find the interest on each of the following deposits under the conditions shown. Round off each answer to the nearest cent.

	Deposit	Number Of Days	Rate of Interest	Interest on $1	Interest on Deposit
a.	$ 400	38	5%	$______	$______
b.	300	44	4%	______	______
c.	1,500	52	6%	______	______
d.	3,400	55	$7\frac{1}{2}$%	______	______

5. The interest period at the Dearborn Mutual Bank and Trust Company closes on August 30. The annual rate of interest paid by this bank is $5\frac{1}{4}$%. How much interest will each of the following deposits receive for the period if deposited on the date shown?

	Deposit	Date of Deposit	Number Of Days	Interest on $1	Interest on Deposit
a.	$ 270	Aug. 14	______	$______	$______
b.	350	Aug. 5	______	______	______
c.	1,240	Aug. 2	______	______	______
d.	962	Aug. 21	______	______	______

6. Find the interest for each of the following deposits for the period in which the deposit was made.

	Deposit	Date Of Deposit	Interest Period Closes	Rate Of Interest	Number Of Days	Interest On $1	Interest on Deposit
a.	$ 700	May 17	June 30	5%	________	$________	$________
b.	800	April 8	June 1	4%	________	________	________
c.	1,500	Aug. 23	Sept. 30	6%	________	________	________
d.	3,200	Jan. 17	March 1	7%	________	________	________
e.	2,100	Oct. 14	Nov. 30	$7\frac{1}{2}$%	________	________	________
f.	650	July 6	Aug. 31	$5\frac{1}{4}$%	________	________	________

Those who can afford to save larger amounts of money for longer periods of time sometimes convert their accounts into "savings certificates." These earn more interest than the regular savings account, but they must be left deposited for over a year.

C

Use the simple interest table in finding your answers to the exercises below.

1. Peter Fleming deposited $342 at his bank on February 17. Interest was paid semiannually on June 1 and December 1 at the rate of $5\frac{1}{4}$%. How much interest did Peter receive on the $342 for the interest period during which this money was deposited? ________
2. Betty Daniels deposited $570 on July 17 and $420 on August 26 at the Central Savings and Loan Association, which has an interest rate of 5%. Interest is paid on April 1 and October 1 of each year.
   a. How much interest did Betty receive for the interest period on the $570 deposit? ________
   b. How much interest did Betty receive for the interest period on the $420 deposit? ________
   c. What was the total interest that Betty received on both deposits for the interest period? ________

Unit 4: Finding the Interest on a Savings Account for an Interest Period

The investigation thus far has concerned itself with determining the amount of interest that is added to a savings account based on a single deposit made during an interest period. Normally, though, a savings account will have some money in it at the beginning of the interest period and, in addition, both deposits and withdrawals will occur during the period. In view of this, it would be well to consider how the bank balance is determined at the end of the period under these conditions.

Since most banks are now giving interest from the day of deposit until the day of withdrawal, and, also, since many banks are adding interest monthly to depositors' accounts, this will be the pattern used in the explanation that follows.

ILLUSTRATION: Frieda Tobin had $2,100 on deposit at the Gerard Savings Bank on April 1. During this month the account had the following activity:

April 3: Deposit of $460
April 9: Deposit of $250
April 16: Withdrawal of $740

If the annual interest rate is $5\frac{1}{4}\%$, how much did Frieda have on deposit on April 30?

SOLUTION:

(1) Interest on \$1 for 30 days = \$.0043151
Interest on \$2,100 for 30 days = 2,100 × \$.0043151
= \$9.06

(2) Interest on \$1 for 27 days = \$.0038836
Interest on \$460 for 27 days = 460 × \$.0038836
= \$1.79

(3) Interest on \$1 for 21 days = \$.0030205
Interest on \$250 for 21 days = 250 × \$.0030205
= \$.76

(4) Interest on \$1 for 14 days = \$.0020137
Interest on \$740 for 14 days = 740 × \$.0020137
= \$1.49

(5) Money on deposit on April 30
= (\$2,100 + \$460 + \$250) + (\$9.06 + \$1.79 + \$.76)
− (\$740 + \$1.49)
= \$2,810 + \$11.61 − \$741.49
= \$2,080.12

EXPLANATION: The solution is separated into five separate sections. In the first of these the interest is found on the \$2,100 for the 30 days in April. In the second section, the interest is found on the deposit of \$460 for the 27 days from April 3 to April 30. Similarly, in the third section, the interest is found for the second deposit of \$250 for the 21 days from April 9 to April 30. Included in the interest on the \$2,100 is the interest on the withdrawal of \$740 made on April 16, hence the interest on that amount of money, in addition to the \$740 itself, must be deducted from whatever the total would have been on April 30. Hence, the interest on \$740 is found in section 4. In section 5, the balance on April 1 is added to the two deposits made during that month; to that sum is added the interest gathered on each of these amounts during the month; and, finally, from that amount is subtracted the withdrawal and the interest that withdrawal would have earned.

EXERCISES A

1. Interest is paid monthly on each of the following accounts. How much interest was added to the account at the end of the month in which each of the following deposits was made?

	Amount on Deposit At Beginning of Month	Deposit	Date of Deposit	Interest Rate	Interest
a.	$2,000	$600	6/8	5%	$______
b.	3,000	500	5/12	6%	______
c.	5,000	400	7/16	7%	______
d.	4,600	800	4/7	6½%	______
e.	2,500	350	8/9	5¼%	______
f.	3,700	520	9/3	7½%	______

2. Interest is paid monthly on each of the following accounts. How much interest was added to the account at the end of the month in which each of the following withdrawals was made?

	Amount on Deposit At Beginning of Month	Withdrawal	Date of Withdrawal	Interest Rate	Interest
a.	$1,000	$300	3/8	4%	$______
b.	7,000	200	5/14	5%	______
c.	8,000	630	11/5	6%	______
d.	4,500	750	1/10	7%	______
e.	5,200	460	2/7	5¼%	______
f.	6,800	810	4/4	6½%	______

***3.** Interest is paid monthly on each of the following accounts. How much interest was added to the account at the end of the month in which the following deposits and withdrawals were made?

	Amount on Deposit At Beginning of Month	Deposit	Date of Deposit	Withdrawal	Date of Withdrawal	Interest Rate	Interest
a.	$4,000	$ 300	5/6	$ 100	5/9	6%	$______
b.	2,000	1,000	7/3	400	7/15	5%	______
c.	6,000	800	4/20	2,000	4/9	5¼%	______
d.	7,000	1,500	6/22	3,000	6/5	4%	______
e.	5,000	750	11/3	450	11/15	6%	______
f.	8,600	420	3/12	1,400	3/20	7%	______

*Optional

B

1. On June 1 George White had $4,500 on deposit in his account at the Wayside Trust Company, which pays an annual interest rate of 5%. Interest is credited to a depositor's account monthly. During the month of June his account showed the following activity:

June 14: Withdrawal of $1,600
June 27: Deposit of $320

How much money did Mr. White have on deposit at the end of June? ______

2. The Mutual Savings Bank of Bayside pays an annual interest rate of $5\frac{1}{4}\%$. Interest is added to depositors' accounts at the end of each month. One of the accounts showed the following activity for the month of March.

Amount on deposit at beginning of month: $1,400
March 5: Withdrawal of $250
March 10: Deposit of $620
March 17: Withdrawal of $350

a. How much interest was added to this account for the month of March? ________

b. How large was this account on March 31? ________

Unit 5: Compound Interest

Section 1: Computing Compound Interest

A rather important thing occurs relative to the interest that grows on a savings account that has not been considered before now. Consider the situation where a person has $6,000 in a bank that pays an annual interest rate of 5% but once a year. Under these conditions the interest earned on this account during the first year would be computed in the usual manner as,

$$\begin{aligned} I &= P \times R \times T \\ &= \$6{,}000 \times 5\% \times 1 \text{ year} \\ &= \$6{,}000 \times .05 \times 1 \\ &= \$300 \end{aligned}$$

Hence, at the end of the first year the depositor would have not only his original $6,000 in the bank but also an additional $300 paid to him by the bank. In view of this he would have a total of $6,300 on deposit.

If no money is deposited or withdrawn during the second year, then the bank would compute the interest earned the second year on the $6,300—not on the $6,000—for the $6,300 is the balance in the account during the second year. And, again, as usual, the interest would be computed as,

$$\begin{aligned} I &= \$6{,}300 \times .05 \times 1 \\ &= \$315 \end{aligned}$$

Thus, it is immediately apparent that while the depositor's money earned only $300 the first year, it earned $315 the second year. The extra $15 was earned on the interest of $300 received at the end of the first year.

Whenever interest is paid upon earlier interest that has been given to a depositor that process is called *compounding interest.* In the illustration just examined, interest was paid but once each year on both the balance and the previous year's interest. This situation is one where the *interest is compounded annually.* As you learned, interest is often given semiannually, quarterly, and even monthly. Under these conditions, interest is said to be *compounded* semiannually, quarterly, or, in the last case, monthly. The following illustration will clarify the computation required in these circumstances.

ILLUSTRATION: Marie Ragin invested \$10,000 at an annual rate of 8% compounded semiannually. How much had this investment grown to at the end of two years?

EXPLANATION: Perhaps the simplest way of examining this situation is to first realize that if the interest rate is 8% for the year, then it will be but 4% for the half-year. Hence, to determine the interest Marie received at the end of the first half-year, you would merely multiply the principal of \$10,000 by the interest rate of 4%.

$$\begin{aligned} I &= \$10{,}000 \times .04 \\ &= \$400 \end{aligned}$$

In view of this, at the end of the first half-year Marie would have \$10,400 in this investment. Therefore, to find the interest for the second half-year, the process above would be repeated. However, now the principal is \$10,400 rather than \$10,000.

$$\begin{aligned} I &= \$10{,}400 \times .04 \\ &= \$416 \end{aligned}$$

Similarly, each succeeding half-year's interest is found until the principal at the end of 4 half-years—that is, at the end of two years—is determined.

SOLUTION:

Interest on 1st half-year
= \$10,000 × .04
= \$400

Principal end of 1st half-year
= \$10,000 + \$400
= \$10,400

Interest on 2nd half-year
= \$10,400 × .04
= \$416

Principal end of 2nd half-year
= \$10,400 + \$416
= \$10,816

Interest on 3rd half-year
= \$10,816 × .04
= \$432.64

Principal end of 3rd half-year
= \$10,816 + \$432.64
= \$11,248.64

Interest on 4th half-year
= \$11,248.64 × .04
= \$449.95

Principal end of 4th half-year
= \$11,248.64 + \$449.95
= \$11,698.59 (answer)

Had the interest been compounded quarterly in the illustration above, then the interest rate for each quarterly period would have been 2%, that is, 1/4 of the 8% which is the annual interest rate. Also, since there are 4 quarterly periods during one year, then over the 2 years there would have been 8 periods in which interest was added to that account.

Hence, in examining situations involving compound interest it is best to ask yourself two questions,

1. What is the interest rate for the *period*?
2. How many *periods* are there during which interest is added to the account?

Thus, in trying to determine the amount of money a person will have at the end of a year and a half at an annual interest rate of 12% compounded monthly, the answer to the first question will be 1%. This is found by dividing the 12% annual rate by 12, which is the number of months in a year. Further, the answer to the second question is 18, since in 1½ years there are 18 months, and this is the number of periods for which interest is added to the account.

Whereas in the Illustration, the process of finding the interest and principal had to be repeated four times, in the case where interest is compounded monthly over one and one-half years, the process will have to be repeated 18 times.

EXERCISES A

1. Each of the following accounts is permitted to remain dormant* over the period shown. How large will each account be at the end of the period if interest is compounded annually?

	Amount on Deposit At Beginning of Period	Interest Rate	Period Of Years	Amount on Deposit At End of Period
a.	$6,000	4%	2	$______
b.	5,000	6%	2	______
c.	9,000	5%	2	______
d.	8,000	7%	3	______
e.	4,000	8%	3	______
f.	5,000	6.5%	2	______

*Neither withdrawals nor deposits were made on the account.

2. If interest is compounded semiannually, what is the interest rate for the period and for how many periods will a person receive interest in each of the following situations?

	Annual Interest Rate	Interest Rate For Period	Number Of Years	Number Of Periods
a.	4%	________	1	________
b.	6%	________	2	________
c.	8%	________	3	________
d.	10%	________	5	________
e.	5%	________	7	________
f.	7%	________	15	________

3. If interest is compounded quarterly, what is the interest rate for the period and for how many periods will a person receive interest in each of the following situations?

	Annual Interest Rate	Interest Rate For Period	Number Of Years	Number Of Periods
a.	4%	________	1	________
b.	8%	________	2	________
c.	12%	________	5	________
d.	16%	________	7	________
e.	6%	________	10	________
f.	7%	________	12	________

4. If interest is compounded monthly, what is the interest rate for the period and for how many periods will a person receive interest in each of the following situations?

	Annual Interest Rate	Interest Rate For Period	Number Of Years	Number Of Periods
a.	12%	________	1	________
b.	24%	________	2	________
c.	18%	________	4	________
d.	30%	________	8	________
e.	6%	________	½	________
f.	9%	________	2½	________

5. Each of the following accounts is permitted to remain dormant over the period shown. How large will each account be at the end of the period if interest is compounded semiannually?

	Amount on Deposit At Beginning of Period	Interest Rate	Number Of Years	Amount on Deposit At End of Period
a.	$4,000	4%	1	$________
b.	3,000	6%	1½	________
c.	4,000	8%	1	________
d.	7,000	7%	1	________

6. Each of the following accounts is permitted to remain dormant over the period shown. How large will each account be at the end of the period if interest is compounded quarterly?

	Amount on Deposit At Beginning of Period	Interest Rate	Period Of Years	Amount on Deposit At End of Period
a.	$8,000	4%	1/2	$________
b.	6,000	8%	1/2	________
c.	9,000	6%	1/2	________
d.	5,000	7%	1/2	________

B

1. Rose Sherman had $5,000 in an account at the Western Savings and Loan Association, where interest is compounded semiannually at 5%. If Rose neither added to nor withdrew any money from this account for a period of 1 year, how much interest did her savings earn? ________
2. The Neighborhood Savings Institution pays an annual interest rate of 6%.
   a. How much will a dormant account of $7,000 earn in interest over a two-year period if interest is compounded annually? ________
   b. How much will this account earn over the two-year period if interest is compounded semiannually? ________
   c. How much more will be earned if interest is compounded semiannually rather than annually? ________
3. Tom Baker has a $3,200 savings account at the Lakewood Bank and Trust Company where interest is paid at an annual rate of 4%. During the period of one year, he makes no deposits or withdrawals from this account.
   a. How much interest will this account earn if interest is compounded semiannually? ________
   b. How much interest will this account earn if interest is compounded quarterly? ________
   c. How much would Tom gain over the year if interest were compounded quarterly rather than semiannually? ________

Section 2: Computing Compound Interest by Table

A few years ago, the pastor of a church was going over some very old records. Among them he found a letter that was written by an officer in the British army during the Revolution to the colonial pastor. It seems that while transporting weapons from one point to another, some British soldiers had damaged a fence that belonged to the church. In the letter, the officer had assured the pastor that the British government would pay $25 at the close of the war to cover this damage. Unfortunately, the debt was never paid.

Newspapers published this story widely. They raised the interesting point as to how much the $25 indebtedness might now have grown at an interest rate of 5%, compounded annually. When you consider how long it took you to do the problems in the first part of this unit, where the period of time was but 2 or 3 years at most, you can imagine the difficulty involved in this computation where the interest has to be compounded over a 200-year period! As you have probably guessed by now, much of the tedious computation that you had to struggle through can be shortened by the use of tables, such as the one that appears on page 234. This table is designed to tell you how much $1 will amount to when interest is compounded at various rates.

ILLUSTRATION 1: One dollar is deposited in a bank that pays a 4% interest rate, compounded annually. If this account remains dormant for 15 years, into how much money will the $1 grow?

EXPLANATION: At the point where the "15-period" row meets the "4%" column, you will find the numeral "1.8009." This is the number of dollars to which $1 will grow after 15 years at a 4% interest rate compounded annually.

SOLUTION:

Value of $1 @ 4% after 15 years = $1.8009, or $1.80

ILLUSTRATION 2: Interest is compounded quarterly at the Belleville Trust Company. If the annual interest rate is 6%, how much will $1 grow to by the end of 5 years?

EXPLANATION: In keeping with what you had learned in the previous section, you must first determine the rate for the quarterly period and, also, the number of periods during which interest was added to the account. Since the annual rate is 6%, by dividing the annual rate by 4 the quarterly rate is found to be 1.5%. Similarly, since a depositor will receive interest 4 times each year, over the 5 years he will receive interest for 20 periods. Hence, the value of the $1 can be found where the "20-period" row meets the "1.5%" column. The numeral there is "1.3469."

SOLUTION:

Value of $1 after 5 years = $1.3469

COMPOUND INTEREST TABLE
Value of $1

Number of Periods	1.5%	2%	2.5%	3%	3.5%	4%	5%	6%	7%	8%	9%	10%
1	1.0150	1.0200	1.0250	1.0300	1.0350	1.0400	1.0500	1.0600	1.0700	1.0800	1.0900	1.1000
2	1.0302	1.0404	1.0506	1.0609	1.0712	1.0816	1.1025	1.1236	1.1449	1.1664	1.1881	1.2100
3	1.0457	1.0612	1.0769	1.0927	1.1087	1.1248	1.1576	1.1910	1.2250	1.2597	1.2950	1.3310
4	1.0614	1.0824	1.1038	1.1255	1.1475	1.1699	1.2155	1.2625	1.3108	1.3605	1.4116	1.4641
5	1.0773	1.1041	1.1314	1.1593	1.1877	1.2167	1.2763	1.3382	1.4026	1.4693	1.5386	1.6105
6	1.0934	1.1262	1.1597	1.1941	1.2293	1.2653	1.3401	1.4186	1.5007	1.5869	1.6771	1.7716
7	1.1098	1.1487	1.1887	1.2299	1.2723	1.3159	1.4071	1.5036	1.6058	1.7138	1.8280	1.9487
8	1.1265	1.1717	1.2184	1.2668	1.3168	1.3686	1.4775	1.5938	1.7182	1.8059	1.9926	2.1436
9	1.1434	1.1951	1.2489	1.3048	1.3629	1.4233	1.5513	1.6895	1.8385	1.9990	2.1719	2.3579
10	1.1605	1.2190	1.2801	1.3439	1.4106	1.4802	1.6289	1.7908	1.9672	2.1589	2.3674	2.5937
11	1.1779	1.2434	1.3121	1.3842	1.4600	1.5395	1.7103	1.8983	2.1049	2.3316	2.5804	2.8531
12	1.1956	1.2682	1.3449	1.4258	1.5111	1.6010	1.7959	2.0122	2.2522	2.5182	2.8127	3.1384
13	1.2136	1.2936	1.3785	1.4685	1.5640	1.6651	1.8856	2.1329	2.4098	2.7196	3.0658	3.4523
14	1.2318	1.3195	1.4130	1.5126	1.6187	1.7317	1.9799	2.2609	2.5785	2.9372	3.3417	3.7975
15	1.2502	1.3459	1.4483	1.5580	1.6753	1.8009	2.0789	2.3966	2.7590	3.1722	3.6425	4.1772
16	1.2690	1.3728	1.4845	1.6047	1.7340	1.8730	2.1829	2.5404	2.9522	3.4259	3.9703	4.5950
17	1.2880	1.4002	1.5216	1.6528	1.7947	1.9479	2.2920	2.6928	3.1588	3.7000	4.3276	5.0545
18	1.3073	1.4282	1.5597	1.7024	1.8575	2.0258	2.4066	2.8543	3.3799	3.9960	4.7171	5.5599
19	1.3270	1.4568	1.5987	1.7535	1.9225	2.1068	2.5270	3.0256	3.6165	4.3157	5.1417	6.1159
20	1.3469	1.4859	1.6386	1.8061	1.9898	2.1911	2.6533	3.2071	3.8697	4.6610	5.6044	6.7275
21	1.3671	1.5157	1.6796	1.8603	2.0594	2.2788	2.7860	3.3996	4.1406	5.0338	6.1088	7.4003
22	1.3876	1.5460	1.7216	1.9161	2.1315	2.3699	2.9253	3.6035	4.4304	5.4365	6.6586	8.1403
23	1.4084	1.5769	1.7646	1.9736	2.2061	2.4647	3.0715	3.8198	4.7405	5.8715	7.2579	8.9543
24	1.4295	1.6084	1.8087	2.0328	2.2833	2.5633	3.2251	4.0489	5.0724	6.3412	7.9111	9.9497
25	1.4509	1.6407	1.8539	2.0938	2.3673	2.6658	3.3864	4.2919	5.4274	6.8485	8.6231	10.8347

With this background it is but a simple step to determine the value of any amount of money when interest is compounded periodically.

ILLUSTRATION 3: Donald Prell opened an account with \$5,300 at the Valley Savings Bank and allowed the account to remain dormant. If interest is compounded semiannually at 7%, how large will this account be at the end of 8 years?

EXPLANATION: As in Illustration 2, it is necessary to determine the rate for the period and, also, the number of periods. The semiannual rate is 3.5%, while the number of periods will be 16. Hence, by examining the table, it is found that \$1 after 16 periods at 3.5% will amount to \$1.7340. Therefore, \$5,300 will amount to 5,300 times as much as \$1.7340.

SOLUTION:

$$\begin{aligned}\text{Value of \$1 after 8 years} &= \$1.7340\\ \text{Value of \$5,300 after 8 years} &= 5{,}300 \times \$1.7340\\ &= \$9{,}190.20\end{aligned}$$

It is not too difficult to compute the interest on the \$25 debt that the British government failed to pay some 200 years ago. The compound interest table appears to be of value only if the period of time is 25 years or less. You can attack the problem, however, by breaking up the 200-year period into several parts. First, you can find the value of the \$25 after 25 years. Knowing this amount, you can then find how much that will amount to after the next 25 years. This answer will represent the value of \$25 after 50 years. This process can then be repeated for each 25-year period. This solution is outlined below:

$$\begin{aligned}\text{Value of \$25 @ 5\% for 25 years} &= 25 \times \$3.3864\\ &= \$84.66\end{aligned}$$

$$\begin{aligned}\text{Value of \$84.66 @ 5\% for the next 25 years} &= 84.66 \times \$3.3864\\ &= \$286.69\end{aligned}$$

This pattern is followed until finally the 200th year is reached at which point it is found that the debt has grown to \$432,360.54. Needless to say, the British government did not give the church that amount of money! It did, however, pay off the original debt of \$25!

Over recent years, in order to attract more and more depositors, banks are not only compounding interest quarterly or monthly, they are doing this as often as each day of the year and some are even doing it "continuously." By this they mean that the interest is being compounded as rapidly as the computers are capable of doing this, and for many banks this happens to be once every 10 minutes.

It might be interesting to examine just what happens as interest is compounded more and more frequently during the period of one year. The pattern below will help demonstrate this point. In each of these situations the value of $10,000 has been found at an annual rate of 8%, which is compounded after different periods of time.

$10,000 @ 8% compounded annually = $10,800.00
$10,000 @ 8% compounded semiannually = $10,816.00
$10,000 @ 8% compounded quarterly = $10,824.32
$10,000 @ 8% compounded monthly = $10,830.00
$10,000 @ 8% compounded daily = $10,832.77

Quite apparently the amount a person would gain over a year on a $10,000 deposit when interest is compounded daily rather than monthly is only $2.77. And were the compounding done "continuously" rather than daily, the depositor would gain just a few pennies on a $10,000 deposit. For most people who have less than $10,000 in a bank, "continuous" compounding or daily compounding will be little more than a good advertising scheme.

EXERCISES A

1. How much will $1 be worth after the number of years shown if interest is compounded annually at each of the following rates?

	Annual Interest Rate	Years	Value Of $1
a.	4%	25	$______
b.	2%	25	______
c.	5%	20	______
d.	8%	10	______
e.	6%	12	______
f.	7%	24	______
g.	9%	15	______
h.	3.5%	18	______
i.	1.5%	8	______
j.	10%	23	______

2. How much will $1 be worth after the number of years shown if interest is compounded semiannually?

	Annual Interest Rate	Interest Rate For Period	Number Of Years	Number of Periods	Value Of $1
a.	4%	________	3	________	$________
b.	6%	________	5	________	________
c.	8%	________	9	________	________
d.	12%	________	7	________	________
e.	14%	________	11	________	________
f.	5%	________	4	________	________
g.	7%	________	8	________	________
h.	3%	________	12	________	________

3. How much will $1 be worth after the number of years shown if interest is compounded quarterly?

	Annual Interest Rate	Interest Rate For Period	Number Of Years	Number of Periods	Value Of $1
a.	16%	________	3	________	$________
b.	8%	________	5	________	________
c.	12%	________	2	________	________
d.	6%	________	1	________	________
e.	10%	________	4	________	________
f.	14%	________	6	________	________

4. How much will $1 be worth after the number of years shown if interest is compounded monthly?

	Annual Interest Rate	Interest Rate For Period	Number Of Years	Number of Periods	Value Of $1
a.	24%	________	1	________	$________
b.	36%	________	2	________	________
c.	18%	________	1/2	________	________
d.	30%	________	1 1/2	________	________

5. Each of the following accounts remained dormant for the number of years shown. How much money was there in each account at the end of the period if interest was compounded annually?

	Deposit	Annual Interest Rate	Number Of Years	Value Of $1	Value of Deposit
a.	$4,000	5%	3	$________	$________
b.	7,000	7%	12	________	________
c.	2,000	8%	16	________	________
d.	5,200	9%	22	________	________
e.	8,400	6%	7	________	________

6. Each of the following accounts remained dormant for the number of years shown. How much money was there in each account at the end of the period if interest was compounded semiannually?

	Deposit	Annual Interest Rate	Number Of Years	Value Of $1	Value of Deposit
a.	$5,000	6%	4	$__________	$__________
b.	6,000	8%	9	__________	__________
c.	9,000	10%	12	__________	__________
d.	4,500	7%	5	__________	__________
e.	8,300	5%	11	__________	__________

7. Each of the following investments remained dormant for the number of years shown. How much money was in each investment at the end of the period if interest was compounded monthly?

	Investment	Annual Interest Rate	Number Of Years	Value Of $1	Value of Investment
a.	$ 2,000	16%	3	$__________	$__________
b.	10,000	8%	5	__________	__________
c.	6,500	12%	6	__________	__________
d.	7,600	6%	2	__________	__________
e.	12,500	10%	4	__________	__________

8. Each of the following investments remained dormant for the number of years shown. How much money was in each investment at the end of the period if interest was compounded monthly?

	Investment	Annual Interest Rate	Number Of Years	Value Of $1	Value of Investment
a.	$ 4,000	24%	2	$__________	$__________
b.	6,000	36%	1	__________	__________
c.	15,000	18%	1½	__________	__________
d.	20,000	30%	½	__________	__________

B

1. If you run your finger down the 4% column on the compound interest table on page 234, you will discover that the first numeral that appears as $2 or over is the numeral $2.0258. This occurs at the 18th period. You can interpret this to mean that $1 becomes approximately $2 at a 4% interest rate compounded annually. Another way of looking at this is to say that money doubles itself in 18 years at an interest rate of 4% compounded annually.

   How long will it take money to double itself at each of the following rates if interest is compounded annually?

   a. 5% __________ c. 4% __________ e. 8% __________

   b. 6% __________ d. 7% __________ f. 10% __________

2. How long will it take money to triple itself at each of the following rates if interest is compounded annually?

   a. 5% __________ b. 7% __________ c. 10% __________

3. Joseph Jackson deposited $5,000 at the Industrial Savings Bank, which paid interest annually. The account remained dormant for a period of 15 years, after which he withdrew the money.
   a. How much money would Joseph have received had the rate of interest been 4%? ________
   b. How much money would Joseph have received had the rate of interest been 7%? ________
   c. How much more would he have received at the 7% rate than at the 4% rate? ________
4. Fifty dollars was deposited at a bank that paid a 5% interest rate, compounded annually. If the account remained dormant for a period of 40 years, how large would the account be at the end of that period? ________
5. The Bank of Dearborn pays an annual interest rate of 6% to its depositors. Carolyn Sloane opened an account there with a deposit of $12,000 and then allowed the account to remain dormant for a period of 5 years.
   a. How much money would Carolyn have in the account at the end of the five-year period if interest is compounded semiannually? ________
   b. How much money would Carolyn have in the account at the end of the five-year period if interest is compounded quarterly? ________
   c. How much more money would Carolyn have in the bank if interest is compounded quarterly rather than semiannually? ________

Unit 6: Growth of Regular Deposits

There are many people who try to plan ahead in order to anticipate what their needs might be some five or ten years in the future. For instance, at the birth of a child, the parents will frequently begin to set aside a fixed amount of money each year in order to provide for that child's college education some twenty years later. In this unit you will be concerned with just how this money grows over the years.

Consider the situation where deposits of $2,000 are made annually at a bank that pays a yearly interest rate of 6% compounded annually. During the first year there will be only the $2,000 in the bank, for this is the amount of the first deposit. At the end of the first year, however, interest will be added to the account.

$$
\begin{aligned}
I &= \$2{,}000 \times .06 \\
&= \$120
\end{aligned}
$$

Hence, after the first year the account will contain both the original deposit of \$2,000 plus the interest of \$120, or a total of \$2,120. With the beginning of the second year another \$2,000 is deposited, bringing the account to \$4,120. Therefore, at the close of the second year the bank will compute the interest for that year on the \$4,120.

$$\begin{aligned} I &= \$4{,}120 \times .06 \\ &= \$247.20 \end{aligned}$$

Again, both this interest of \$247.20 plus another \$2,000 will be added to the \$4,120, making a total of \$6,367.20 that is on deposit for the third year. And so this process is repeated year after year for so long as deposits are made. The computation is not really very difficult but it is rather lengthy. By now it should be apparent that whenever the arithmetic process repeats itself as it does here, there is usually a table available to simplify the work. The table shown below was designed to show how \$1 deposits made annually would grow over the years at various rates of interest.

GROWTH OF \$1 ANNUAL DEPOSITS

Years At End of:	Rate					
	4%	5%	6%	7%	8%	9%
1	1.0400	1.0500	1.0600	1.0700	1.0800	1.0900
2	2.1216	2.1525	2.1836	2.2149	2.2464	2.2781
3	3.2465	3.3101	3.3746	3.4399	3.5061	3.5731
4	4.4163	4.5256	4.6371	4.7507	4.8666	4.9841
5	5.6330	5.8019	5.9753	6.1533	6.3359	6.5233
6	6.8983	7.1420	7.3938	7.6540	7.9228	8.2004
7	8.2142	8.5491	8.8975	9.2598	9.6366	10.0285
8	9.5828	10.0266	10.4913	10.9780	11.4876	12.0210
9	11.0061	11.5779	12.1808	12.8164	13.4866	14.1929
10	12.4864	13.2068	13.9716	14.7836	15.6455	16.5603
11	14.0258	14.9171	15.8699	16.8884	17.9771	19.1407
12	15.6268	16.7130	17.8821	19.1406	20.4953	21.9534
13	17.2919	18.5986	20.0151	21.5505	23.2149	25.0192
14	19.0236	20.5786	22.2760	24.1290	26.1521	28.3609
15	20.8245	22.6575	24.6725	26.8881	29.3243	32.0034
16	22.6975	24.8404	27.2129	29.8402	32.7502	35.9737
17	24.6454	27.1324	29.9057	32.9990	36.4502	40.3013
18	26.6712	29.5390	32.7600	36.3790	40.4463	45.0185
19	28.7781	32.0660	35.7856	39.9955	44.7620	50.1601
20	30.9692	34.7193	38.9927	43.8642	49.4229	55.7645
21	33.2480	37.5052	42.3923	48.0057	54.4568	61.8733
22	35.6179	40.4305	45.9958	52.4361	59.8933	68.5319
23	38.0826	43.5020	49.8156	57.1767	65.7648	75.7898
24	40.6459	46.7271	53.8645	62.2490	72.1059	83.7009
25	43.3317	50.1135	58.1564	67.6765	78.9544	92.3240

ILLUSTRATION 1: Deposits of $1 are made annually over a period of 15 years. If interest is compounded annually at 5%, how large will the account be at the end of this period?

EXPLANATION: At the point where the "15-year" row meets the "5%" column, you will find the numeral 22.6575. This is the number of dollars to which $1 annual deposits will grow at a 5% annual rate after a period of 15 years.

SOLUTION:

Value of annual deposits of $1 @ 5% over 15 years = $22.6575, or $22.66

ILLUSTRATION 2: Annual deposits of $500 are made over a 21-year period. If the interest is compounded annually at 7%, how large will the account be at the end of this period?

EXPLANATION: The method of Illustration 1 is used to find the value of $1 deposits over the 21-year period. The value of the $1 deposits turns out to be $48.0057; therefore the value of $500 deposits will be 500 times as great.

SOLUTION:

Value of annual deposits of $1 @ 7% over 21 years = $48.0057
Value of annual deposits of $500 @ 7% over 21 years = 500 × $48.0057
= $24,002.85

EXERCISES A

1. Deposits of $1 are made annually over each of the following periods of years. If interest is compounded annually, how large will each account be at the close of the period?

	Interest Rate	Period Of Years	Value Of Account At Close Of Period
a.	4%	8	$________
b.	6%	19	________
c.	8%	23	________
d.	9%	12	________
e.	5%	17	________
f.	7%	21	________

2. The following deposits are made annually over the period of years shown. If interest is compounded annually, how large will each account be at the close of the period?

	Annual Deposits	Interest Rate	Period Of Years	Value Of $1 Deposits	Value Of Account At Close Of Period
a.	$ 400	5%	12	$______	$______
b.	900	6%	18	______	______
c.	500	9%	25	______	______
d.	650	8%	9	______	______
e.	1,300	4%	16	______	______
f.	2,500	7%	17	______	______
g.	3,400	9%	20	______	______
h.	4,350	5%	10	______	______
i.	1,270	7%	15	______	______
j.	3,580	6%	25	______	______

3. The following deposits are made annually over the period of years shown. If interest is compounded annually, how much interest will these accounts have earned over the period of years?

	Annual Deposits	Interest Rate	Period Of Years	Value Of $1 Deposits	Value Of Account At Close Of Period	Interest Accumulated Over the Period
a.	$ 800	4%	10	$______	$______	$______
b.	800	5%	10	______	______	______
c.	3,000	8%	6	______	______	______
d.	2,500	7%	18	______	______	______
e.	1,400	9%	22	______	______	______
f.	1,600	6%	25	______	______	______

B

1. On the day George was born, his father began to put aside $500 each year to pay for George's college education. The money was deposited annually in a bank that paid a 6% interest rate, compounded annually. On George's 19th birthday, his father made the last deposit of $500 and then turned the account over to George. How much money was in the account at that time? ______

2. On the day that Frank Roberts was 45 years old, he and his wife decided to deposit $400 each year on his birthday so that they would have their own retirement fund when Mr. Roberts retired at 65. Their deposits were made at a bank where interest was compounded annually.

a. How much money will be in their account on Mr. Roberts' 65th birthday if the annual rate of interest is 5%? The last deposit was made on that day. ______

b. How much money will be in their account on Mr. Roberts' 65th birthday if the annual rate of interest is 7%? ______

c. How much better off financially would the Roberts have been had the bank paid 7% rather than 5%? ______

3. Each Christmas for 25 years, Margaret Riley and the other employees of the Arco Drill Company received a bonus of $250. Instead of spending the money, she deposited it in a special bank account to which she made no other deposits. Interest was compounded annually at 6%.
   a. How large was the account at the end of the 25-year period? ________
   b. How much interest had been added to the account over the period of years? ________

Unit 7: Chapter Review and Test

A

1. Complete each of the following deposit slips.

a.

	Dollars	Cents
Bills	56	00
Coin		96
Checks	84	50
Total	____	____

b.

	Dollars	Cents
Bills	182	00
Coin	5	68
Checks	76	43
	153	69
Total	____	____

2. Find the interest on each of the following accounts for one period.

	Principal	Interest Rate	Period	Interest
a.	$ 700	5%	Annually	$________
b.	800	6%	Annually	________
c.	1,400	6%	Semiannually	________
d.	2,000	8%	Semiannually	________
e.	2,400	8%	Quarterly	________
f.	1,600	7%	Semiannually	________

3. Find the interest on each of the following deposits for the period of time shown.

	Principal	Interest Rate	Period In Days	Interest
a.	$ 900	6%	100	$________
b.	500	8%	200	________
c.	4,000	5%	50	________
d.	2,000	$4\frac{1}{2}$%	60	________
e.	3,600	$5\frac{1}{2}$%	80	________

4. Find the number of days between the dates in each of the following exercises. Use the timetable on page 218.

a. From June 17 to December 2 of the same year. ________

b. From October 14 to January 31 of the following year. ________

5. Use the Simple Interest Table shown on page 219 to find the interest on each of the following deposits. Round off each answer to the nearest cent.

	Deposit	Number of Days	Interest Rate	Interest on $1	Interest
a.	$4,000	20	6%	$______	$______
b.	2,000	26	7%	______	______
c.	6,000	40	6.5%	______	______

6. Find the interest on each of the following deposits for the period in which the deposit was made. In finding your answer, use both the timetable and the Simple Interest Table.

	Deposit	Date Of Deposit	Interest Period Closes	Interest Rate	Number Of Days	Interest On $1	Interest
a.	$ 600	May 2	May 30	5%	______	$______	$______
b.	5,000	November 17	December 1	4%	______	______	______
c.	4,500	June 5	July 31	5.25%	______	______	______

7. Each of the following accounts remained dormant for the period of time shown. How large will the account be at the end of the period if interest is compounded annually? In finding your answer, use the Compound Interest Table on page 234.

	Amount On Deposit At Beginning Of Period	Interest Rate	Period Of Years	Value of $1	Amount On Deposit At End Of Period
a.	$6,000	5%	24	$______	$______
b.	8,500	7%	15	______	______

8. Each of the following accounts remained dormant for the period of time shown. How large will the account be at the end of the period if interest is compounded periodically as indicated? In finding your answer, use the Compound Interest Table.

	Original Deposit	Interest Compounded	Years	Interest Rate	Value of $1	Account At End Of Period
a.	$6,000	Semiannually	8	4%	$______	$______
b.	3,000	Semiannually	12	5%	______	______
c.	8,000	Quarterly	5	10%	______	______

9. The following deposits are made annually over the period of years shown. If interest is compounded annually, how large will each account be at the close of the period? In finding your answer, use the table on page 240.

	Annual Deposits	Interest Rate	Period Of Years	Value Of $1 Deposits	Account At End Of Period
a.	$ 200	4%	16	$________	$________
b.	800	6%	22	________	________
c.	1,400	9%	18	________	________

B

In finding your answer to each of the following problems, use whatever tables in this chapter you feel are necessary.

1. An $8,000 savings account remained dormant over a period of 10 years in a bank where interest is compounded semiannually at 5%. How much interest was added to this account over the 10-year period? ________
2. Joanne Arben opened a savings account with a $10,000 deposit, and then she permitted the account to remain dormant over a period of 10 years. The bank paid an interest rate of 7%. How much more will Joanne have in her account at the end of the 10 years if interest is compounded semiannually rather than annually? ________
3. At 20, George West decided that when he reached 40, he would take a trip around the world. To prepare for this, he planned to deposit $400 annually at a bank that paid an interest rate of 6% compounded annually.

   a. At the end of 20 years, how much money did George have for his world trip? ________
   b. How much more would George have had if he had kept his money in a bank that paid 7% compounded semiannually? ________

CHAPTER 7

BANKING SERVICES

In chapter 6 you examined banking only from the point of view of the interest a person earns by keeping his money in a savings account. At this time you are going to take a look at some of the other services that can be had at most banks.

Unit 1: Checking Accounts

Section 1: The Cost of a Checking Account

There are thousands upon thousands of banks in the United States and each of them appears to have its own system of charges for its checking-account services. In fact, quite frequently, even a single bank will have several different types of checking accounts available for its depositors depending on whether they are businessmen or private individuals, or whether they want to keep large balances in their accounts or just a few dollars to pay off an occasional small bill. Although the cost differs from bank to bank, basically the computation of this cost falls into one of the patterns described here.

A. The Special Checking Account

Computing the cost to maintain this type of account is relatively simple. Usually there is a maintenance charge of, say, 50¢ per month. In addition, the person is required to pay 10¢ for each check he writes.

ILLUSTRATION 1: Barbara Welch has a special checking account at the Mayfair Trust Company. During the past month she wrote 9 checks. How much will be charged against her checking account if this bank uses the plan described above?

SOLUTION:

Monthly maintenance charge = \$.50
Charge for 9 checks = 9 × \$.10
= \$.90
Total charge = \$.50 + \$.90
= \$1.40

B. The Flat-Payment Plan

Under this plan a person is permitted to write all the checks he wants and the only charge is \$2 per year. However, in order to take full advantage of this plan the depositor must keep a minimum balance of, say, \$300 in his checking account. If one month the balance happens to drop between \$200 and \$300, then for the month in which this occurs he will be charged \$1. If he allows the balance to fall below \$200 one month, then for that month the service charge is \$2. And finally, if it drops below \$100, the charge for the month is \$3.

Flat-Payment Plan
Annual service charge: $2 (payable in October)
Monthly service charge:
Nothing, if min. bal. is $300 or more
$1, if minimum balance is from $200-$299.99
$2, if minimum balance is from $100-$199.99
$3, if minimum balance is from $0-$99.99

ILLUSTRATION 2: Walter Bryan has a checking account at a bank that uses the flat-payment plan. During two months of last year, Mr. Bryan permitted the balance in his account to reach $225. On four other months, it dropped to as low as $110. For the remainder of the year, a balance was maintained that was above $300. What was the total amount of money that Walter had to pay for issuing checks last year?

SOLUTION:

Cost for 2 months in which the balance was $225 = 2 × $1
= $2

Cost for 4 months in which the balance was $110 = 4 × $2
= $8

Basic service charge for the year = $2

Total cost for the year = $2 + $8 + $2
= $12

Actually, the person who has a checking account under the flat-payment plan frequently gets the impression that his only cost for maintaining this account is $2 per year so long as he keeps the balance above $300. This is not quite correct, for there is a hidden cost that he should know about. By keeping $300 constantly on deposit in the checking account, he cannot have this same $300 in his savings account, where it might earn interest at the rate of perhaps 5% or 6% a year. This loss of interest should be considered as part of the cost of having this type of account.

ILLUSTRATION 3: A person maintains an average balance of $450 in his checking account over a period of a year. If he had had this money in his savings account, it would have drawn 5% interest. How much interest did this person lose on the $450 over the period of the year?

SOLUTION:

$$\begin{aligned} I &= P \times R \times T \\ &= \$450 \times 5\% \times 1 \\ &= \$450 \times .05 \times 1 \\ &= \$22.50 \end{aligned}$$

EXPLANATION: Finding the interest is just a matter of applying the interest formula where the "Time" is 1 year.

C. The Analysis Plan

This plan is a bit more involved than the previous two. To determine the monthly charge, it is necessary to refer to a table such as the following. Notice that the word "Items" appears in the headings of the third and fourth columns. An item, when used in reference to a checking account, implies either a check that is drawn against the account, or a deposit that is made to the account. Thus, if a person wrote 7 checks during a month in which he made 2 deposits, he would be charged with 9 items for that period.

Minimum Balance	Basic Charge	Items Allowed	Charge Per Additional Item
Under $100.00	75¢	10	5¢
$100.00 to $199.99	50¢	10	5¢
$200.00 to $299.99	25¢	10	5¢
$300.00 to $399.99	0	15	5¢
$400.00 and over	0	20	5¢

ILLUSTRATION 4: Janice Young issued 17 checks during September. During this period she made 4 deposits. When examining her checkbook she found that the smallest amount of money she had in her checking account during September was $247.56. If her bank used the "analysis plan" for computing the cost, how much was her checking account charge for the month?

SOLUTION:

$$\text{Basic charge} = 25¢$$

$$\begin{aligned} \text{Number of items during month} &= 17 + 4 \\ &= 21 \end{aligned}$$

$$\begin{aligned} \text{Number of items that will be charged} &= 21 - 10 \\ &= 11 \end{aligned}$$

$$\begin{aligned} \text{Charge for additional items} &= 11 \times 5¢ \\ &= 55¢ \end{aligned}$$

$$\begin{aligned} \text{Total charge} &= 25¢ + 55¢ \\ &= 80¢ \end{aligned}$$

EXPLANATION: Janice's lowest balance for the month was $247.56.

Since this fell between \$200.00 and \$299.99, the basic charge was 25¢. Also, under this balance she was permitted to have 10 items at no additional charge. However, Janice had issued 17 checks and made 4 deposits, or a total of 21 items. For each item over 10 she had to pay 5¢. Since there were 11 items over the 10 that were free, she had to pay 11 times 5¢, or 55¢. By adding the basic charge of 25¢ to the additional charge of 55¢, the total charge of 80¢ is found.

EXERCISES A

The plans referred to in the following problems are the ones described on the preceding pages.

1. Use the Special Checking-Account Plan to find the charge for the month in each of the following exercises.

	Number Of Checks Issued	Charge		Number Of Checks Issued	Charge
a.	12	\$______	d.	23	\$______
b.	17	______	e.	14	______
c.	8	______	f.	38	______

2. Use the Flat-Payment Plan to find the charge for the month in each of the following exercises. Do not consider the yearly charge when finding your answer.

	Minimum Balance For the Month	Charge		Minimum Balance For the Month	Charge
a.	\$462.75	\$______	d.	\$163.48	\$______
b.	249.52	______	e.	87.25	______
c.	304.16	______	f.	203.12	______

3. Use the Analysis Plan to find the charge for the month in each of the following exercises.

	Minimum Balance For the Month	Number Of Checks Issued	Number Of Deposits Made	Charge
a.	\$473.26	18	0	\$______
b.	314.65	19	0	______
c.	415.18	32	0	______
d.	347.09	27	0	______
e.	256.12	24	0	______
f.	207.91	36	1	______
g.	141.52	17	1	______
h.	183.40	42	3	______
i.	76.57	35	2	______
j.	54.21	48	4	______

4. How much interest will be lost during the year by keeping the following average balance in a checking account rather than a savings account?

	Average Balance	Interest Rate	Interest		Average Balance	Interest Rate	Interest
a.	$600	5%	$________	e.	$500	$4\frac{1}{2}$%	$________
b.	500	4%	________	f.	700	$5\frac{1}{2}$%	________
c.	800	6%	________	g.	900	$6\frac{1}{2}$%	________
d.	450	7%	________	h.	800	$6\frac{1}{4}$%	________

B

1. Betty Palmer had a checking account at a bank that used the Flat-Payment Plan for computing the cost. During the past year, the minimum balance in her checking account for each month was as follows:

January $627	April $259	July $485	October $712
February $302	May $523	August $192	November $410
March $146	June $267	September $317	December $252

What was the total amount that Betty had to pay to maintain this checking account during the past year? ________

2. During the month of October, the balance in Walter McGrath's checking account dropped to $227.34. He issued 26 checks during the month.

a. If the checking account was in a bank that used the Special-Checking-Account Plan, what would the charge have been? ________

b. If the checking account was in a bank that used the Analysis Plan, what would the charge have been? ________

c. How much could he have saved by using one of these plans rather than the other? ________

3. Daniel Groel's checking account is in a bank that uses the Flat-Payment Plan. During the past year, he maintained an average balance of $620, and he never permitted the balance to drop below $300. Had the money been in a savings account, he would have received an interest rate of $5\frac{1}{2}$%. What was the total cost of maintaining this account last year? Include both the loss of interest and the charge on the checking account. ________

Section 2: Writing Checks

Now that you have learned what the cost of maintaining a checking account can be, it might be well to take some time to learn how to write a check. The form of most checks is very much the same as the one here.

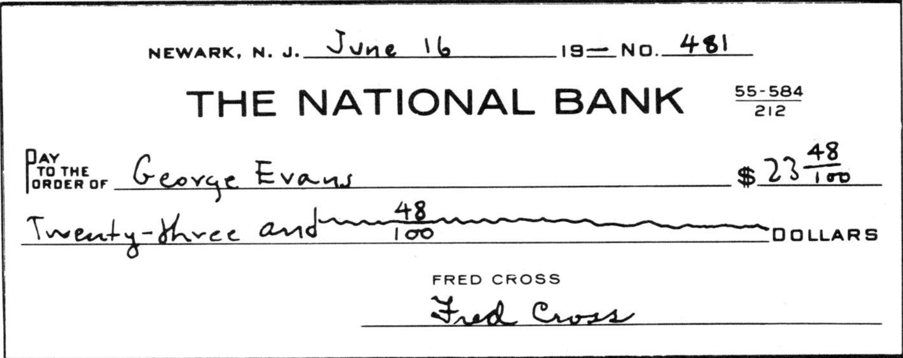
NEWARK, N. J. June 16 19— NO. 481

THE NATIONAL BANK 55-584/212

PAY TO THE ORDER OF George Evans $ $23\frac{48}{100}$

Twenty-three and $\frac{48}{100}$ DOLLARS

FRED CROSS

Fred Cross

The purpose of a check number is to help you find the check easily at some later date if you want to refer to it. The name of the person to whom you are giving the check—and who will receive cash for it—is written after the words, "Pay to the Order of." Directly after that appears the amount of the check. This amount is written in Arabic numerals. The dollar part of the amount—in this case $23—is written quite large, while the cents part immediately after it is written over the numeral 100. The numeral 2 in the 23 is written as close as possible to the dollar sign. The fraction line in $\frac{48}{100}$ must also be written as close to the numeral 3 in the 23 as possible. The purpose of this is to prevent a dishonest person from writing another numeral or two into the amount of the check to increase the size of the check. The purpose of writing out the amount of the check on the center line is to lessen the chance of having the check altered. The use of the wavy line that appears here is to prevent any possible change being made in the amount of the check. Finally, the person who writes out the check signs his name in the lower right-hand corner.

If the check had been for exactly twenty-three dollars, then the numeral would appear as $23\frac{00}{100}$, while the written form would be:

"Twenty-three and ~~~ $\frac{00}{100}$ ~~~ Dollars"

Two zeros must appear in the numerator of the fraction. If only one were written there, a 9 could be inserted in front of it, making the amount 90¢ rather than 0¢, as it was meant to be. Similarly, if the amount were twenty-three dollars and four cents, then the numeral should be written as $\$23\frac{04}{100}$ where a zero appears before the 4 in the numerator of the fraction.

DATE		DEPOSITS			RECORD OF CHECKS AS DRAWN	AMOUNT	
		BALANCE FORWARD	427	18	No. 481 DATE June 16 19— PAY TO George Evans (Repair for TV set)	23	48
6	18		75	—	No. 482 DATE June 19 19— PAY TO Public Utilities, Inc. (Electric and gas bill)	16	25
					No. 483 DATE June 20 19— PAY TO Trion Lumber Co. (Lumber for shelving)	41	83
TOTAL BALANCE AND DEPOSITS			502	18			
LESS CHECKS DRAWN			81	56			
BALANCE FORWARD			420	62	TOTAL CHECKS DRAWN	81	56

Each time a check is written, you also record, for your own information, the number of the check, the date of issue, the name of the person for whom it was written, and the amount of the check. This record appears on a page of the checkbook, and often resembles the illustration on page 254. If the checkbook from which this illustration was taken were opened before you, there would be three checks on the page at the right, and the record pertaining to these three checks would appear on the page at the left. Thus, for check #481, the date that it was written was June 16, 19__. It was made payable to George Evans. The amount Mr. Evans received was $23.48. Notice that the words "Repair for TV set" appear below the name George Evans. Although this information does not appear on the check, it is written here to remind you who George Evans happens to be and why you had paid him $23.48.

The $81.56 that appears in the lower right-hand corner is the sum of the amounts for which the three checks on this page were written. This numeral appears again in the lower-left corner, to the right of the words "Less Checks Drawn." It was rewritten here, for you are about to subtract the $81.56 from the "Total Balance and Deposits." This is the amount that would have been in the checking account had the three checks never been written. At the top-left corner of the page is the numeral $427.18. This is the balance that was in the checking account before check #481 was made out for George Evans. On June 18, $75 was deposited to the checking account, thus bringing the total of the original balance of $427.18 and this deposit to $502.18. After $81.56 is deducted from this amount, the new balance is $420.62. The $420.62 is now written at the top left corner of the next page of the checkbook in exactly the same position as $427.18.

EXERCISES A

1. From your local bank you may be able to obtain a number of blank checks. If not, draw check forms similar to the one on page 253 and then write a check for each of the following. Fill in your own check number and date.

	Issued to:	Amount	Issued by:
a.	Smith Brothers Oil Company	$64.50	Eugene Farrell
b.	Richard Peterson	17.86	Edward Hawkins
c.	William Helms, Inc.	3.49	Claire Dobson
d.	Leonard Motors	136.25	Bernard Mosby
e.	Henry Schmidt	247.58	Leslie Meehan
f.	Firemen's Insurance Company	368.47	Joann Williams
g.	May's Transport Company	31.05	Alma Jackson

	Issued to:	Amount	Issued by:
h.	Dorothy Hamilton	214.09	Herman Feder
i.	Joseph Day	352.00	Sarah Morrison
j.	Carr's Service Station	104.00	James Seton

2. Draw forms similar to the one on page 254. After recording the information for each set of the following checks, complete each form by finding the balance to be forwarded to the following page of the checkbook.

a. Balance brought forward: $227.89
Checks issued: May 9, Service Bureau Corp., $56.20
May 12, Arthur Myers, $19.45
May 14, Julia Nadler, $7.84

b. Balance brought forward: $509.18
Checks issued: February 14, Ann Nagy, $173.50
February 14, Robert Linnon, $15.20
February 15, Exclusives, Inc., $90.89

c. Balance brought forward: $294.06
Checks issued: July 26, Lionel Hoppler, $81.55
July 26, Rose Pittman and Co., $175.20
July 28, Paul Underwood, $62.37
Deposit: July 27, $114.75

d. Balance brought forward: $413.82
Checks issued: October 3, Turnpike Sales, $49.95
October 3, Grace Newhouse, $71.50
October 4, Oliver Holder, $118.27
Deposit: October 4, $316.85

e. Balance brought forward: $712.58
Checks issued: April 12, Internal Revenue Service, $424.70
April 14, Home Oil Company, $88.42
April 15, Thompson's Dairy, $23.60
Deposits: April 12, $55.00
April 15, $106.50

f. Balance brought forward: $1,241.20
Checks issued: June 4, Hanlon and Wilson, $394.25
June 8, Fred Austin, $226.92
June 10, Ruth Morrow, $471.88
Deposits: June 5, $192.37
June 8, $247.50
June 10, $86.87

Section 3: Reconciling the Checking Account Statement

Periodically—usually once a month—the bank will send you a statement such as the one shown below. The information that appears on this form includes:

1. The checks you have written that have been cashed during the month

*　　　　　　　　*

Mr. William Allyn
53 Somerset Road
Westbrook, N. Y.

4

*　　　　　　　　*

VOUCHERS ENCLOSED 6

CHECKS	DEPOSITS	DATE	BALANCE
AMOUNT BROUGHT FORWARD		AUG 29	856.41
83.21		SEP 2	773.20
41.50		SEP 9	731.70
273.20		SEP 11	458.50
	320.50	SEP 16	779.00
9.14		SEP 17	769.86
	104.20	SEP 29	874.06
.85 s.c.			873.21

KEY

EC—ERROR CORRECTED　SC—SERVICE CHARGE - PREVIOUS MONTH
RT—RETURN ITEM　LS—LIST
CC—CERTIFIED CHECK　DM—DEBIT MEMO
DC—DEPOSIT CORRECTION　CM—CREDIT MEMO

PLEASE EXAMINE THIS STATEMENT UPON RECEIPT AND REPORT ANY DIFFERENCES AT ONCE

YOUR BALANCE IS THE LAST AMOUNT PRINTED IN THIS COLUMN

National, State, and County Banking Company

2. The deposits you have made
3. The service charges the bank has made against your account (See Section 1 of this unit.)
4. And, finally, the balance of your checkbook account

The objective now is to check the balance shown in the bank statement against the one that you have recorded in your own checkbook. If the two do not agree, there is always the slight possibility that the computers at the bank may be in error. The chance of this, though, is quite remote.

There are other reasons why you should want to compare your checkbook balance with that of the bank's. If nothing else, the monthly service charge for issuing checks would not have appeared in your own records. And you would want to deduct this amount from your account. In addition, there will be times when you write a check while away from home and then forget to record the information in your checkbook upon returning home. In the same way, a deposit that you may have made in the morning might be completely forgotten some eight hours later when you are back home again. Each of these will, of course, tend to make your bank balance different from that shown in the bank's records.

In addition to this, there is still another factor that may make the two accounts differ. Quite often there are a few checks that you wrote that were not cashed before the statement was mailed to you. In view of this, the bank balance will be much higher than yours. The process of comparing your records with those of the bank is called *reconciling a bank statement*.

ILLUSTRATION: Reconcile the checkbook balance with the bank statement balance based on the following information.

Balance recorded in the checkbook: \$423.78
Balance recorded on the bank statement: \$509.09
Checks written that have not yet cleared the bank: \$14.67, \$29.50, \$5.84
Service charge for the period: \$1.45
Check written but never recorded: \$19.75
Deposit made but never recorded: \$56.50

SOLUTION:

Reconciling the Two Statements

Checkbook balance:		$423.78	Bank balance:		$509.09
Add deposit not recorded:		56.50	Deduct outstanding		
		480.28	checks:	14.67	
Deduct:				29.50	
Forgotten				5.84	50.01
check:	19.75				
Service charge:	1.45	21.20			
Actual checkbook balance:		$459.08	Actual bank balance:		$459.08

EXPLANATION: The objective of reconciling the checkbook balance with the bank balance is not only to see if an error has been made, but also to determine exactly what your actual checkbook balance is. This quite simply means how much money you have in the checking account. Hence, both the checkbook balance and the bank balance are examined specifically toward showing that the actual amount of money you have in your checking account is the same as the amount of money that the bank should have recorded there. The left side of the solution is devoted to computing the actual checkbook balance, while the right side is for the actual bank balance. In examining the left side, notice that a deposit of $56.50 had not been recorded at the time it was made. Hence, the balance of $423.78 had to be increased by $56.50. In addition, the person had written a check for $19.75 and had failed to record this in his checkbook. This means that he really has $19.75 less in his checking account than he thought he had. Further, the service charge for the month was $1.45. Taking both the service charge and the forgotten check into account, the actual amount of the checkbook balance should be $21.20 less than the $480.28. The difference between $480.28 and $21.20, which is $459.08, is the actual checkbook balance.

In the right section of the solution you can see that there is but one thing that affects the bank balance, and that is the item called outstanding checks. These are the checks that the person has written, but, as yet, the checks have not cleared the bank, that is, they have not reached the bank. Since the bank is not aware that they have even been written, the amount of these checks has not been subtracted from its balance. On the other hand, in but a few days these checks will be presented to the bank for payment, and hence the actual bank balance should be less than the $509.09 shown. In fact, the amount that must be deducted is $50.01. This is the sum of the three outstanding checks. Thus, when $50.01 is subtracted from the bank balance of $509.09, you find that the *actual bank balance* of $459.08 is the same as the *actual checkbook balance*.

EXERCISES

A

When doing the problems in this set of exercises, draw reconciliation forms similar to the one on page 257.

Reconcile the bank balance with the checkbook balance in each of the following exercises.

	Bank Balance	Checkbook Balance	Service Charge	Outstanding Checks	
1.	$246.50	$203.90	$ .60	$43.20	$________
2.	512.40	446.45	.85	$66.80	________
3.	604.70	588.00	1.20	$17.90	________
4.	393.20	389.10	.85	$4.95	________
5.	827.60	745.55	1.45	$83.50	________
6.	752.20	685.60	1.10	$43.20, $24.50	________
7.	629.74	555.77	.90	$57.25, $17.62	________
8.	483.12	449.34	.65	$9.48, $24.95	________
9.	279.06	226.43	1.05	$46.52, $7.16	________
10.	941.82	869.50	1.75	$16.58, $4.69, $52.80	________

B

1. Reconcile the checkbook balance with the bank balance, using the following information.
   Checkbook balance: $694.23 Bank balance: $620.63
   Checks written that have not cleared the bank: $12.75
   Service charge: $1.15
   Check written but never recorded: $85.20 ____________
2. Reconcile the checkbook balance with the bank balance, using the following information.
   Checkbook balance: $467.82 Bank balance: $631.63
   Checks written that have not cleared the bank: $62.45, $18.75
   Service charge: $.95
   Deposit made but never recorded: $83.56 ____________
3. Reconcile the checkbook balance with the bank balance, using the following information.
   Checkbook balance: $762.54 Bank balance: $744.72
   Checks written that have not cleared the bank: $12.75, $42.80, $26.18
   Service charge: $1.40
   Check written but never recorded: $169.40
   Deposit made but never recorded: $71.25 ____________
4. When Fred Johnson received his bank statement on May 2, he noticed that the balance recorded on it was $513.78. In reconciling his checkbook balance of $647.52 with the bank balance, he discovered that a deposit of $84.50 that he had mailed to the bank on

April 30 had not arrived in time to be credited to his account. In addition, his examination of the bank statement revealed the following:
Checks written that had not cleared the bank: \$20.75, \$12.50
Service charge: \$1.25
Check written that had never been recorded: \$81.24
Prepare a reconciliation statement showing the actual checkbook balance and the actual bank balance for Fred's account.

Unit 2: Cashing Checks

There are a great number of people who have neither checking accounts nor savings accounts. And, unfortunately, there are many banks that will not cash a check for a person unless he is a depositor at that bank. Hence people who find themselves in this position will turn to check-cashing firms to cash either their paychecks or any other checks that may have been given to them.

Although the fees charged by these companies vary from state to state and from company to company, the manner in which the fees are quoted is quite similar and much the same as the rates in the table below.

CHECK-CASHING CHARGES

Company A

Checks written on in-state banks: Amount of check	Cost
\$0 to \$40.00	25¢
\$40.01 to \$49.99	1/2% + 5¢
\$50.00 and over	1/2% + 10¢
Checks written on out-of-state banks:	
\$0 to \$20.00	25¢
\$20.01 to \$49.99	1% + 5¢
\$50.00 and over	1% + 10¢

Company B

Checks written on in-state banks: Amount of check	Cost
\$0 to \$49.99	35¢
\$50.00 and over	3/4%
Checks written on out-of-state banks:	
\$0 to \$49.99	45¢
\$50.00 and over	1 1/4%

Notice that for both of these check-cashing companies, the rates for cashing out-of-state checks are quite a bit higher than the rates for cashing in-state checks. The reason for this is that the company not only has to wait longer for the out-of-state checks to clear but also seems to run a greater risk that these checks may not be good.

ILLUSTRATION 1: How much will it cost to cash an out-of-state check for $127.60 at Company B?

EXPLANATION: Since the check is written against an out-of-state bank, it is necessary to look at that section of the Company B rate table. There you will notice that the cost for a check written in an amount over $50 is 1¼% of the amount of the check, which in this case is $127.60. Before finding 1¼% of $127.60, change 1¼% to the form 1.25% and then express this as a decimal in the usual way by moving the decimal point two places to the left.

SOLUTION:

$$\begin{aligned}\text{Charge for cashing a \$127.60-check} &= 1\tfrac{1}{4}\% \text{ of } \$127.60\\ &= 1.25\% \times \$127.60\\ &= .0125 \times \$127.60\\ &= \$1.595, \text{ or } \$1.60\end{aligned}$$

ILLUSTRATION 2: How much will it cost to cash an in-state check for $154.75 at Company A?

SOLUTION:

$$\begin{aligned}\text{Charge for cashing a \$154.75-check} &= \tfrac{1}{2}\% \text{ of } \$154.75 + 10¢\\ &= .5\% \times \$154.75 + 10¢\\ &= .005 \times \$154.75 + 10¢\\ &= \$.77 + \$.10\\ &= \$.87\end{aligned}$$

EXPLANATION: As in Illustration 1, it is first necessary to rewrite ½% as .5% before changing it to its decimal equivalent of .005. After finding the product of .005 and $154.75, remember that there is an additional 10¢ charge that must be added to that product.

EXERCISES A

Write each of the following percent values as a decimal. If you do not recall how this is done, refer to pages 514–516 for help.

a. 1½%	________	c. 1¾%	________	e. ¼%	________
b. 1¼%	________	d. ½%	________	f. ¾%	________

B

1. What is the cost for cashing each of the following out-of-state checks at Company A?

	Amount of Check	Cost		Amount of Check	Cost
a.	$ 15.40	$______	g.	$ 46.50	$______
b.	17.95	______	h.	39.70	______
c.	6.49	______	i.	84.20	______
d.	30.00	______	j.	136.40	______
e.	70.00	______	k.	106.55	______
f.	120.00	______	l.	142.17	______

2. What is the cost for cashing each of the following in-state checks at Company B?

	Amount of Check	Cost		Amount of Check	Cost
a.	$23.00	$______	f.	$ 52.00	$______
b.	14.75	______	g.	64.50	______
c.	29.98	______	h.	93.20	______
d.	60.00	______	i.	123.60	______
e.	80.00	______	j.	148.75	______

3. What is the cost for cashing each of the following out-of-state checks at Company B?

	Amount of Check	Cost		Amount of Check	Cost
a.	$36.00	$______	f.	$ 58.00	$______
b.	27.45	______	g.	71.50	______
c.	19.50	______	h.	84.50	______
d.	70.00	______	i.	106.25	______
e.	90.00	______	j.	158.45	______

4. What is the cost for cashing each of the following in-state checks at Company A?

	Amount of Check	Cost		Amount of Check	Cost
a.	$12.50	$______	f.	$ 41.60	$______
b.	14.50	______	g.	47.30	______
c.	41.00	______	h.	92.65	______
d.	45.00	______	i.	139.50	______
e.	87.00	______	j.	178.75	______

C

1. Charles Putnam cashed a check for $158.20 at Company A.
   a. What will the charge be if this is an out-of-state check? ________
   b. What will the charge be if this is an in-state check? ________
   c. How much more will Charles have to pay if the check is from out of state? ________
2. Nancy Evans' paycheck amounts to $126.90 each week. The check is drawn against an in-state bank and she cashes it weekly at Company A.
   a. What charge does Nancy pay each week for cashing her paycheck? ________
   b. How much does Nancy pay over the period of one year for having these checks cashed? ________
3. A check for $237.50 drawn on an out-of-state bank is cashed at a check-cashing service.
   a. How much will the charge be if it is cashed at Company A? ________
   b. How much will the charge be if it is cashed at Company B? ________
   c. How much more is the charge at Company B than at Company A? ________

Unit 3: Borrowing Money from a Bank

Thus far you have been concerned with the services of a bank from the point of view of the depositor who has either a savings account or a checking account or possibly both. There is another very important service with which you are provided by a bank—the lending of money. Actually, it is through this last service that most banks earn their money in order to operate.

There are three basic types of loans that most banks have available for the private individual. Each of these will be investigated in this unit.

Section 1: The Monthly Payment Loan

In reality you have already examined this type of loan, for one form of it is simply the automobile loan that was studied in Chapter 1. Banks also lend money under this same arrangement at the time a person plans to build an addition to his home or perhaps to just repair it. Just as you learned earlier, the amount borrowed is paid off in monthly installments in accordance with an arrangement such as those shown in the advertisements below.

NATIONAL SUSSEX BANK

You'll Like Our Low Bank Rates (12.9%)

Unpaid Balance	12 Months Amount Per Month	18 Months Amount Per Month	36 Months Amount Per Month
$1,500	$133.91	$ 92.10	$50.47
2,000	178.54	122.80	67.29
2,400	214.25	147.36	80.75

THE STATE BANK OF PLEASANTVILLE

See Us For a Home Improvement Loan (14.6%)

Amount Of Note	12 Months Monthly Payment	24 Months Monthly Payment	30 Months Monthly Payment
$1,200	$108.08	$ 55.96	$ 46.70
2,600	234.18	121.24	101.18
3,800	342.26	177.20	147.88

ILLUSTRATION: Gloria Byrne borrowed $1,500 from the National Sussex Bank in order to remodel the kitchen of her home. How much more did she return to the bank than she borrowed if she paid off the loan over a period of 18 months?

SOLUTION:

$$\begin{aligned}\text{Amount repaid to bank} &= 18 \times \$92.10\\ &= \$1{,}657.80\\ \text{Amount extra repaid} &= \$1{,}657.80 - \$1{,}500\\ &= \$157.80\end{aligned}$$

EXPLANATION: The monthly payment is found in the table at the point where the "$1,500" row meets the "18 Months" column. This monthly payment of $92.10 is multiplied by 18 in order to determine the total repaid the bank. The excess Gloria paid is found by subtracting the $1,500 she received from the $1,657.80 she returned.

EXERCISES A

1. What is the monthly payment to the National Sussex Bank on each of the following loans?

	Amount Borrowed	Period of Loan	Monthly Payment
a.	$1,500	18 months	$________
b.	2,000	12 months	________
c.	2,000	36 months	________
d.	2,400	18 months	________
e.	1,500	36 months	________

2. How much money is repaid to the State Bank of Pleasantville on each of the following loans?

	Amount Borrowed	Period of Loan	Monthly Payment	Amount Repaid
a.	$1,200	12 months	$________	$________
b.	2,600	30 months	________	________
c.	3,800	12 months	________	________
d.	2,600	24 months	________	________
e.	3,800	30 months	________	________

3. How much more money will be repaid to the National Sussex Bank than was borrowed in each of the following loans?

	Amount Borrowed	Amount of Loan	Monthly Payment	Amount Repaid	Excess Repaid
a.	$2,000	36 months	$________	$________	$________
b.	2,400	12 months	________	________	________
c.	2,000	18 months	________	________	________
d.	1,500	12 months	________	________	________
e.	2,400	36 months	________	________	________

B

Eric Swenson borrowed $1,200 from the State Bank of Pleasantville.

a. How much would he return to the bank if he paid the debt off over a 24-month period? ________

b. How much would he return to the bank if he paid the debt off over a 30-month period? ________

c. How much more would the 30-month loan cost him than the 24-month loan? ________

Section 2: The Discounted Loan

With this type of loan the charge for borrowing money is computed in exactly the same manner as was used earlier when finding the interest on a deposit. Earnings that are paid for the use of money are called either interest or discount depending on when the earnings are given. If they are paid at the end of the period, they are called *interest*, while if they are paid at the beginning of the period, they are called *discount*. Thus, when you deposit money in a savings account you do not receive any earnings on this money until the end of an interest period. At that point the earnings are added to your account. Since you receive this money at the end of the period, these earnings are called interest. When money is borrowed from a bank under a *discounted loan*, the charge for this loan must be paid in advance. As an illustration, if $500 is borrowed and the charge is $20, then you must pay the bank the $20 before the $500 is turned over to you. In reality, the bank actually subtracts the $20 charge from the $500 and turns over to you only $480. In this illustration:

the $500 is called the *principal* of the debt;
the $20 is called the *discount;*
the $480 is called the *proceeds*.

ILLUSTRATION: Find the discount and proceeds on a $600 loan. The discount rate is 8% and the money was borrowed for 90 days.

SOLUTION:

$$\begin{aligned} D &= P \times R \times T \\ &= \$600 \times 8\% \times 90/360 \\ &= \$600 \times .08 \times 90/360 \\ &= \$12 \text{ (Discount)} \\ \text{Proceeds} &= \$600 - \$12 \\ &= \$588 \end{aligned}$$

EXPLANATION: Where earlier the formula was called the "interest formula," now it is called the "discount formula." What had been "interest" in the previous formula is now "discount," and what had been "interest rate" is now "discount rate." However, the computation remains exactly the same, or, rather, almost the same. Notice that where formerly the number 365 was used as the number of days in a year, now the number 360 replaces it. Originally banks used the 360-day year since all the computations were done by hand and most loans were for 30, 60, 90, or 120 days. In view of this, division by 360 was far, far easier than by 365. Now, though, computers do this tedious labor and it makes no difference to the computer whether it is asked to divide by 365 or 360. Then why do banks still use 360 as the number of days in a year for the purpose of lending money? As you might imagine, they do this because they earn more money under this arrangement.

EXERCISES A

1. Find the discount on each of the following loans.

	Principal	Discount Rate	Number Of Days	Discount
a.	$ 700	8%	90	$______
b.	500	8%	40	______
c.	300	8%	72	______
d.	600	9%	96	______
e.	1,200	9%	48	______
f.	1,000	10%	108	______
g.	900	10%	84	______
h.	1,800	8½%	132	______
i.	900	10½%	120	______
j.	800	10½%	144	______

2. Find the proceeds on each of the following loans.

	Principal	Discount Rate	Number Of Days	Discount	Proceeds
a.	$ 200	8%	60	$______	$______
b.	400	9%	90	______	______
c.	2,000	9%	100	______	______
d.	600	10%	30	______	______
e.	720	11%	80	______	______
f.	3,600	8½%	50	______	______
g.	4,000	9½%	72	______	______
h.	4,500	10½%	64	______	______

B

1. Howard Fleming borrowed $750 from a bank for a period of 80 days at a discount rate of 10%.
   a. How much money did he receive from the bank? ______
   b. How much money did he return to the bank? ______
2. On May 23, Charles Cosgrove borrowed $800 from a bank for a period of three months at a discount rate of 9%.
   a. If the bank computed the charge on a monthly basis, how much would the discount have been? ______
   b. If the bank computed the charge on a daily basis, how much would the discount have been? (There are 92 days in this period.) ______
   c. How much would Charles have saved had the discount been computed on a monthly basis rather than on a daily basis? ______
3. Arlene Lawson borrowed $10,000 from the Grove Savings Bank at a discount rate of 8% for a period of 90 days.

a. In computing the discount, the loan clerk used the 360-day year. What was the amount of the discount? ________

b. If the loan clerk had used the 365-day year, what would the amount of the discount have been? ________

c. How much would Arlene have saved if the 365-day year had been used rather than the 360-day year? ________

4. Raymond Goodwin borrowed $800 for which he had to pay a charge of $50.

a. If the $50 was called a discount charge, how much did Mr. Goodwin receive and how much did he have to return? ________

b. If the $50 was called an interest charge, how much did Mr. Goodwin receive and how much did he have to return? ________

Section 3: The Interest-Bearing Loan

Perhaps the most popular type of loan used by many banks is the *demand note.* Under this arrangement, the borrower will leave with the bank either his passbook (bankbook), or a life insurance policy, or stocks, or bonds, or other such items that have greater value than the amount of money being borrowed. Frequently, there will be no date set at which time the person borrowing the money must return it to the bank. Whenever the bank *demands* the money be returned, the person must do so. Also, the borrower is permitted to pay off the debt at any time convenient to himself.

However, the borrower must pay the bank interest on this debt in exactly the same manner in which the bank pays interest to its depositors. That is, if the bank pays interest quarterly, then every three months the borrower must go to the bank and pay the interest that has accumulated on the loan. Similarly, if interest is paid *by* the bank monthly, then the borrower must pay interest *to* the bank monthly. Should the borrower miss making one of these payments, then the entire loan becomes due immediately. Needless to say, the interest rate the borrower pays the bank is more than the interest rate paid by the bank to its depositors.

Since the computation involved in finding the interest due at the close of each interest period is quite lengthy, a table similar to the one on page 270 is used to ease the labor. The design of this table is almost identical to that of the Simple Interest Table on page 219 in Chapter 6. In that table the interest was based on a 365-day year; now the interest is based on the 360-day year. Other than that, the application of the table is the same as earlier.

SIMPLE INTEREST ON $1
(360-Day Year)

Days	8%	8.5%	9%	9.5%	10%	11%	12%
1	.0002222	.0002361	.0002500	.0002639	.0002778	.0003056	.0003333
2	.0004444	.0004722	.0005000	.0005278	.0005556	.0006111	.0006667
3	.0006667	.0007083	.0007500	.0007917	.0008333	.0009167	.0010000
4	.0008889	.0009444	.0010000	.0010556	.0011111	.0012222	.0013333
5	.0011111	.0011806	.0012500	.0013194	.0013889	.0015278	.0016667
6	.0013333	.0014167	.0015000	.0015833	.0016667	.0018333	.0020000
7	.0015556	.0016528	.0017500	.0018472	.0019444	.0021389	.0023333
8	.0017778	.0018889	.0020000	.0021111	.0022222	.0024444	.0026667
9	.0020000	.0021250	.0022500	.0023750	.0025000	.0027500	.0030000
10	.0022222	.0023611	.0025000	.0026389	.0027778	.0030556	.0033333
11	.0024444	.0025972	.0027500	.0029028	.0030556	.0033611	.0036667
12	.0026667	.0028333	.0030000	.0031667	.0033333	.0036667	.0040000
13	.0028889	.0030694	.0032500	.0034306	.0036111	.0039722	.0043333
14	.0031111	.0033056	.0035000	.0036944	.0038889	.0042778	.0046667
15	.0033333	.0035417	.0037500	.0039583	.0041667	.0045833	.0050000
16	.0035556	.0037778	.0040000	.0042222	.0044444	.0048889	.0053333
17	.0037778	.0040139	.0042500	.0044861	.0047222	.0051944	.0056667
18	.0040000	.0042500	.0045000	.0047500	.0050000	.0055000	.0060000
19	.0042222	.0044861	.0047500	.0050139	.0052778	.0058056	.0063333
20	.0044444	.0047222	.0050000	.0052778	.0055556	.0061111	.0066667
21	.0046667	.0049583	.0052500	.0055417	.0058333	.0064167	.0070000
22	.0048889	.0051944	.0055000	.0058056	.0061111	.0067222	.0073333
23	.0051111	.0054306	.0057500	.0060694	.0063889	.0070278	.0076667
24	.0053333	.0056667	.0060000	.0063333	.0066667	.0073333	.0080000
25	.0055556	.0059028	.0062500	.0065972	.0069444	.0076389	.0083333
26	.0057778	.0061389	.0065000	.0068611	.0072222	.0079444	.0086667
27	.0060000	.0063750	.0067500	.0071250	.0075000	.0082500	.0090000
28	.0062222	.0066111	.0070000	.0073889	.0077778	.0085556	.0093333
29	.0064444	.0068472	.0072500	.0076528	.0080556	.0088611	.0096667
30	.0066667	.0070833	.0075000	.0079167	.0083333	.0091667	.0100000
31	.0068889	.0073194	.0077500	.0081806	.0086111	.0094722	.0103333

ILLUSTRATION 1: Joseph Raynor borrowed $900 on a passbook loan from the Passaic Valley Bank at an interest rate of 9½%. Interest payments had to be made on this loan on the last day of each month. How much did Joseph give the bank on May 17 when he paid off the debt?

SOLUTION:

Number of days in May for which interest must be paid: 17
Interest on \$1 @ $9\frac{1}{2}\%$ for 17 days = \$.0044861
Interest on \$900 @ $9\frac{1}{2}\%$ for 17 days = 900 × \$.0044861
= \$4.03749, or \$4.04
Amount returned to bank on May 17 = \$900 + \$4.04
= \$904.04

EXPLANATION: The last interest payment Joseph had made was on April 30. Hence at the time he paid his debt on May 17, he not only had to pay the \$900, but also, the interest on the 17 days in May. The interest found in the table on \$1 @ $9\frac{1}{2}\%$ turned out to be \$.0044861 and, therefore, the interest on \$900 is 900 times as much, or \$4.04. In view of this, Joseph gave the bank \$900 plus \$4.04, or \$904.04.

ILLUSTRATION 2: If Joseph Raynor of Illustration 1 borrowed the \$900 on March 3, how large was the first interest payment?

EXPLANATION: Since interest payments had to be made on the last day of each month and since there are 31 days in March, then Joseph had to pay interest for the 28 days in March during which he held the bank's money. The rest of the solution is completed in exactly the same manner as the interest was found in Illustration 1. Incidentally, should you have trouble recalling the number of days in any particular month, refer to the timetable on page 218.

SOLUTION:

Number of days from March 3 to March 31: 28
Interest on \$1 @ $9\frac{1}{2}\%$ for 28 days = \$.0073889
Interest on \$900 @ $9\frac{1}{2}\%$ for 28 days = 900 × \$.0073889
= \$6.65001, or \$6.65

The simple interest table on page 270 is to be used in each of the exercises below.

EXERCISES A

1. Find the interest on \$1 under each of the conditions given here.

	Rate of Interest	Number of Days	Interest
a.	8%	5	\$________
b.	8%	11	________
c.	9%	25	________
d.	10%	7	________

	Rate of Interest	Number of Days	Interest
e.	11%	18	$______
f.	12%	23	______
g.	8.5%	12	______
h.	9.5%	29	______
i.	$8\frac{1}{2}$%	4	______
j.	$9\frac{1}{2}$%	24	______
k.	$9\frac{1}{2}$%	12	______

2. Find the interest on each of the following loans.

	Loan	Rate of Interest	Number of Days	Interest
a.	$ 600	8%	18	$______
b.	500	10%	9	______
c.	400	9%	22	______
d.	1,200	8.5%	28	______
e.	1,500	9.5%	8	______
f.	2,600	11%	26	______
g.	750	12%	20	______

3. Interest payments must be made monthly on the last day of each month. How much interest will each of the following borrowers have to pay the bank on the day these debts are repaid?

	Loan	Rate of Interest	Date Repaid	Number of Days	Interest
a.	$ 800	9%	April 12	______	$______
b.	700	10%	June 18	______	______
c.	300	11%	Sept. 23	______	______
d.	1,000	8.5%	Feb. 15	______	______
e.	1,400	9.5%	Oct. 6	______	______
f.	2,000	12%	Dec. 11	______	______

4. Interest payments must be made on the last day of each month. How much money will each of the following borrowers have to pay the bank on the day these debts are repaid?

	Loan	Rate of Interest	Date Repaid	Number of Days	Interest	Amount Returned
a.	$ 600	10%	Jan. 16	______	$______	$______
b.	900	8%	July 9	______	______	______
c.	1,300	9%	Nov. 27	______	______	______
d.	2,200	8.5%	April 6	______	______	______
e.	1,700	11%	March 13	______	______	______
f.	2,500	9.5%	June 24	______	______	______

5. Interest payments must be made monthly on the last day of each month. How large will the first interest payment have to be on each of the following loans? (See Illustration 2, page 271.)

	Loan	Rate of Interest	Date Borrowed	Number Of Days	Interest
a.	$ 500	8%	June 10	________	$________
b.	800	9%	April 20	________	________
c.	400	9.5%	July 16	________	________
d.	1,600	11%	Aug. 11	________	________
e.	2,300	12%	Oct. 14	________	________
f.	3,000	8.5%	Nov. 3	________	________
g.	3,200	10%	Jan. 25	________	________
h.	3,500	9%	March 8	________	________

B

1. Linda Tucker borrowed $10,000 from her bank for a period of 30 days.
   a. How much interest will she pay if the interest rate is 8%? ________
   b. How much interest will she pay if the interest rate is 12%? ________
   c. How much would she save if she is able to get the loan at the 8% rather than the 12% rate? ________
2. Using the Simple Interest Table on page 270, determine the interest on $1 at an interest rate of 8% for a period of 40 days. ________
3. Patrick Turner borrowed $4,000 from the Wayne State Bank at an interest rate of 10%. The date he borrowed this money was 52 days before the first interest payment fell due.
   a. How much interest will Patrick have to pay on each dollar of the loan for the first period? ________
   b. How much interest will Patrick have to pay on the loan for the first period? ________

Unit 4: Chapter Review and Test

1. In terms of the Special Checking Account described on page 248, determine the charge for the month that would have to be paid if the following number of checks were issued:
   a. 7 ________ b. 15 ________ c. 36 ________
2. In terms of the Flat-Payment Checking Account described on page 249, determine the charge for the month that would have to be paid for the following minimum balances. Do not consider the

yearly charge when finding your answer.
a. $523.17 ________ b. $114.86 ________ c. $295.24 ________

3. In terms of the Analysis-Checking-Account Plan described on page 250, determine the charge for the month that would have to be paid on accounts that had the following activity:
   a. Minimum balance: $456; number of checks issued: 27 ________
   b. Minimum balance: $242; number of checks issued: 19 ________
   c. Minimum balance: $196; number of checks issued: 22; number of deposits: 2 ________

4. Draw a checkbook page form similar to the one on page 254. Use the following information to complete this form, including the balance that is to be forwarded to the following page of the checkbook.
   Balance brought forward: $456.32
   Checks issued: June 14, Roger's Motors, $42.70
   June 14, John Soyden, $14.10
   June 15, Bednar Door Company, $145.00
   Deposit: June 15, $87.35 ________

5. Use the following information to reconcile the checkbook balance with the bank balance.
   Checkbook balance: $342.80 Bank balance: $458.60
   Checks written that have not cleared the bank: $52, $65
   Service charge: $1.20 ________

6. What is the cost of cashing each of the following checks at Company A whose rates are shown on page 261?

Amount of Check	Location of Bank	Cost
a. $36.00	In-state	$________
b. 15.98	Out-of-state	________
c. 37.00	Out-of-state	________
d. 76.50	In-state	________

7. Julia Hernandez borrowed $2,600 from the State Bank of Pleasantville, whose loans are described on page 265. She paid off this debt in 30 monthly installments.
   a. How large was each monthly installment? ________
   b. How much did she return to the bank over the 30-month period? ________
   c. How much more did she return to the bank than she received? ________

8. How large is the discount on a loan of $600 at a discount rate of 7% for a period of 90 days? ________

9. William Gans borrowed $400 from a bank at a discount rate of 7½% for a period of 120 days.

a. How much did William actually receive from the bank? ________

b. How much did William return to the bank? ________

10. Use the Simple Interest Table on page 270 to find the interest on each of the following loans.

a. $600 at 8% for 27 days ________

b. $1,000 at 9½% for 40 days ________

11. At the Grove Township Federal Bank, interest payments on a debt must be made on the last day of each month. Simeon Fletcher borrowed $3,000 from this bank at an interest rate of 9½%. The loan was made on April 12 and the debt was repaid on July 17. Refer to the interest table on page 270 when answering the following questions.

a. How much interest did Simeon have to pay for the period in July during which he kept the money? ________

b. How much money did he give the bank on July 17 when he paid off the debt? ________

c. For how many days in April did he have to pay interest? ________

d. How much interest did he pay the bank on April 30? ________

PERSONAL LOANS

CHAPTER 8

SMALL LOANS

Although banks earn their money primarily through lending money, they often are unwilling to make loans to a great number of people. These people are considered to be "high risk" borrowers, that is, the banks fear that there is a good possibility that money loaned to these people may never be returned. In view of this, the person who finds that he can not borrow from a bank and yet is in need of money will turn to some other agency for a loan. In this chapter the lending practices of several of these types of agencies will be examined.

Unit 1: The Small-Loan Agency

Among the many other things the mailman drops into your mailbox each week, you can usually count on advertisements such as the following:

"**IN DEBT?** We will assist you in getting out of debt. One weekly payment can possibly pay your bills and overdue debts."

"I'm behind in my house payments . . . bills are coming due . . . the kids need clothes . . . **who'll lend a hand? WE WILL!**"

"It's time to fix up your home! Get a FIX–UP loan."

"Don't be bothered by bills. Here's the CASH you need."

"Exclusive for Engineers! Dear engineer . . . **Borrow $200 to $1,000 or more** in complete confidence by mail! Write us at RST"

As is evident, these companies are most anxious to help you get out of debt. And of course they should be. By lending you the money you supposedly need, they, in turn, reap a profitable reward by charging a high rate of interest. In fact, as you will see, it is much, much higher than your own money can possibly earn by being in the bank.

In all fairness to the small-loan agency, it should be pointed out that there are situations in which it is actually possible to save money by borrowing from these institutions. Notice that three of the advertisements stressed the fact that they wanted to lend you money to clear up bills. When these bills happen to be for articles purchased on the installment plan, you may be much better off by borrowing the money from the small-loan agency to get yourself out of debt. The interest rates charged by these agencies are restricted by state laws, while there are often no restrictions on the rates that can be charged the buyer on an installment purchase. In view of this, you will find that it is usually cheaper to borrow money and pay cash for an article you need rather than buy it on the installment plan.

This is not the case, though, for many other bills that you will have to pay. The gas and electric bill, the water bill, the telephone bill, the doctor's bill, the dentist's bill—all these carry no interest charge with them. If you borrow money to pay them off, you will only be freeing yourself from many small debts on which you pay no interest to get yourself involved in a single large debt that carries with it a substantial interest charge.

Loans made to clear up an accumulation of small debts are called consolidation loans. The theory behind them is that rather than be confused by what seems to be an endless number of small debts, you borrow enough money to pay them off and then have only one large debt to contend with. As was pointed out earlier, the wisdom of investing in a consolidation loan depends on what the small debts happen to be.

The small-loan agency is so called because it deals in small loans. These loans have different meanings in different states. In some, they can be any amount up to \$500, while in others the amount might be as high as \$2,000. Furthermore, state laws differ on what is considered to be a fair rate of interest that should be charged the borrower. The legal maximum limit (highest rate) in several states happens to be 2½% *per month* on the unpaid balance. Notice that this rate is quoted by the month, not by the year. On a yearly basis it comes to 30%. There is at least one state in which the legal yearly interest rate on a \$100-loan runs as high as 80%. This, though, is unusual.

A number of states prefer to have a decreasing rate scale such as the one below:

3% per month on the unpaid balance up to \$500
2% per month on the unpaid balance over \$500 and under \$1,000
1% per month on the unpaid balance over \$1,000

Here, again, as is usual with small loans, the rate is quoted as a monthly rate.

It has only been within recent years that the federal government has passed a "Truth-in-lending" law requiring that a lender notify a borrower exactly what annual rate of interest he will have to pay. Unfortunately, the law does not require that the borrower be told just how much the cost of the loan will actually be.

Facts Chart

Select Your Loan Here . . .

Amount Of Loan	Number of Monthly Payments	Amount of Each Monthly Payment	Annual Rate
$1,000	36	$41.34	29.34%
900	36	37.53	30.04%
800	36	33.70	30.82%
700	36	29.85	31.79%
600	30	29.21	33.07%
500	24	28.82	34.61%

ILLUSTRATION 1: The RST Consumer Loan Company mailed the advertisement above to people throughout the country. How much will it cost someone to borrow $800 if he pays back the money over a period of 36 months?

SOLUTION:

Monthly payment = $33.70
Total of monthly payments = 36 × $33.70
= $1,213.20
Debt charge or interest = $1,213.20 − $800
= $413.20

ILLUSTRATION 2: The Economy Credit Corporation placed the following advertisement in a newspaper.

WE'LL LEND YOU A HELPING HAND

$25 to $2,500

If You Owe	Pay As Low As	Time Length
$ 750	$16.87 per week	12 months
1,500	28.80 per week	15 months
2,500	40.36 per week	18 months

Annual Rate: 31.65%

How much interest will the borrower be paying if he makes the $1,500 loan?

EXPLANATION: To find the number of weeks in 15 months, consider this time as consisting of two periods. The first of these is 12 months, which is the equivalent of one year, which, in turn, can be thought of as 52 weeks. The second period will be the remaining 3 months. This is equivalent to ¼ of a year, or ¼ of 52 weeks. Thus, 3 months can be rewritten as 13 weeks. Hence, the total number of weeks in 15 months is 65. Chances are that the time length in the advertisement was deliberately stated in months rather than weeks to make it appear much shorter. Since 65 is a much larger number than 15, you tend to associate 65 weeks with a much longer period of time than 15 months.

SOLUTION:

Number of weeks in 15 months = 65
Total of weekly payments = 65 × $28.80
= $1,872
Interest = $1,872 − $1,500
= $372

EXERCISES A

Use the following table to answer the questions that follow it.

SELECT YOUR LOAN FROM THIS TABLE

(Rates set by law)

24-Month Plan

Amount of Loan	Monthly Payment	Annual Rate
$ 400	$22.09	28.66%
500	27.18	26.96%
800	41.88	22.95%
1,200	61.00	19.87%
1,500	75.23	18.47%

1. How much did the borrowers repay the loan company for each of the loans below?

	Amount of Loan	Total Repaid
a.	$1,200	$__________
b.	400	__________
c.	800	__________

2. Using your answers to the exercises above, determine the amount of interest paid on each of those loans.

	Amount of Loan	Interest
a.	$1,200	$__________
b.	400	__________
c.	800	__________

3. a. Is the interest on the $800-loan twice as much as the interest on the $400-loan? ________
   b. How do you account for your answer to Part a? ________

B

Use the advertisement below to answer the questions that follow it.

TERMS TO SUIT YOUR BUDGET

Cash To You	24 Months	18 Months	12 Months	Annual Rate of Interest
$ 500	$30.18	$ 37.00	$ 50.85	38.46%
1,000	58.14	71.83	99.60	34.28%
1,500	83.98	104.61	146.33	30.14%

1. How much money did the borrower repay the loan company on each of the following loans?

	Amount of Loan	Period of Loan	Total Repaid
a.	$ 500	18 months	$________
b.	1,000	24 months	________
c.	1,500	12 months	________

2. How much interest is paid on each of the following loans?

	Amount of Loan	Period of Loan	Total Repaid	Interest
a.	$1,000	12 months	$________	$________
b.	500	12 months	________	________
c.	1,500	18 months	________	________

C

1. How much interest will a person have to pay if he borrows $500 for a 24-month period from the loan company in Exercise A? ________
2. How much interest will a person have to pay if he borrows $500 for a 24-month period from the loan company in Exercise B? ________
3. How much money can someone save by borrowing $500 from the loan company in Exercise A rather than the one in Exercise B? ________

D

1. A color television set can be purchased for $400 cash. This set can also be purchased on the installment plan by making no down payment and monthly payments of $25 over a period of two years.
   a. How much will the installment purchaser have to pay for the set? ________
   b. How much more will a person have to pay for the set if he buys it on the installment plan rather than for cash? ________
   c. If the installment purchaser had borrowed the $400 for the 24-month period from the loan company in Exercise A, what would the loan have cost him? ________
   d. How much could the installment purchaser have saved by borrowing the $400 from the loan company in Exercise A and paying cash for the television set? ________
2. Use the advertisement in Illustration 2, page 280, to answer each of the following questions.
   a. How much interest will a borrower have to pay on the $750 loan for the 12-month period? ________
   b. How much interest will a borrower have to pay on the $2,500 loan for the 18-month period? ________

E

The Confidential Cash Loan Corporation mailed advertising circulars to people, urging them to "Consolidate Your Bills." The advertisement read as follows:

CUT YOUR MONTHLY PAYMENTS 1/3 TO 1/2 AND GET EXTRA CASH BESIDES

(Annual rate 29.49%)

Take 24 months to pay

Here's a typical problem that many families face.

Here's how a loan from us Solved the Problem.

Accounts	Amount Owed	Monthly Payments		
Clothing	$ 48	$ 6	Amount of Loan	$500
Appliance	100	10	Amount Needed to Pay Bills	457
Hospital	110	10	Extra Cash for You	43
Doctor	24	12		
Dentist	105	15	Monthly Payment	
Car Repair	20	5	For a loan of $500	$27.81
Home Repair	50	10	Here's how payments of	
Total	$457	$68 ⟷	$68 were cut to $27.81	

1. For how many months will the borrower have to make the monthly payments of $27.81? ________
2. If the loan were not made then:
   a. In how many months will the clothing bill be paid? ________
   b. In how many months will the appliance bill be paid? ________
   c. In how many months will the hospital bill be paid? ________
   d. In how many months will the doctor's bill be paid? ________
   e. In how many months will the dentist's bill be paid? ________
   f. In how many months will the car repair bill be paid? ________
   g. In how many months will the home repair bill be paid? ________
3. In view of your answers in exercise 2, how long would it be before the last of the bills is paid? ________
4. In what way would you criticize the advertisement? ________
5. How much interest would the borrower have to pay on the loan of $500? ________

Unit 2: The Pawnshop Loan

Many people prefer to borrow money from a pawnshop rather than from a small-loan agency. The pawnshop owner seems to be more willing to lend money to "high risk" borrowers than any other legal lending agency. And contrary to what most people believe, the cost of a pawnshop loan in most states is not much more—if any more at all—than that charged by the small-loan company. There are a few states, though, in which the rate of interest on a pawnshop loan can run as high as 10% per month—this comes to 120% per year.

All pawnshop loans are *collateral* loans. This simply means that the borrower turns over to the pawnbroker some article of goods to be held until the debt is paid. The type of goods that is acceptable varies from broker to broker. Some will accept clothing, shoes, window drapes, and the like, while others will not. They reason that people using this merchandise for collateral are probably just trying to get rid of some old, used articles and have no other way of disposing of them. Such things as watches, rings, cameras, musical instruments, radios, and TV sets are accepted by all pawnbrokers. These are items that can be sold quite easily in the event they are not claimed.

There is no fixed period by which the pawnshop loan must be paid. Some brokers insist on payment within one month, or they will sell the collateral, while contracts with other brokers permit the borrower to keep the money for an entire year. Usually, though, if the person

Private finance companies, banks, and firms that issue credit cards usually check the financial status of all potential borrowers to make sure they are good credit risks.

makes a small payment at the time the loan is due—even the interest is enough—the pawnbroker will extend the period by which the debt must be paid. On the other hand, whenever the borrower is ready and willing to pay off the debt plus interest, he can do so. There is one small point that shouldn't be overlooked, though. Interest always appears to be charged for a full month's time and never for a fractional part of it. Thus, if the debt were paid off after 2 months and 23 days, the borrower would have to pay 3 months' interest on the loan. In fact, even if the period were 2 months and 1 day, the interest would be computed for the period of 3 months.

ILLUSTRATION 1: For what period of time will interest have to be paid on a pawnshop loan that was made April 4 and paid off on August 15?

EXPLANATION: In counting the months from April 4 to August 15, you find that May 4 will be one month; June 4, two months; July 4, three months; and August 4, four months. Since any days after August 4 and prior to September 4 have to be considered as a full month, then the time from August 4 to August 15 will bring the interest period to five months.

SOLUTION:

Interest period from April 4 to August 15 = 5 months

ILLUSTRATION 2: Jerry Campbell borrowed $75 from a pawnbroker on March 12 and returned the money with interest on September 9. How much money did Jerry return if state law permitted the pawnbroker to charge the following rates?

On that part of the loan up to and including $50:	$2\frac{1}{2}\%$ per month
On that part of the loan over $50:	2% per month

EXPLANATION: On the first $50 of the loan, Jerry paid an interest rate of $2\frac{1}{2}\%$ per month. Since he borrowed $75, altogether, then on the remaining $25, he had to pay a rate of 2% per month. The period of time from March 12 to September 9 is considered as 6 months because the fractional part of the last month is counted as an entire month. Hence, in determining the interest on the loan, you first compute it for one month and then multiply this answer by 6 to find the interest for the entire 6 months.

SOLUTION:

Interest period from March 12 to September 9 = 6 months

Interest on first \$50 for 1 month = $\$50 \times 2\frac{1}{2}\%$
$= \$50 \times .025$
$= \$1.25$

Interest on remaining \$25 for 1 month = $\$25 \times 2\%$
$= \$.50$

Interest on \$75 for 1 month = $\$1.25 + \$.50$
$= \$1.75$

Interest on \$75 for 6 months = $6 \times \$1.75$
$= \$10.50$

Total repaid on September 9 = $\$75 + \$10.50$
$= \$85.50$

In the preceding illustration, the interest for 1 month is an exact amount of money—$1.75. This will not always be the case. In those situations where it is not, do not round off any answer to the nearest penny until you have found the total interest for the full period of time.

EXERCISES

A

If you do not recall how to find the answers to the following exercises you will probably want to refer to the pages indicated for help.

1. Change each of the following percent numerals to its equivalent decimal numeral. (See page 514.)

a. 2%	________	g. 4.25%	________	m. $3\frac{1}{4}\%$	________
b. 3%	________	h. 3.75%	________	n. $2\frac{1}{4}\%$	________
c. 1%	________	i. $2\frac{1}{2}\%$	________	o. $4\frac{3}{4}\%$	________
d. 5%	________	j. $1\frac{1}{2}\%$	________	p. $5\frac{3}{4}\%$	________
e. 2.5%	________	k. $4\frac{1}{2}\%$	________	q. $5\frac{1}{2}\%$	________
f. 3.5%	________	l. $6\frac{1}{2}\%$	________	r. $6\frac{3}{4}\%$	________

2. Find the product in each of the following. (See page 518.)

a. $30 \times 2\% =$ ________	g. $26 \times 3.5\% =$ ________
b. $50 \times 3\% =$ ________	h. $58 \times 1.5\% =$ ________
c. $45 \times 1\% =$ ________	i. $70 \times 2\frac{1}{2}\% =$ ________
d. $18 \times 6\% =$ ________	j. $32 \times 4\frac{1}{2}\% =$ ________
e. $60 \times 2.5\% =$ ________	k. $46 \times 2\frac{1}{4}\% =$ ________
f. $40 \times 5.5\% =$ ________	l. $81 \times 5\frac{3}{4}\% =$ ________

B

1. Determine the interest period on each of the following pawnshop loans.

	Date Borrowed	Date Returned	Interest Period In Months
a.	March 5	March 17	________
b.	May 18	June 2	________
c.	February 6	April 12	________
d.	September 9	December 20	________
e.	June 16	October 25	________
f.	April 10	June 5	________
g.	July 23	October 11	________
h.	January 9	May 5	________
i.	December 14	February 25	________
j.	October 23	January 29	________
k.	November 6	February 3	________
l.	September 27	March 20	________

2. How much interest will have to be paid on each of the following pawnshop loans in which the interest period is one month?

	Amount Borrowed	Monthly Rate Of Interest	Interest
a.	$50	2%	$______
b.	40	3%	______
c.	15	4%	______
d.	25	5%	______
e.	12	6%	______
f.	35	7%	______
g.	65	8%	______
h.	70	9%	______
i.	96	4½%	______
j.	47	5½%	______

3. How much interest will have to be paid on each of the following pawnshop loans?

	Amount Borrowed	Monthly Rate Of Interest	Period Of Loan	Interest
a.	$ 80	3%	2 months	$______
b.	10	4%	3 months	______
c.	45	5%	5 months	______
d.	26	6%	4 months	______
e.	18	7%	2 months	______
f.	120	4½%	6 months	______

4. How much interest will have to be paid on each of the following pawnshop loans?

	Amount Borrowed	Monthly Rate Of Interest	Date Borrowed	Date Returned	Period Of Loan (Months)	Interest
a.	$ 20	4%	May 3	June 20	______	$______
b.	60	6%	April 24	July 31	______	______
c.	68	3%	February 21	July 10	______	______
d.	110	2%	June 14	September 2	______	______
e.	75	5%	March 3	August 17	______	______
f.	132	3%	December 5	March 15	______	______
g.	24	3½%	January 16	June 10	______	______
h.	39	2½%	September 21	January 28	______	______

5. How much money will have to be repaid on each of the following pawnshop loans?

	Amount Borrowed	Monthly Rate	Date Borrowed	Date Returned	Period Of Loan (Months)	Interest	Amount Repaid
a.	$ 50	2%	June 12	October 3	______	$______	$______
b.	16	4%	February 17	June 14	______	______	______
c.	41	3%	May 2	October 20	______	______	______

	Amount Borrowed	Monthly Rate	Date Borrowed	Date Returned	Period Of Loan (Months)	Interest	Amount Repaid
d.	$140	5%	March 15	July 27	______	$______	$______
e.	58	$2\frac{1}{2}$%	October 30	January 20	______	______	______
f.	87	$3\frac{1}{2}$%	November 16	March 21	______	______	______

C

1. In one of the states, the law permits pawnbrokers to charge the following interest rates:

On first $100	5% per month
On excess above $100	3% per month

How much interest will have to be paid on each of the following loans in which the interest period is one month?

	Amount Borrowed	Interest
a.	$ 80	$______
b.	120	______
c.	160	______
d.	135	______
e.	108	______
f.	175	______

2. The following pawnshop loans were made in the state whose rates are quoted in Problem 1, above. How much interest had to be paid?

	Amount Borrowed	Date Borrowed	Date Returned	Period Of Loan (Months)	Interest For 1 Month	Total Interest
a.	$ 75	May 20	July 16	______	$______	$______
b.	130	March 6	August 4	______	______	______
c.	150	June 15	September 25	______	______	______
d.	142	February 11	February 26	______	______	______
e.	196	November 24	January 20	______	______	______
f.	231	October 14	March 23	______	______	______

3. How much interest will have to be paid on each of the following loans that were made for the period shown? The monthly rate charged by the pawnbroker is:

$4\frac{1}{2}$% on the amount up to and including $50
3% on the amount in excess of $50

	Amount Borrowed	Period Of Loan	Interest For 1 Month	Total Interest
a.	$ 30	1 month	$______	$______
b.	45	3 months	______	______
c.	85	1 month	______	______
d.	90	4 months	______	______
e.	120	2 months	______	______
f.	175	5 months	______	______

4. The following loans were made at the pawnshop whose rates are quoted in Problem 3, above. How much money had to be returned by the borrower? Include interest.

	Amount Borrowed	Date Borrowed	Date Returned	Period Of Loan	Interest For 1 Month	Total Interest	Amount Repaid
a.	$ 40	May 10	June 1	______	$______	$______	$______
b.	26	July 6	September 4	______	______	______	______
c.	80	February 15	March 12	______	______	______	______
d.	100	June 17	August 25	______	______	______	______
e.	130	March 20	September 15	______	______	______	______
f.	150	December 12	January 10	______	______	______	______
g.	185	November 25	February 6	______	______	______	______
h.	225	September 10	March 21	______	______	______	______

Unit 3: The Credit-Union Loan

Perhaps the least expensive agency from which a person can borrow money is the *credit union*. The difficulty with this, though, is that in order to borrow from such an organization, you must be a member of the group. Credit unions are formed by people who have some common bond. They may be members of the same church, or employees of the same company, or teachers in the same city, or people living in the same apartment house, and so on. One of their purposes in organizing is to give them some place to save their money. More important also, though, is that it gives them some place where they can borrow money at a cost that is usually a good deal less than at the small-loan agency, or the pawnshop, or the installment house, or, indeed, most places.

To form a credit union, the people must first get permission to do so from either the federal or state government. They do this by obtaining a charter to organize. In addition, the federal or state government sends inspectors around periodically to make certain that no one is illegally helping himself to the funds.

Since most of the work is done by volunteers who are members of the credit union, there are very few expenses involved in running such an agency. What little there are usually involve the rent for a small office, expenses for stationery, and, possibly, the salary of a secretary. Hence, practically all the interest collected from borrowers is distributed among the members of the group as interest on their savings. Thus, if the borrowers are asked to pay an interest rate of 8% or 9%, very likely as much as 6% interest rate is paid to the depositors. Usually the 2% or 3% left over is all that is needed to cover expenses. This is much, much less than is needed by other lending agencies to meet their overhead (expenses).

As was pointed out earlier, the depositors and the borrowers in a credit union are exactly the same people. It is not possible to borrow any money from a credit union unless you belong to the association and have some money on deposit with the group. Furthermore, the amount of money you can borrow is limited by how much you can afford to borrow. Thus, the more you earn, the more you are permitted to borrow—within certain limits. The loans are primarily designed for the payment of small debts, or to help you buy such things as TV sets or washing machines without having to pay the high interest rates asked for on installment purchases. However, you could never borrow the money needed to buy a house or, in some cases, a new car. A credit union just does not have that much money to lend. And even if it did, it could not afford to lend so much to one person, for then it would not have any left to lend to someone else in the group.

Finding the cost of borrowing money from a credit union merely involves an application of the interest formula.

ILLUSTRATION 1: Bob Aikens borrowed \$250 from a credit union of which he is a member. He paid off the debt at the end of four months. If the interest rate charged was 7½%, how much money did the loan cost him?

SOLUTION:

$$\begin{aligned} I &= P \times R \times T \\ &= \$250 \times 7\tfrac{1}{2}\% \times 4 \text{ months} \\ &= \$250 \times 7.5\% \times \tfrac{4}{12} \\ &= \$250 \times \overset{.025}{\cancel{.075}} \times \frac{\overset{1}{\cancel{4}}}{\underset{\underset{1}{\cancel{3}}}{\cancel{12}}} \\ &= \$6.25 \end{aligned}$$

EXPLANATION: Just a word of caution: remember to rewrite 7½% in the form 7.5% before changing it to a decimal. Also, the 4 months must be expressed as 4/12 of a year since the interest rate is quoted in terms of a yearly period.

ILLUSTRATION 2: Joan Becker borrowed \$500 from her credit union to purchase a color TV set. At the end of two months, she repaid \$200 with interest, and at the end of five months, she paid off the balance of the debt with interest. If the annual interest rate was 7%, what was the total she returned to the credit union?

SOLUTION:

$$\text{Interest on \$500 for 2 months} = \$500 \times 7\% \times 2 \text{ months}$$
$$= \$500 \times .07 \times \frac{\overset{1}{\cancel{2}}}{\underset{6}{\cancel{12}}}$$
$$= \frac{\$35}{6}$$
$$= \$5.833, \text{ or } \$5.83$$
$$\text{Debt after first 2 months} = \$500 - \$200$$
$$= \$300$$
$$\text{Interest on \$300 for 3 months} = \$300 \times 7\% \times 3 \text{ months}$$
$$= \$300 \times .07 \times \frac{\overset{1}{\cancel{3}}}{\underset{4}{\cancel{12}}}$$
$$= \frac{\$21}{4}$$
$$= \$5.25$$
$$\text{Total repaid} = \$200 + \$300 + \$5.25 + \$5.83$$
$$= \$511.08$$

EXPLANATION: Since Joan kept the full \$500 for only the first two months, she paid interest on that amount for the 2-month period only. At the end of that time, having paid off \$200 with all the interest owed to that date, she still owed the credit union \$300. When the final payment of \$300 was made, she had to pay interest on that amount for three months, for this was the period of time she had kept the \$300.

In the illustrations above, the interest rate was quoted on an annual basis. There are, however, a very large number of credit unions that prefer to quote the interest rate by the month. When this is done, the computation for finding the interest is the same as used when finding the interest on a pawnshop loan.

EXERCISES A

1. Determine the interest on each of the following credit-union loans.

	Principal	Annual Interest Rate	Number Of Months	Interest
a.	$400	7%	3	$______
b.	200	8%	4	______
c.	500	7%	6	______
d.	210	8%	3	______
e.	275	9%	8	______
f.	685	9%	4	______
g.	800	7½%	9	______
h.	400	8½%	8	______
i.	520	8½%	6	______
j.	640	9½%	3	______

2. Determine the amount of money that was returned to the credit union on each of the following loans.

	Principal	Annual Interest Rate	Number Of Months	Interest	Amount Returned
a.	$100	7%	6	$______	$______
b.	90	8%	2	______	______
c.	140	6%	3	______	______
d.	80	9%	1	______	______
e.	150	8½%	4	______	______
f.	240	7½%	3	______	______

B

1. In each of the following loans, the borrower returned the money in two payments. Thus, in exercise "a," he made the first payment with interest at the end of 3 months and paid off the balance 6 months after he had borrowed the money. How much interest was paid on each loan?

	Principal	Annual Interest Rate	Amount Of First Payment	First Payment Made At End of:	Balance Paid At End of:	Total Interest
a.	$600	7%	$200	3 months	6 months	$______
b.	800	8%	400	2 months	5 months	______
c.	900	8%	300	4 months	7 months	______
d.	700	9%	300	6 months	12 months	______
e.	500	9%	100	1 month	5 months	______
f.	400	10%	50	1 month	4 months	______

2. The payments on the following loans were made in the same manner as those in Problem 1, above. What was the total amount of money that was repaid on each loan?

	Principal	Annual Interest Rate	Amount Of First Payment	First Payment Made At End of:	Balance Paid At End of:	Total Interest	Amount Repaid
a.	$200	8%	$100	3 months	6 months	$_____	$_____
b.	400	8%	300	4 months	7 months	_____	_____
c.	900	7%	400	6 months	12 months	_____	_____
d.	800	9%	500	2 months	5 months	_____	_____

C

The credit unions in each of the following exercises charged their members a monthly interest rate for borrowing money. Determine the interest on each of these loans.

	Principal	Monthly Interest Rate	Number Of Months	Interest
a.	$300	1%	1	$_____
b.	350	1%	1	_____
c.	375	1%	2	_____
d.	425	1%	3	_____
e.	100	2%	1	_____
f.	150	2%	2	_____
g.	325	2%	4	_____
h.	175	2%	5	_____
i.	200	$1\frac{1}{2}$%	1	_____
j.	350	$1\frac{1}{2}$%	3	_____
k.	470	$1\frac{1}{2}$%	6	_____
l.	400	$2\frac{1}{2}$%	4	_____
m.	600	$\frac{3}{4}$%	1	_____
n.	800	$\frac{3}{4}$%	8	_____

Unit 4: The Credit-Card Loan

In the early chapters you investigated the use of credit cards when purchasing gasoline, paying for a night's lodging, and even buying clothing. There are a number of credit cards, such as Master Charge, BankAmericard, and American Express, which can be used for borrowing money. This can be done by merely showing the credit card at any of the offices of these companies or at any of the branches of participating banks.

Before a credit card is issued, a check is made to determine how much money the person earns and just how reliable he is in paying off his debts. On the basis of this, a decision is made as to how much money can safely be loaned to this person without fear of it not being returned. Hence, were a person in need of money and had he a Master Charge credit card—or any of the others—he would simply go to a bank that is part of the Master Charge system. The bank would check to see whether the balance owed by this person permitted the lending of the amount he was asking. If the balance showed that the loan could be made, he would receive the money immediately.

Thus, consider the situation where Master Charge had originally decided that you would be allowed to charge purchases up to a total of $1,000. Were you in a position where you already owed $600 for items you had charged against your Master Charge account, then you would not be able to borrow more than $400 until some of the debt was paid.

Computing the charge on a credit card loan is usually done on a daily basis. That is, although the interest rate is quoted as an annual rate, that number is divided by 365 and the daily rate also appears on the statement the credit card holder receives monthly from the company. Thus, if the annual rate is 12%, then the daily rate shown will be .03287%, for this is the quotient when 12% is divided by 365.

ILLUSTRATION 1: During a billing period of 28 days the balance of a credit card loan was $600. If the daily interest rate is .03287%, how much interest will gather on this loan over these 28 days?

EXPLANATION: The interest formula is applied here in exactly the same way as was done in the past. However, since the interest rate is quoted in terms of 1 day and the "time" is stated in terms of "days," then the formula can be used directly.

SOLUTION:

$$\begin{aligned} I &= P \times R \times T \\ &= \$600 \times .03287\% \text{ per day} \times 28 \text{ days} \\ &= \$600 \times .0003287 \times 28 \\ &= \$5.52216, \text{ or } \$5.52 \end{aligned}$$

EXPLANATION (continued): Notice that as usual the percent, .03287%, is changed to a decimal, .0003287, by moving the decimal point two places to the left. The product of $600 and .0003287 gives the amount of interest for 1 day. Multiplying that product by 28 gives the amount of interest for 28 days.

There is a rather unfortunate thing that occurs with a credit card loan, though. As an illustration, on May 10 the credit card company completes its computation of the amount you owe and then mails you the bill for, say, $400. The bill, however, does not reach your home until May 14, and on that day you write a check for the $400 and mail it immediately. Your check finally reaches the company on May 19. Now, although you paid the debt 4 days after the bill was due, you will have to pay 9 days interest since your check was not received until 9 days after May 10, the billing date.

ILLUSTRATION 2: Linda Murray received her credit card statement on February 12. The billing date on the statement was 2/8, while the balance shown for a loan she had made was $450. On February 14, she wrote a check for $450 and mailed it to the credit card company, which received her check on February 19. What was the "balance" that appeared on Linda's statement the following month if the daily rate is .04109%?

EXPLANATION: The only dates of importance when paying off a credit card loan are the date when the bill was completed by the company and the date it received the payment on the loan. In this situation the bill was completed on February 8 and the check was received on February 19. In view of this, Linda will have to pay interest for 11 days.

SOLUTION:

$$
\begin{aligned}
I &= P \times R \times T \\
&= \$450 \times .04109\% \text{ per day} \times 11 \text{ days} \\
&= \$450 \times .0004109 \times 11 \\
&= \$2.033955, \text{ or } \$2.03
\end{aligned}
$$

EXPLANATION (continued): The $2.03 found in the solution above is the balance that Linda still has to pay on the loan.

ILLUSTRATION 3: On the billing date, April 14, the balance on a credit card loan was $500. A check for $200 was received for this loan on April 22. How large was the balance on the next billing date, May 12, if the daily interest rate was .04931%?

EXPLANATION: The interest in this illustration is examined as two separate situations. First, the interest on $500 is found for the period from April 14 to April 22, when the payment was received. This is a period of 8 days. Following this, the interest for the period from April 22 to May 12 is found on $300, which is the amount of debt remaining after the $200-payment was made. The number of days from April 22 to May 12 is 20—see the timetable on page 218. Hence, the balance on May 12 will be the sum of the $500 and the two interest charges less the $200-payment that was made.

SOLUTION:

$$
\begin{aligned}
\text{1st Int.} &= P \times R \times T \\
&= \$500 \times .04931\% \text{ per day} \times 8 \text{ days} \\
&= \$500 \times .0004931 \times 8 \\
&= \$1.9724, \text{ or } \$1.97
\end{aligned}
$$

$$
\begin{aligned}
\text{Balance after payment} &= \$500 - \$200 \\
&= \$300
\end{aligned}
$$

2nd Int. = \$300 × .0004931 × 20
= \$2.9586, or \$2.96
Balance on May 12 = (\$500 + \$1.97 + \$2.96) − \$200
= \$304.93

EXERCISES

A

If you do not recall how to find the answers to the following exercises, you will probably want to refer to the pages indicated for help.

1. Change each of the following percent numerals to its equivalent decimal numeral. (See page 514.)

a. .04527% ________ d. .03076% ________
b. .03621% ________ e. .04127% ________
c. .02984% ________ f. .04062% ________

2. Find the product in each of the following. (See page 518.)

a. \$400 × .03823% = ________
b. \$600 × .05217% = ________
c. \$800 × .02506% = ________
d. \$900 × .03162% = ________
e. \$500 × .04178% = ________

3. Find the product in each of the following. Round off each answer to the nearest cent. (See page 518.)

a. \$700 × .03412% × 10 = ________
b. \$600 × .04235% × 12 = ________
c. \$450 × .03981% × 6 = ________
d. \$350 × .02762% × 15 = ________
e. \$240 × .03052% × 26 = ________

B

1. Each of the following people paid the entire balance on their credit card statement on the date shown below. For how many days will they owe interest on the statement balance?

	Billing Date	Date Bill Was Received	Date Check Arrived	Number of Days
a.	March 12	March 14	March 18	________
b.	June 5	June 9	June 16	________
c.	April 20	April 23	April 27	________
d.	September 28	October 2	October 8	________
e.	January 27	January 29	February 5	________
f.	May 24	May 28	June 10	________

2. How much interest was charged on each of the following credit card loans for the billing period shown?

	Amount of Loan	Number of Days in Billing Period	Daily Rate	Interest
a.	$100	30	.03287%	$_____
b.	200	31	.03287%	_____
c.	600	26	.04109%	_____
d.	500	28	.04109%	_____
e.	700	32	.04931%	_____
f.	400	29	.04931%	_____

3. The loan balance shown on the credit card statement was paid by check and received a number of days after the billing date as shown below. What is the new balance on the loan, that is, how much interest gathered before the check was received by the credit card company?

	Balance	Number of Days	Daily Rate	New Balance
a.	$300	6	.03835%	$_____
b.	500	8	.03835%	_____
c.	750	10	.04383%	_____
d.	450	20	.04383%	_____
e.	240	15	.05753%	_____
f.	360	23	.05753%	_____

4. Each of the following credit card loan balances was paid in full. What will the new loan balance be?

	Balance	Billing Date	Check Received	Number of Days	Daily Rate	New Balance
a.	$400	2/10	2/16	_____	.03424%	$_____
b.	600	3/12	3/22	_____	.03424%	_____
c.	800	5/7	5/20	_____	.03698%	_____
d.	700	7/14	7/26	_____	.03698%	_____
e.	550	6/28	7/5	_____	.03972%	_____
f.	310	11/22	12/3	_____	.03972%	_____

5. The payments shown below were made on credit card loans. What will the new loan balance be? (See Illustration 3.)

	Balance	Billing Date	Amount Of Check	Check Received	Next Billing Date	Daily Rate	New Balance
a.	$500	5/4	$100	5/10	6/2	.04246%	$_____
b.	600	8/16	200	8/26	9/15	.04246%	_____
c.	400	9/21	300	9/29	10/20	.02876%	_____
d.	800	2/8	500	2/14	3/10	.02876%	_____
e.	900	4/12	400	4/20	5/10	.04521%	_____
f.	700	7/16	200	7/28	8/15	.04521%	_____

C

1. The daily interest rate on a credit card loan is .05479%. What is the annual rate on this loan? ________
2. Bruce Dodge repaid a debt of $800 on a credit card loan. His check was in the mail for a period of five days. How much interest did Bruce have to pay as a result of just the mailing time? The daily interest rate was .03506%. ________
3. On March 17, Martha Fuller received a credit card statement dated March 5. The balance of her loan as shown on this statement was $650. How much interest accumulated on this loan during the period of mailing if the daily rate was .04794%? ________

Unit 5: Chapter Review and Test

1. The Alliance Finance Corporation placed the following advertisement in a local newspaper.

LOANS TO FIT YOUR NEEDS

Cash Received By You	Amount of Monthly Payment	Number of Months
$106	$19.47	6
147	14.63	12
387	27.78	18

(annual rate of interest: 34.16%)

   a. How much money will the borrower repay the loan company on the $106 loan? ________
   b. How much money will the borrower repay the loan company on the $387 loan? ________
2. If a person borrowed money from a pawnshop on August 17 and paid off the debt on January 5, for how many months would he be charged interest? ________
3. Steve Billings borrowed $75 from a pawnshop that charged an interest rate of 4% per month on the unpaid balance of the debt. He returned the money with interest at the end of four months.
   a. How much interest did Steve have to pay? ________
   b. What amount did he return to the pawnbroker? ________
4. A pawnbroker has his shop in a state where he is permitted to charge the following monthly interest rates:

On the first $50 of the debt	3½%
On the amount over $50	2%

a. If a person borrows $40 for one month, how much interest will he have to pay? ________

b. If a person borrows $85 for one month, how much interest will he have to pay? ________

c. If a person borrows $125 for five months, how much interest will he have to pay? ________

5. Nancy Brookfield belongs to the credit union at her church. In order to buy a used car, she borrowed $400 from the credit union, agreeing to return the money at the end of nine months. If she was charged an annual interest rate of 8%, how much did she have to return? ________

6. When Phyllis Riley bought her sewing machine, she borrowed $180 from the credit union to which she belonged. She paid off $80 of the loan at the end of two months and the balance of the debt five months after she had borrowed the money. Her credit union charges an annual rate of 9% on money loaned to its members. How much interest did Phyllis have to pay on her debt? ________

7. The Clearfield Firemen's Credit Union charges its members an interest rate of 2% per month on the unpaid balance of money borrowed. When Jim Freeman bought an outboard motor for his boat, he borrowed $650 from this credit union. At the end of five months, he paid off his debt.

   a. How much interest did he have to pay on the loan? ________

   b. How much money did he return to the credit union at the end of the five months? Include interest. ________

8. The billing date on a credit card loan statement is May 15. The borrower receives the bill on May 19 and mails a check for the entire balance of the loan on May 21. The check arrives on May 24. For how many days will the borrower be billed for interest on his next credit card statement? ________

9. The daily interest rate charged by a credit card company is .04794%. How much interest will a borrower have to pay for a 30-day billing period on a loan of $500? ________

10. Edith Bradley received a credit card statement showing a balance of $300 on money she had borrowed. The billing date was June 14 and the date the company received her check for the $300 was June 25. For how much interest will she be billed on her next credit card statement if the daily rate is .04054%? ________

12:07
6
5

CHAPTER 9

INVESTMENTS

For several chapters you have been learning what happens when you go into debt and how you can borrow money. From this you might think that you will always be just one jump ahead of the bill collector. This will just not be so, for the great majority of you will find that you are managing to build up quite a sizable savings account. You will very likely be troubled more by what you should do with your savings than you will be by next month's telephone bill.

The idea of not knowing what to do with the money left over after paying off your bills may strike you as a bit odd at this point. However, jump ahead a few years in your life, and imagine that this will actually happen to you. Even at your age you have no doubt heard of so many people investing their money in stocks and bonds that you begin to wonder whether some day you will do the same. There seems to be little point in talking about investing in stocks and bonds, though, until you find out just what they are.

In this chapter, you are going to take a look at these two ways of having your money work for you. It should give you some thoughts about what you can do with your money other than keep it in a bank.

Unit 1: The Stock Market

Section 1: The Stock Market Report

Suppose that five of you get together and form a company for producing a new flavored soda that is to be sold in a pressurized can. You find that you need $600 for the expenses involved in starting the business. One of you contributes $200; a second, only $50; a third, $150; a fourth, $100; and the fifth also $100. In order to be fair to everyone, you decide that each of you will be given sheets of paper on which is stated that every sheet of paper represents $10 in the value of the company. This means that there will be 60 sheets of paper altogether. The person who contributed the $200 will receive 20 of these sheets, while the one who gave $50 will get 5.

Each sheet of paper, called a *stock certificate*, actually indicates that you own 10 shares of stock in the company. It signifies that each of you is a part owner of this company. The person contributing the greater amount will own the greater part of the company.

Imagine that when once people tasted the soda, they just drank more and more of it. In fact, business was so good that the original $600 invested by the five of you jumped to $1,800 in value. Thus, the 60 shares of stock that had originally been worth $10 each were now worth $30 each. Hence, the 20 shares owned by the person who had invested $200 jumped to $600 in value. If he wants to sell either some of these shares, or all of them, to anyone else, he can do so at the $30 price per share.

In time business takes a turn for the worse. People find that a good part of the soda spray from the pressurized can wets their clothing. It isn't long before the value of the company drops from a high point of $1,800 to a low point of $300. When this happens, each of the 60 shares of stock that had been worth $30 is now worth only $5. Hence, people buying these shares of stock will now pay no more than $5 each for them, although when the business was started, each of these pieces of paper was worth twice as much.

Most companies today get started in exactly the same way as the small soda business above. Since a great deal of money is needed to operate a business, a great many people are needed to become part owners. When the company is first organized and shares of stock are sold, it is relatively simple to determine the value of each share, for all shares together represent the value of the company. In the little company you organized, the entire value was only $600, thus making each of the 60 shares worth $10. The original value of each share of stock is called the *par value* of the stock. In time, however, the value of each share fluctuates (varies), depending on how the company prospers.

But, how can you go about buying stock? It is very unlikely that you would personally know someone who happens to own shares in the company in which you wish to invest. Hence, you will probably go to a *stockbroker*—a man who buys and sells stock for other people. He, in turn, will go to a *stock market*—a place where stocks are bought and sold. There he will inquire of other brokers if they know of anyone who would like to sell the stock that you want to purchase. Usually, there will be some such person. In that event, your broker will arrange to buy the stock for you and then bill you not only for the amount he had to pay, but also a small additional fee to cover the cost of his services.

In the event you want to sell some stocks that you hold, you would follow exactly the same procedure. Now, however, the broker would turn over to you the amount he had received from the buyer, only withholding a small amount to pay for his services. Thus, you have to pay the broker at the time he buys the stock for you and again at the time he sells it for you.

The marketplaces where stocks are bought and sold are called *stock exchanges*. The stocks of all companies are not handled at every exchange, but only those stocks that the brokers in that exchange decide they want to handle. The largest of these exchanges is the New York Stock Exchange, which is located in New York City. Another exchange located in New York is the American Stock Exchange. There are a number of other exchanges located throughout the country and throughout the world.

So many people are interested in stock investments that most newspapers publish the daily sales transactions in at least one or more of the stock exchanges. These stock-market reports appear in the form shown on page 306.

Chances are that the first thing that strikes you as you look at this table is the large number of fractions that appear. Actually, there are only seven different fractions that you have to deal with, and these are:

$$1/8,\ 1/4,\ 3/8,\ 1/2,\ 5/8,\ 3/4,\ 7/8$$

Each of these fractions represents a fractional part of a dollar, and these are the only fractional parts of a dollar at which stocks are sold. That is, even if you wanted to, you couldn't purchase a share of stock at $12.57, for it is not sold anywhere at that price. Notice that these fractions are all eighths of a dollar. The fraction $1/4$ is really $2/8$ that has been reduced to its lowest terms, while the fraction $1/2$ was originally the fraction $4/8$.

Since each of the fractions represents a part of a dollar, it might be well if they are written in their decimal form, for this is the way you will be using them.

$$
\begin{aligned}
\$\tfrac{1}{8} &= 12\tfrac{1}{2}\text{¢} = \$.125\\
\$\tfrac{1}{4} &= 25\text{¢} = \$.25\\
\$\tfrac{3}{8} &= 37\tfrac{1}{2}\text{¢} = \$.375\\
\$\tfrac{1}{2} &= 50\text{¢} = \$.50\\
\$\tfrac{5}{8} &= 62\tfrac{1}{2}\text{¢} = \$.625\\
\$\tfrac{3}{4} &= 75\text{¢} = \$.75\\
\$\tfrac{7}{8} &= 87\tfrac{1}{2}\text{¢} = \$.875
\end{aligned}
$$

Hence, if a share of stock is selling at 14⅞, this would mean that the purchaser had to pay $14⅞, or $14.875 for the share. Similarly, when you say that you will buy a share at 14½, it means that you are willing to pay $14.50 for it.

STOCK MARKET QUOTATIONS

Year To Date High	Year To Date Low	Stocks & Dividend	Sales In 100's	Open	High	Low	Close	Net Change
19½	12	Abacus Corp. 2	16	15½	16	15	15¼	+½
85	72	Abbott Markets 5	4	75	75½	75	75	−1
16¾	12½	Adams Department Store 1	29	15¼	15¾	14⅞	15	+¼
39	25¼	Alabama Electric Co. 2	1	36⅞	36⅞	36⅞	36⅞	+½
16⅝	12⅞	Allen, Inc. 1.20	32	13¼	13⅜	13⅛	13¼	+⅛
78	64	American Bakers pf. 2½	6	64	64¾	64	64¼	−½
96⅞	71½	American Corporation 2	58	84½	85¼	83¼	84½	+1½
12¼	5¾	Atlas Industries	24	8	8¾	8	8½	
48⅝	41⅛	Baldwin Tools 2.50	26	44⅞	45¼	44¾	45	+⅜
58¼	44⅞	Baltimore Credit 1	31	47½	48¼	47⅛	47⅝	−½
65⅜	50¾	Baxter, Inc., pf. 3	7	62⅝	63⅞	62⅜	63¾	+1¼
5⅞	3⅛	Beech Instruments .15	81	4¼	4⅜	4⅛	4⅜	+⅛
17¾	13	Bliss Petroleum 1	9	15¼	15⅝	15¼	15½	+⅞
55½	41½	Bond Foods pf. 2½	14	48½	49	48¼	48¾	−¼
40⅜	23¼	Bullard and Sons 1.70	38	27¾	28	27½	28	+¼
36⅞	29⅝	California Breweries 2	6	30⅝	30⅝	30⅝	30⅝	
46½	37½	Canadian Gas Co. 2	14	38¼	39½	38	38	−1
81⅞	62¼	Carpenter Corp. 1.80	55	78¾	79½	78¼	79	+⅞
43½	35¼	Cenco Chemicals 1.50	26	42	42½	41	42¼	−½
31½	27	Champion Soup Co. 1.06	18	28	28	27	28	
46¾	37⅞	City R. R. Services 1½	16	39⅛	39⅞	38¾	39½	−⅛
82¼	75	Colonial, Inc. 3.25	88	78½	78¾	78	78½	+2
20⅝	14¾	Crane Industries pf. 1½	75	19⅛	19¼	17⅝	18⅜	+¾
33	29⅝	Dana Power and Light Co. 1.60	9	30½	30½	30¼	30½	+⅛
34½	19⅞	Diamond Airlines	68	28⅜	28½	26	28	+1⅛
20¼	13½	Dobbs Productions .37	14	14	14¼	13⅞	13⅞	−⅞
36¾	30¾	Dow Aircraft .84	92	34	35	33	34½	+1
36	25¼	Drexel Mines .70	44	28	28½	28	28	−⅜
23⅜	18¼	Dunhill Limited pf. 1.05	27	23	23⅛	22½	22⅞	+¼
24¼	16½	Dynamics, Inc. 1.20	16	18¼	18½	17½	18	+⅝

Now you are ready to find out what each of the columns in the stock market report represents. You can do this by examining the quotation for the first company listed.

Year To Date		Stocks & Dividend	Sales In 100's	Open	High	Low	Close	Net Change
High	Low							
19½	12	Abacus Corp. 2	16	15½	16	15	15¼	+½

Year to Date: There are two words that appear under the heading "Year to Date." These are the words "High" and "Low." The numeral 19½ written under the word "High" signifies that the highest price anyone paid for a share of the Abacus Corporation stock thus far that year was $19.50. What does the 12 under the word "Low" represent?

Stocks and Dividend: Obviously, the word "Stocks" refers to the name of the company that is listed in this column, and in this illustration, the company is Abacus Corporation. The explanation for the word "Dividend" is a little more involved. As was pointed out earlier, a stockholder in a company is actually a part owner of the company. He and a great number of other people jointly own the company. Either once or twice a year, or, perhaps, even four times a year, the directors of the company meet to determine how much profit the company had earned for that period of time—assuming that there has been a profit. This profit is then divided among all the shareholders. As you can easily see, it would not be right to give all shareholders the same amount of profit, for some might own as many as 500 shares, while others might own only 5 shares. To distribute the profit fairly, the same amount is allotted for each share of stock. Thus, a person who owns 10 shares of stock will receive 10 times the amount that a person who owns 1 share of stock receives. In the illustration, the numeral "2" to the right of the name of the company tells you that during the previous year, the Abacus Corporation gave its stockholders $2 for each share of stock they held. Thus, a stockholder who owned 400 shares would have received $800 as his part of the company's profit. The $2 profit allotted for each share of stock is called a *stock dividend*.

There is another feature about dividends that should be pointed out. Stocks can be divided roughly into two different types—*preferred* and *common*. The owner of preferred stock in a company is usually guaranteed a certain percent of the par value each year as his share of the profit. Remember that the par value of the stock is its original value. Thus, if the par value of the stock is $50, and if he owns "5% preferred" stock of the company, it would mean that he will receive 5% of $50, or $2.50 each year on each share he owns. In fact, the preferred stockholders must receive their guaranteed share of the profit before even one penny is distributed among the common stockholders. If no profit is left over, then the common stockholders get nothing. If a great deal of profit remains, then the common stockholders share what remains.

Sales in 100's: Although the stocks in a few companies are sold in groups of 10 shares each—called "lots of 10"—the sales of the great bulk of companies listed on any exchange can be made only in lots of 100. Thus, these sales take place only in what are called *round* lots, that is, in amounts of 100 shares, or 200 shares, or 300 shares, and so on. This is not to say that you couldn't ask your broker to buy 37 shares of stock of a certain company for you. This can be done, but not in the normal way in which stocks are bought at a stock exchange.

Return now to the numerals under the words "Sales in 100's." The numeral "16" for the Abacus Corporation implies that 16 hundred (1600) shares of this company's stock were sold that day at that stock exchange.

Open, High, Low, Close: The numerals under these words tell a little about what happened to the price at which the stocks were sold that day. For instance, on the very first sale that day the purchaser had to pay 15½, or $15.50, for each share of the Abacus Corporation stock. During the day, the highest that anyone had to pay for a share of this company's stock was $16 per share. The numeral 15¼ under the word "Close" tells you that the last person to buy Abacus Corporation stock that day had to pay $15.25 for each share.

These common-stock certificates represent shares of ownership in American corporations. Stocks of more than 1,400 companies are traded on the New York Stock Exchange.

Net Change: One of the things that a person likes to know when he examines the quotations of a particular stock is whether the price that day is higher or lower than it was the day before. It is the numeral that appears under the words "Net Change" that gives him some idea of this. This numeral indicates the amount the closing price per share that day has risen or fallen over the closing price of the previous day. If there is a positive sign (+) in front of the numeral, then the price has risen. If there is a negative (−) sign, then the price has fallen. In the illustration of the Abacus Corporation, the numeral is $+1/2$. This means that the closing price of $15\frac{1}{4}$ is $1/2$ dollar more than the closing price of the day before. Hence, the closing price of the previous day must have been $14\frac{3}{4}$, or $14.75.

ILLUSTRATION: Joe Manning purchased 400 shares of the Baxter, Inc., preferred stock at the "Low" of the day shown in the stock-market report on page 306. How much did he have to pay for these stocks?

EXPLANATION: The price that Joe paid for each share is found in the column under the word "Low." For Baxter, Inc., it is $62\frac{3}{8}$ or, $62.375. Since this is the price for 1 share, the price for 400 shares will be 400 times as much as this.

SOLUTION:

$$\begin{aligned}\text{"Low" of day} &= 62\tfrac{3}{8}\\ &= \$62.375\\ \text{Cost of 400 shares} &= 400 \times \$62.375\\ &= \$24{,}950\end{aligned}$$

EXPLANATION (continued): It is important that you realize that Joe had to pay more than the $24,950 for the 400 shares of stock. Not only did he have to pay a broker's commission, but also, possibly, some other small charges in connection with the purchase. None of these fees will be considered in any of this work.

EXERCISES A

1. Rewrite each of these numerals in its equivalent decimal form.

a. $15½	________	f. $57⅛	________	k. $1⅝	________
b. $32¼	________	g. $85⅛	________	l. $9⅞	________
c. $49¾	________	h. $43⅛	________	m. $14⅞	________
d. $27¼	________	i. $7⅝	________	n. $26⅞	________
e. $16⅛	________	j. $2⅝	________	o. $81⅞	________

2. Find the product in each of the following exercises. Change each of the numerals to decimal form before multiplying.

a. 10 × $2½ = ______	m. 100 × $54⅝ = ______
b. 20 × $5¼ = ______	n. 100 × $18⅝ = ______
c. 60 × $7¾ = ______	o. 100 × $36⅝ = ______
d. 25 × $6½ = ______	p. 200 × $60⅝ = ______
e. 55 × $9¼ = ______	q. 200 × $17⅛ = ______
f. 75 × $8¾ = ______	r. 300 × $4⅛ = ______
g. 45 × $12¼ = ______	s. 400 × $5⅜ = ______
h. 65 × $15½ = ______	t. 600 × $16⅜ = ______
i. 35 × $32¼ = ______	u. 200 × $26⅝ = ______
j. 100 × $14⅛ = ______	v. 500 × $12⅝ = ______
k. 100 × $26⅜ = ______	w. 300 × $40⅞ = ______
l. 100 × $42⅜ = ______	x. 400 × $32⅞ = ______

3. Determine the sum in each of the following exercises. Change each of the numerals to decimal form before adding.

a. $16 + $½ = ______	l. $18⅛ + $¼ = ______
b. $27 + $¼ = ______	m. $23⅜ + $½ = ______
c. $41 + $¾ = ______	n. $15¾ + $⅝ = ______
d. $8½ + $¼ = ______	o. $29⅞ + $¼ = ______
e. $5¾ + $½ = ______	p. $76⅝ + $⅜ = ______
f. $14¼ + $¾ = ______	q. $41½ + $⅞ = ______
g. $62¾ + $1 = ______	r. $59⅛ + $1¼ = ______
h. $27½ + $¾ = ______	s. $62⅜ + $1⅝ = ______
i. $85¼ + $½ = ______	t. $37¼ + $2⅛ = ______
j. $27¾ + $¾ = ______	u. $94½ + $1⅜ = ______
k. $52¼ + $¼ = ______	v. $80⅛ + $2⅝ = ______

4. Determine the difference in each of the following exercises. Change each of the numerals to decimal form before finding the difference.

a. $12 − $½ = ______	h. $42⅞ − $¾ = ______
b. $25 − $¾ = ______	i. $31¾ − $⅝ = ______
c. $56 − $⅝ = ______	j. $65½ − $¾ = ______
d. $39 − $⅜ = ______	k. $51¼ − $1⅛ = ______
e. $9½ − $¼ = ______	l. $72⅜ − $2¾ = ______
f. $7¾ − $½ = ______	m. $45⅛ − $1½ = ______
g. $16⅝ − $¼ = ______	n. $29¼ − $1⅝ = ______

B

The stock quotations that appear on page 306 are to be used in answering each of the questions in the following exercises. Express each answer in decimal form.

1. What was the highest price paid this year prior to the day of this stock table for a share of stock in each of the following companies?

Company	Price per Share
a. Alabama Electric Co.	$________
b. Bond Foods pf.	________
c. Baltimore Credit	________
d. Bliss Petroleum	________
e. Baxter, Inc., pf.	________
f. California Breweries	________

2. What was the first price paid that day for a share of stock in each of the following companies?

Company	Price per Share
a. Abbott Markets	$________
b. American Corporation	________
c. Bullard and Sons	________
d. City R.R. Services	________
e. Diamond Airlines	________
f. Baldwin Tools	________

3. What was the lowest price paid that day for a share of stock in each of the following companies?

Company	Price per Share
a. Atlas Industries	$________
b. Drexel Mines	________
c. Dynamics, Inc.	________
d. Dana Power and Light Co.	________
e. City R.R. Services	________
f. Adams Department Store	________

4. What was the net change that day for a share of stock in each of the following companies? Indicate whether the price had increased or decreased over the closing price of the previous day.

Company	Net Change	Increase Or Decrease
a. Colonial, Inc.	$________	________
b. Abbott Markets	________	________
c. Alabama Electric Co.	________	________
d. American Corporation	________	________
e. Beech Instruments	________	________
f. Drexel Mines	________	________
g. Diamond Airlines	________	________
h. Dobbs Productions	________	________

5. What was the last price paid for a share of stock in each of the following companies on the day prior to the one shown in the quotations on page 306?

Company	Last Price For Day Shown	Net Change	Last Price Of Previous Day
a. Dow Aircraft	$________	$________	$________
b. Canadian Gas Co.	________	________	________
c. Champion Soup Co.	________	________	________
d. Adams Department Store	________	________	________
e. Bond Foods pf.	________	________	________
f. Cenco Chemicals	________	________	________
g. Baldwin Tools	________	________	________
h. Bliss Petroleum	________	________	________
i. Baltimore Credit	________	________	________
j. Crane Industries pf.	________	________	________

C

1. How much will the buyer have to pay on each of the following stock purchases?

	Price per Share	Number Of Shares	Total Price
a.	42	100	$________
b.	17½	100	________
c.	15¾	100	________
d.	52¼	100	________
e.	31⅜	100	________
f.	67⅛	200	________
g.	46⅝	400	________
h.	25⅞	300	________

2. How much did the buyer have to pay on each of the following stock purchases that were made on the day of the stock-market quotations on page 306?

Company	Number Of Shares	Price Per Share	Price Per Share In Dollars	Total Price
a. Atlas Industries	100	Open	$________	$________
b. Abbott Markets	100	Low	________	________
c. Bullard and Sons	100	Low	________	________
d. Baldwin Tools	100	High	________	________
e. Baxter, Inc., pf.	200	Close	________	________
f. Allen, Inc.	200	High	________	________
g. Crane Industries pf.	200	Open	________	________
h. Dobbs Productions	300	Low	________	________
i. Dunhill Limited pf.	300	Close	________	________
j. Baltimore Credit	400	Low	________	________

D

1. Timothy Crane purchased 200 shares of Adams Department Store stock at the closing price in the quotations on page 306.
   a. How much did he pay for the stock? ________
   b. How much would the stock have cost him had he made the purchase at the closing price of the previous day? ________
   c. How much could he have saved had he been able to make the purchase at the closing price of the previous day? ________
2. Frank Delman purchased 300 shares of Baxter, Inc., preferred stock at the "Low" of the day in the quotations that appear on page 306.
   a. How much did he save on each share of stock by not having to buy it at the "High" of the day? ________
   b. How much did he save on the 300 shares by buying them at the "Low" of the day rather than the "High"? ________
3. Patricia Trent was lucky enough to have been able to purchase 100 shares of Bullard and Sons at the "Low" of the year (see page 306).
   a. How much did these stocks cost her? ________
   b. Had she been equally lucky and sold them at the "High" of the year, how much would she have received? ________
   c. How much profit would she have made on the purchase and sale of this stock? ________

Section 2: Computing Dividends

The common stockholder does not know from year to year how large the dividends on his shares will be. Since the company's profits vary over the years, he has every reason to believe that the dividends he receives will also vary. However, when you examine a large number of companies, you find that the dividend distributed on each share remains pretty much the same over the years, although the earnings and the profits of the companies change a great deal. It would seem that if you planned to purchase the stock of a company and wanted to know what you might expect to receive as a dividend on each share, you would be fairly safe in assuming that the dividend for the coming year would be much the same as it had been for the past one. Hence, by examining the quotations on page 306, you can see that the American Corporation paid its shareholders $2 per share in dividends during the previous year. In view of this, it is likely that it will pay $2 in dividends during the coming year. Incidentally, by looking at the quotations, it is not possible to tell whether the $2 was paid in a lump sum, or in two installments during the year (semiannually), or, perhaps, in four installments (quarterly).

ILLUSTRATION 1: Raymond DaSilva owns 200 shares of Bullard and Sons stock. How much did Raymond receive in dividends from the company last year? (Use the quotations on page 306.)

EXPLANATION: Next to the words "Bullard and Sons" appears the numeral 1.70. This means that $1.70 was the dividend given for each share of stock last year. Since Raymond owns 200 shares, he received 200 times this amount.

SOLUTION:

$$\begin{aligned} \text{Dividend per share} &= \$1.70 \\ \text{Dividends on 200 shares} &= 200 \times \$1.70 \\ &= \$340 \end{aligned}$$

The person who owns preferred stock is a little more certain of how much he can expect annually in dividends than the holder of common stock. His stock certificate specifically states that either annually, or semiannually, or quarterly, he will receive a fixed percent of the par value of the stock.

ILLUSTRATION 2: Mary Ryan owns 200 shares of the Sunshine Drug Company 6% preferred stock. When she purchased the stock, she paid 46⅛ for each share. However, the par value of the stock is $50. How large was her annual dividend check?

EXPLANATION: The amount a person pays for preferred stock has absolutely nothing to do with the dividends he receives. The dividends are computed on the basis of the par value, and, hence, you completely ignore the 46⅛ price that Mary paid for each share. The dividend on one share is determined by finding 6% of $50, while the dividends on 200 shares are 200 times this amount.

SOLUTION:

$$\begin{aligned} \text{Dividend per share} &= 6\% \text{ of } \$50 \\ &= .06 \times \$50 \\ &= \$3.00 \\ \text{Dividends on 200 shares} &= 200 \times \$3 \\ &= \$600 \end{aligned}$$

ILLUSTRATION 3: Fred Persing purchased 80 shares of Texas Oil Company's 5½% preferred stock at 104½ per share. If the par value of the stock is $100, how much is Fred's quarterly dividend payment?

EXPLANATION: Here, again, you ignore the purchase price of the stock and use only the par value in computing the dividends. As in Illustration 1, the annual dividends are found for the entire 80 shares.

This amount is divided by 4 to determine the quarterly dividend.

SOLUTION:

$$\begin{aligned}\text{Annual dividend per share} &= 5\tfrac{1}{2}\% \text{ of } \$100\\ &= .055 \times \$100\\ &= \$5.50\\ \text{Annual dividends on 80 shares} &= 80 \times \$5.50\\ &= \$440.00\\ \text{Quarterly dividends on 80 shares} &= \tfrac{1}{4} \times \$440\\ &= \$110\end{aligned}$$

EXERCISES A

1. Use the quotations that appear on page 306 to determine the dividend per share that was paid by each of the following companies during the previous year.

Company	Dividend	Company	Dividend
a. Baltimore Credit	$______	f. California Breweries	$______
b. Colonial, Inc.	______	g. Dobbs Productions	______
c. Dunhill Limited pf.	______	h. Champion Soup Co.	______
d. Crane Industries pf.	______	i. Beech Instruments	______
e. Diamond Airlines	______	j. American Bakers pf.	______

2. Determine the annual dividends received by each of the following people who owned the number of shares of stock indicated.

	Number Of Shares	Annual Dividend Per Share	Dividend
a.	100	50¢	$______
b.	100	75¢	______
c.	80	65¢	______
d.	40	$1.20	______
e.	75	$2.25	______
f.	200	62½¢	______
g.	250	18½¢	______
h.	300	67½¢	______

3. Use the quotations on page 306 to determine the dividends paid the previous year to the stockholders in the following companies.

Company	Number Of Shares	Dividend Per Share	Total Dividends
a. Alabama Electric Co.	100	$______	$______
b. Baldwin Tools	100	______	______
c. Bullard and Sons	200	______	______
d. Dow Aircraft	800	______	______
e. Bond Foods pf.	75	______	______
f. City R.R. Services	35	______	______

4. What annual dividend can each of the following preferred stockholders expect to receive on each share of stock? Do not round off your answers.

	Par Value Per Share	Annual Dividend Rate	Annual Dividend
a.	$ 50	5%	$______
b.	100	5%	______
c.	100	5½%	______
d.	50	5½%	______
e.	50	6¼%	______
f.	100	4¾%	______
g.	50	4¾%	______
h.	25	5%	______
i.	25	4½%	______
j.	10	8%	______
k.	10	6%	______
l.	10	5½%	______

5. What annual dividend can each of the following preferred stockholders expect to receive?

	Number Of Shares	Par Value Per Share	Annual Dividend Rate	Annual Dividend Per Share	Total Dividends
a.	100	$ 50	6%	$______	$______
b.	100	50	7%	______	______
c.	100	100	6%	______	______
d.	50	100	4%	______	______
e.	75	50	6½%	______	______
f.	200	100	6½%	______	______
g.	200	100	4½%	______	______
h.	100	100	4.75%	______	______
i.	100	50	5.35%	______	______
j.	40	10	8%	______	______

6. What semiannual dividend can each of the following preferred stockholders expect to receive?

	Number Of Shares	Par Value Per Share	Annual Dividend Rate	Annual Dividend Per Share	Total Annual Dividends	Total Semiannual Dividends
a.	100	$100	7%	$______	$______	$______
b.	50	100	3%	______	______	______
c.	40	50	4%	______	______	______
d.	100	50	4½%	______	______	______
e.	70	50	7½%	______	______	______
f.	60	100	6.3%	______	______	______
g.	200	100	5.8%	______	______	______
h.	200	50	6.45%	______	______	______

7. What quarterly dividend can each of the following preferred stockholders expect to receive?

	Number Of Shares	Par Value Per Share	Annual Dividend Rate	Annual Dividend Per Share	Total Annual Dividends	Total Quarterly Dividends
a.	200	$100	7%	$______	$______	$______
b.	100	50	6%	______	______	______
c.	100	50	4.2%	______	______	______
d.	30	50	5.3%	______	______	______
e.	50	10	6.5%	______	______	______
f.	300	10	7.2%	______	______	______

B

1. Bill Stanton purchased 65 shares of common stock and 200 shares of 5% preferred stock of the Manhattan Business Corporation.
   a. If the company has been paying an annual dividend of $1.07 per share on its common stock, how much in dividends should Bill expect to receive over the period of one year on his common stock? ______
   b. If the par value of the preferred stock is $50, how much in dividends should he expect to receive over the period of one year on his preferred stock? ______
   c. What total dividends should he expect to receive from the Manhattan Business Corporation over the period of one year? ______

2. For some years now, Mona Feret has owned 200 shares of Dynamics, Inc., stock and 350 shares of Cenco Chemicals stock. The stock of both of these companies is sold at the exchange whose quotations appear on page 306.
   a. How much did she receive in dividends from the Dynamics company last year? ______
   b. How much did she receive in dividends from Cenco Chemicals last year? ______
   c. What total dividends did she receive from both of these companies last year? ______

3. The 5% preferred stock of the Trans-Atlantic Airlines Company is selling for $75 per share, but it has a par value of $100. The 6% preferred stock of the Southern Airlines Company is also selling for $75 per share, but it has a par value of $50.
   a. What is the annual dividend paid per share by the Trans-Atlantic Company? ______
   b. What is the annual dividend paid per share by the Southern Airlines Company? ______
   c. When you consider only the dividend and cost of each of these stocks, which is the better buy? ______

Section 3: Profit or Loss on Stock Investments

The person who spends his time buying stocks one day and selling them the next after a slight rise in price is probably doing nothing more than supporting his broker. When you consider the broker's fees and the various other expenses on stock transactions, an investor's added costs will run anywhere from a high of 9% to a low of 1/2% of the price of the stocks each time he buys or sells. The person investing around $300 to $400 will find that his charges are at about the 4% rate. Had he been able to invest around $5,000, the added fees would be in the neighborhood of 1%. In general, the average person buying stock can count on paying about 2% of the price in broker's fees and other expenses. This is the rate that will be used in the work that follows in this section.

ILLUSTRATION 1: What was the approximate total amount that Leonard Shanks had to pay when he purchased 100 shares of Hayes Products, Inc., at 23 1/2?

SOLUTION:

Cost per share = 23 1/2, or $23.50
Cost of 100 shares = 100 × $23.50
= $2,350
Approximate amount of additional fees = 2% of $2,350
= .02 × $2,350
= $47
Approximate total cost of purchase = $2,350 + $47
= $2,397

EXPLANATION: The approximate amount of the additional fees is about 2% of the cost of 100 shares. Hence, it is simply a matter of computing 2% of $2,350 to determine these fees. To do this, you rewrite the percent numeral 2% in its decimal numeral equivalent form as .02. The fees of $47, when added to the cost of $2,350, give you the approximate total amount that Leonard had to pay for the purchase.

ILLUSTRATION 2: Approximately how much money did Marie Larson receive from her broker at the time she sold her 50 shares of Howard Nickel Company stock at 42 3/8?

SOLUTION:

Selling price per share = 42 3/8, or $42.375
Selling price of 50 shares = 50 × $42.375
= $2,118.75

$$\begin{aligned}\text{Approximate amount of additional fees} &= 2\% \text{ of } \$2{,}118.75\\ &= .02 \times \$2{,}118.75\\ &= \$42.375, \text{ or } \$42.38\\ \text{Approximate amount received by Marie} &= \$2{,}118.75 - \$42.38\\ &= \$2{,}076.37\end{aligned}$$

EXPLANATION: The computation in this solution is much the same as it is for Illustration 1. They differ, though, in the very last step, for now the fees have to be subtracted from the selling price of the stock. This is much the same as a situation in which you might bring a camera to someone and ask him to sell it for you. He agrees to do this on the condition that you pay him $5 for his services. After selling the camera for, say, $70, instead of turning this amount over to you, he gives you only $65. The remaining $5 he keeps as his fee. Similarly, in this illustration, the charges came to approximately $42.38. This is deducted from the selling price of $2,118.75, and the balance, $2,076.37, is turned over to Marie.

The goal in this section is to develop some means of finding the profit (or loss) in the purchase and sale of stock. Consider, for instance, what the total fees might be in buying stock for $1,000 and selling it for $2,000.

$$\begin{aligned}\text{Fees paid on purchase of stock} &= 2\% \text{ of } \$1{,}000\\ &= .02 \times \$1{,}000\\ &= \$20\\ \text{Fees paid on sale of stock} &= 2\% \text{ of } \$2{,}000\\ &= .02 \times \$2{,}000\\ &= \$40\\ \text{Total fees paid on purchase and sale} &= \$20 + \$40\\ &= \$60\end{aligned}$$

The cost of the stock plus the selling price comes to $3,000. When you take 2% of this sum, it again equals $60, which is the total of the fees paid on both purchase and sale.

$$\begin{aligned}2\% \text{ of } \$3{,}000 &= .02 \times \$3{,}000\\ &= \$60\end{aligned}$$

It would appear, therefore, that if you are interested in finding the total fees paid on both the purchase and sale of the same stock, time can be saved by adding these two amounts and taking 2% of the sum. This is much easier than finding 2% of each number individually and then determining the sum.

ILLUSTRATION 3: How much profit or loss did Michael O'Hara

have when he bought 100 shares of Reliable Products, Inc., at 37 and sold them at 38½?

SOLUTION:

$$\text{Total cost} = 100 \times \$37$$
$$= \$3{,}700$$
$$\text{Total selling price} = 100 \times \$38.50$$
$$= \$3{,}850$$
$$\text{Total profit before considering fees} = \$3{,}850 - \$3{,}700$$
$$= \$150$$
$$\text{Approximate fees} = 2\% \text{ of } (\$3{,}700 + \$3{,}850)$$
$$= .02 \times \$7{,}550$$
$$= \$151$$
$$\text{Approximate loss after considering fees} = \$151 - \$150$$
$$= \$1$$

EXPLANATION: In determining the approximate fees on both the buying and selling of the stock, you first add the purchase price to the selling price, and then find 2% of the total. It is interesting to note that the profit of $150 that Michael may have thought he was going to make dwindled to a loss of $1 after the fees were deducted.

EXERCISES A

1. Determine the approximate fees that will have to be paid on each of the following stock orders.

	Total Selling Price	Approximate Fees		Total Selling Price	Approximate Fees
a.	$2,000	$______	e.	$875	$______
b.	3,000	______	f.	618	______
c.	1,500	______	g.	746	______
d.	2,300	______	h.	957	______

2. Determine the approximate fees that will have to be paid on each of the following stock sales.

	Number Of Shares	Selling Price Per Share	Total Selling Price	Approximate Fees
a.	100	25	$______	$______
b.	100	27½	______	______
c.	100	38¾	______	______
d.	100	16⅛	______	______
e.	100	22⅝	______	______
f.	50	45¼	______	______
g.	50	62⅜	______	______
h.	40	71⅞	______	______

3. Use the stock quotations on page 306 to determine the approximate fees that had to be paid on each of the following stock sales.

	Number Of Shares	Name Of Company	Selling at:	Total Selling Price	Approximate Fees
a.	100	Atlas Industries	Open	$________	$________
b.	100	Bond Foods pf.	High	________	________
c.	200	Abacus Corp.	Low	________	________
d.	200	Cenco Chemicals	Low	________	________
e.	200	American Bankers pf.	Close	________	________
f.	500	Beech Instruments	High	________	________

4. What is the approximate total cost, including fees, that will have to be paid by the buyer on each of the following stock purchases?

	Total Purchase Price	Approximate Fees	Approximate Total Cost
a.	$1,000	$________	$________
b.	4,000	________	________
c.	2,500	________	________
d.	3,600	________	________
e.	1,250	________	________
f.	2,375	________	________

5. What is the approximate amount the seller will receive after fees are deducted on each of the following stock sales?

	Total Selling Price	Approximate Fees	Approximate Amount Received
a.	$5,000	$________	$________
b.	3,500	________	________
c.	2,700	________	________
d.	4,300	________	________
e.	2,450	________	________
f.	1,325	________	________

6. What is the approximate total amount, including fees, that will have to be paid by the buyer on each of the following stock purchases?

	Number Of Shares	Cost Per Share	Purchase Price	Approximate Fees	Approximate Total Purchase Price
a.	100	15	$________	$________	$________
b.	100	$21\frac{1}{2}$	________	________	________
c.	100	$34\frac{1}{4}$	________	________	________
d.	200	$42\frac{3}{4}$	________	________	________
e.	200	$26\frac{3}{4}$	________	________	________
f.	400	$12\frac{5}{8}$	________	________	________

7. What is the approximate total amount, less fees, that will be received by the seller on each of the following stock sales? Use the quotations on page 306.

	Number Of Shares	Name Of Company	Selling at:	Selling Price	Approximate Fees	Approximate Amount Received
a.	100	Bullard and Sons	Close	$____	$____	$____
b.	100	Abbott Markets	Low	____	____	____
c.	100	Bliss Petroleum	Close	____	____	____
d.	200	Dobbs Productions	High	____	____	____
e.	200	Diamond Airlines	Open	____	____	____
f.	300	City R.R. Services	High	____	____	____

B

1. Determine the approximate fees paid on both the purchase and sale in the following stock transactions.

	Purchase Price	Selling Price	Total of Purchase and Selling Prices	Approximate Fees
a.	$2,000	$3,000	$____	$____
b.	2,400	2,500	____	____
c.	1,900	1,700	____	____
d.	1,450	1,650	____	____
e.	3,240	3,150	____	____
f.	1,025	1,475	____	____

2. Determine the approximate fees paid on both the purchase and sale in the following stock transactions.

	Number Of Shares	Purchase Price Per Share	Purchase Price	Selling Price Per Share	Selling Price	Total of Purchase and Selling Prices	Approximate Fees
a.	100	12	$____	14	$____	$____	$____
b.	200	18	____	21	____	____	____
c.	100	$24\frac{1}{2}$	____	25	____	____	____
d.	100	36	____	$34\frac{1}{2}$	____	____	____
e.	200	$30\frac{3}{4}$	____	$36\frac{1}{2}$	____	____	____
f.	200	$25\frac{1}{2}$	____	$20\frac{1}{4}$	____	____	____

3. Determine the profit or loss on each of the following stock transactions when the fees for buying and selling are not taken into account.

	Number Of Shares	Purchase Price Per Share	Purchase Price	Selling Price Per Share	Selling Price	Profit Or Loss
a.	100	50	$____	56	$____	$____
b.	40	28	____	37	____	____
c.	100	$17\frac{1}{2}$	____	$25\frac{1}{4}$	____	____
d.	100	$31\frac{3}{4}$	____	$47\frac{5}{8}$	____	____
e.	65	$12\frac{1}{2}$	____	$9\frac{3}{4}$	____	____
f.	30	$54\frac{1}{8}$	____	$42\frac{1}{4}$	____	____

4. Determine the profit or loss on each of the following stock transactions when the fees for buying and selling are taken into account.

	Number Of Shares	Purchase Price Per Share	Purchase Price	Selling Price Per Share	Selling Price	Profit Or Loss	Fees	Total Profit Or Loss
a.	100	24	$_____	30	$_____	$_____	$_____	$_____
b.	100	32	_____	46	_____	_____	_____	_____
c.	100	16	_____	17	_____	_____	_____	_____
d.	100	50	_____	51	_____	_____	_____	_____
e.	100	20	_____	16	_____	_____	_____	_____
f.	100	42	_____	37	_____	_____	_____	_____

Section 4: Rate of Return on Stock Investments (Optional)

There are a great many people who purchase stock simply with the idea of holding it for only a short period. They hope that during this time the stock will rise in value and, therefore, they will be able to sell it at a profit. There are an equally large number of people who purchase stock solely for the purpose of getting a higher rate of interest on their money than they would if they kept it in a bank.

We will consider the rate paid by most banks to be somewhere between 4% and 8% per year. Hence, the person who invests in stock for the dividend alone will have to receive a rate higher than the 8% or it would probably be to his advantage to keep his money in a bank. In order to determine what rate of interest a person does receive on a stock investment, you consider the dividends in exactly the same way as you would the interest that a bank pays its depositors. This is the way it should be, for both dividends and interest represent the money earned by putting your savings to work. In the one case, you are allowing the bank to use your savings, while in the other, you are permitting the management of a company to use your money. In both instances, you are really being paid a rent for the use of this money.

Since dividends and interest can be thought of as being interchangeable terms, it is possible to use the interest formula in connection with the work on dividends.

$$\text{Interest Formula: Principal} \times \text{Rate} = \text{Interest}$$
$$P \times R = I$$

This is exactly what was done at the time you were finding the dividends on preferred stock. Now, however, the problem is somewhat different. Where, before, you knew the interest rate and had to determine the dividends the investor received, at this time you happen to know the dividends that were given to him and you would like to know the rate of interest he received. Expressing this somewhat differently, your object is to find the value of R—the rate of interest—in the formula above. To do this, the Product of Two Numbers Principle is used (see page 518) and the formula is rewritten as follows:

$$R = I \div P$$

There is a slight change that should be made in this formula. In view of the fact that you are dealing with dividends rather than interest, it would be best to use the symbol "D" rather than "I" when writing the formula. Just one more small point—the people involved in stock investments seem to prefer to call the rate of interest by the name *rate of return*. Thus, the formula becomes:

$$\text{Rate of Return} = \text{Dividend} \div \text{Principal Invested}$$
$$\text{or} \quad R = D \div P$$

The application of this formula is relatively simple as you will see in the following illustration.

ILLUSTRATION 1: Ralph Tucker purchased 100 shares of Bullard and Sons stock at the "High" of the day shown in the quotations on page 306. What rate of return can he expect from his investment?

EXPLANATION: In examining the quotations on page 306, notice that Bullard and Sons paid \$1.70 in dividends on each share of stock during the previous year. In computing the rate of return that Mr. Tucker can expect, assume that the company will pay the same amount this year. Rather than compute the rate of return on the total cost and the total dividends for the 100 shares, you do this for only 1 share. Actually, the rate of return is identical, whether it is based on 100 shares or 1 share. However, the computation is much easier when 1 share is used. Also, in finding the rate of return, ignore all fees charged in connection with the purchase and sale of the stock. These fees are relatively small when compared to the cost of the stock. Hence they do not affect the rate of return to any extent worth noticing. The number that is to be used as the replacement for the principal in the formula is \$28, for this is the amount invested in each share.

SOLUTION:

$$\begin{aligned} R &= D \div P \\ &= \$1.70 \div \$28 \\ &= .061, \text{ or } 6.1\% \end{aligned}$$

ILLUSTRATION 2: The 4% preferred stock of the Potomac Glass Company is selling at 37½. What rate of return will an investor receive if the par value of the stock is 50?

EXPLANATION: Before it is possible to determine the rate of return, it is first necessary to find the dividend the investor receives. This dividend, as you recall, is based on the par value of the stock.

SOLUTION:

$$\text{Dividend} = 4\% \text{ of } \$50$$
$$= .04 \times \$50$$
$$= \$2.00$$
$$R = D \div P$$
$$= \$2 \div \$37.50$$
$$= .053, \text{ or } 5.3\%$$

EXERCISES A

1. Determine the rate of return to the nearest tenth of a percent on each of the following stock purchases.

	Annual Dividends	Cost Per Share	Rate Of Return		Annual Dividends	Cost Per Share	Rate Of Return
a.	$3.00	$52.00	____%	e.	$1.80	$30.50	____%
b.	4.00	65.00	____%	f.	2.30	28.25	____%
c.	2.50	46.00	____%	g.	4.75	83.75	____%
d.	1.50	27.00	____%	h.	5.20	96.50	____%

2. Determine the rate of return to the nearest tenth of a percent that the purchaser can expect on the following stock. The quotations for these stocks appear on page 306.

Name Of Company	Purchased at:	Cost Per Share	Dividends	Rate Of Return
a. Canadian Gas Co.	Close	$____	$____	____%
b. Colonial, Inc.	Low	____	____	____%
c. American Bakers pf.	Low	____	____	____%
d. Allen, Inc.	Open	____	____	____%
e. Abacus Corp.	Close	____	____	____%
f. Dobbs Productions	Open	____	____	____%
g. Dunhill Limited pf.	Low	____	____	____%
h. Beech Instruments	Open	____	____	____%

3. What rate of return to the nearest tenth of a percent can the purchaser of the following preferred stock expect to receive?

	Interest Rate	Par Value	Dividend	Purchase Price	Rate Of Return
a.	5%	$100	$____	$110	____%
b.	6%	100	____	112	____%
c.	4%	100	____	84	____%
d.	5%	50	____	41	____%

	Interest Rate	Par Value	Dividend	Purchase Price	Rate Of Return
e.	$4\frac{1}{2}\%$	$ 50	$______	$38	______%
f.	$5\frac{1}{2}\%$	50	______	55	______%
g.	4.8%	100	______	82	______%
h.	6.1%	100	______	95	______%

B

1. Bernard Caswell purchased 100 shares of Drexel Mines at the "High" for the year shown in the quotations on page 306.
   a. To the nearest tenth of a percent, what rate of return can Mr. Caswell expect to receive on his investment? ______
   b. If Mr. Caswell had purchased the stock at the "Low" of the year, what rate of return could he have expected to receive? ______
   c. Based on the rate of return alone, should Mr. Caswell have invested in this stock, or should he have deposited his money in the bank? ______
2. a. What rate of return can the purchaser of 100 shares of Atlas Industries expect to receive if he paid the opening price shown in the quotations? ______
   b. Why would a person want to invest his money in Atlas Industries stock? ______

Section 5: The Mutual Funds

Whatever a person's objective may be in the purchase of stock, the research he has to do before he can make up his mind as to what the best buy will be for his needs may take endless hours of time. To avoid the problem of making a personal investigation, many an investor will simply purchase shares of stock in a *mutual fund.* A mutual fund is a company that simply owns shares of stock in a great number of other companies. The mutual-fund company does not manufacture anything, nor does it own any buildings, nor does it sell any merchandise. It is simply in the business of investing in other businesses. By buying the stock of many different companies, the mutual fund reduces the risk of any large loss it might suffer by having one company go bankrupt.

Over the past 100 years, the general trend of the value of stocks has very definitely been upward. You, as an individual, cannot possibly buy the stocks of many different companies, for you just don't have that much money to invest. Hence, there is always the possibility that the companies you do invest in may suffer large losses while most other companies are operating at a profit. The mutual-fund company works on the premise that business in the United States is basically sound, and that the general trend of stock prices will continue to rise in the future. Hence, even if a few of their investments turn bad, the bulk of them will be making enough money to outweigh the losses they suffer in a few companies.

To avoid even a small loss by making an unwise investment, the mutual funds employ people who are experts in analyzing stock investments. These men decide what stocks the fund should purchase and which ones they should sell. It is their judgment—good or bad—that determines how successful the fund will be. And when you buy stock in a mutual fund, you really give your savings to these men and ask them to invest it for you.

Although the stock of a few of the mutual-fund companies can be purchased at a stock market, the majority of these companies sell their shares only at a stockbroker's office, or through the door-to-door salesmen that the stockbroker hires. This is just where the debate over mutual funds starts. Quite a substantial fee has to be paid to a salesman for making his sale. At the time you investigated the cost of buying and selling stock, you found that the fee that had to be paid to the broker ran on the average somewhere around 2% for buying the stock and another 2% for selling it. However, on the purchase of most mutual-fund stocks you have to pay the salesman around 8 to 9 percent for his commission. Some of this money he keeps; some goes to the broker who employs him, and a small amount filters back to the mutual-fund company itself. In spite of the fact that this charge is rather high, most people agree that the small investor who does not have the time to investigate before he invests is a lot better off buying mutual funds than buying stock as a result of, say, a tip from a good friend.

There are two basic ways in which it is possible to purchase mutual funds from a salesman. In the first of these, you make a lump-sum payment and buy whatever number of shares this amount will purchase. This method is called the Single-Payment Plan. In the second method, you invest a fixed amount monthly, such as $25, or $50, or $100, and so on. As soon as the total of the monthly payments amounts to enough money to purchase a share of stock, this is done and the stock is mailed to you. This method is called the Monthly-Systematic-Investment Plan.

Many people find fault with the monthly plan because at least half of the first year's payments are deducted for sales charges. Hence, if you should decide, after the first year, not to go on with this program, half of your money would have been used up in fees. On the other hand, the people who run the funds say that this is a good way to force people to save. These monthly plans are designed, usually, to cover a 10-year period. Since the fees drop drastically after the first year, it is only by continuing to make payments over the remaining 9 years that you get the average charges down to the point where they seem reasonable.

ILLUSTRATION 1: Under the Single-Payment Plan, a person invested $10,000 in shares in a mutual fund. If the sales charge was 8½%, how much of the $10,000 was actually used for the purchase of stock?

SOLUTION:

$$\begin{aligned} \text{Fees} &= 8\tfrac{1}{2}\% \text{ of } \$10{,}000 \\ &= .085 \times \$10{,}000 \\ &= \$850 \end{aligned}$$

$$\begin{aligned} \text{Amount remaining for stock purchase} &= \$10{,}000 - \$850 \\ &= \$9{,}150 \end{aligned}$$

EXPLANATION: Since $850 went for fees, the remainder, which is the difference between the original $10,000 and the $850, is used for buying stock in the mutual fund.

ILLUSTRATION 2: Carol Thomas enrolled in a $25 Monthly-Systematic-Investment Plan, which consisted in making an initial payment (first payment) of $50 and remaining payments of $25 each over a period of ten years. Sales charges for the first year amounted to half of each payment, while for the remaining nine years, the charge was $12 per year. In addition, she was charged 75¢ per month to pay for the salaries of the experts employed to run the fund. What was the total charge that Carol had to pay over the ten-year period?

SOLUTION:

$$\text{Charge on initial payment of } \$50 = \$25$$

$$\begin{aligned} \text{Monthly charge during the first year} &= \tfrac{1}{2} \times \$25 \\ &= \$12.50 \end{aligned}$$

$$\begin{aligned} \text{Total of monthly charges for first year} &= 12 \times \$12.50 \\ &= \$150 \end{aligned}$$

$$\begin{aligned} \text{Total of annual charges for remaining 9 years} &= 9 \times \$12 \\ &= \$108 \end{aligned}$$

$$\begin{aligned} \text{Annual charge for salaries of experts} &= 12 \times \$.75 \\ &= \$9 \end{aligned}$$

$$\begin{aligned} \text{Total charge for salaries of experts} &= 10 \times \$9 \\ &= \$90 \end{aligned}$$

$$\begin{aligned} \text{Total charges over the ten-year period} &= \$25 + \$150 + \$108 + \$90 \\ &= \$373 \end{aligned}$$

EXPLANATION: The charges over the ten-year period consisted of the following three parts:

1. The charges for the first year, which amounted to one half of the money she paid in that year; notice that during the first year there is an initial payment, plus 12 additional monthly payments—not 11 payments
2. Annual payments of $12 each over a period of 9 years
3. Monthly charges of 75¢ each for the payment of the salaries of employees to oversee the fund.

The total of each of these charges is $175, $108, and $90 respectively, for a grand total of $373.

EXERCISES A

1. Determine the sales charge that will have to be paid by an investor in mutual funds under each of the following Single-Payment-Plan Investments.

	Amount Invested	Sales Rate Charge	Sales Charge
a.	$ 2,000	8%	$______
b.	4,000	9%	______
c.	6,000	7%	______
d.	3,000	8½%	______
e.	8,000	7½%	______
f.	10,000	9½%	______

2. Determine the amount of money that will remain to be invested in mutual funds after the sales charge is deducted in each of the following Single-Payment-Plan Investments.

	Amount Invested	Sales Rate Charge	Sales Charge	Amount Remaining For Investment
a.	$5,000	9%	$______	$______
b.	1,000	6%	______	______
c.	7,000	8%	______	______
d.	6,400	7½%	______	______
e.	8,500	8½%	______	______
f.	9,200	9½%	______	______

3. The sales charge that has to be paid to a mutual fund during the first year consists of one half of the initial payment, plus one half of the remaining 12 payments made during the first year. What is the total charge for the first year under each of the following plans?

	Initial Payment	Monthly Payment	Amount Paid During First Year	Sales Charge During First Year
a.	$ 100	$ 50	$______	$______
b.	300	50	______	______

	Initial Payment	Monthly Payment	Amount Paid During First Year	Sales Charge During First Year
c.	$ 150	$ 75	$________	$________
d.	200	100	________	________
e.	500	100	________	________
f.	1,400	200	________	________

4. James Elroy agreed to make payments into a Monthly-Systematic-Investment Plan. He was told that after the first year, he would have to pay a sales charge of $12 per year on every $25 he contributed on his monthly payments. That is, if he invested $50 per month, the sales charge after the first year would be $24 per year. How much will the annual sales charge be after the first year in each of the following plans?

	Monthly Payment	Number of $25's In Monthly Payment	Annual Sales Charge
a.	$ 75	________	$________
b.	100	________	________
c.	150	________	________
d.	200	________	________
e.	300	________	________
f.	500	________	________

5. To pay for the salaries of the employees who operate the mutual fund, each investor has to pay a fee of 75¢ per month. How much will an investor in this fund have to pay for this fee if he makes payments for the following periods of time?

	Monthly Payments for:	Total Of Supervisory Fees		Monthly Payments for:	Total Of Supervisory Fees
a.	60 months	$________	e.	6 years	$________
b.	80 months	________	f.	8 years	________
c.	95 months	________	g.	9 years	________
d.	115 months	________	h.	10 years	________

6. Many mutual funds charge their investors ½% per month of the monthly payment. How much will this amount to each month on the following plans?

	Monthly Payment	Monthly Fee		Monthly Payment	Monthly Fee
a.	$ 50	$________	d.	$120	$________
b.	100	________	e.	25	________
c.	400	________	f.	75	________

B

On page 234, there is a table showing how much money will be worth if placed in a bank and allowed to remain there over a long period of time. Use this table to determine the amount of money each depositor will have in the bank after the period of time shown. Interest is compounded annually in each case. (Review exercises.)

	Amount on Deposit At Beginning of Period	Interest Rate	Period Of Years	Value of $1 At End of Period	Amount on Deposit At End of Period
a.	$ 6,000	5%	10	$________	$________
b.	2,000	6%	10	________	________
c.	10,000	6%	12	________	________
d.	7,500	7%	15	________	________
e.	5,400	8%	8	________	________
f.	6,800	5%	11	________	________

C

1. The Seagrave Fund advertised that, over a period of 9 years, an investment of $10,000 in its fund increased in value to a point where, at the end of the period, it was worth $32,500.
   a. If a person had deposited $10,000 in the bank at an interest rate of 7% compounded annually, how much would he have had in the account at the end of 9 years? ________
   b. How much would a person gain by having invested the $10,000 in the Seagrave Fund rather than by depositing it in the bank? ________

2. The Midwest Mutual Fund claims that an investment of $5,000 in its fund at the beginning of a particular 10-year period would have been worth $23,600 at the end of the period.
   a. How much would $5,000 have been worth at the end of the 10 years had it been deposited in a bank at an interest rate of 6% compounded annually? ________
   b. How much more money would a person have if he had purchased $5,000 worth of shares in the Midwest Mutual Fund instead of depositing it in a bank? ________

Unit 2: The Bond Market

Section 1: The Bond Market Report

At the time you studied the services of a bank, you found that one of these services concerned itself with the lending of money. A bank will not give money to a person unless it receives, in return, a written statement assuring it that the money will be returned. The piece of paper bearing this statement and the signature of the borrower is called a *promissory note.*

A bond is pretty much the same as a promissory note, except that there is much more money involved. When a company starts in business, or, perhaps, when it wants to expand its business, it issues these promissory notes, called *bonds*, to anyone who will lend it money. Usually, these bonds are valued at $1,000 each, and a person buying one is in reality lending the company $1,000. On the bond itself there is a statement to the effect that the company, at some date in the future, will pay back the $1,000. In addition, there is also some statement about the rate of interest the company is going to pay the lender for the use of his money.

The big difference between a stockholder and a bondholder is this:

A stockholder is a part owner of a company. If the company makes a great deal of money, he shares in the profit. If the company goes bankrupt, he stands to lose his entire investment. A bondholder is a person from whom the company has borrowed money. Whether the company does well or does poorly, all he receives is the interest on the money the company owes him. Should the company go bankrupt, then whatever money it may have—such as from the sale of its buildings—must be used to pay off the bondholders first. If any money happens to be left over, it is distributed among the stockholders.

Such a long period of time exists between the day a bond is issued and the day it is redeemed (paid off) that many people want to sell it at some time between these dates. Since the company does not want the bond back before it is due, these people try to sell their bonds at marketplaces that resemble stock markets and are called bond markets. As in the case of stock markets, the only persons permitted into these areas are brokers who are members of that bond-market organization. Hence, in order either to buy or to sell a bond, you must ask a broker to do it for you, and for this service he charges you a small fee.

Bond-market sales appear daily in newspapers in much the same way that stock-market sales do. On page 334, there is a sample of a section of bond-market quotations as they might appear in a newspaper. In order to explain the meaning of each item, the report of the first company listed follows.

Year to Date		Bonds & Rate	Sales In $1,000	High	Low	Last	Net Change
High	Low						
106½	85	Eastern Mfg. Co. 5s 92	85	89	88¼	88⅜	+⅛

Perhaps the most confusing part about bond quotations is the fact that all the decimal points are in the wrong places. To save space—and time, too—the decimal point appears one place farther to the left in the quotation than it should be. For instance, a bond that is selling at a quoted price of "95" actually means that it is being sold for $950. As stated a moment ago, the decimal point in the numeral 95 is one place farther to the left than it should be, as follows:

95.0.

Similarly, a quotation of 94 3/8 should first be written in the following form:

94.375

Now, by moving the decimal point one place to the right, you find that the value of the bond is as follows:

$943.75

From the example above, it would seem best that each time you write a bond quotation, it should be written as a decimal numeral in which three digits fall to the right of the decimal point. If the fraction is 3/8 as it is above, then the three digits will be .375. If the fraction is 3/4, then the three digits will be .750. In fact, the fractions that are used in bond quotations are the same as those used in stock quotations, but you express them with a decimal point followed by three digits.

1/8 = .125	1/2 = .500
1/4 = .250	5/8 = .625
3/8 = .375	3/4 = .750
7/8 = .875	

And, of course, if there is no fraction in the quotation, as in 95, then you write the quotation with a decimal point followed by 3 zeros:

The quotation of 95 becomes 95.000.
Hence the price of the bond becomes $950.00.

An explanation of the quotations for the Eastern Manufacturing Company follows.

Year to Date: As in the case of the stock quotations, the numerals below the words "High" and "Low" refer to the highest and lowest prices at which a bond of this company had been sold during the year prior to the date of the quotation. You must remember, though, that the "High" quotation of 106 1/2 must be written as 106.500, which, in turn, implies that the price was $1,065.00. Similarly, the "Low" quotation of 85 gives you the low price of $850.00.

BOND MARKET QUOTATIONS

Year to Date High	Year to Date Low	Bonds & Rate	Sales In $1,000	High	Low	Last	Net Change
106½	85	Eastern Manufacturing Co. 5s 92	85	89	88¼	88⅜	+⅛
155	99¾	Electronic Associates 3½s 87	22	116	115½	116	+1
135	98⅛	Emerson-Brody Corp. 5s 89	17	108	106	107	−½
104½	97	Equitable Light Co. 6s 93	33	103	102½	102½	
96	92	Evans Storage Battery Co. 6s 94	5	94¾	94¾	94½	−1⅛
27	18	Falstaff Finance Corp. 5s 2020	1	20¼	20¼	20¼	+¼
29	20⅛	Family Food Stores 4½s 2015	47	24½	24	24	−1
40	36	Federal Mineral Co. 3⅛s 2000	2	38	38	38	−½
102	71⅜	Florida Products, Inc. 4⅜s 92	17	77½	76⅞	77¼	+1
124	104	Foremost Tire Co. 5½s 87	15	109	108	108½	−1
80¾	74	Franklin Sulphur Co. 3¼s 88	12	80¾	79½	80¾	+1½
97⅞	59⅝	General Department Stores 5½s 2011	58	90	84¼	89⅛	+8⅛
73	68½	Gibraltar Power Co. 5s 2001	2	72¾	72⅜	72⅜	
84½	70	Glenn-Holmes Corp. 4.80s 89	31	78	77	77	+1
163¼	124	Gulf National, Inc. 5½s 90	25	161⅛	159	160⅝	−4⅛
90	82½	Harvey Grace Motors, Inc. 7s 88	137	84¾	83⅜	84	+⅛
129½	109⅜	Hayes Products 5.30s 92	15	120⅞	120⅛	120½	+2⅛
145	112	Hotels International 4¼s 90	13	125	124¼	124⅝	+6
120	98¾	Household Services, Ltd. 6¼s 87	3	105	104½	104½	−½
124	104	Hunt-Portland Engineering Company 4¼s 92	8	116	114	115	−⅛
74	70¼	Idaho Paper Co. 3¼s 86	5	74	72½	73	−1
85½	80	Ideal Powder Co. 5½s 92	16	85¼	84⅜	85	
105	101⅛	Illinois Telephone Co. 4¼s 93	62	103½	102½	102⅝	−⅜
144¾	112	International Sugar Co. 4¾s 91	37	117½	116½	117	−½
103	94⅝	Interstate Transportations 4s 92	36	95½	94¾	95⅜	−2¼
131	109¾	Iowa Refrigerator Co. 5¾s 88	39	125⅞	123¼	124	−⅞
58½	49	Johnson Manufacturing Co. 4s 91	25	54¾	54	54¼	+1¼
106⅝	103⅝	Jonathon and Sons, Inc. 7⅜s 88	54	104½	104	104⅛	−¼
84	74⅞	Jones and Kendall, Inc. 4⅞s 90	10	81⅞	80⅝	81¾	+¼
100¾	93⅞	Joy Steel Corp. 6½s 87	16	98	97¼	97⅝	−1

Bonds & Rate: As you might guess, the name under the word "Bonds" refers to the company that issued the bond. In this case, it is the Eastern Manufacturing Company. The numeral "5" and letter "s" that appear immediately to the right of the name of the company indicate that the company is paying an interest rate of 5% per year.

After the "5s" is the numeral "92." This numeral tells you that the bonds mature in 1992. This means that the company will pay off the debt owed on these bonds in 1992.

Sales in $1,000: The heading of this column actually omits a word. It should appear as "Sales in $1,000 Bonds" so that for the Eastern Manufacturing Co., you can say that 85 $1,000 bonds were sold that day. Each bond on that day may not have been worth $1,000. That is the value of the bond when issued, and again it is its value at the time the bonds will eventually be paid off. At any time between those dates, the value of the bond may vary, depending on the fortunes of the company.

High, Low, Last: As in the case of stock-market quotations, the numerals found in these columns show the highest, lowest, and last prices paid for bonds of that company during the day of quotation. Again you must keep in mind that the decimal points in the numerals are in the wrong place. The quotation of "89" for the "High" of Eastern Manufacturing Company really means that the highest price paid was \$890.00. Similarly, the "Low" quotation of 88¼ indicates that that price was \$882.50.

Net Change: Once again, the meaning of the words "Net Change," as used in bond-market quotations, is the same as the meaning given to it in stock-market quotations. The numerals under these words tell you the amount the closing price that day rose or fell over the closing price of the previous day. Thus, in the case of the Eastern Manufacturing Company, the price rose ⅛. Here, again, the decimal point is in the wrong place. As before, write the net change first as a decimal and then move the decimal point one place to the right to find the price change. In terms of a net change of ⅛, this would mean:

$$1/8 = .125$$

Therefore, the price change is \$1.25.

ILLUSTRATION 1: Find the amount paid for 5 bonds of Florida Products, Inc., that were purchased at the "Low" of the day shown on page 334.

SOLUTION:

Quotation for "Low" = 76⅞, or 76.875
Low price per bond = \$768.75
Cost of 5 bonds = 5 × \$768.75
= \$3,843.75

EXPLANATION: Possibly the most difficult part of the solution is in changing the mixed numeral 76⅞ to its equivalent form as the decimal numeral 76.875. In the event that you do not recall the decimal equivalents of the fractions, it is always possible to find them on page 306. However, it would be best to memorize them, since you will be using them so often.

ILLUSTRATION 2: What was the closing price paid for a bond of Evans Storage Battery Co., on the day before the one shown for the quotations on page 334?

SOLUTION:

Closing quotation on day shown = $94\frac{1}{2}$, or 94.500
Closing price on day shown = \$945.00
Net change = $-1\frac{1}{8}$, or -1.125
Net price change = −\$11.25 (down \$11.25)
Closing price of previous day = \$945.00 + \$11.25
= \$956.25

EXPLANATION: The negative sign in front of the $1\frac{1}{8}$ shows you that the price was down $1\frac{1}{8}$ from what it had been the previous day. This means that the closing price was \$11.25 more on the previous day. Hence, by adding \$11.25 to the closing price of the day shown, you can find the closing price of the day before.

EXERCISES

A

1. Change the following bond quotations to actual prices.

	Quotation	Price		Quotation	Price
a.	$96\frac{1}{2}$	\$______	h.	$104\frac{3}{4}$	\$______
b.	$85\frac{3}{4}$	______	i.	$117\frac{1}{2}$	______
c.	$52\frac{1}{4}$	______	j.	$123\frac{1}{4}$	______
d.	$78\frac{3}{8}$	______	k.	$112\frac{7}{8}$	______
e.	$61\frac{5}{8}$	______	l.	126	______
f.	76	______	m.	$110\frac{3}{8}$	______
g.	$80\frac{1}{8}$	______	n.	$135\frac{5}{8}$	______

2. Change the following net changes for bonds to actual price changes.

	Quotation	Price Change		Quotation	Price Change
a.	$+\frac{1}{4}$	\$______	g.	$+1\frac{1}{2}$	\$______
b.	$+\frac{3}{8}$	______	h.	-7	______
c.	$-\frac{5}{8}$	______	i.	$-2\frac{3}{4}$	______
d.	$+\frac{3}{4}$	______	j.	$+4\frac{1}{8}$	______
e.	$+\frac{7}{8}$	______	k.	$-5\frac{3}{8}$	______
f.	$-\frac{1}{2}$	______	l.	$+3\frac{7}{8}$	______

B

The bond-market quotations that appear on page 334 are to be used in answering each of the questions in the following exercises.

1. During what year will the bonds of each of the following companies mature (have to be paid off)?

Company	Year
a. Equitable Light Co.	___
b. Hotels International	___
c. Iowa Refrigerator Co.	___
d. General Department Stores	___
e. Federal Mineral Co.	___

2. What was the lowest price paid that year for a bond in each of the following companies?

Company	Quotation	Price
a. Gibraltar Power Co.	___	$___
b. Iowa Refrigerator Co.	___	___
c. Idaho Paper Co.	___	___
d. Florida Products, Inc.	___	___
e. General Department Stores	___	___

3. What was the highest price paid that day for a bond in each of the following companies?

Company	Quotation	Price
a. Franklin Sulphur Co.	___	$___
b. Ideal Powder Co.	___	___
c. International Sugar Co.	___	___
d. Household Services, Ltd.	___	___
e. Gulf National, Inc.	___	___

4. What was the last price paid that day for a bond in each of the following companies?

Company	Quotation	Price
a. Evans Storage Battery Co.	___	$___
b. General Department Stores	___	___
c. Hunt-Portland Eng.	___	___
d. Illinois Telephone Co.	___	___
e. Joy Steel Corp.	___	___

5. What was the net price change that day for a bond in each of the following companies? Indicate whether the price had increased or decreased over the closing price of the previous day.

Company	Net Change	Net Price Change	Increase Or Decrease
a. Falstaff Finance Corp.	___	$___	___
b. Family Food Stores	___	___	___
c. Interstate Transportations	___	___	___
d. Hotels International	___	___	___
e. Ideal Powder Co.	___	___	___

6. What was the last price paid for a bond in each of the following companies on the day prior to the one shown in the quotations?

Company	Last Price For Day Shown	Net Price Change	Last Price Of Previous Day
a. Emerson-Brody Corp.	$_____	$_____	$_____
b. Idaho Paper Co.	_____	_____	_____
c. Glenn-Holmes Corp.	_____	_____	_____
d. Gibraltar Power Co.	_____	_____	_____
e. Florida Products, Inc.	_____	_____	_____
f. Federal Mineral Co.	_____	_____	_____
g. International Sugar Co.	_____	_____	_____
h. Hayes Products	_____	_____	_____
i. Franklin Sulphur Co.	_____	_____	_____
j. Jonathon and Sons, Inc.	_____	_____	_____

C

1. How much will the buyer have to pay on each of the following bond purchases?

	Number Of Bonds	Quotation Per Bond	Price Per Bond	Total Price
a.	2	87	$_____	$_____
b.	3	96 1/2	_____	_____
c.	5	75 3/4	_____	_____
d.	5	68 1/4	_____	_____
e.	4	103 5/8	_____	_____
f.	4	107 1/8	_____	_____
g.	8	121 3/8	_____	_____
h.	6	100 7/8	_____	_____
i.	15	91 3/4	_____	_____
j.	25	59 5/8	_____	_____

2. How much did the buyer have to pay on each of the following bond purchases that were made on the day of the bond-market quotations?

Company	Number Of Bonds	Quotation Per Bond	Price Per Bond	Total Price
a. Equitable Light Co.	3	High	$_____	$_____
b. Family Food Stores	10	High	_____	_____
c. Franklin Sulphur Co.	5	Low	_____	_____
d. Ideal Powder Co.	4	High	_____	_____
e. Jones and Kendall, Inc.	6	Last	_____	_____
f. Interstate Transportations	20	Low	_____	_____
g. Hayes Products	8	Low	_____	_____
h. Gulf National, Inc.	3	Last	_____	_____
i. Florida Products, Inc.	7	Low	_____	_____
j. Iowa Refrigerator Co.	16	High	_____	_____

D

1. Robert Perle purchased 5 bonds of Hunt-Portland Engineering Company.
   a. How much would he have had to pay for these bonds had he purchased them at the "High" of the year for the quotations shown on page 334? ________
   b. How much would he have had to pay for them had he purchased them at the "Low" of the year? ________
   c. How much money might he have saved had he been able to buy the bonds at the "Low" rather than the "High" of the year? ________

2. Linda Turner purchased 10 bonds of Hotels International at the closing price shown in the quotations on page 334. How much more did she have to pay for these bonds than she would have had to pay had she purchased them at the closing price of the previous day? ________

Section 2: Interest Payments

At the time you were examining the bond quotations in the previous section it was mentioned that symbols such as "6s" or "4³/₈s" that are found immediately after the name of the company represent the rate of interest that the company is paying to holders of its bonds. These interest payments are made either annually (once a year), or semiannually (twice a year), or, possibly, quarterly (four times per year), depending on the arrangements the company made at the time it borrowed the money. The rate of interest shown in the quotations, however, is an annual rate, which is usually the way an interest rate is expressed. Hence, if you have to determine the amount of interest you will receive on a quarterly basis, you must first determine it for an annual period and then divide that answer by 4.

ILLUSTRATION: Fred Shaeffer owns 6 bonds of Florida Products, Inc. (See page 334.) If interest is paid quarterly, how much interest will he receive on these bonds at each interest period?

SOLUTION:

$$\text{Interest rate} = 4\tfrac{3}{8}\% = 4.375\% = .04375$$

$$\text{Interest on 1 bond for 1 year} = 4\tfrac{3}{8}\% \text{ of } \$1{,}000 = .04375 \times \$1{,}000 = \$43.75$$

Interest on 6 bonds for 1 year = 6 × $43.75
= $262.50
Interest on 6 bonds for $\frac{1}{4}$ year = $262.50 ÷ 4
= $65.625, or $65.63

EXPLANATION: The fractions that appear in the interest rates are the same fractions that appear in the stock and bond quotations. Hence, you have nothing new to learn. After writing the percent numeral 4⅜% in its equivalent form of 4.375%, you can easily change it to its decimal form of .04375 by moving the decimal point two places to the left. From this point on, the solution is quite simple. First you find the interest on 1 bond for 1 year. This answer is then multiplied by 6 to determine the interest on 6 bonds for the 1 year. The solution is completed by dividing the annual interest by 4, since the interest is given in quarterly periods.

EXERCISES A

1. Change each of the following percent numerals to its equivalent decimal numeral.

a. 4.80% ____	f. 4½% ____	k. 4⅞% ____
b. 5.30% ____	g. 5¼% ____	l. 6⅜% ____
c. 6.20% ____	h. 6¾% ____	m. 4⅝% ____
d. 4.60% ____	i. 7⅛% ____	n. 3⅞% ____
e. 5.70% ____	j. 5⅜% ____	o. 6⅛% ____

2. Determine the annual interest payments on each of the following $1,000 bonds.

	Interest Rate	Interest
a.	4%	$____
b.	5%	____
c.	6%	____
d.	7%	____
e.	4½%	____
f.	5¼%	____
g.	5¾%	____
h.	5⅛%	____
i.	6⅞%	____
j.	4⅜%	____
k.	5.80%	____
l.	6.30%	____
m.	4.70%	____
n.	5.40%	____

3. Determine the semiannual interest payments on each of the following $1,000 bonds.

	Annual Interest Rate	Annual Interest	Semiannual Interest
a.	5½%	$_______	$_______
b.	6¼%	_______	_______
c.	4¾%	_______	_______
d.	4⅛%	_______	_______
e.	5⅜%	_______	_______
f.	6.20%	_______	_______

4. Determine the quarterly interest payments on each of the following $1,000 bonds.

	Annual Interest Rate	Annual Interest	Quarterly Interest
a.	6½%	$_______	$_______
b.	6¾%	_______	_______
c.	4⅝%	_______	_______
d.	5⅞%	_______	_______
e.	7.30%	_______	_______
f.	5.70%	_______	_______

5. Determine the total interest payments made to the owners of the following number of $1,000 bonds for the period of time indicated.

	Number Of Bonds	Annual Interest Rate	Payments Made	Interest per Bond Per Year	Total Interest
a.	2	5%	Annually	$_______	$_______
b.	4	8%	Annually	_______	_______
c.	3	4½%	Semiannually	_______	_______
d.	5	7½%	Semiannually	_______	_______
e.	4	5¾%	Semiannually	_______	_______
f.	7	6⅛%	Semiannually	_______	_______
g.	10	4¼%	Quarterly	_______	_______
h.	14	7¾%	Quarterly	_______	_______
i.	12	6.20%	Quarterly	_______	_______
j.	25	5.80%	Quarterly	_______	_______

B

The bond-market quotations that appear on page 334 are to be used in answering each of the questions in the following exercises.

1. Determine the annual payments made by the following companies on each of their bonds.

Name Of Company	Annual Interest Rate	Interest
a. Emerson-Brody Corp.	______%	$______
b. Family Food Stores	______%	______
c. Hunt-Portland Engineering Company	______%	______
d. International Sugar Co.	______%	______
e. Jonathan and Sons, Inc.	______%	______

2. Determine the semiannual interest payments made by the following companies on each of their bonds.

Name Of Company	Annual Interest Rate	Annual Interest	Semiannual Interest
a. Eastern Manufacturing Co.	______%	$______	$______
b. Equitable Light Co.	______%	______	______
c. Foremost Tire Co.	______%	______	______
d. Franklin Sulphur Co.	______%	______	______
e. Hayes Products	______%	______	______

3. Determine the quarterly interest payments made by the following companies on each of their bonds.

Name Of Company	Annual Interest Rate	Annual Interest	Quarterly Interest
a. Evans Storage Battery Co.	______%	$______	$______
b. Gibraltar Power Co.	______%	______	______
c. General Department Stores	______%	______	______
d. Iowa Refrigerator Co.	______%	______	______
e. Jones and Kendall, Inc.	______%	______	______

4. Determine the total interest payments made to the owners of the following number of bonds of the companies shown for the period of time indicated.

Name Of Company	Number Of Bonds	Payments Made	Annual Interest Rate	Total Interest
a. Falstaff Finance Corp.	4	Annually	______%	$______
b. Harvey Grace Motors, Inc.	6	Semiannually	______%	______
c. Electronic Associates	10	Semiannually	______%	______
d. Gulf National, Inc.	5	Semiannually	______%	______
e. Household Services, Ltd.	3	Semiannually	______%	______
f. Joy Steel Corp.	12	Quarterly	______%	______
g. Jones and Kendall, Inc.	16	Quarterly	______%	______
h. Glenn-Holmes Corp.	8	Quarterly	______%	______

Section 3: Rate of Return on Bond Investments (Optional)

The person who invests in bonds is hoping to get more for his money than he might if he deposited it in a bank. However, finding the interest rate a bond investor receives is not just the simple process of merely looking at the bond quotations to see what rate is listed there. The rate of interest listed is based on the original value of the bond, which was $1,000. But, as you can see by examining the quotations on page 334, most people are buying bonds at a price other than $1,000. Hence, the problem is to find the rate of interest you will receive on the amount *you* paid for the bond and not the rate of interest paid to the original buyer on the original $1,000 debt.

When the first person bought the $1,000 bond, the company may have agreed to pay him an annual interest rate of 5%. This amounted to $50 a year. When you buy the bond a few years later, the company continues to pay this interest of $50 each year. However, and this is the important point, you may have paid only $800 for the bond. Thus, you are receiving $50 on an $800 investment rather than on a $1,000 investment and, hence, the rate of interest you are receiving will be more than the rate the original lender received. If you paid more than $1,000 for the bond, then your rate of interest would be less than 5%.

The method for determining the rate of interest you receive on a bond investment is the same as you used earlier for determining the rate of interest received on a stock investment. That rate was called the rate of return on a stock investment, and you found it by using the following formula:

$$\text{Rate of Return} = \text{Dividend} \div \text{Principal Invested}$$

or

$$R = D \div P$$

The only difference is that now the money you receive from the company is called the interest on the bond rather than the dividend on the stock. Hence, the formula becomes:

$$\text{Rate of Return} = \text{Interest} \div \text{Principal Invested}$$

or

$$R = I \div P$$

ILLUSTRATION 1: To the nearest tenth of a percent, what rate of return will the purchaser of 5 bonds of General Department Stores receive on his investment if he were able to buy these bonds at the "Low" of the day shown in the quotations on page 334?

SOLUTION:

$$\begin{aligned}\text{Rate of interest} &= 5\tfrac{1}{2}\% \\ &= .055 \\ \text{Annual interest} &= 5\tfrac{1}{2}\% \text{ of } \$1{,}000 \\ &= .055 \times \$1{,}000 \\ &= \$55 \\ \text{“Low” of day} &= 84\tfrac{1}{4}, \text{ or } \$842.50 \\ \text{Rate of return} &= \text{I} \div \text{P} \\ &= \$55 \div \$842.50 \\ &= .065, \text{ or } 6.5\%\end{aligned}$$

EXPLANATION: Before you can compute the rate of return, you must know both the cost of the bond and the amount of interest paid on the bond. These turned out to be $842.50 and $55 respectively. Hence, by dividing the interest by the cost to the investor, you find that he is receiving a rate of return of 6.5%. Notice that you ignore the fact thathe had purchased 5 bonds. The rate of return on 1 bond is the same as that on 5 bonds.

ILLUSTRATION 2: Julia Carslaw received a quarterly dividend payment of $27 on a bond that she owned. If she had paid a quoted price of 106⅜ for the bond, to the nearest tenth of a percent what rate of return was she receiving?

EXPLANATION: Since the rate of return is an annual rate, the first thing you must determine is the amount Julia receives over the period of 1 year. Having received $27 for a quarter of a year, she will receive 4 times this amount for the entire year. The rest of the solution is completed as in Illustration 1.

SOLUTION:

$$\begin{aligned}\text{Quarterly interest} &= \$27 \\ \text{Annual interest} &= 4 \times \$27 \\ &= \$108 \\ \text{Investment} &= 106\tfrac{3}{8}, \text{ or } \$1{,}063.75 \\ \text{Rate of return} &= \$108 \div \$1{,}063.75 \\ &= .102, \text{ or } 10.2\%\end{aligned}$$

EXERCISES A

1. Determine the annual rate of return to the nearest tenth of a percent on each of the following bond purchases.

	Annual Interest	Price Paid	Rate of Return
a.	$53	$ 950.00	______%
b.	65	870.00	______%
c.	46	917.50	______%
d.	72	1,075.00	______%
e.	68	1,052.50	______%

2. Determine the annual rate of return to the nearest tenth of a percent on each of the following bond purchases.

	Semiannual Interest	Annual Interest	Quotation Paid	Price Paid	Rate Of Return
a.	$25	$______	84	$______	______%
b.	32	______	96	______	______%
c.	36	______	92 1/2	______	______%
d.	41	______	104 1/2	______	______%
e.	47	______	123 3/4	______	______%

3. Determine the annual rate of return to the nearest tenth of a percent on each of the following bond purchases.

	Quarterly Interest	Annual Interest	Quotation Paid	Price Paid	Rate Of Return
a.	$13	$______	72	$______	______%
b.	16	______	91	______	______%
c.	22	______	95 1/2	______	______%
d.	33	______	102 3/8	______	______%
e.	39	______	115 7/8	______	______%

B

Use the bond-market quotations on page 334 to determine the rate of return in each of the following exercises.

Name Of Company	Interest Rate	Annual Interest	Quotation Paid	Price Paid	Rate Of Return
a. Eastern Manufacturing Co.	______%	$______	High	$______	______%
b. Harvey Grace Motors, Inc.	______%	______	Last	______	______%
c. Emerson-Brady Corp.	______%	______	Low	______	______%
d. Family Food Stores	______%	______	High	______	______%
e. Foremost Tire Co.	______%	______	Last	______	______%
f. Franklin Sulphur Co.	______%	______	High	______	______%
g. Gulf National, Inc.	______%	______	Low	______	______%
h. Ideal Powder Co.	______%	______	Low	______	______%

Section 4: Federal Government Bonds and Municipal Bonds

There are only two other types of bonds that you might be interested in investigating. These are municipal bonds and federal government bonds. Since the municipal bonds are the easier of the two to examine, this will be done first.

City governments need to raise money to build schools, or roads, or sewerage systems and the like. To get this money as quickly as possible, they usually borrow it by selling bonds. They then pay off the debt over a 20-year period, or a 25-year period, or whatever other period suits them best. In most cases, the bonds are sold directly to banks, or large insurance firms, or large investment companies rather than to individuals. However, these bonds may eventually be resold to individual investors.

Although municipal bonds usually pay a much lower interest rate than the bonds of private corporations, they are sought after by banks, insurance companies, and people who earn a great deal of money. The big advantage these bonds have over other bonds is that no income tax has to be paid on the interest earned by them. In the case of some people, an interest rate of 6% on which no tax has to be paid might be the equivalent of an interest rate of 9% or 10% on which taxes have to be paid. This in turn might be a great deal better than the interest rate a person would receive from the bank were he to keep his money there.

Federal government bonds carry with them an advantage similar to municipal bonds. However, the advantage here is only a delaying action. In the case of federal government E bonds, the tax on the interest can be delayed until the maturity date of the bond, at which time the government pays off both the debt and all the interest that has accumulated. It is at that time that the tax has to be paid by the owner of the bond.

People who buy federal bonds usually do so for one of two reasons. They hope that by the time they collect the interest, the income tax laws will have been changed so that the tax may be much lower than at the time they bought the bonds. Or they know that by the time the bonds mature, they will have retired. Hence, their income will be a great deal less than when they bought the bonds. As a result, the amount of income tax they will have to pay on the bond interest will be a great deal less than if they received the interest immediately.

The federal government presently issues two types of bonds:

Series E bonds, which are sold in denominations of $25, $50, $75, $100, $200, $500, and $1,000.

Series H bonds, which are sold in denominations of $500, $1,000, and $5,000.

Holders of the Series H bonds do not have to wait until maturity to receive the interest on their bonds, but receive it semiannually at an interest rate of 6%. The big advantage of owning these bonds—and the other government bonds, too—is that they are not subject to any state income tax. And since most states do have income taxes, the fact that you do not have to pay this tax on the interest on federal bonds can amount to a substantial savings for some taxpayers. The Series E bonds also pay an *average* annual interest rate of 6% compounded semiannually over 5 years.

When the Series E bond was originally issued, its maturity value was $25, $50, $75, $100, $200, $500, $1,000, or $10,000, depending on what size bond was purchased. Now, however, although they are still called "$25 bonds," or "$50 bonds," and so on, their maturity value is actually slightly higher than these amounts. For instance, the maturity value of a $25 bond is really $25.20; the $50 bond would have a maturity value of twice this amount, while that of the $75 bond would be three times this amount.

A Series E bond can be sold back to the federal government at any time beginning within two months after the date of purchase. The amount returned to you includes not only the price you paid, but also the interest that accumulated over the period of time you kept the bond. Should you ask for your money during the first 6 months, you will receive absolutely no interest. In fact, even during the second 6-months' period, you will receive very little interest on your money. However, the interest does begin to increase after that time so that by the end of the 5-year period, when the bond falls due, the average interest rate comes to 6%. The following table shows the redemption value on a $25 bond for which you initially paid $18.75.

REDEMPTION VALUE ON A $25 SERIES E BOND

If Held:	Amount Returned
0 to 1/2 year	$18.75
1/2 to 1 year	19.10
1 to 1 1/2 years	19.61
1 1/2 to 2 years	20.10
2 to 2 1/2 years	20.60
2 1/2 to 3 years	21.14
3 to 3 1/2 years	21.71
3 1/2 to 4 years	22.31
4 to 4 1/2 years	22.97
4 1/2 to 5 years	23.67
5 years from issue date	25.20

In a brokerage office, investors and brokers map the strategy for building an investment portfolio. Behind them the board flashes the latest quotations.

ILLUSTRATION 1: What is the cost of a $200 Series E bond?

EXPLANATION: Since a $200 bond has 8 times the value of a $25 bond, the cost of a $200 bond will be 8 times the cost of the $25 bond. Hence, the computation simply involves multiplying $18.75 by 8. (The cost of a $25 bond is $18.75.)

SOLUTION:

Cost of a $25 bond = $18.75
Number of $25 amounts in $200 = 200 ÷ 25
= 8
Cost of a $200 bond = 8 × $18.75
= $150.00

ILLUSTRATION 2: Bruce Davidson purchased two $500 Series E bonds and kept them until maturity. How much more will he receive for the bonds than he paid for them?

EXPLANATION: The computation involves finding the amount received on the bonds at maturity and the amount paid for the bonds. The difference between these two numbers is the amount that Bruce received above what he paid for the bonds.

SOLUTION:

Amount paid for a $25 bond = $18.75
Number of $25 amounts in $500 = 500 ÷ 25
= 20
Amount paid for a $500 bond = 20 × $18.75
= $375
Maturity value of a $25 bond = $25.20
Maturity value of a $500 bond = 20 × $25.20
= $504
Profit on 1 bond = $504 − $375
= $129
Profit on 2 bonds = 2 × $129
= $258

EXERCISES

1. What is the cost of the following Series E bonds?

	Bond	Cost		Bond	Cost
a.	$50	$________	c.	$100	$________
b.	75	________	d.	500	________

2. What is the maturity value of each of the following Series E bonds?

	Bond	Maturity Value		Bond	Maturity Value
a.	$50	$________	c.	$100	$________
b.	75	________	d.	500	________

3. How much money will a person receive if he keeps each of the following Series E bonds for the period of time indicated?

	Bond	Period Held	Amount Returned On $25 Bond	Amount Received
a.	$ 25	1 year 2 months	$________	$________
b.	25	3 years 5 months	________	________
c.	50	4 years 1 month	________	________
d.	50	5 years	________	________
e.	200	2 years 4 months	________	________
f.	100	3 years 2 months	________	________
g.	500	3 years 10 months	________	________
h.	1,000	4 years 7 months	________	________

4. How much more will a person receive than he pays for the number of Series E bonds shown?

	Bond	Number Of Bonds	Period Held	Cost Per Bond	Amount Returned Per Bond	Profit Per Bond	Total Profit
a.	$ 50	2	3 yr. 2 mo.	$________	$________	$________	$________
b.	75	5	4 yr. 7 mo.	________	________	________	________
c.	100	6	5 yr.	________	________	________	________
d.	200	8	2 yr. 10 mo.	________	________	________	________
e.	500	14	1 yr. 1 mo.	________	________	________	________

5. How much interest will a person receive annually on each of the following municipal bonds?

	Par Value	Annual Interest Rate	Interest
a.	$ 500	4%	$________
b.	500	4½%	________
c.	1,000	3½%	________
d.	5,000	3.8%	________
e.	5,000	4.2%	________
f.	10,000	3.9%	________

6. What will be the semiannual interest payment to the holders of each of the following number of municipal bonds?

	Par Value	Number Of Bonds	Annual Interest Rate	Interest Per Bond	Total Annual Interest	Total Semiannual Interest
a.	$ 500	2	3%	$________	$________	$________
b.	500	4	4¼%	________	________	________

	Par Value	Number Of Bonds	Annual Interest Rate	Interest Per Bond	Total Annual Interest	Total Semiannual Interest
c.	$ 1,000	5	$5\frac{1}{4}\%$	$______	$______	$______
d.	1,000	6	$4\frac{3}{4}\%$	______	______	______
e.	5,000	3	$3\frac{3}{4}\%$	______	______	______
f.	5,000	7	4.7%	______	______	______
g.	10,000	8	4.3%	______	______	______
h.	10,000	3	5.1%	______	______	______

Unit 3: Chapter Review and Test

The exercises with an asterisk (*) refer to optional material.

1. Use the stock-market quotations on page 306 to answer each of the following questions.
   a. What was the lowest price paid that year prior to the day shown for a share of Bullard and Sons stock? ______
   b. What was the lowest price paid that day for a share of Carpenter Corp. stock? ______
   c. What was the last price paid that day for a share of Dow Aircraft stock? ______
   d. How much more did the last buyer of that day have to pay for each share of Colonial, Inc., stock than the last buyer of the previous day? ______
2. What was the last price paid per share by the buyer of American Bakers preferred stock on the day prior to the one shown in the quotations on page 306? ______
3. If the broker's fees are not considered, how much will each of the following purchases cost?
   a. The purchase of 100 shares of stock quoted at $17\frac{3}{4}$ ______
   b. The purchase of 300 shares of Bliss Petroleum stock purchased at the "High" of the day shown in the stock-market quotations on page 306. ______
4. If broker's fees are not considered, how much profit would Joyce Blake have made if she purchased 100 shares of Diamond Airlines at the "Low" of the year and sold them at the "High" of the year shown in the quotations on page 306? ______
5. Approximately how much would Carla Sims have to pay in fees when she purchased stock that cost her $2,350? ______
6. Thomas Paterno owns 300 shares of Allen, Inc., stock. If he owned them the year prior to the quotations shown on page 306, how much would he have received in dividends from the company? ______

7. What annual dividend payment will the holder of 200 shares of a $5\frac{1}{2}\%$ preferred stock receive if the par value of the stock is \$100? ________

8. Joe Skinner owns 100 shares of 4.40% preferred stock of the Reed Chain Corporation. The par value of the stock is \$50, but Joe paid only $\$34\frac{3}{4}$ for each share. How much will he receive at each quarterly dividend period? ________

*9. Determine the rate of return to the nearest tenth of a percent on each of the following stock purchases:
   a. A stock that is paying an annual dividend of \$3.50 and was purchased for \$48 ________
   b. A share of stock of Cenco Chemicals that was purchased at the "High" of the day shown in the quotations on page 306. ________
   c. A share of $4\frac{1}{2}\%$ preferred stock that was purchased at $44\frac{3}{4}$, but has a par value of \$50 ________

10. Ben Newton invested \$4,500 in mutual funds under a Single-Payment-Plan Investment.
   a. If the sales charge was $8\frac{1}{2}\%$ of the investment, how large was this fee? ________
   b. How much money remained to be invested in the mutual fund after the sales charge was deducted? ________

11. Regina Wiley invested in mutual funds under a Monthly-Systematic-Investment Plan. During the first year, she made an initial payment of \$200, plus 12 monthly payments of \$50 each. If the service charge for the first year was one half of the total amount paid to the fund, how much was this in Regina's case? ________

12. Change each of the following bond quotations to actual prices.

	Quotation	Price
a.	$87\frac{1}{2}$	\$________
b.	$124\frac{5}{8}$	________

13. Use the bond-market quotations on page 334 to answer each of the following questions.
   a. What was the lowest price paid that day for a bond of the Emerson-Brody Corporation?

      Quotation: ________ Price: \$________

   b. What was the lowest price paid that year to the day shown for a bond of the Gibraltar Power Company?

      Quotation: ________ Price: \$________

   c. How much less did the last buyer of a bond of the Joy Steel

Corporation have to pay for it the day shown than he would have had to pay for it had it been purchased the previous day?

Amount less: $________

14. Robert Kooms purchased 5 bonds of the Franklin Sulphur Co., at the closing price shown in the quotations on page 000. How much did he have to pay for these bonds? ________

15. a. What annual interest payment will the holder of two $5\frac{1}{4}\%$ bonds receive if the par value of the bonds is $1,000? ________

b. What semiannual interest payment will the holder of six Iowa Refrigerator Co. bonds receive? (See the bond-market quotations on page 334.) ________

***16. a.** To the nearest tenth of a percent, what rate of return will an investor receive on a bond for which he paid $940, and which gives an annual interest of $62? ________

b. To the nearest tenth of a percent, what rate of return will the purchaser receive on a bond of the Equitable Light Co. that was purchased at the low price of the day shown in the quotations on page 334? ________

17. a. What is the cost of a $50 Series E bond? ________

b. What is the cost of a $200 Series E bond? ________

18. a. How much will a person receive if he returns a $200 Series E bond after 4 years and 3 months? ________

b. How much will a person receive if he returns a $100 Series E bond after 11 months? ________

CHAPTER 10

INSURANCE

Basically, the principles of insurance rest pretty much on the idea about to be described. Suppose 40 of you owned motorbikes, each of which is valued at approximately \$400. Over the years you discovered that every year one of these bikes is completely destroyed. This accident does not happen to the same person every year. Since \$400 is a good deal of money for any one of you to put out in order to buy another motorbike, you decide that every year each of you will contribute \$10 to a fund to pay for the replacement of the bike that may be cracked up that year. By doing this, the person involved in the accident suffers a loss of only \$10—the cost of his contribution—rather than a \$400 loss.

You might say to yourself, "Well, I'm just not going to be involved in an accident, so why should I pay even the small amount of \$10 a year?" This would be fine if only you were absolutely sure that this were true. But, unfortunately, you cannot foresee the future, and what you think cannot happen to you may very well happen. And hence, you try to avoid this financial risk by joining with others to help pay off a large loss that is quite certain to happen to some of you in the group.

Through experience, insurance companies know just how many people of a certain age will die each year, or how many automobile accidents there will be in a certain city each year, or how many homes will be destroyed by fire each year. They also know just how much money all of this is going to cost. What they don't know is just who is going to be involved in these mishaps. All of you, therefore, are charged enough money to pay for the loss that will most assuredly happen to a few of you. In addition, you have to pay a little more to cover the expenses needed to operate the company. By doing this, each of you knows that should the worst happen, at least you might not have any financial problems.

Unit 1: Life Insurance

Section 1: Life Expectancy and the Mortality Tables

Insurance companies keep records that help them determine what the cost of insurance should be. In the case of life insurance companies, these records are called *mortality tables* and resemble those shown on page 357. These tables were purposely placed side by side so that you could compare the two. The first is based on the total population in the United States over the three-year period 1939–1941, while the second is based on the total population of the United States over the three-year period 1959–1961. Perhaps the most dramatic change that occurred in the intervening twenty years happens to be in the very first year of a person's life. Back in 1940, approximately 47 babies in every 1,000 died during their first year of life. In 1960, however, that number was just about half, for approximately only 26 of every 1,000 babies died. By now, the number is likely to be down even more.

These tables also tell you how long you can expect to live when you are at any given age. Thus, in 1940, a boy of 16 could, under normal circumstances, expect to live another 52.17 years. Hence, he could look forward to reaching the age of 68. In 1960, though, the boy of 16 could plan on another 56.37 years of life, to the age of 72. That 20-year period showed a very definite increase in the number of years you could expect to live.

Actually, there has been an increase in man's life expectancy for sometime now. However, this increase has been most apparent over the last 100 years because of the tremendous growth in medical knowledge. A person born in 1860 could look forward to reaching only 41. As you can see from the table, a baby born 100 years later has a good chance of reaching 70, or 29 years more than his great-great-grandfather!

ILLUSTRATION 1: Use the mortality table based on the years 1939–1941 to find to what age a person of 16 can expect to live.

EXPLANATION: Follow the "Age" column down until you reach the numeral 16. Then place the edge of a piece of paper along the row containing this numeral. Run your finger along the edge of the paper until it comes to the numeral 52.17 in the column headed "Expectation of Life—Years." Make certain you are using the 1939–1941 part of the table. The numeral 52.17 represents the number of years more that a person of 16 can expect to live. Hence, by adding 52.17 to 16, you can determine the age he should reach.

MORTALITY TABLES

Age	United States Total Population (1939–1941) Deaths Per 1,000	United States Total Population (1939–1941) Expectation of Life (Years)	United States Total Population (1959–1961) Deaths Per 1,000	United States Total Population (1959–1961) Expectation of Life (Years)	Age	United States Total Population (1939–1941) Deaths Per 1,000	United States Total Population (1939–1941) Expectation of Life (Years)	United States Total Population (1959–1961) Deaths Per 1,000	United States Total Population (1959–1961) Expectation of Life (Years)
0	47.10	63.62	25.93	69.89	55	15.64	19.31	11.61	21.37
1	5.21	65.76	1.70	70.75	56	16.84	18.60	12.49	20.62
2	2.67	65.10	1.04	69.87	57	18.12	17.92	13.52	19.87
3	1.88	64.28	.80	68.94	58	19.49	17.24	14.73	19.14
4	1.51	63.40	.67	67.99	59	20.95	16.57	16.11	18.42
5	1.32	62.49	.59	67.04	60	22.51	15.91	17.61	17.71
6	1.17	61.57	.52	66.08	61	24.19	15.27	19.17	17.02
7	1.05	60.65	.47	65.11	62	26.01	14.63	20.82	16.34
8	.96	59.71	.43	64.14	63	27.97	14.01	22.52	15.68
9	.91	58.77	.39	63.17	64	30.12	13.40	24.31	15.03
10	.90	57.82	.37	62.19	65	32.48	12.80	26.22	14.39
11	.92	56.87	.37	61.22	66	35.09	12.21	28.28	13.76
12	.97	55.92	.40	60.24	67	37.98	11.64	30.53	13.15
13	1.07	54.98	.48	59.26	68	41.20	11.08	33.01	12.55
14	1.22	54.04	.59	58.29	69	44.77	10.53	35.73	11.96
15	1.39	53.10	.71	57.33	70	48.73	10.00	38.66	11.38
16	1.57	52.17	.82	56.37	71	53.12	9.49	41.82	10.82
17	1.73	51.26	.93	55.41	72	57.98	9.00	45.30	10.27
18	1.88	50.34	1.02	54.46	73	63.33	8.52	49.15	9.74
19	2.03	49.44	1.08	53.52	74	69.18	8.06	53.42	9.21
20	2.17	48.54	1.15	52.58	75	75.54	7.62	57.99	8.71
21	2.30	47.64	1.22	51.64	76	82.39	7.20	62.96	8.21
22	2.42	46.75	1.27	50.70	77	89.75	6.81	68.67	7.73
23	2.50	45.86	1.28	49.76	78	97.61	6.43	75.35	7.26
24	2.56	44.98	1.27	48.83	79	105.99	6.07	83.02	6.81
25	2.62	44.09	1.26	47.89	80	114.91	5.73	92.08	6.39
26	2.67	43.21	1.25	46.95	81	124.38	5.41	102.19	5.98
27	2.75	42.32	1.26	46.00	82	134.44	5.11	112.44	5.61
28	2.85	41.44	1.30	45.06	83	145.08	4.82	121.95	5.25
29	2.95	40.55	1.36	44.12	84	156.25	4.56	130.67	4.91
30	3.07	39.67	1.43	43.18	85	167.88	4.31	143.80	4.58
31	3.20	38.79	1.51	42.24	86	179.92	4.08	158.16	4.26
32	3.35	37.91	1.60	41.30	87	192.29	3.86	173.55	3.97
33	3.51	37.04	1.70	40.37	88	204.93	3.66	190.32	3.70
34	3.69	36.17	1.81	39.44	89	217.79	3.47	208.35	3.45
35	3.90	35.30	1.94	38.51	90	230.81	3.30	227.09	3.22
36	4.12	34.44	2.09	37.58	91	243.94	3.14	245.98	3.02
37	4.36	33.58	2.28	36.66	92	257.11	2.99	264.77	2.85
38	4.62	32.72	2.49	35.74	93	270.31	2.86	282.84	2.69
39	4.91	31.87	2.73	34.83	94	283.44	2.73	299.52	2.55
40	5.24	31.03	3.00	33.92	95	296.46	2.61	314.16	2.43
41	5.59	30.19	3.30	33.02	96	309.35	2.50	329.15	2.32
42	5.99	29.35	3.62	32.13	97	322.10	2.40	344.50	2.21
43	6.43	28.53	3.97	31.25	98	334.75	2.31	360.18	2.10
44	6.91	27.71	4.35	30.37	99	347.36	2.21	376.16	2.01
45	7.44	26.90	4.76	29.50	100	360.05	2.13	392.42	1.91
46	8.01	26.10	5.21	28.64	101	372.98	2.04	408.91	1.83
47	8.62	25.30	5.73	27.79	102	386.34	1.96	425.62	1.75
48	9.28	24.52	6.33	26.94	103	400.36	1.88	442.50	1.67
49	9.99	23.74	7.00	26.11	104	415.25	1.80	459.51	1.60
50	10.76	22.98	7.74	25.29	105	431.17	1.72	476.62	1.53
51	11.59	22.22	8.52	24.49	106	448.20	1.64	493.78	1.46
52	12.49	21.48	9.29	23.69	107	466.33	1.56	510.95	1.40
53	13.46	20.74	10.05	22.91	108	485.39	1.48	528.10	1.35
54	14.51	20.02	10.82	22.14	109	505.10	1.41	545.19	1.29

SOLUTION:

Expectation of life at 16 = 52.17 years
Age a person of 16 should reach = 16 + 52.17
= 68.17

ILLUSTRATION 2: How many people in a group of 50,000, age 55, will die before they reach 56? Use the mortality table for the years 1959–1961.

EXPLANATION: The table shows that 11.61 people in each 1,000 who are alive at 55 will die during that year. Since 50,000 is 50 times as much as 1,000, to find the total number of people who will die you need only multiply 50 by 11.61.

SOLUTION:

Number per 1,000 who will die = 11.61
Number of 1,000's in 50,000 = 50,000 ÷ 1,000
= 50
Total number who will die in 50,000 = 50 × 11.61
= 580.50, or 581

EXPLANATION (continued): Notice that the answer is rounded off to the nearest whole number. Since these are people you are considering, it would not be acceptable to leave an answer in terms of 50 hundredths of a person.

When you talk about the age a person should reach as is done in Illustration 1, you are thinking about the average person. For instance, in that illustration, the average person of 16 should expect to reach 68.17. As you all know, some people will die before this, while others will live well beyond it. The average person is the one who is exactly in the middle of this group, that is to say, he is the one who will die at 68.17. Half the people who started out with him at 16 will die before he does, and half of them will outlive him.

EXERCISES A

Refer to the mortality tables on page 357 when doing the computations for the following problems.

1. According to the mortality table based on the period 1939–1941, how many years can people at the following ages expect to live?

	Age	Life Expectancy		Age	Life Expectancy
a.	10	________	c.	28	________
b.	15	________	d.	34	________

	Age	Life Expectancy		Age	Life Expectancy
e.	42	________	h.	79	________
f.	56	________	i.	96	________
g.	65	________	j.	107	________

2. According to the mortality table based on the years 1959–1961, until what age can people at the following ages expect to live?

	Age	Age Expectancy		Age	Age Expectancy
a.	1	________	f.	61	________
b.	5	________	g.	69	________
c.	18	________	h.	82	________
d.	25	________	i.	95	________
e.	43	________	j.	104	________

3. According to the mortality table based on the years 1939–1941, how many of the following number of persons at each of the ages shown can be expected to die before they reach their next birthday?

	Age	Number Of People	Deaths Per 1,000	Total Number Of Deaths
a.	1	100,000	________	________
b.	7	400,000	________	________
c.	16	500,000	________	________
d.	21	200,000	________	________
e.	46	80,000	________	________
f.	57	70,000	________	________
g.	69	60,000	________	________
h.	86	50,000	________	________

4. According to the mortality table based on the years 1959–1961, how many of the following number of people, at each of the ages shown, can be expected to live until their next birthday?

	Age	Number Of People	Deaths Per 1,000	Total Number Of Deaths	Total Number Surviving
a.	4	100,000	________	________	________
b.	15	700,000	________	________	________
c.	19	900,000	________	________	________
d.	37	600,000	________	________	________
e.	54	300,000	________	________	________
f.	65	200,000	________	________	________
g.	78	60,000	________	________	________
h.	95	20,000	________	________	________

B

1. a. Of 200,000 babies born in 1940, how many died during their first year of life? ________

b. Of 200,000 babies born in 1960, how many died during their first year of life? ________

c. How many more died in 1940 than in 1960? ________

2. A boy who was 16 in 1960 could expect to live how many more years than a boy who was 16 in 1940? ________

Section 2: Life Insurance

PART 1: TERM INSURANCE

With the information in the mortality tables, life insurance companies are able to predict the number of people at each age who will die each year. On the basis of this, they can determine, in advance, how much money they will need to pay the *beneficiaries* upon the death of the people who are insured. The beneficiary is simply the person who is named in the policy as the one to collect the money when an insured person dies. And the amount that he receives is called the *face value* of the policy.

The least expensive type of life insurance a person can purchase is *term insurance.* Recall that when you studied about automobile insurance, you learned that after you paid the premium you were insured for one year. At the end of this period, you were no longer insured, nor did you get any money back from the insurance company. If you wanted to continue to protect yourself in the event of an automobile accident, you had to pay the premium again for another year.

This is much the same situation in a *term* policy for life insurance. Now, however, the period for which insurance is purchased is usually 5 or 10 years. At the end of that time, if you are still alive, neither you nor the beneficiary receives anything for the money you paid in. If you want to continue to protect your beneficiaries in the event of your death, you have to purchase another policy for another 5- or 10-year period.

In the table on page 361 you can see that the cost of term insurance for a male is exactly the same as the cost for a female who is three years older. Research has shown that women tend to live longer than men. For this reason, a woman who is the same age as a man can buy insurance at a cheaper rate.

Notice, also, that the rates depend on the amount of insurance you purchase. For instance, if at 20 a man were to purchase a 5-year term-insurance policy that had a face value of between $5,000 and $9,999, he would have to pay $6.44 each year for each $1,000 worth of insurance. However, if the face value were between $10,000 and $19,999, then the cost for each $1,000 of insurance would be only $5.69.

It is also possible to purchase less than $5,000 worth of term insurance and more than $20,000 worth. The rates, though, will be different than those shown in the table below.

ANNUAL PREMIUM PER $1,000 OF TERM INSURANCE

Age		5-Year Term Policy		10-Year Term Policy	
Male	Female	$5,000–$9,999	$10,000–$19,999	$5,000–$9,999	$10,000–$19,999
20	23	$ 6.44	$ 5.69	$ 6.51	$ 5.76
25	28	6.59	5.84	6.72	5.97
30	33	6.88	6.13	7.19	6.44
35	38	7.56	6.81	8.27	7.52
40	43	9.11	8.36	10.24	9.49
45	48	11.60	10.85	13.43	12.68
50	53	15.66	14.91	18.47	17.72
55	58	21.95	21.20	26.28	25.53
60	63	31.80	31.05	38.40	37.65

ILLUSTRATION 1: What annual premium will Martin Jenkins have to pay on a $12,000, 10-year term policy that he took out at age 35?

EXPLANATION: Follow down the "Age" column for males until you reach the numeral 35. Run your finger across the row containing this numeral until you reach the two columns headed by the words "10-Year." Since the amount of insurance purchased is $12,000, the rate you want will be in the column headed by the numerals "$10,000–$19,999." The $7.52 that your finger will be pointing to is the cost per $1,000 of insurance. For the $12,000 that Martin purchased, he will have to pay 12 times $7.52.

SOLUTION:

Annual premium per $1,000 = $7.52
Annual premium for $12,000 = 12 × $7.52
= $90.24

There are quite a number of people who feel that they need a great deal of insurance protection early in their married lives. Then, as time goes on and their children get older, their need for this protection becomes smaller. In order to get as much insurance as possible for the least cost, these people buy what is called *decreasing-term insurance.* In most respects, this insurance is the same as normal-term insurance. There is one very important difference, though, and that is that, as the years go by, the amount for which they are insured grows less and less. For instance, in the first year they may be insured for $1,000, while in the second it may be only $925, in the third, $845, and so on.

Since the amount of insurance protection grows smaller each year in decreasing-term insurance, it is cheaper to buy than normal-term insurance. Hence, the same amount of money will purchase more decreasing-term insurance than the normal-term insurance.

ANNUAL PREMIUM FOR $1,000 INITIAL AMOUNT OF DECREASING—TERM INSURANCE

Age		10-Year	20-Year
Male	Female		
20	23	$ 2.72	$ 2.62
25	28	2.85	2.78
30	33	3.14	3.03
35	38	3.77	3.89
40	43	4.96	5.38
45	48	6.94	7.92
50	53	10.20	11.90
55	58	15.36	18.06
60	63	23.45	

AMOUNT OF DECREASING—TERM INSURANCE FOR EACH $1,000 INITIAL AMOUNT

Year	10-Year Term	15-Year Term
1	$1,000	$1,000
2	925	958
3	845	913
4	760	865
5	670	814
6	575	761
7	473	703
8	365	643
9	251	578
10	129	510
11		437
12		360
13		278
14		191
15		99

ILLUSTRATION 2: Nora Morales is 43 years old. How much will she save annually by purchasing an $8,000 decreasing 10-year term policy rather than an $8,000 normal 10-year term policy?

SOLUTION:

Annual premium per $1,000 on decreasing-term policy = $4.96
Annual premium per $1,000 on normal-term policy = $10.24
Annual saving per $1,000 insurance = $10.24 − $4.96
= $5.28
Annual saving on $8,000 insurance = 8 × $5.28
= $42.24

Actually, the preceding problem is a little misleading. There is really no such thing as cheaper insurance. Although Nora Morales would be paying $42.24 per year less on the decreasing-term insurance, she would also be insured for a great deal less. During the first year she would be insured for $8,000 on both policies. After the first year, however, on the normal-term policy, she would still be insured for the $8,000, but on the decreasing-term policy, she would be insured for less than $8,000. Each year thereafter, the amount of protection on the decreasing-term policy would grow less and less. The table on the right gives you some idea of the amount of protection a person has on a decreasing-term policy as the years go by. It is interesting to notice that although you are paying the same premium every year, in the first year you are insured for $1,000, while in the fifteenth year, you are insured for only $99. That is why decreasing-term insurance is so inexpensive a form of insurance.

ILLUSTRATION 3: A person originally bought $9,000 worth of decreasing 15-year term insurance. For how much was he insured during the sixth year after the date of purchase?

SOLUTION:

Value of $1,000 worth of decreasing-term insurance in the 6th year = $761

Value of $9,000 worth of decreasing-term insurance in the 6th year = 9 × $761
= $6,849

EXPLANATION: Although the person was insured for $9,000 during the first year after buying the insurance, he was insured for only $6,849 during the sixth year.

EXERCISES A

In doing the following exercises, you will have to refer to the tables in this section.

1. Determine the annual premium on each of the following term-insurance policies.

	Age	Sex	Face Value	Term	Rate per $1,000	Premium
a.	30	M	$ 6,000	5-Year	$______	$______
b.	45	M	8,000	5-Year	______	______
c.	50	M	7,000	10-Year	______	______
d.	23	F	9,000	5-Year	______	______
e.	38	F	15,000	10-Year	______	______
f.	55	M	7,500	10-Year	______	______
g.	53	F	6,500	5-Year	______	______
h.	60	M	18,500	5-Year	______	______
i.	28	F	15,500	10-Year	______	______
j.	23	F	9,500	5-Year	______	______

2. Determine the annual premium on each of the following decreasing-term insurance policies.

	Age	Sex	Face Value	Term	Rate per $1,000	Premium
a.	35	M	$ 4,000	10-Year	$______	$______
b.	50	M	6,000	20-Year	______	______

	Age	Sex	Face Value	Term	Rate per $1,000	Premium
c.	38	F	$ 3,000	10-Year	$________	$________
d.	23	F	7,000	10-Year	________	________
e.	30	M	15,000	20-Year	________	________
f.	25	M	25,000	20-Year	________	________

3. For what amount will a person be insured during the year shown on each of the following decreasing-term policies?

	Year	Term	Initial Value	Amount per $1,000	Total Insurance
a.	1st	10-Year	$ 8,000	$________	$________
b.	3rd	10-Year	6,000	________	________
c.	7th	10-Year	9,000	________	________
d.	10th	10-Year	10,000	________	________
e.	3rd	15-Year	8,000	________	________
f.	9th	15-Year	20,000	________	________
g.	14th	15-Year	75,000	________	________
h.	12th	15-Year	25,000	________	________
i.	1st	15-Year	30,000	________	________
j.	15th	15-Year	30,000	________	________

B

1. Ronald Baker purchased a $10,000 5-year term policy.
   a. How much will his beneficiary receive if he dies two years after he purchased the policy? ________
   b. How much will his beneficiary receive if he dies one day after he pays his first premium? ________
   c. How much will his beneficiary receive if he dies six years after he pays his first premium? ________
2. Debra Bigelow purchased a decreasing-term policy, the initial value of which was $15,000.
   a. For how much will she be insured in the third year if it is a 10-year policy? ________
   b. For how much will she be insured in the third year if it is a 15-year policy? ________
   c. For how much more will she be insured under the 15-year policy than under the 10-year policy during the third year? ________
3. At age 30, William Kent purchased a $15,000 10-year term policy. He lived the entire 10-year period.
   a. If he had purchased a normal-term policy, what would his total premium have been for the 10-year period? ________
   b. If he had purchased a decreasing-term policy, what would his total premium have been for the 10-year period? ________
   c. How much less would he have to pay under the decreasing-term policy over the 10-year period? ________

PART 2: ORDINARY-LIFE, LIMITED-PAYMENT LIFE, AND ENDOWMENT INSURANCE

There are three basic types of life insurance other than term insurance. In the case of term insurance, if the insured does not die during the period that the policy is in effect, then neither he, nor his beneficiary, receives any money from the insurance company. In the case of each of the other three types of insurance, someone, at sometime, must get some money back from the company. Therefore, one of these policies costs more than a term policy with the same face value.

The three types of policies are: the ordinary, or whole-life, policy, the limited-payment life policy, and the endowment policy. Just as you found that there were variations of term insurance, such as decreasing-term insurance, so, too, are there variations of each of these three. The following explanations will try to point out not only the manner in which you are protected under each of these policies, but also some of the variations of them which exist.

Ordinary-Life or Whole-Life Insurance

If you buy this type of insurance, you agree to pay premiums for your entire life. The company agrees that, at the time of your death, they will pay your beneficiary the face value of the policy. Thus, according to the mortality tables, if you take out insurance at 18 and happen to be the one and only person in 1,000 who dies the first year, then the insurance company will pay the full face value of the policy to the beneficiary you named. On the other hand, if you live for the 54 years beyond age 18 that the insurance company expects you to live, you will have to pay the premium for the entire period, but the company will still pay your beneficiary only the face value of the policy. In fact, even if you live until 109—the mortality tables end at that point—you must still continue to pay the premiums every year.

A variation of this policy is one involving an ordinary-life policy paid up at a certain age. For instance, if you felt you did not want to pay for insurance after 65, you could agree to pay the company slightly higher premiums each year than you would under the ordinary-life policy. Then, at 65 you will no longer have to make any further payments. However, after that age you will still be insured, that is, at the time of your death your beneficiary will receive the face value of the policy. Of course, should you die before 65, your beneficiary would get the face value of the policy at that time.

Limited-Payment Life Policy

This type of insurance is much the same as the ordinary-life policy, except that you agree to pay the premiums for a limited period only.

This period may be 20 years, or 25 years, or 30 years. At the end of that period, although you no longer make any payments, you are insured for the rest of your life as in the ordinary-life policy paid up at age 65. Hence, from the day you pay the first premium until the day you die, you are fully insured. A limited-payment life policy in which you pay premiums for 20 years is called a 20-payment life insurance policy. What would the policy be called if you paid the premiums for 30 years?

Endowment Policy

In each of the life-insurance policies already examined, you yourself never receive one penny of the amount you pay in premiums. In the endowment policy, however, you personally may get your money back—in fact, you may get back the face value of the policy. Here, as in the limited-payment life policy, premiums are paid for a fixed number of years. If you do not die during that period, the company agrees to give you the face value of the policy at the end of the period, and then you are no longer insured. Should you die during that period, the face value of the policy will go to your beneficiary. For instance, on a $5,000, 20-year endowment policy, if you die at any time during the 20-year period, your beneficiary will receive the $5,000. In the event you live to make the 20 annual payments, then, at the end of the 20 years, the insurance company will give you the $5,000. Once you receive the money, though, you are no longer insured.

A variation of the endowment policy is a policy that is similar to the ordinary-life policy paid up at age 65. In the latter policy, you pay premiums until 65 and then make no further payments. Then, at the time of your death, and not before, your beneficiary receives the face value of the policy. In the case of the endowment policy paid up at 65, you yourself get the face value of the policy at that age and then you are no longer insured. A person buying this type of insurance is usually interested in using this money as part of his retirement fund if he manages to live to age 65.

ILLUSTRATION 1: Use the table on page 367 to find the annual premium Fred Ellis would have to pay on a $6,000, 20-year-endowment policy that he purchased at age 35.

EXPLANATION: The method for finding the annual premium is exactly the same here as it was in the case of term insurance.

SOLUTION:

$$\text{Annual premium per } \$1{,}000 = \$48.19$$
$$\text{Annual premium for } \$6{,}000 = 6 \times \$48.19$$
$$= \$289.14$$

ANNUAL LIFE–INSURANCE PREMIUM RATES PER $1,000

Age		Ordinary-Life		Life-Paid-Up-At-Age-65 (Male Only)		20-Payment-Life		Endowment-At-Age-65 (Male Only)		20-Year-Endowment	
Male	Female	$5,000–$9,999	$10,000–$19,999	$5,000–$9,999	$10,000–$19,999	$5,000–$9,999	$10,000–$19,999	$5,000–$9,999	$10,000–$19,999	$5,000–$9,999	$10,000–$19,999
20	23	$ 15.07	$ 14.32	$15.98	$15.23	$ 22.90	$ 22.15	$ 18.74	$ 17.99	$ 46.70	$ 45.95
25	28	17.08	16.33	18.41	17.66	25.43	24.68	21.85	21.10	46.93	46.18
30	33	19.63	18.88	21.65	20.90	28.42	27.67	26.00	25.25	47.36	46.61
35	38	22.94	22.19	26.09	25.34	32.02	31.27	31.71	30.96	48.19	47.44
40	43	27.25	26.50	32.39	31.64	36.40	35.65	39.88	39.13	49.66	48.91
45	48	32.85	32.10	41.72	40.97	41.72	40.97	52.01	51.26	52.01	51.26
50	53	40.23	39.48	57.21	56.46	48.33	47.58	70.72	69.97	55.76	55.01
55	58	49.93	49.18	86.46	85.71	56.64	55.89	109.55	108.80	61.64	60.89
60	63	62.47	61.72			67.60	66.85			70.59	69.84
65	68	79.43	78.68			82.77	82.02			84.27	83.52
70	73	102.25	101.50			103.94	103.19			104.53	103.78

Although at one time most people paid their life-insurance premiums on a weekly, or monthly, basis, they no longer do so, for they found this to be much too expensive. The more frequently premiums are paid, the higher the cost of insurance. On the other hand, some people might find it difficult to make a single lump-sum payment of \$289.14 once each year, as Fred Ellis did in Illustration 1, above. Hence, for a small additional cost arrangements can be made to make payments semiannually, quarterly, or even monthly. The following table shows the percent of annual premium charged by some insurance companies if payments are made other than annually.

Period	Percent of Annual Premium
Semiannually	51%
Quarterly	26%
Monthly	9%

If you were charged nothing extra, the semiannual premium should be one half, or 50%, of the annual premium. However, you are being asked to pay 51% of the annual premium, or 1% more than you should on each payment. What percent extra are you being asked to pay on each quarterly payment?

ILLUSTRATION 2: Gracie Hammond purchased a \$12,000 ordinary-life-insurance policy at age 28.

a. If she pays her premiums monthly, how much will each payment be?
b. How much can she save each year by making annual payments rather than quarterly payments?

EXPLANATION: The annual payment is found in exactly the same manner as in the first illustration. By computing 9% of the annual premium, the monthly premium is found.

SOLUTION:

(a) Annual premium per \$1,000 = \$16.33
Annual premium for \$12,000 = 12 × \$16.33
= \$195.96
Quarterly premium for \$12,000 = 9% of \$195.96
= .09 × \$195.96
= \$17.6364, or \$17.64

(b) Annual cost when premiums are paid monthly = 12 × \$17.64
= \$211.68
Annual cost when premiums are paid once each year
= \$195.96 (See above for annual premium on \$12,000.)
Saving per year = \$211.68 − \$195.96
= \$15.72

EXERCISES A

1. Determine the annual premium on each of the following policies purchased at the age indicated.

	Sex	Age	Policy	Face Value	Premium Per $1,000	Total Premium
a.	M	40	20-Year-Endowment	$ 8,000	$______	$______
b.	M	25	Ordinary-Life	6,000	______	______
c.	M	50	Life-Paid-Up-at-65	7,000	______	______
d.	F	38	20-Payment-Life	12,000	______	______
e.	M	55	Endowment-at-65	15,000	______	______
f.	M	20	Ordinary-Life	16,000	______	______
g.	M	45	20-Year-Endowment	7,500	______	______
h.	M	20	Life-Paid-Up-at-65	12,500	______	______
i.	M	35	Endowment-at-65	17,500	______	______
j.	F	28	20-Payment-Life	18,500	______	______

2. Determine the semiannual premium for each of the annual premiums shown.

	Annual Premium	Semiannual Premium		Annual Premium	Semiannual Premium
a.	$200	$______	f.	$125.50	$______
b.	168	______	g.	146.50	______
c.	175	______	h.	185.46	______
d.	209	______	i.	238.57	______
e.	257	______	j.	269.85	______

3. Determine the quarterly premium for each of the annual premiums shown.

	Annual Premium	Quarterly Premium		Annual Premium	Quarterly Premium
a.	$300	$______	f.	$240.04	$______
b.	240	______	g.	123.50	______
c.	180	______	h.	184.30	______
d.	164	______	i.	237.62	______
e.	235	______	j.	268.16	______

4. Determine the semiannual premium on each of the following policies purchased at the age indicated.

	Sex	Age	Policy	Face Value	Premium Per $1,000	Annual Premium	Semiannual Premium
a.	M	20	Ordinary-Life	$ 5,000	$______	$______	$______
b.	M	35	Life-Paid-Up-at-65	7,000	______	______	______
c.	F	43	20-Year-Endowment	10,000	______	______	______
d.	M	50	Endowment-at-65	8,000	______	______	______
e.	F	28	20-Payment-Life	11,000	______	______	______
f.	M	40	Life-Paid-Up-at-65	16,000	______	______	______

5. Determine the quarterly premium on each of the following policies purchased at the age indicated.

	Sex	Age	Policy	Face Value	Premium Per $1,000	Annual Premium	Quarterly Premium
a.	M	35	20-Payment-Life	$ 6,000	$______	$______	$______
b.	M	70	20-Year-Endowment	8,000	______	______	______
c.	F	63	Ordinary-Life	10,000	______	______	______
d.	M	55	Endowment-at-65	5,000	______	______	______
e.	M	45	Life-Paid-Up-at-65	14,000	______	______	______
f.	F	23	20-Year-Endowment	17,000	______	______	______

6. Determine the monthly premium on each of the following policies purchased at the age indicated.

	Sex	Age	Policy	Face Value	Premium Per $1,000	Annual Premium	Monthly Premium
a.	F	48	20-Payment-Life	$ 8,000	$______	$______	$______
b.	F	33	20-Year-Endowment	12,000	______	______	______
c.	M	30	Endowment-at-65	15,000	______	______	______
d.	F	53	Ordinary-Life	11,000	______	______	______
e.	M	25	Life-Paid-Up-at-65	7,000	______	______	______
f.	F	68	20-Payment-Life	18,000	______	______	______

B

1. James Hayden purchased a $15,000 20-payment life-insurance policy at age 25.
   a. If he paid his premiums annually, what would each payment be? ______
   b. If he paid his premiums quarterly, what would each payment be? ______
   c. How much could he save each year by making annual payments rather than quarterly payments? ______
2. At age 23, Mary Parker purchased a $10,000 20-year-endowment policy.
   a. What annual premium will she have to pay? ______
   b. If she lives the entire 20 years, what will be the total of the premiums she will have paid? ______
   c. How much will she receive from the company at the end of the 20-year period? ______
   d. How much more will she receive from the company than she paid in premiums? ______
3. George Chapman purchased a $5,000 ordinary-life policy at age 50.
   a. What annual premium will he have to pay? ______
   b. According to the mortality table for the years 1959–1961 on page 357 indicate, to the nearest year, how many years the insurance company expects George to live. ______

c. If he should live exactly the number of years he is supposed to, what will be the total of the premiums he will have paid the insurance company? ________

d. How much more (or less) will he have paid the company than his beneficiary will receive at the time of his death? ________

C

Refer to the table on page 367 in order to answer each of the following questions.

1. Why should the rates at 45 be exactly the same for a 20-payment life policy as they are for a life-paid-up-at-65 policy? ________
2. a. Why should the rates for an endowment-at-65 policy be less than the rates for a 20-year-endowment when a person is under 45? ________

   b. Why should the rates for an endowment-at-65 policy be more than the rates for a 20-year-endowment when a person is over 45? ________
3. a. Why should the rates for a life-paid-up-at-65 policy be less than the rates for a 20-payment life policy when the person is under 45? ________

   b. Why should the rates for a life-paid-up-at-65 policy be more than the rates for a 20-payment-life policy when a person is over 45? ________
4. Why should the rates on a 20-year-endowment policy be more than the rates on a 20-payment-life policy taken out at the same age?

____

Unit 2: Disability Insurance

In the previous unit you learned how a person could continue to provide for his family in the event his income was cut off by his death. However, a person does not have to die in order to lose his income. He may be involved in a serious accident, or have a long siege of illness. Either of these will prevent him from working and thus lead to a loss of salary.

People who are concerned that this will happen to them, and thus leave them with no money to support either themselves or their families, usually protect themselves by buying *disability insurance*, that is, insurance in the event of sickness or accident. Under this insurance, if you are unable to work because of either of these causes, the insurance company will send you monthly checks to replace, in some way, the income you may no longer be receiving from your employer.

The greater the premium you pay, the greater will be your monthly allotment.

There are two other factors that determine how large the premiums will be. The first of these concerns itself with when you want the insurance company to begin sending you monthly checks. If this income is to start the very first day that you can no longer work, then the rates are going to be quite high. Most people who become ill or are injured in an accident are often back at work within a few days. Hence, if you arrange so that payments do not begin until the second week of your illness, the rates will be a great deal lower than if payments include the very first day of illness. Similarly, the rates are even lower if payments begin only after you have been out of work for at least two weeks. The longer the delay in your receiving money from the insurance company, the lower the premiums will be. The usual time, though, is about a two-week delay.

The last factor contributing to the cost of disability insurance concerns itself with just how long you want the insurance company to send you monthly payments. If you want the payments to last for only the first year you are disabled, your premiums will be less than if you want them to last for two years, or, perhaps, even for life. It is always

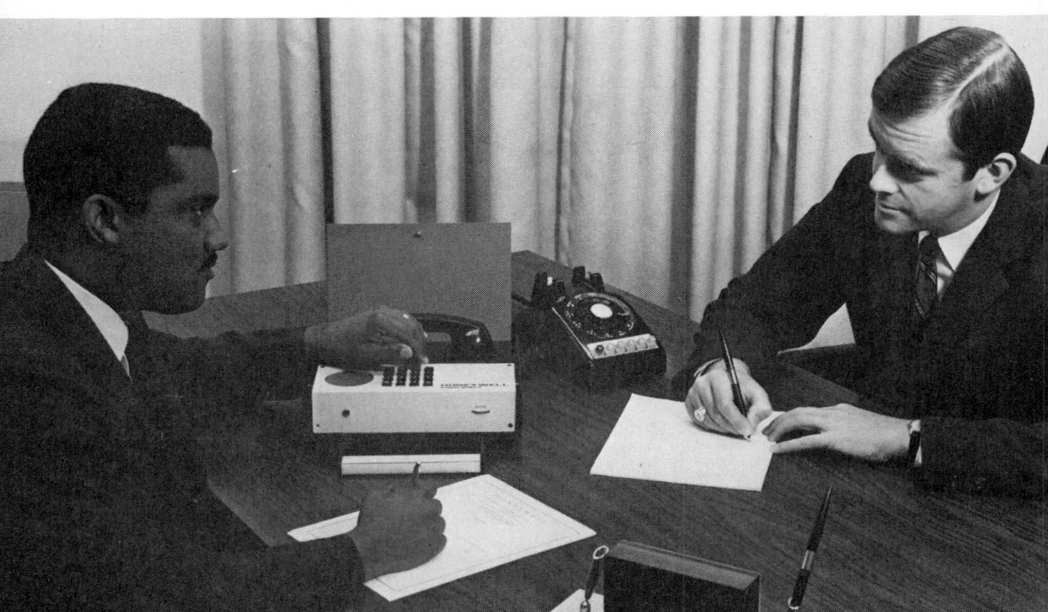

Not just the American homeowner – but businesses as well – purchase many kinds of insurance policies to protect their investments against fire or other costly accidents.

possible that you can be so injured, or become so ill—such as with a heart ailment—that you may never be able to return to work. To cover such an eventuality, you may want to think in terms of having the insurance payments continue for life. If you do, though, the cost will be a great deal more than if the payments were to last for only one year.

Incidentally, insurance companies will not permit everyone to protect himself with disability coverage. If you happen to be an airline pilot, or a tunnel worker, or a window cleaner, or a miner, or an aerial photographer, to name a few occupations, the insurance companies will not give you disability insurance. All other people are separated into four occupation classifications: AAA, AA, A, and B, with the people in the AAA occupations paying the lowest rates and the B people paying the highest. Some of the occupations that fall into the AAA ratings are: accountants, office workers, cashiers, clerks, executives, physicians, studio photographers, and classroom teachers. The B occupations include farmhands, bartenders, boiler makers, road laborers, elevator repairmen, firemen, motorcycle policemen (but not foot patrolmen, who get an A rating), and welders.

The table below shows a sampling of what the rates are for people in the AAA, AA, and A occupations if they purchase disability insurance. The "1-Year," "2-year," and "Lifetime" columns refer to the period of time monthly payments are to be received. Notice, also, that this table can be used only if no disability payments are sent covering the first 14 days of illness. Other tables will have to be used in the event that only the first 7 days are to be eliminated from payments or, actually, any other period but 14 days. It is interesting to notice that this company feels that the A occupations are so dangerous they will not permit anyone in these occupations to insure himself for more than $300 of monthly payments to last over a lifetime.

DISABILITY INSURANCE

Annual Premium per $100 of Monthly Income—Male

14-Day Elimination Period

	AAA			AA			A		
Age	1-Year	2-Year	Lifetime	1-Year	2-Year	Lifetime	1-Year	2-Year	Lifetime *
20	$23.10	$27.90	$ 66.30	$29.10	$33.90	$ 83.50	$37.10	$41.90	$107.50
25	25.00	30.40	73.10	31.00	36.40	89.90	39.00	44.40	114.10
30	27.80	33.80	81.20	33.80	39.80	98.10	41.80	47.80	122.50
35	31.50	38.50	90.80	37.50	44.50	107.80	45.50	52.50	132.30
40	36.30	44.50	101.80	42.30	50.50	118.80	50.30	58.50	143.40
45	42.00	51.90	117.60	48.00	57.90	134.70	56.00	65.90	159.30
50	50.40	62.40	139.80	56.40	68.40	157.00	64.40	76.40	131.70
55	60.30	75.10	156.80	66.30	81.10	173.30	74.30	89.10	196.90

* Not used for a monthly income of more than $300.

ILLUSTRATION 1: Use the disability insurance table to determine how much it would cost Walter Evans annually if he wanted to be covered by a monthly disability insurance income of $400 that would be paid for two years. Walter is employed in a AA occupation, and he is 40 years of age.

EXPLANATION: Place the edge of a piece of paper along the row containing the age "40." Run your finger along the paper to the three columns in the AA occupations. Since Walter wants to be paid for a 2-year period in the event he is disabled, the rate per $100 of monthly income is $50.50. To find the cost for a monthly income of $400, multiply $50.50 by 4.

SOLUTION:

Premium per $100 of monthly income = $50.50
Number of 100's in 400 = 400 ÷ 100
= 4
Premium for $400 of monthly income = 4 × $50.50
= $202.00

The heading in the disability insurance table tells you that it can be used only for men. If you want to determine the cost of this insurance for a woman, you must first find the cost for a man in the same occupation and at the same age and then determine 150% of that premium. Thus, women have to pay 50% more for disability insurance than do men. It would appear, then, that although women, on the average, live longer than men, they tend to be away from work for either sickness or accident many more days than men.

Just as in the case of life insurance, it is possible to pay disability insurance premiums either semiannually or quarterly at the same rates used earlier. That is:

Semiannual premium = 51% of annual premium
Quarterly premium = 26% of annual premium

ILLUSTRATION 2: Brenda McAdams works in a AAA occupation. At 25, she purchased an insurance policy to pay her a $250 monthly income for one year in the event she became disabled. What semiannual premium will she have to pay?

SOLUTION:

Annual premium per $100 of monthly income (male) = $25.00
Number of 100's in 250 = 250 ÷ 100
= 2.5
Annual premium for $250 of monthly income (male) = 2.5 × $25
= $62.50

Annual premium for \$250 of monthly income (female)

$$= 150\% \text{ of } \$62.50$$
$$= 1.50 \times \$62.50$$
$$= \$93.75$$

$$\text{Semiannual premium} = 51\% \text{ of } \$93.75$$
$$= .51 \times \$93.75$$
$$= \$47.8125, \text{ or } \$47.81$$

EXERCISES A

1. Determine the annual premium per \$100 of monthly income that a man will have to pay on each of the following disability policies.

	Age	Occupation Rating	Years For Monthly Income	Annual Premium Per \$100
a.	30	AAA	1	\$________
b.	45	AA	2	________
c.	20	A	1	________
d.	25	AA	Lifetime	________
e.	50	AAA	2	________
f.	35	AA	1	________
g.	40	AAA	Lifetime	________
h.	40	AA	Lifetime	________

2. Determine the annual premium a man will have to pay on each of the following disability policies.

	Age	Occupation Rating	Monthly Income	Years Of Monthly Income	Annual Premium Per \$100	Total Annual Premium
a.	25	AAA	\$300	2	\$________	\$________
b.	40	A	400	1	________	________
c.	30	AA	200	Lifetime	________	________
d.	45	A	500	1	________	________
e.	50	AAA	350	2	________	________
f.	20	AA	450	1	________	________
g.	35	AAA	150	Lifetime	________	________
h.	55	A	250	Lifetime	________	________

3. What annual premium will a woman have to pay if the male at the same age and in the same occupation has to pay the following annual premiums?

	Male Premium	Female Premium		Male Premium	Female Premium
a.	\$ 60	\$________	d.	\$137	\$________
b.	80	________	e.	159	________
c.	126	________	f.	48.20	________

	Male Premium	Female Premium		Male Premium	Female Premium
g.	$67.30	$_____	i.	$109.65	_____
h.	97.62	_____	j.	134.87	_____

4. Determine the annual premium a woman will have to pay on each of the following disability insurance policies.

	Age	Occupation Rating	Monthly Income	Years Of Monthly Income	Annual Premium Per $100	Male Premium	Female Premium
a.	20	AAA	$200	1	$_____	$_____	$_____
b.	30	AA	300	2	_____	_____	_____
c.	45	A	100	Lifetime	_____	_____	_____
d.	25	AA	400	2	_____	_____	_____
e.	40	A	250	1	_____	_____	_____
f.	50	AAA	350	2	_____	_____	_____

5. Determine the semiannual premium a man will have to pay on each of the following disability insurance policies.

	Age	Occupation Rating	Monthly Income	Years Of Monthly Income	Annual Premium Per $100	Annual Premium	Semiannual Premium
a.	30	AA	$100	1	$_____	$_____	$_____
b.	40	AAA	200	Lifetime	_____	_____	_____
c.	25	A	500	2	_____	_____	_____
d.	50	AAA	400	1	_____	_____	_____
e.	45	AA	150	Lifetime	_____	_____	_____
f.	35	AAA	450	2	_____	_____	_____

6. Determine the quarterly premium a man will have to pay on each of the following disability insurance policies.

	Age	Occupation Rating	Monthly Income	Years Of Monthly Income	Annual Premium Per $100	Annual Premium	Quarterly Premium
a.	25	AAA	$100	2	$_____	$_____	$_____
b.	35	A	200	1	_____	_____	_____
c.	45	AA	500	Lifetime	_____	_____	_____
d.	40	A	250	2	_____	_____	_____

B

1. At 35, Paul Fleming purchased a disability-insurance policy that would pay him $300 per month over a period of two years in the event that he was disabled. His occupation was classified as an AA risk.

a. How much were his annual premiums? _____

b. By renewing the policy year after year, he continued to pay the same rate that he paid at age 35. If he did this for a period of 8 years, what did this insurance cost him? ________

c. During the eighth year, he received disability payments from the insurance company for a period of nine months because of a serious illness. What was the total of these payments? ________

d. How much more did he receive from the company than he had paid them in premiums? ________

2. An insurance company wrote a policy for a 20-year-old cashier—AAA rating—that would pay $200 monthly for life in the event the person was permanently disabled.

a. If the person were a male, what annual premium would he have to pay? ________

b. If the person were a female, what annual premium would she have to pay? ________

c. How much less does a male have to pay annually than a female? ________

Unit 3: Hospital, Surgical, and Medical Insurance

In recent years, the increased cost of operating a hospital has so skyrocketed the price of hospital care that very few people can truly afford to spend any time in one. Fortunately, for most people, many employers have taken on the task of paying hospitalization insurance as part of their employee benefits. No matter who pays for it, though, the cost is high.

Some insurance companies will write two different policies. One of these will cover just hospital expenses, while the other will cover only the fees that have to be paid to the surgeon for an operation. In this way, you can purchase one policy or the other, or, if you prefer, both. Other insurance companies include both hospital and surgical expenses in a single policy, as is done in the table of premiums shown. Notice that this company offers two different plans. In the first, the maximum amount the company pays for the use of a hospital bed is $20 per day. In the event the charge is $23 per day, then you, yourself, will have to pay the additional $3 for each day you spend in the hospital. Similarly, the company will pay the surgeon no more than $300 for the operation he performs. If the operation is relatively minor, then the $300 will probably cover his fees. But if it is not, then any amount over the $300 will have to come out of your pocket. The second of the plans available to you through this insurance company has a $25 maximum daily hospital benefit and a $400 maximum surgical benefit.

In the particular policies that are shown on page 378, the insured has to pay annual premiums until 65. At that time, social security

HOSPITAL EXPENSE PREMIUMS

	$20 Maximum Daily Hospital Benefit $300 Maximum Surgical Expense Benefit $4 Maximum Daily Medical Expense Benefit			$25 Maximum Daily Hospital Benefit $400 Maximum Surgical Expense Benefit $5 Maximum Daily Medical Expense Benefit		
Age	Individual Male	Individual Female	Wife	Individual Male	Individual Female	Wife
20	$ 80.20	$106.78	$122.00	$ 99.26	$132.52	$151.00
25	86.53	114.73	122.00	106.97	142.27	151.00
30	95.18	125.12	122.00	117.72	159.98	151.00
35	107.22	136.97	125.00	132.48	169.53	154.90
40	123.88	149.28	131.46	153.02	184.62	162.84
45	145.54	164.84	145.13	179.66	203.76	179.67
50	177.56	193.12	170.08	219.24	238.58	210.42
55	231.85	245.84	219.38	286.45	303.74	271.42
60	382.50	386.48	345.44	471.90	476.82	426.66

For 1 child, add $42.40 annually
For 2 or more children, add $84.80

For 1 child, add $52.70 annually
For 2 or more children, add $105.40

Semiannual premiums = 51% of annual premiums
Quarterly premiums = 26% of annual premiums

benefits cover most of these same costs, so people do not continue purchasing this insurance. Notice that there are three rates: the first one for the individual male, the second for the individual female, and the last for a wife. A family consisting of a husband and wife pays the sum of the individual male's premium and the wife's premium. That isn't all, though. If there are children in the family, and if they are to be covered, too, the cost is still more.

ILLUSTRATION 1: Joe Boswell is 30 years old, while his wife is 25. They have three children—1, 2, and 4. If Mr. Boswell insured the entire family under the less expensive of the two hospital-expense plans, how much would his semiannual premium be?

SOLUTION:

$$\begin{aligned}
\text{Mr. Boswell's premium} &= \$95.18\\
\text{Mrs. Boswell's premium} &= \$122.00\\
\text{Premium for the three children} &= \$84.80\\
\text{Total annual premium} &= \$95.18 + \$122.00 + \$84.80\\
&= \$301.98\\
\text{Semiannual premium} &= 51\% \text{ of } \$301.98\\
&= .51 \times \$301.98\\
&= \$154.0098, \text{ or } \$154.01
\end{aligned}$$

As mentioned earlier, a surgeon's fees will rarely run under the $300 or $400 maximum you are allowed under the hospital-expense insurance of this company. Similarly, the costs of drugs, operating-room fees, oxygen-tent fees, private nurses, and on and on tend to run the extra charges well beyond the means of most people. Hence, within recent years, a new type of policy, called the *major-medical insurance plan*, has been designed to protect you against any large hospital or surgical bills that you might incur. Under this type of policy, you have to pay the first $500 of these expenses, after which the company pays the rest of the costs, that is, the rest of the costs within certain limits. In the case of the policy whose premiums are shown here, this limit is $10,000. With other policies for other companies, the maximum benefit may run as high as $20,000 or $25,000. Similarly, the amount deductible may be $750, or even $1,000, rather than the $500.

People will frequently purchase both major-medical and hospital-expense insurance. By doing this, they can cover the first $500 of their expenses by the second policy and the remainder of their costs by the first. This usually leaves them with little or nothing that they, themselves, have to pay—except the premiums, of course.

MAJOR–MEDICAL PREMIUMS

$500 Deductible Amount
$10,000 Maximum Benefit

Age At Issue	Individual Male	Individual Female	Wife
25	$ 33.45	$ 49.38	$ 39.80
30	37.66	54.99	45.39
35	43.11	61.21	51.58
40	50.35	68.42	58.76
45	59.62	77.22	67.50
50	71.26	88.67	78.88
55	86.63	108.42	94.55
60	108.22	127.01	117.02

For 1 or more children, add $20 annually.

ILLUSTRATION 2: At 35, Louisa Atwell insured herself under both the major-medical and the $25-per-day hospital plan. How much will her total insurance premium be if she pays it on a quarterly basis?

SOLUTION:

Hospital-expense premium = $169.53
Major-medical premium = $61.21
Total annual premium = $169.53 + $61.21
= $230.74
Quarterly premium = 26% of $230.74
= .26 × $230.74
= $59.9924, or $59.99

EXERCISES A

In doing the following exercises, refer to the tables in this unit.

1. Determine the annual premium on each of the following hospital-expense insurance policies.

	Age	Person	Maximum Daily Benefit	Annual Premium
a.	25	Male	$20	$______
b.	40	Female	20	______
c.	55	Male	25	______
d.	35	Wife	25	______
e.	20	Female	25	______
f.	45	Male	20	______

2. Determine the annual premium on each of the following major-medical insurance policies.

	Age	Person	Annual Premium		Age	Person	Annual Premium
a.	30	Male	$______	c.	60	Wife	$______
b.	45	Female	______	d.	55	Male	______

3. How much of the medical costs in column 1 will each of the following medical policies pay?

	Medical Cost	Amount Deductible	Maximum Limit	Cost Covered
a.	$ 600	$500	$10,000	$______
b.	450	500	10,000	______
c.	1,200	500	10,000	______
d.	1,200	750	10,000	______
e.	659	750	10,000	______
f.	7,460	500	10,000	______
g.	12,500	500	10,000	______
h.	12,500	500	20,000	______

4. Determine the total annual family premium on each of the following hospital-expense insurance policies.

	Husband's Age	Wife's Age	Number Of Children	Maximum Daily Benefit	Husband's Premium	Wife's Premium	Children's Premium	Total Premium
a.	40	Deceased	1	$20	$____	$____	$____	$____
b.	50	Deceased	2	20	____	____	____	____
c.	Deceased	35	4	20	____	____	____	____
d.	Deceased	40	3	25	____	____	____	____
e.	30	30	2	25	____	____	____	____
f.	45	40	1	25	____	____	____	____
g.	25	20	1	20	____	____	____	____
h.	35	25	3	25	____	____	____	____

5. Determine the total annual premium that has to be paid by the following individuals who purchase both a hospital-expense policy and a major-medical policy.

	Sex	Age	Maximum Daily Hospital Benefit	Hospital-Expense Premium	Major-Medical Premium	Total Premium
a.	M	30	$25	$______	$______	$______
b.	F	40	20	______	______	______
c.	F	45	25	______	______	______
d.	M	35	20	______	______	______
e.	M	55	25	______	______	______
f.	F	55	25	______	______	______

6. Determine the semiannual premium on each of the following hospital-expense insurance policies.

	Age	Person	Maximum Daily Benefit	Annual Premium	Semiannual Premium
a.	30	Male	$20	$______	$______
b.	40	Male	25	______	______
c.	35	Female	20	______	______
d.	55	Female	25	______	______

7. Determine the quarterly premium on each of the following major-medical policies.

	Age	Person	Annual Premium	Quarterly Premium
a.	40	Female	$______	$______
b.	35	Male	______	______
c.	60	Male	______	______
d.	50	Female	______	______

B

1. Stephen Barnard is a bachelor. At 30, he purchased both the $25 hospital-expense insurance policy and the major-medical insurance policy.
   a. If he paid the premiums annually, what was the total amount he had to pay each year? ______
   b. If he paid the premiums quarterly, what was the total amount he had to pay each quarter? ______
   c. If he paid the premiums quarterly, how much did this amount to on an annual basis? ______
   d. How much can he save each year by paying the premiums annually rather than quarterly? ______
2. Mr. Ellis, 40, and Mrs. Ellis, 35, have 4 children—16, 12, 10, 9.

a. What annual premium will Mr. Ellis have to pay for the family under the major-medical plan? ________
b. What annual premium will Mr. Ellis have to pay for the family under the $25-maximum-daily-hospital-expense plan? ________
c. What total annual premium will Mr. Ellis have to pay for the family under both plans? ________
d. If Mr. Ellis preferred to pay his premiums semiannually, what would his payments be? ________

Unit 4: Unemployment Insurance

You have learned how a person can protect himself against loss of income in the event of death, sickness, or accident. You have also examined how he can help make certain that his hospital and doctor bills can be paid should he require the services of either. Usually, though, the greatest concern about loss of income is not from any one of these, but, rather, from loss of job. There is nothing that distresses a person more than the thought of being unemployed for a long period with no income to support his family and/or himself.

To soften the blow of unemployment, every state in the nation now has some form of unemployment insurance. The laws governing the amount a person receives differ so widely from state to state that it is rather difficult to show any uniform method by which benefits are paid. In only three states—Alabama, Alaska, and New Jersey—is the employee required to make any contributions to the unemployment fund. In all funds, including those of these three states, the employer pays for the unemployment insurance.

Although there is no uniformity in state unemployment laws, there are a few generalizations about all of them. For instance, every state has a minimum number of weeks that you have to work or a minimum amount you have to earn before you are eligible to receive unemployment insurance. The minimum earnings required range from as little as $300 per year to as much as $1,250 per year, while the number of weeks of employment required ranges all the way from 14 to 40. Practically all states require a waiting period of 1 week before you can start collecting weekly benefits. A few states will even give you the benefits lost during that first week if you are unemployed for a long enough period. No state pays unemployment benefits indefinitely. The majority seem to favor a maximum period of 26 weeks after you have become unemployed. On the other hand, although you might use up all your benefits in less than 9 weeks, no state will pay you benefits for less than this period—if you remain unemployed. There appears to be only a handful of states that base their unemployment benefits on the number of dependents you have. All other states base benefits solely on a certain fraction of what your wages were at the time you were employed. Incidentally, you must show that you are willing to accept reasonable employment if it can be found for you, or you will not be given the weekly benefits.

Here are a few situations that arise most often in the payment of state unemployment insurance.

ILLUSTRATION 1: In a number of states, the maximum amount that a person can collect in unemployment insurance during any one year is 1/3 of the amount he has earned the previous year. If Fred Barclay's earnings this year are $8,400, how much might he be able to collect in unemployment compensation next year in one of these states?

SOLUTION:

Previous year's earnings = $8,400

Maximum Fred can receive in unemployment compensation

$$= \frac{1}{3} \times \$8{,}400$$
$$= \$2{,}800$$

ILLUSTRATION 2: In a certain state, the weekly benefit a person can receive is 1/26 of the amount he earned during the best 3-month period of the previous year. If, during the previous year, Robert's best quarterly earnings were $2,680, how much might he receive as his weekly benefit if he is unemployed?

SOLUTION:

$$\text{Best quarterly earnings} = \$2{,}680$$
$$\text{Weekly benefit} = 1/26 \times \$2{,}680$$
$$= \$2{,}680/26$$
$$= \$103.08$$

EXPLANATION: The only trouble with the answer above is the fact that only five states will pay an unemployed person that large a weekly benefit. For most states, the largest amount he can be paid will be somewhere between $49 and $85 weekly. Hence, Robert would receive whatever the maximum happened to be in the state where he lived.

ILLUSTRATION 3: In the state where Eve Walker lives, it is possible to receive unemployment benefits for a total of 2/5 of her annual earnings, which are $8,150. Her weekly unemployment benefit is $70. For how many weeks will she be entitled to receive this benefit?

SOLUTION:

Total unemployment benefits Eve can receive = $\frac{2}{5} \times \$8{,}150$
= $3,260

Number of weeks she can receive these benefits = $3,260 ÷ 70
= 46 full weeks
($40 will remain for the 47th week)

EXPLANATION: No state will pay Eve $70 for 46 consecutive weeks. As explained earlier, most states would pay her $70 for the maximum number of weeks permitted by their state laws. Let us say that in the state where Eve lives, this maximum happens to be 26 weeks in the year. If Eve is still unemployed the following year, the state will then pay her for the remaining 20 weeks of the 46 weeks and in the 21st week of that year she will receive only $40 rather than $70.

EXERCISES

1. In the following exercises, the state gave each of these people a certain percent of their average weekly wage. However, they could not receive less than the minimum, nor more than the maximum shown. How large was each of the weekly unemployment benefits?

	Average Weekly Wage	Weekly Minimum Possible	Weekly Maximum Possible	Percent Given	Weekly Benefit
a.	$ 84	$15	$85	50%	$________
b.	124	15	85	50%	________
c.	131	15	85	50%	________
d.	174	15	85	50%	________
e.	174	23	92	50%	________
f.	100	20	75	65%	________
g.	120	20	75	65%	________
h.	30	20	75	65%	________
i.	98	12	82	55%	________
j.	124	12	82	55%	________
k.	135	12	82	55%	________
l.	185	12	82	55%	________

2. In the following exercises, each week the state gave each of these people a certain percent of their annual wages. However, they could not receive less than the minimum nor more than the maximum shown. How large was each of the weekly unemployment checks?

	Annual Wages	Weekly Minimum Possible	Weekly Maximum Possible	Percent Given	Weekly Benefit
a.	$ 3,000	$12	$64	2.0%	$________

	Annual Wages	Weekly Minimum Possible	Weekly Maximum Possible	Percent Given	Weekly Benefit
b.	$ 2,800	$12	$64	2.0%	$______
c.	5,400	12	64	2.0%	______
d.	5,600	12	64	1.1%	______
e.	4,900	12	64	1.1%	______
f.	5,100	12	84	1.6%	______
g.	8,300	12	84	1.6%	______
h.	3,200	14	80	2.3%	______
i.	570	14	80	2.3%	______
j.	6,590	14	80	1.2%	______
k.	6,130	14	80	1.2%	______
l.	8,300	12	84	.8%	______
m.	10,400	12	84	.8%	______

3. In the following exercises, each week the state gave each of these people a certain fraction of their quarterly wages. However, they could not receive less than the minimum nor more than the maximum shown. How large was each of the weekly unemployment checks?

	Quarterly Wages	Weekly Minimum Possible	Weekly Maximum Possible	Fraction Given	Weekly Benefit
a.	$1,260	$10	$ 75	1/20	$______
b.	1,470	10	75	1/20	______
c.	1,685	10	75	1/20	______
d.	1,635	10	67	1/25	______
e.	1,455	10	67	1/25	______
f.	210	10	67	1/25	______
g.	1,785	17	104	1/21	______
h.	1,932	17	104	1/21	______
i.	2,163	17	104	1/21	______
j.	1,690	15	68	1/26	______
k.	364	15	68	1/26	______
l.	3,250	15	68	1/26	______
m.	1,680	13	78	1/24	______
n.	1,800	13	78	1/24	______

4. Each of the following fractions shows the fractional amount of their annual wages that unemployed persons in these states can receive in total unemployment benefits if they are without work for a long enough period of time. How much will this amount be for each of the following persons?

	Annual Wages	Fraction of Annual Wages They Can Receive	Amount Possible		Annual Wages	Fraction of Annual Wages They Can Receive	Amount Possible
a.	$4,620	1/3	$______	c.	$8,600	1/4	$______
b.	3,750	1/3	______	d.	7,540	1/4	______

	Annual Wages	Fraction of Annual Wages They Can Receive	Amount Possible		Annual Wages	Fraction of Annual Wages They Can Receive	Amount Possible
e.	$5,390	2/5	$______	i.	$ 9,420	3/10	$______
f.	4,265	2/5	______	j.	10,650	3/10	______
g.	6,270	3/5	______	k.	11,280	3/4	______
h.	12,135	3/5	______	l.	8,396	3/4	______

5. The weekly unemployment benefit and the total amount that a person can receive are shown. If he is totally unemployed, what is the maximum number of weeks in one year that a person will receive these benefits. Consider any fractional part of a week as an entire week.

	Weekly Benefit	Total Benefit	Minimum Number of Weeks If Totally Unemployed	Maximum Number of Weeks If Totally Unemployed	Number Of Weeks
a.	$40	$ 800	10	26	______
b.	32	576	10	26	______
c.	53	1,113	15	28	______
d.	38	1,026	17	34	______
e.	41	492	17	34	______
f.	27	702	18	30	______
g.	35	615	12	26	______
h.	44	1,150	10	22	______
i.	39	1,262	14	34	______
j.	51	1,085	22	36	______

Unit 5: Homeowners' and Fire Insurance

Section 1: The Cost of Fire Insurance

There is one variety of insurance that a person should not be without—and this is fire insurance. Anyone who owns their own home should have this insurance on both the house and its contents. Those who rent an apartment should buy fire insurance to cover their furniture and other valuables. These policies protect a person not only from the loss due to damage caused by fire but also from the damage caused by lightning or smoke. For an additional fee—and this cost is somewhat high—it is possible to buy what is called *extended coverage.* This protects the insured from any loss caused by windstorm, hail, riot, civil commotion, aircraft, and vehicles. A person interested in this type of protection, though, would be a lot better off purchasing a homeowners' policy. With a homeowners' policy, he would get a lot more protection for just a little more money.

FIRE INSURANCE

Rates per $100

Town Class	House 1 Year	House 3 Years	Contents 1 Year	Contents 3 Years
Brick				
A	$.066	$.188	$.128	$ .36
B	.071	.202	.133	.38
C	.076	.217	.138	.39
D	.081	.231	.143	.41
E	.086	.245	.148	.42
F	.096	.270	.158	.45
G	.136	.390	.198	.56
H	.250	.710	.290	.83
K	.300	.860	.350	1.00
Frame				
A	.102	.29	.165	.47
B	.107	.30	.170	.48
C	.112	.32	.175	.50
D	.117	.33	.180	.51
E	.122	.35	.185	.53
F	.132	.38	.195	.56
G	.172	.49	.235	.67
H	.270	.77	.310	.88
K	.320	.91	.360	1.03

By examining the rate table shown above, you can see that the cost of fire insurance depends on two things. One of these is the fire protection available in the community in which the house is located. This is shown in the column headed by the words "Town Class." The better the fire department, the lower are the fire insurance rates. Notice that the rate takes a big jump between town class G and town class H. In the first of these classes of towns, there are fire hydrants but they are not necessarily near the house. In the second, there are no fire hydrants available at all. For class H, the fire department is within 5 miles of the house. Town class K not only has no fire hydrants but the fire department is more than 5 miles from the house. The insurance company really does not expect any part of a house in a class-K town to be saved by the time the fire engines arrive. That is why the rates for this town class are so high.

The other factor that determines how high the rates will be is the material from which the house is constructed, usually either brick or wood. A brick house is less likely to be completely destroyed by a fire than a wood frame house. Hence the rates on a brick house are are less.

There are two different ways in which a person can buy fire insurance. In the first of these he can buy a new policy each year. In the second he can buy a policy that will last for three years. The advantage of the three-year policy is not so much the small saving that the person gains but rather that he is guaranteed by the insurance company that the cost of the insurance will not go up during the three-year period.

ILLUSTRATION: A brick house in a town-class-D community was insured for $18,000 against damage by fire.

a. If the owner purchased a 3-year policy, how much did this cost him?

Disability insurance for a telephone company lineman is either very expensive or unavailable due to the high risk of injury from electric wires or falling from a pole.

b. If the owner purchased three 1-year policies, how much did this cost him?

c. How much can he save by buying the 3-year policy?

SOLUTION:

(a) Rate per \$100 on a 3-year policy = \$.231
Number of 100's in 18,000 = 18,000 ÷ 100
= 180
Cost of the 3-year policy = 180 × \$.231
= \$41.58

(b) Rate per \$100 on a 1-year policy = \$.081
Cost of the 1-year policy = 180 × \$.081
= \$14.58
Cost of the 1-year policy for 3 years = 3 × \$14.58
= \$43.74

(c) Saving = \$43.74 − \$41.58
= \$2.16

EXERCISES A

1. Find the cost of each of the following one-year fire-insurance policies.

	Town Class	Type Of Structure	Insured For:	Amount Of Insurance	Rate	Total Cost
a.	C	Brick	House	\$10,000	\$________	\$________
b.	F	Brick	House	12,000	________	________
c.	D	Brick	Contents	4,000	________	________
d.	E	Frame	Contents	5,000	________	________
e.	E	Brick	Contents	5,000	________	________
f.	B	Frame	House	20,000	________	________
g.	H	Frame	House	23,000	________	________
h.	K	Brick	House	27,000	________	________

2. Find the cost of each of the following three-year fire-insurance policies.

	Town Class	Type Of Structure	Insured For:	Amount Of Insurance	Rate	Total Cost
a.	E	Frame	House	\$ 9,000	\$________	\$________
b.	C	Frame	House	14,000	________	________
c.	A	Frame	Contents	6,000	________	________
d.	G	Brick	Contents	23,000	________	________
e.	B	Brick	House	17,000	________	________
f.	H	Frame	Contents	2,500	________	________
g.	D	Brick	Contents	3,500	________	________
h.	F	Brick	House	16,500	________	________

B

1. A brick house was insured for $25,000 under a three-year fire insurance policy.
   a. If the house is located in an A-community, how much will the cost of the insurance be? ________
   b. If the house is located in a K-community, how much will the cost of the insurance be? ________
   c. How much less is the cost of the insurance in the A-community than in the K-community? ________
2. A three-year $20,000 fire-insurance policy was purchased on a frame house in an F-community.
   a. What was the cost of this insurance? ________
   b. If the owner had purchased three one-year policies over the period of three years, what would the cost have been? ________
   c. How much did the owner save by buying the three-year policy? ________
3. A frame house in an H-community was insured against fire for one year for $45,000, while its contents were insured for $12,000. What was the total cost of the insurance? ________

Section 2: Homeowners' Insurance

It was mentioned earlier that a person who owned his own home would be better off buying a *homeowners' policy* than buying fire insurance with extended coverage. Under homeowners' insurance a person is not only protected against all the losses covered by fire insurance but he also has the following additional coverage:

1. 10% of the face value to cover damage to other buildings on the land such as a garage, or barn, or shed.
2. 20% of the face value to cover expenses he might have by renting an apartment while his home is being repaired as a result of a fire.
3. 50% of the face value to cover damage to the contents of the house.
4. 1% of the face value to cover damage he might cause to someone else's property—other than by automobile.
5. 100% of the face value for injury that he caused some other person or for injuries a person might have incurred while being on his property.

ILLUSTRATION 1: Fred Yerby purchased a $25,000 homeowners' policy. Describe the coverages under which he was protected.

SOLUTION:

Basic coverage on house = \$25,000

1. Coverage to additional buildings = 10% × \$25,000
   = .10 × \$25,000
   = \$2,500
2. Coverage for living expenses = 20% × \$25,000
   = \$5,000
3. Coverage for contents = 50% × \$25,000
   = \$12,500
4. Coverage for damage to others' property = 1% × \$25,000
   = \$250
5. Coverage for injury to people = 100% × \$25,000
   = \$25,000

Most states require that a homeowners' policy contain a "\$50-deductible" clause. This clause is not quite the same as the deductible clause connected with collision insurance on a car. In a homeowners' policy it is frequently interpreted as follows:

1. If the damage is \$50 or less, the insurance company will pay for *nothing*.
2. If the damage is over \$500, the insurance company will pay for *everything*.
3. If the damage is between \$50 and \$500, the insurance company will pay for 111% of that part of the damage that is in excess of \$50.

ILLUSTRATION 2: The extent of fire damage to a house was \$375. If the loss was covered by a \$50-deductible homeowners' policy, how much did the insurance company have to pay?

SOLUTION:

Excess above \$50 = \$375 − \$50
= \$325

Amount paid by insurance company = 111% of \$325
= 1.11 × \$325
= \$360.75

EXPLANATION: Since the extent of the damage was somewhere between \$50 and \$500, the insurance company will determine just what it has to pay based on that part of the loss that is above \$50. In this case the excess over \$50 is \$325. Hence, the computation consists in finding 111% of \$325.

EXERCISES A

1. Determine the various coverages a person will have under the following homeowners' policies.

	Coverage For House	Additional Buildings (10%)	Living Expenses (20%)	Contents (50%)	Others' Property (1%)	Injury to People (100%)
a.	$20,000	$______	$______	$______	$______	$______
b.	30,000	______	______	______	______	______
c.	40,000	______	______	______	______	______
d.	50,000	______	______	______	______	______
e.	35,000	______	______	______	______	______
f.	23,000	______	______	______	______	______
g.	29,000	______	______	______	______	______
h.	56,000	______	______	______	______	______

2. Fire damaged each of the following homes to the extent indicated. How much of this loss will be paid for by the insurance company if the property is insured under a $50-deductible homeowners' policy?

	Extent of Damage	Excess Above $50	Amount Paid by Insurance Company
a.	$200	$______	$______
b.	400	______	______
c.	350	______	______
d.	250	______	______
e.	175	______	______
f.	425	______	______
g.	387	______	______
h.	296	______	______

3. Fire damaged each of the following homes to the extent indicated. How much of each loss will be paid for by the insurance company if each property is insured under a $50-deductible homeowners' policy for $30,000?

	Extent of Damage	Amount Paid by Insurance Company		Extent of Damage	Amount Paid by Insurance Company
a.	$ 47	$______	d.	$ 21	$______
b.	658	______	e.	12,460	______
c.	4,925	______	f.	35,000	______

B

1. Brenda Gramby insured her home for $24,000 under a homeowners' policy. During a fire the extent of damage to the furniture, clothing, and jewelry amounted to $14,950.

a. To what extent did the insurance company cover the loss to the contents of the house? ________

b. How much of the damage to the contents will Brenda herself have to pay? ________

2. Ralph Collins drove a golfball through a window and damaged a painting valued at \$850. He is insured under a homeowners' policy to the extent of \$42,000.

a. For how much of the damage will the insurance company pay? ________

b. For how much of the damage will Ralph have to pay? ________

Section 3: The 80% Clause

Practically all homeowners' policies contain an important statement in them that should not be overlooked. This statement is called the "80% clause." Through it, the owner agrees to insure his property for at least 80% of its value. If it is insured for less than that, he further agrees that he will share part of the loss caused by the fire. Thus, if he insures the property for ½ of 80% of its value, the company will pay for ½ of the fire damage and he will have to pay for the other half. Or, if he insures it for ¾ of 80% of its value, the company will pay for ¾ of any fire damage and he will have to pay for the remaining ¼. The following few illustrations should help clear up this point.

ILLUSTRATION 1: A house is valued at \$25,000, but insured against fire for only \$22,000. If fire destroys the property to the extent of \$6,000, how much of this will the fire insurance company have to pay?

SOLUTION:

80% of the value = 80% of \$25,000
= .80 × \$25,000
= \$20,000
Amount of insurance = \$22,000
Amount paid by company = \$6,000

EXPLANATION: Since 80% of the value of the house is \$20,000, and since the house is insured for more than that amount, the insurance company must pay the full cost of the damage of \$6,000.

ILLUSTRATION 2: A house is valued at \$25,000, but insured against fire for only \$15,000. If fire destroys the property to the extent of \$6,000, how much of this will the fire insurance company have to pay?

SOLUTION:

$$
\begin{aligned}
80\% \text{ of the value} &= 80\% \text{ of } \$25{,}000\\
&= .80 \times \$25{,}000\\
&= \$20{,}000
\end{aligned}
$$

Amount of insurance $= \$15{,}000$

Fraction of loss the insurance company will have to pay

$$
\begin{aligned}
&= \$15{,}000/\$20{,}000\\
&= 3/4
\end{aligned}
$$

Amount of loss the insurance company will have to pay

$$
\begin{aligned}
&= 3/4 \text{ of } \$6{,}000\\
&= 3/4 \times \$6{,}000\\
&= \$4{,}500
\end{aligned}
$$

EXPLANATION: The house is insured for only $15,000, while 80% of the value of the house is $20,000. Hence, the insurance company will pay for only $15,000/$20,000, or 3/4 of any loss. And 3/4 of the $6,000 loss in this case is $4,500. How much of the $6,000 loss will the owner have to pay?

EXERCISES

1. For at least what amount of money will each of the following properties have to be insured under the 80% clause if the insurance company is to pay the entire fire loss?

	Property Value	Amount Of Insurance		Property Value	Amount Of Insurance
a.	$20,000	$______	e.	$35,000	$______
b.	30,000	______	f.	29,000	______
c.	24,000	______	g.	37,000	______
d.	18,000	______	h.	46,000	______

2. What fraction of the fire damage will the insurance company have to pay in each of the following exercises if the policies contain an 80% clause?

	80% Of the Property Value	Amount Of Insurance	Fraction of Loss Paid By Insurance Company
a.	$20,000	$10,000	______
b.	16,000	12,000	______
c.	25,000	15,000	______
d.	30,000	20,000	______
e.	28,000	24,000	______

3. In each of the following exercises, the policies contain an 80% clause. How much of the loss will the insurance company pay?

	80% Of the Property Value	Amount Of Insurance	Fraction of Loss Paid By Insurance Company	Fire Loss	Amount Paid by Insurance Company
a.	$15,000	$10,000	______	$6,000	$______
b.	12,000	10,000	______	1,800	______
c.	24,000	18,000	______	1,500	______
d.	27,000	24,000	______	3,600	______
e.	25,000	15,000	______	1,300	______
f.	30,000	32,000	______	1,700	______
g.	30,000	27,000	______	2,100	______
h.	32,000	30,000	______	6,400	______

4. What fraction of the fire damage will the insurance company have to pay in each of the following exercises if the policies contain an 80% clause?

	Property Value	80% Of the Property Value	Amount Of Insurance	Fraction of Loss Paid By Insurance Company
a.	$20,000	$______	$12,000	______
b.	30,000	______	20,000	______
c.	25,000	______	18,000	______
d.	40,000	______	28,000	______
e.	35,000	______	20,000	______
f.	24,000	______	19,200	______

5. In each of the following exercises, the policies contain an 80% clause. How much of the loss will the insurance company have to pay?

	Property Value	80% Of the Property Value	Amount Of Insurance	Fire Loss	Amount Paid By Insurance Company
a.	$20,000	$______	$ 8,000	$6,000	$______
b.	30,000	______	18,000	8,000	______
c.	40,000	______	24,000	1,600	______
d.	50,000	______	36,000	2,500	______
e.	15,000	______	10,000	2,400	______
f.	25,000	______	16,000	1,200	______
g.	35,000	______	24,000	3,500	______
h.	32,000	______	29,000	4,200	______

Unit 6: Chapter Review and Test

Refer to the tables in this chapter when doing the computation for the problems below.

1. a. According to the mortality table for the years 1959–1961, until what age can a person of 15 expect to live? ______

b. According to the mortality table for the years 1959–1961, how many people per 1,000 at age 60 will die before they reach the age of 61? ________

2. According to the mortality table for the years 1959–1961, in a group of 400,000 of age 50, how many will not live to age 51? ________

3. a. Elroy Sandford purchased a $10,000 20-year-term policy. If he lived the entire 20 years, how much would he receive from the insurance company at the end of that time? ________
   b. If the policy had been a 20-year-endowment policy, how much would he have received? ________
4. What is the annual premium on a $9,000 decreasing 10-year-term policy? It was purchased by a man when he was 45. ________
5. Anthony DeMeo purchased a $25,000 15-year decreasing-term policy. For how much was he insured during the sixth year after he made the purchase? ________
6. At 33, Betty Higgins purchased a $14,000 20-payment life-insurance policy.
   a. If she paid the premiums annually, how large would each payment be? ________
   b. If she paid the premiums semiannually, how large would each payment be? ________
   c. In one year, how much could she save by paying the premiums annually rather than semiannually? ________
   d. In twenty years, how much could she save by paying the premiums annually rather than semiannually? ________
   e. Will Betty receive the $14,000 from the company at the end of the 20 years? ________
7. Mr. Porter, who is employed in an AA risk occupation, purchased a disability-insurance policy to cover him for two years in the event he was ill and could not work. Were this to happen, he would receive $300 per month in benefits. Mr. Porter is 45.
   a. How much was his annual premium for this coverage? ________
   b. If Mrs. Porter had had the same job as her husband and purchased the same insurance, what would her annual premium have been? Mrs. Porter is 45. ________
8. The cost of Bruce Mallon's surgical and hospital bills totaled $4,726 when he was injured in an accident. If he carried major-medical insurance that had a $500 deductible clause and a $10,000 maximum limit and no other insurance, how much of the surgical and hospital bill did Bruce have to pay? ________
9. Thomas Johnson insured both himself and his wife under a $25

maximum-daily-hospital-expense-insurance policy. Mr. Johnson is 30 years of age and his wife is 25.

a. What total annual premium would he have to pay for the two of them? ________

b. What total quarterly premium would he have to pay for the two of them? ________

10. Grace Bigelow lives in a state where the weekly unemployment compensation payments are 63% of the average weekly wage that the person has been earning. However, these payments cannot be less than $12, nor more than $76. If Grace's average weekly salary before she became unemployed was $94.50, how much did she receive each week in unemployment benefits? ________

11. Norman Palmer lives in a C-community and owns a brick house which he insured under a 3-year fire-insurance policy for $25,000. What is the cost of this insurance? ________

12. What is the annual premium on a $20,000 fire-insurance policy on a frame house in a D-community? ________

13. A house is insured under a homeowners' policy for $34,000. During a fire the contents were destroyed to the extent of $21,000. How much of this loss will be paid for by the insurance company? ________

14. Lynne Farrington owns a $30,000 home which she insured under a homeowners' policy that contains an 80% clause. Fire damaged her property to the extent of $6,000.

a. If she had insured the house for $25,000, how much of the loss would the insurance company have had to pay? ________

b. If she had insured the house for $20,000, how much of the loss would the insurance company have had to pay? ________

U. S. BUREAU OF THE CENSUS
U.S. CENSUS

CHAPTER 11

RETIREMENT INCOME

It may seem a bit odd that you should be studying about retirement benefits when you have not even completed high school. As pointed out in an earlier chapter on personal income, however, you have little to say about whether you want to save for retirement or not. From the very first salary check you get—at least in most jobs—deductions are made to provide an income for you when you retire. Earlier you investigated how these deductions were computed. Now you are going to find out what you get for the money that is sent to the federal government for your retirement benefits.

Unit 1: Social Security Benefits

Section 1: The Primary Insurance Amount

It is not possible to understand social security insurance without knowing the meaning of a *quarter of coverage.* A person receives a quarter of coverage if during any one of the following four quarterly periods he earned at least $50 at a job where social security deduc-

QUARTERLY PERIODS

January February March	April May June
July August September	October November December

tions were taken from his pay. In fact, if a person earned $13,200 (see page 170) or more during one year, even if this were earned in a single day, he would immediately be given four quarters of coverage. On the other hand, suppose that someone earned only $13,000 during the year and that $10,000 of this was earned during the months of January and February, while the remaining $3,000 was earned during May. Then that person would be credited with only two quarters of coverage. The important amount under the present law is $13,200. Since he earned less than $13,200 during the year and since he earned it all during only two quarters of the year, he receives credit for only two quarters. Had he earned $13,200 rather than $13,000 during these same months, then by law he would be entitled to four quarters of coverage instead of two. Or, had his $13,000 earnings been spread evenly throughout the year, then he would have earned more than $50 in each quarter of the year. Under these circumstances, he also would have earned four quarters of coverage that year.

There are two ways in which a person can be insured under the social security law. In the first of these he is covered by what is called being *currently insured.* This means that during the previous 12 quarters—three years—he was employed in occupations where he earned at least 6 quarters of coverage. The advantage of being currently insured falls not to the person himself but rather to his family in the event of his death. At that time the survivors, that is a spouse and any children, receive monthly benefits. In addition, they receive a small lump-sum payment.

The second way in which a person can be insured under the social security laws is to be *fully insured.* To get this type of coverage he will have to earn 40 quarters of coverage. When this happens, even if he does not earn another penny, he will be insured under the social security law for the rest of his life. Exactly what it means to be insured under this law is what you will investigate at this time.

The amount a person receives depends entirely on an amount called the *average yearly earnings.* This number is determined by adding up all the money a person earns from the time he reaches 22 until he retires at 65 or 62, if he desires. To make this number as large as possible, the five years of lowest earnings are dropped off before the sum is computed. For instance, in the case of a college student, he may not start working until 24. Hence, the years in which he was 23 and 24 will be eliminated, for he earned nothing at that time. In addition, three other years will also be eliminated. This sum is then divided by the number of years in that period to give the average yearly earnings.

Under the present law, there will never be a year in which your income as used in this averaging process can be greater than $13,200, for this is the largest annual income from which social security deductions are taken. Because of this, it is unlikely that any person will receive the greatest benefits possible under the social security law.

At the time a worker decides to retire, the social security agency computes his average yearly earnings. On the basis of that average an amount called the *primary insurance amount* (P.I.A.) is determined. All monthly benefits—both those to him and those to his dependents

SOCIAL SECURITY PRIMARY INSURANCE AMOUNT (P.I.A.)

Average Yearly Earnings	Primary Insurance Amount	Maximum Family Benefit	Average Yearly Earnings	Primary Insurance Amount	Maximum Family Benefit
$1,150	$114.40	$171.60	$ 5,500	$282.10	$524.70
1,500	138.90	208.40	5,600	285.80	530.00
2,200	163.40	245.10	5,700	289.60	535.80
2,850	188.10	282.20	5,800	293.60	541.20
3,550	212.20	346.00	6,600	320.20	579.80
3,850	224.30	378.90	6,800	327.10	588.10
4,000	228.50	390.60	6,950	333.70	596.20
4,200	236.80	411.50	7,200	343.90	608.60
4,400	244.70	433.90	7,400	350.70	616.70
4,650	252.90	455.30	7,550	357.40	625.40
4,900	263.00	483.20	7,800	367.50	643.10
5,050	266.80	493.60	9,000	393.50	688.70
5,150	270.70	505.40	10,800	426.80	747.00
5,250	274.70	513.60	12,000	449.00	785.80
5,400	278.20	519.40			

—are computed in terms of this amount. The table on page 401 gives a sampling of the primary insurance (P.I.A.) for a number of average yearly earnings.

ILLUSTRATION: What is the P.I.A. for average yearly earnings of $6,950?

EXPLANATION: The numeral immediately to the right of the average yearly earnings of $6,950 is $333.70. This is the primary insurance amount. The numeral to the right of that one, which in this case is $596.20, is the maximum benefit a family can receive for a P.I.A. of $333.70. After the benefit for the entire family is computed, if the sum is more than $596.20, the social security agency will send the family a check for no more than $596.20.

SOLUTION:

$$\text{P.I.A.} = \$333.70$$

EXERCISES

1. Determine the P.I.A. on each of the following average yearly earnings.

a. $5,400	________	f. $ 4,650	________
b. 5,800	________	g. 6,950	________
c. 4,200	________	h. 7,400	________
d. 6,600	________	i. 10,800	________
e. 3,850	________	j. 7,550	________

2. Determine the maximum family benefit on each of the following average yearly earnings.

a. $2,200	________	f. $ 5,050	________
b. 7,800	________	g. 3,850	________
c. 5,500	________	h. 9,000	________
d. 4,900	________	i. 5,600	________
e. 1,500	________	j. 12,000	________

Section 2: Retirement Benefits

In this section you will examine how the social security agency computes the benefits for the entire family at the time the husband retires. In all the discussions from this point on it will be assumed that it was the husband who was covered by social security insurance and not the wife.

If the husband retires at age 65, then he receives the full primary insurance amount. However, should he retire at an age earlier than 65, he will lost 20/36ths of 1% of the P.I.A. for each month prior to age 65 that he retires. Thus, were he to retire at age 64, his monthly benefit would be only 93.33% of the P.I.A.; were he to retire at age 63, it would be but 86.67% of the P.I.A. However, 62 is the very earliest age at which a man can retire and still receive benefits.

Once a husband starts to collect benefits, both his wife and each child under the age of 18 will receive 50% of the P.I.A. However, if a child is not going to school, as soon as he reaches 18, his benefits are cut off. Should he be in school, whether high school or college, his benefits will continue until he reaches 22, at which time they are stopped. On the other hand, his mother can receive benefits only if he is under 18. Once he is beyond that age, she will no longer receive anything until she, herself, reaches retirement age.

If the husband is retired, then the wife's retirement age can be as early as 62. Should she begin taking her benefits at that time, though, they will not be as great as they will be if she waits until 65. In the table below, you can see that if the wife begins to take her payments at 62, then she receives only 37.5% of the P.I.A. If she waits, though, until she is 65, she receives 50% of the P.I.A. As long as she is taking care of a child under 18, though—no matter what her own age may be—the wife will receive 50% of the P.I.A.

FAMILY RETIREMENT BENEFITS

Family Member	Percent of P.I.A.
Husband,	
65 or older	100%
64	93.33%
63	86.67%
62	80%
Wife,	
65 or older	50%
64	45.83%
63	41.67%
62	37.5%
. . . .	
Wife with child under 18	50%
Child under 18	50%
Child under 22 attending school	50%

ILLUSTRATION 1: Mr. Swenson retired at 66, at which time his wife was 65. If his average yearly earnings were $5,500, how much will both he and his wife receive in social security benefits each month?

SOLUTION:

Mr. Swensen's benefit = \$282.10
Mrs. Swensen's benefit = 50% of \$282.10
= \$141.05, or \$141.10
Total benefit of both husband and wife = \$282.10 + \$141.10
= \$423.20

EXPLANATION: Since Mr. Swensen is over 65 he will receive the entire P.I.A. On average yearly earnings of \$5,500, this will amount to \$282.10. Since Mrs. Swensen is 65, she will receive 50% of the P.I.A., which comes to \$141.05. However, the amount sent to her will be \$141.10. Social security checks are always rounded off so that the "cents" part is a multiple of 10¢. Whenever the computation indicates that the monthly benefit will fall between two multiples of 10¢, the check is always written for the larger of the two values. In this illustration, the benefit should have been \$141.05. However, it was rounded off to the next higher multiple of 10¢, which made the check turn out to be \$141.10. Had the benefit been computed as \$141.01, it would still have been rounded off to \$141.10.

ILLUSTRATION 2: When Mr. Williams reached 63, he retired and asked the social security agency to begin sending him his monthly benefits. Mrs. Williams was 55 at the time and they had one child under the age of 18. What is the total monthly family benefit if Mr. Williams average yearly earnings were \$7,400?

SOLUTION:

P.I.A. = \$350.70
Mr. Williams' benefit = 86.67% of \$350.70
= .8667 × \$350.70
= \$303.95, or \$304
Mrs. Williams' benefit = 50% of \$350.70
= \$175.35, or \$175.40
Child's benefit = 50% of \$350.70
= \$175.40
Total family benefit = \$304 + \$175.40 + \$175.40
= \$654.80
Maximum family benefit received = \$616.70

EXPLANATION: The interesting feature of this problem is that the family benefit is not the total of the three benefits received by Mr. Williams, Mrs. Williams, and their child. That sum comes to more than the amount given to any single family whose average yearly earnings were \$7,400. The maximum for this income is only \$616.70 and that is all the Williams family will receive each month. When the child reaches the age of 18, if he is not attending school, his benefit of $175.40 will be subtracted from $654.80—not $616.70—and the family will receive the balance of $479.40.

The social security law provides for disability payments in exactly the same manner as retirement payments. A disabled person will receive the primary amount, while his wife and children will receive the same percents of the primary amount as if the husband had retired. To be covered for disability payments, a person must have earned 5 years of social security credits in the 10 years prior to the time he became disabled. This statement isn't quite true for everybody, though. If the person happens to be under 31, he will need fewer than 5 years of credits to qualify for disability payments. And if he happens to be under 24, he will need fewer still. In any event, he can receive these payments only if his disability is expected to last for at least 12 months. Also of interest is the fact that the payments do not begin until after the fifth month of disability.

EXERCISES A

1. Round off each of the following to the next higher 10¢ amount.

a.	$123.67	e.	$205.21	i.	$456.94		
b.	156.89	f.	317.02	j.	129.98		
c.	137.52	g.	238.92	k.	249.93		
d.	243.76	h.	341.97	l.	199.91		

2. Use the following average yearly earnings to determine how much a wife will receive monthly if she is over 65.

	Average Yearly Earnings	P.I.A.	Wife's Benefit
a.	$4,200	$	$
b.	5,050		
c.	5,400		
d.	7,550		
e.	3,850		
f.	4,650		
g.	6,800		
h.	7,800		

3. Use the following average yearly earnings to determine how much a husband will receive monthly if he retires on his 62nd birthday and begins to collect his benefits at that time.

	Average Yearly Earnings	P.I.A.	Husband's Benefit
a.	$12,000	$________	$________
b.	6,600	________	________
c.	3,550	________	________
d.	4,200	________	________
e.	5,500	________	________
f.	9,000	________	________
g.	7,400	________	________
h.	5,700	________	________

4. Use the following average yearly earnings to determine how much a wife will receive if she elects to begin taking her benefits on her 62nd birthday.

	Average Yearly Earnings	P.I.A.	Wife's Benefit
a.	$1,150	$________	$________
b.	4,900	________	________
c.	4,650	________	________
d.	5,400	________	________
e.	5,800	________	________
f.	7,550	________	________

5. In the following exercises the ages of both husband and wife are shown. There are no children under the age of 22 in these families. What is the total family benefit in each situation?

	Average Yearly Earnings	Husband's Age	Wife's Age	P.I.A.	Husband's Benefit	Wife's Benefit	Family Benefit
a.	$4,000	65	57	$________	$________	$________	$________
b.	7,550	66	60	________	________	________	________
c.	2,850	67	66	________	________	________	________
d.	9,000	68	65	________	________	________	________
e.	5,050	62	65	________	________	________	________
f.	7,400	63	66	________	________	________	________
g.	3,850	64	67	________	________	________	________
h.	6,800	65	62	________	________	________	________
i.	2,200	67	63	________	________	________	________
j.	7,800	70	64	________	________	________	________
k.	4,650	62	62	________	________	________	________
l.	7,550	64	63	________	________	________	________

6. In the following exercises the ages of husband, wife, and child are shown. If the child is 18 or over, assume that he is no longer attending school. What is the total family benefit in each situation (compare with maximum family benefit)?

	Average Yearly Earnings	Husband's Age	Wife's Age	Child's Age	Family Benefit
a.	$ 3,550	65	57	24	$______
b.	10,800	65	65	31	______
c.	5,400	65	52	16	______
d.	6,600	69	55	17	______
e.	5,150	66	50	17	______
f.	7,400	62	59	16	______
g.	9,000	64	53	16	______

B

1. Mr. Burns is collecting disability insurance under the social security law. His average yearly earnings are $5,050. He has a wife of 32 and two children—14 and 16.
   a. What is the total monthly benefit the family will receive? ______
   b. What is the total monthly benefit the family will receive when the oldest child reaches 18? ______
2. Mr. Campara retired at 65 and began receiving his social security benefits based on average yearly earnings of $7,200.
   a. How much did he receive each month? ______
   b. How much would he have received each month had he retired at 62 at the same average yearly earnings? ______
   c. How much more does he receive monthly by having retired at 65 rather than at 62? ______
3. The social security agency found that Mr. Flanagan's average yearly earnings were $4,650 at the time he retired at 66.
   a. How much will Mr. Flanagan's monthly benefit be? ______
   b. According to the mortality table for the years 1959–1961 on page 357, how many years, to the nearest year, can Mr. Flanagan expect to live? ______
   c. How much should the social security agency plan on paying Mr. Flanagan over his expected lifetime? ______

Section 3: Survivors' Benefits

Whenever you hear of someone receiving social security benefits, your immediate reaction is that the person must be old and retired. As you learned in the preceding section, this could be quite far from the truth, for some of you, although under 18, might be receiving these benefits, based on your father's retirement payments. In addition to this, there are a great many more of you who may be receiving monthly social security payments because either your dad or mother died and you are under 18, or perhaps still attending school and under 22. In this section, you will learn how large these payments will be in the event of the death of the father of the family. Remember, of course, that the father has to be fully insured or currently insured for the family to collect any benefits.

Should the widow begin collecting her benefits at age 65 or over, she will receive 100% of the primary insurance amount. However, should she choose to start collecting these payments at some younger age, her benefits will be reduced by 19/40ths of 1% for each month prior to age 65 in which the first payment began. Thus, if she were to begin collecting payments on her 64th birthday, her monthly checks will be 94.3% of the P.I.A.; were these checks to begin coming on her 61st birthday, they would amount to 77.2% of the P.I.A. However, if there are no dependents she can not receive any benefits until she reaches the age of 60.

Notice that in the table below, provision is made for making payments to a widow caring for a disabled child no matter what the age of the child or the age of the mother. Actually, these same benefits can be received if the husband is retired rather than deceased. In both cases the child must have been disabled before reaching the age of 22.

SURVIVORS' BENEFITS

Family Member	Percent of P.I.A.
Widow,	
65 or older	100%
64	94.3%
63	88.6%
62	82.9%
61	77.2%
60	71.5%
. . . .	
Widow any age caring for either a child under 18 or a disabled child	75%
Child under 18	75%
Child under 22 attending school	75%
Child disabled before 22	75%

Lump-sum death payment: $255

ILLUSTRATION 1: Mrs. Bailey was 63 at the time of her husband's death. His average yearly earnings were $7,400.

a. How large will the lump-sum death payment be?
b. How much will Mrs. Bailey's monthly benefit be?

SOLUTION:

P.I.A. for $7,400 = $350.70

(a) Lump-sum death payment = $255

(b) Mrs. Bailey's monthly benefit = 88.6% of $350.70
= .886 × $350.70
= $310.72, or $310.80

EXPLANATION: The lump-sum death payment of $255 is exactly the same for everyone. Mrs. Bailey's monthly benefit, though, is found by determining 88.6% of the P.I.A. This is so since her age was 63 at the time her benefits began. In this computation it is assumed that her very first payment was sent during the month of her 63rd birthday.

ILLUSTRATION 2: Mr. Newman died leaving a wife of 40 and two children aged 12 and 14. The social security agency computed his average yearly earnings at $5,700.

a. What total monthly benefit will the family receive?
b. What total monthly benefit will the family receive after the oldest child reaches 18, assuming he is no longer attending school?

SOLUTION:

P.I.A. for $5,700 = $289.60

(a) Mrs. Newman's benefit = 75% of $289.60
= .75 × $289.60
= $217.20

Benefit of child, 12 = 75% of $289.60
= $217.20

Benefit of child, 14 = 75% of $289.60
= $217.20

Total monthly benefit = $217.20 + 217.20 + $217.20
= $651.60

Actual monthly benefit = $535.80 (maximum given for a P.I.A. of $289.60)

(b) Total monthly benefit after oldest child reaches 18
= $651.60 − $217.20
= $434.40

EXERCISES A

1. Determine the widow's monthly benefit if she is under 60 but caring for a child who is under 18.

	Average Yearly Earnings Of Husband	P.I.A.	Widow's Benefit
a.	$ 5,800	$______	$______
b.	2,200	______	______
c.	5,050	______	______
d.	7,400	______	______
e.	6,950	______	______
f.	10,800	______	______

2. Determine the widow's monthly payment if she begins to receive her monthly benefits on her birthday at the age shown.

	Average Yearly Earnings Of Husband	Age of Widow	P.I.A.	Widow's Benefit
a.	$4,900	65	$______	$______
b.	7,550	65	______	______
c.	4,000	64	______	______
d.	7,800	64	______	______
e.	5,250	63	______	______
f.	2,850	62	______	______
g.	9,000	61	______	______
h.	7,800	60	______	______

3. The father in each of the following families has died. Determine the monthly benefit his family will receive.

	Average Yearly Earnings Of Husband	Age of Widow	Ages of Children	P.I.A.	Family Benefit
a.	$ 5,700	37	10	$______	$______
b.	4,200	29	6	______	______
c.	6,600	56	32	______	______
d.	6,950	64	40	______	______
e.	1,500	25	2	______	______
f.	2,850	32	12	______	______
g.	10,800	24	5, 1	______	______
h.	12,000	43	17, 14, 11	______	______

B

1. When Mr. Pitt died, the social security agency found his average yearly earnings to be $5,500. At the time of his death his wife was 48. Mrs. Pitt was left with the care of a disabled son, who was 25 years old. The young man had been permanently disabled at 14.
   a. What monthly benefit did Mrs. Pitt receive? ______
   b. What monthly benefit did the son receive? ______
2. When Mr. Waring died, his wife was 42 and his daughter, who was attending college, was 20. Mr. Waring's average yearly earnings were computed to be $7,800.

a. What lump-sum death payment did the family receive? ________

b. What monthly benefit did Mrs. Waring receive? ________

c. What monthly benefit did the daughter receive? ________

Section 4: The Medicare Program

It has just been within recent years that medicare has been added to the social security program. Medicare consists of two different types of insurance, for neither of which you are eligible until you reach 65. The cost of the first of these—hospital insurance—is tacked on to the social security deductions that are taken from your weekly salary checks. You really have no choice as to whether you want to buy this insurance or not, for deductions are made before you receive your earnings.

Coverage under the second insurance—medical insurance—is voluntary. At the time you reach 65, you simply notify the social security agency that you want this coverage. To pay for it, a small deduction will be made from your social security monthly benefits. The premium changes periodically, depending on how much it costs to run the program. Incidentally, the federal government contributes an amount equal to what you have paid so that, in reality, you are getting relatively cheap insurance for you are paying only half the cost.

Actually, the medicare program has been a real aid to the elderly. Before this law was passed, many aged people feared to become so ill that they would have to be taken to a hospital. They knew that the extremely high cost of hospital care would soon devour the small savings that had taken them a lifetime to accumulate.

Here is how you will be covered under the hospital insurance program when you reach 65.

Hospital care for a single period of illness:

For first 60 days . . . . . . Total payment less $84
For next 30 days . . . . . . Total payment less $18 per day

Nursing-home care following hospital care:

For first 20 days . . . . . . Total payment
For next 80 days . . . . . . Total payment less $9 per day

In addition to the above, the hospital insurance provides for a *lifetime-reserve* of 60 days, during which all but $36 per day of your hospital bill will be paid. For instance, if, during a single period of illness you had to be in the hospital 100 days, this would be 10 days more than the total of 90 days in the table. For those last 10 days the insurance company will pay all but $36 of each day's cost. This will leave you, however, with only 50 more days in the lifetime-reserve. Once you use up the full 60 days in this reserve, you can never use them again.

The 90 days in the single period of illness are quite different from the lifetime-reserve days. These 90 days can be used over and over again each time you have to be taken to the hospital. If you go to the hospital for 35 days, for example, the insurance company will pay all but the first $84 of the bill. If it then becomes necessary for you to go to the hospital for another 50 days, the insurance company will again pay for all but the first $84 of the bill. The first stay of 35 days has no effect on the second stay of 50 days. This can be repeated as often as required. So long as 60 days elapse between the end of the first hospital stay and the beginning of the second hospital stay, then they are considered as two separate periods of illness.

Should it be necessary for you to have to go to a nursing home for care after you have been released from the hospital, then you must be admitted within 14 days after leaving the hospital. If you are admitted after the 14 days are over, then you, yourself, will have to pay the bill. Just one other point pertaining to this. Unless you have been in a hospital for at least 3 days before entering the nursing home, you will not be covered by the insurance program.

There is one more costly item whose expense is covered by this insurance. If you have been in the hospital for at least 3 days, then you are entitled to 100 visits to your home, if needed, by nurses and physical therapists—but not doctors. Here, again, the insurance company will not pay the cost of the treatment unless your doctor sets up a plan for this within 14 days after you leave the hospital. Also, the treatments have to be completed within one year.

ILLUSTRATION 1: Mr. Sherman, who is covered by medicare, spent 75 days in the hospital. The total bill amounted to $2,625. How much of this did the insurance company have to pay?

SOLUTION:

Amount deducted for first 60 days = $84
Amount deducted for remaining 15 days = 15 × $18
= $270

Total deducted = $84 + $270
= $354

Amount paid by the insurance company = $2,625 − $354
= $2,271

EXPLANATION: Mr. Sherman had to pay the first $84 of whatever the cost had been during the first 60 days. In addition, he had to pay $18 of the cost for each of the 15 days he stayed in the hospital beyond the 60 days. The cost to Mr. Sherman for the 15 days was $270. Hence, the total he had to pay for the 75 days was $354. Therefore, the insurance company paid the difference between $2,625 and $354, or $2,271.

ILLUSTRATION 2: Mr. Williamson is 66 and covered by the medicare program. Because of a serious illness, he was hospitalized for 96 days. How much will this cost him?

SOLUTION:

Cost for first 60 days = $84
Cost for next 30 days = 30 × $18
= $540
Cost for remaining 6 days = 6 × $36
= $216
Total cost = $84 + $540 + $216
= $840

EXPLANATION: The computation here is much the same as in the early part of the previous illustration, except that in this case, 6 days of the lifetime-reserve must be used. For each of these days, Mr. Williamson has to pay $36 of the hospital cost, or a total of $216.

The second part of the medicare program, that is, the part you help to pay for after you reach 65, covers almost all doctor's and medical bills. During any single year, if these bills amount to more than $60, then you pay only the first $60, in addition to 20% of the remaining amount. The insurance company pays the rest. Among the costs that are covered are:

> Physician's services, up to 100 visits by either a nurse or a physical therapist; x-ray treatments, surgical dressings, casts, artificial limbs, wheelchairs, hospital beds, and drugs.

ILLUSTRATION 3: Last year, Mr. Harper, who is covered by medical insurance under the medicare program, had a total cost of $856 for doctor's bills and medical bills. How much of this amount did the insurance company have to pay?

SOLUTION:

Amount Mr. Harper paid:

Deductible amount = $60

20% of balance = 20% of ($856 − $60)

= .20 × $796

= $159.20

Total = $60 + $159.20

= $219.20

Amount paid by insurance company = $856 − $219.20

= $636.80

EXPLANATION: Mr. Harper had to pay the first $60 of the cost. In addition, he paid 20% of the balance of $796, and this amounted to $159.20. Hence, the total he paid was $219.20. Therefore, the amount remaining for the insurance company to pay was the difference between $856 and $219.20. This is $636.80.

EXERCISES A

1. In each of the following exercises, the person was covered by the medicare program. How much will his part of the bill be if he was in the hospital the number of days shown?

a. 15 days ______ d. 65 days ______ g. 78 days ______
b. 27 days ______ e. 69 days ______ h. 87 days ______
c. 53 days ______ f. 85 days ______

2. Each of the people in the following exercises was admitted into a nursing home under the medicare program. How much of the bill will each person have to pay if he remains in the home for the number of days shown?

a. 8 days ______ d. 47 days ______ g. 84 days ______
b. 14 days ______ e. 25 days ______ h. 95 days ______
c. 17 days ______ f. 78 days ______

3. Each of the people in the following exercises was admitted to a hospital under the medicare program. If none of them had used any of his lifetime-reserve days, how much of the bill will each have to pay if he remains in the hospital for the number of days shown?

a. 100 days ______ c. 120 days ______ e. 135 days ______
b. 107 days ______ d. 126 days ______ f. 148 days ______

4. How much of each of the following hospital bills will have to be paid by the insurance company if the person is covered by the medicare program?

	Hospital Cost	Number Of Days Hospitalized	Amount Paid By Insured	Amount Paid By Insurance Company
a.	$ 378	10	$______	$______
b.	759	22	______	______
c.	1,510	45	______	______
d.	2,014	53	______	______
e.	2,653	65	______	______
f.	2,912	74	______	______
g.	2,714	82	______	______
h.	3,158	88	______	______

5. How much of each of the following nursing-home bills will have to be paid by the insurance company if the person is covered by the medicare program?

	Nursing-Home Cost	Number Of Days In Nursing Home	Amount Paid By Insured	Amount Paid By Insurance Company
a.	$ 154	7	$______	$______
b.	225	10	______	______
c.	341	14	______	______
d.	456	20	______	______
e.	678	30	______	______
f.	783	35	______	______
g.	1,237	56	______	______
h.	1,978	84	______	______

6. The following are medical costs that persons had over the period of one year. If each of them was covered by the medicare program, how much of these bills did each person have to pay himself?

	Medical Cost	Deductible Amount	Remainder	20% Of Remainder	Insured's Cost
a.	$ 150	$______	$______	$______	$______
b.	200	______	______	______	______
c.	280	______	______	______	______
d.	575	______	______	______	______
e.	40	______	______	______	______
f.	37	______	______	______	______
g.	856	______	______	______	______
h.	1,050	______	______	______	______
i.	1,762	______	______	______	______
j.	4,374	______	______	______	______

7. The following are medical costs that persons had over the period of one year. If each of them was covered by the medicare program, how much of the bill did the insurance company have to pay?

	Medical Cost	Deductible Amount	Remainder	20% Of Remainder	Amount Paid By Insured	Amount Paid By Insurance Company
a.	$ 170	$______	$______	$______	$______	$______
b.	260	______	______	______	______	______
c.	45	______	______	______	______	______
d.	640	______	______	______	______	______
e.	782	______	______	______	______	______
f.	2,390	______	______	______	______	______

B

1. Mrs. Yarby was covered by the medicare program at the time she was taken ill and had to go to the hospital. She spent 27 days there, for which the cost ran to $1,809, and another 16 days in a nursing home at a cost of $432.
   a. How much of the hospital bill did Mrs. Yarby have to pay? ______
   b. How much of the nursing-home bill did she have to pay? ______
   c. What is the total amount that Mrs. Yarby had to pay to both institutions? ______
2. Mr. Darden, who is covered by medicare for both hospital and medical insurance, had a serious operation for which the surgeon's charge was $1,400. He spent 70 days in the hospital and another 38 days in a nursing home before returning to his own home. The hospital costs came to $4,410, while the nursing home charged him $1,026.
   a. How much of the hospital bill did Mr. Darden have to pay? ______
   b. How much of the nursing-home bill did Mr. Darden have to pay? ______
   c. How much of the surgeon's fee did Mr. Darden have to pay? ______
   d. How much of the entire bill did the insurance company have to pay? ______

Unit 2: Private Retirement Plans

There are a great many companies that offer their employees a retirement plan in addition to the one they will receive under the social security program. Most of these plans operate as a joint responsibility —that is, part of the cost is paid for by the employer and the rest is paid for by the employee. Unfortunately, every private retirement plan is different from every other one. However, the one described below is somewhat typical of a great number of them.

In this retirement program, the amount contributed depends upon whether the employee is a man or a woman, and also upon the age at which the person began working for the firm. The rates for women are higher than those for men at the same age, since women, in general, are expected to live longer than men. And, therefore, since women will be collecting retirement benefits for a greater period of time, they have to contribute a greater amount into the fund. Notice, also, that the older you are at the time you begin to work for this company, the higher your contribution rate will be.

PRICE–DAVIS CORPORATION
Employee Contribution Rate

Entrance Age	Percent of Contribution		Entrance Age	Percent of Contribution	
	Men	Women		Men	Women
20	4.80	5.27	40	6.04	6.81
21	4.80	5.31	41	6.14	6.92
22	4.81	5.36	42	6.23	7.04
23	4.83	5.40	43	6.34	7.15
24	4.87	5.45	44	6.44	7.27
25	4.91	5.51	45	6.55	7.39
26	4.96	5.57	46	6.65	7.50
27	5.01	5.64	47	6.77	7.62
28	5.06	5.71	48	6.88	7.75
29	5.12	5.78	49	7.00	7.88
30	5.19	5.85	50	7.12	8.02
31	5.26	5.93	51	7.25	8.18
32	5.34	6.02	52	7.39	8.34
33	5.43	6.11	53	7.54	8.51
34	5.51	6.21	54	7.69	8.67
35	5.59	6.30	55	7.84	8.83
36	5.67	6.39	56	7.99	9.00
37	5.76	6.50	57	8.14	9.16
38	5.86	6.60	58	8.30	9.33
39	5.95	6.71	59	8.45	9.51

ILLUSTRATION 1: Ben Nelson began working for the Price-Davis Corporation when he was 24. His annual income now is $12,356. How large will his contribution to the fund be this year?

EXPLANATION: Ben's contribution rate will be 4.87%, as he entered the company at age 24. To determine his contribution, you will have to determine 4.87% of $12,356.

SOLUTION:

$$\begin{aligned}\text{Contribution rate} &= 4.87\% \\ &= .0487 \\ \text{Contribution that year} &= 4.87\% \text{ of } \$12{,}356 \\ &= .0487 \times \$12{,}356 \\ &= \$601.7372, \text{ or } \$601.74\end{aligned}$$

As an employee, equally important to you as the amount you contribute is the question of how much you will get back in benefits at the time you retire. The method used for finding the monthly benefits received by the Price-Davis employees is one that involves their average annual earnings over the last five years of employment and also the number of years they have been employed by the company. A fraction is found, made up of the numerator, which represents the number of years of employment, and the denominator, which is always 60. This fraction is then multiplied by the average annual earnings of the last five years. Their product equals the annual benefit the employee receives.

$$\text{Annual Benefit} = \frac{\text{Number of Years of Employment}}{60} \times \text{Average Annual Salary of Last Five Years}$$

ILLUSTRATION 2: For the last five years before retirement Clara Lee had an average annual income with the Price-Davis Corporation of $11,450. If she worked for the company for 28 years, how large was her annual retirement benefit?

SOLUTION:

$$\begin{aligned}\text{Annual benefit} &= 28/60 \times \$11{,}450 \\ &= \$320{,}600/60 \\ &= \$5{,}343.33\end{aligned}$$

EXERCISES A

The following exercises are based on the retirement plan of the Price-Davis Corporation.

1. Change each of the following percent numerals to its equivalent decimal numeral.

a. 4.93% ________	c. 5.40% ________	e. 7.03% ________
b. 5.02% ________	d. 6.39% ________	f. 8.00% ________

2. How much will each of the following employees have to contribute to the fund during the year shown?

	Annual Earnings	Entrance Age	Sex	Contribution Rate	Contribution
a.	$ 8,000	49	Male	____%	$____
b.	6,400	35	Female	____%	____
c.	7,500	41	Male	____%	____
d.	9,300	46	Female	____%	____
e.	5,420	21	Male	____%	____
f.	5,420	21	Female	____%	____
g.	7,370	28	Male	____%	____
h.	10,450	52	Male	____%	____
i.	12,360	49	Female	____%	____
j.	14,630	44	Male	____%	____

3. Determine the annual benefit received by each of the following retired employees of the Price-Davis Corporation.

	Number of Years Of Employment	Average Annual Earnings Of Last 5 Years	Annual Benefit
a.	30	$ 7,200	$____
b.	20	9,000	____
c.	15	8,400	____
d.	10	9,600	____
e.	40	12,000	____
f.	45	10,800	____
g.	35	11,400	____
h.	25	12,300	____
i.	32	13,500	____
j.	36	14,580	____

B

1. Maria Torres began working for the Price-Davis Corporation at 22 and retired at 64. Her average annual salary during the last five years before retirement was $12,960.

a. What was her annual retirement benefit? ____

b. If she was paid this benefit on a monthly basis, how much was her check each month? ____

2. Jack Freeman retired from the Price-Davis Corporation at 65. He had begun working for the corporation at age 31. His average annual earnings during the last five years of employment were $12,360.

a. What was his annual retirement benefit? ____

b. According to the mortality table for the years 1959–1961 on page 357, how many years, to the nearest whole number of years, is Mr. Freeman expected to live after retirement? ____

c. If he lives the number of years predicted, what total amount of money will he collect under the retirement plan? ____

Unit 3: Retirement Income from Annuities

Many people feel that social security benefits alone at the time of retirement will not give them nearly enough income to live on in the manner they would like. Some of these people are also covered by company retirement plans and yet they still feel that they will need additional income. If they can afford it, they will probably purchase their own retirement program, called an *annuity*. A retirement plan of this type consists simply of a contract drawn up between a person and, usually, an insurance company whereby the person agrees to pay the insurance company a certain amount of money. The company, in turn, agrees that starting when the person reaches a certain age, it will pay him a fixed amount of money for the rest of his life.

It would not be quite right if, after the insurance company sent the person the first payment, he happened to die. Were this to occur, he would have received far too little in return for the amount he had contributed. Hence, the contract frequently states that the company guarantees to pay someone, either the person himself—if he lives long enough—or someone he names—if he happens to die first—for at least a 10-year period. This annuity is called a *10-Year Certain Annuity*. As mentioned before, should the person live more than 10 years, the company will continue to pay him this monthly income for the rest of his life.

The payments can be made to the insurance company in one of two forms. Either the company is given a lump-sum and no other payments are ever again made, or the person pays the company a fixed amount each year until such time as the company begins to pay him back. The first of these is called a *single-premium annuity*, while the second is an *annual-premium annuity*. As an illustration, with a single-premium annuity, the person might arrange to pay the company $1,000 at age 20 and then make no further payments. When he reaches 60, the company will begin to send him $15.11 every single month as long as he lives. With the annual-premium annuity, the arrangement might be to pay the insurance company $100 every year starting at age 20. When the person reaches 60 he will stop making payments to the company and at that time the company will begin making payments to him of $35.74 every month until the day he dies.

Notice in the Single-Premium Annuity Table on the next page that a male who pays $1,000 at age 20 will get back $15.11 each month starting at 60, while a female will receive only $13.49 monthly for the same $1,000. Do you know why this is so?

SINGLE–PREMIUM ANNUITY							ANNUAL–PREMIUM ANNUITY						
Monthly Life Income Purchased by $1,000 Single Premium							Monthly Life Income (10 Year Certain) Purchased by $100 Annual Premium				Monthly Life Income (10 Year Certain) Purchased by $100 Annual Premium		
MALE				FEMALE			MALE				FEMALE		
Age at Date Of Maturity				Age at Date Of Maturity			Age at Date Of Maturity				Age at Date Of Maturity		
60	65	70	Age	60	65	70	60	65	70	Age	60	65	70
$15.11	$19.43	$24.98	20	$13.49	$17.31	$22.26	$35.74	$48.98	$66.33	20	$31.92	$43.62	$59.11
14.71	18.91	24.31	21	13.13	16.84	21.66	34.29	47.12	63.93	21	30.63	41.96	56.97
14.31	18.41	23.66	22	12.78	16.39	21.08	32.88	45.30	61.60	22	29.37	40.34	54.89
13.93	17.92	23.03	23	12.44	15.95	20.52	31.51	43.53	59.33	23	28.14	38.77	52.87
13.56	17.44	22.41	24	12.11	15.53	19.97	30.17	41.81	57.12	24	26.94	37.23	50.90
13.19	16.97	21.81	25	11.78	15.11	19.43	28.87	40.14	54.97	25	25.78	35.74	48.98
12.84	16.51	21.23	26	11.47	14.71	18.91	27.60	38.51	52.87	26	24.65	34.29	47.12
12.50	16.07	20.66	27	11.16	14.31	18.41	26.37	36.93	50.84	27	23.55	32.88	45.30
12.16	15.64	20.10	28	10.86	13.93	17.92	25.17	35.38	48.85	28	22.48	31.51	43.53
11.84	15.22	19.57	29	10.57	13.56	17.44	24.00	33.88	46.92	29	21.44	30.17	41.81
11.52	14.82	19.04	30	10.29	13.19	16.97	22.87	32.42	45.05	30	20.42	28.87	40.14
11.21	14.42	18.53	31	10.01	12.84	16.51	21.76	31.00	43.22	31	19.44	27.60	38.51
10.91	14.03	18.04	32	9.74	12.50	16.07	20.69	29.62	41.44	32	18.47	26.37	36.93
10.62	13.66	17.55	33	9.48	12.16	15.64	19.64	28.27	39.71	33	17.54	25.17	35.38
10.34	13.29	17.08	34	9.23	11.84	15.22	18.62	26.96	38.02	34	16.63	24.00	33.88
10.06	12.94	16.63	35	8.98	11.52	14.82	17.63	25.68	36.38	35	15.74	22.87	32.42
9.79	12.59	16.18	36	8.74	11.21	14.42	16.66	24.44	34.79	36	14.88	21.76	31.00
9.53	12.25	15.75	37	8.51	10.91	14.03	15.72	23.23	33.23	37	14.04	20.69	29.62
9.27	11.93	15.33	38	8.28	10.62	13.66	14.81	22.06	31.72	38	13.22	19.64	28.27
9.02	11.61	14.92	39	8.06	10.34	13.29	13.92	20.91	30.25	39	12.43	18.62	26.96
8.78	11.30	14.52	40	7.84	10.06	12.94	13.05	19.80	28.82	40	11.66	17.63	25.68
8.55	10.99	14.13	41	7.63	9.79	12.59	12.21	18.71	27.43	41	10.90	16.66	24.44
8.32	10.70	13.75	42	7.43	9.53	12.25	11.39	17.66	26.07	42	10.17	15.72	23.23
8.10	10.41	13.38	43	7.23	9.27	11.93	10.59	16.63	24.75	43	9.46	14.81	22.06
7.88	10.13	13.03	44	7.04	9.02	11.61	9.81	15.63	23.47	44	8.76	13.92	20.91
7.67	9.86	12.68	45	6.85	8.78	11.30	9.06	14.66	22.22	45	8.09	13.05	19.80
7.46	9.60	12.34	46	6.67	8.55	10.99	8.32	13.71	21.00	46	7.43	12.21	18.71
7.26	9.34	12.01	47	6.49	8.32	10.70	7.60	12.79	19.81	47	6.79	11.39	17.66
7.07	9.09	11.69	48	6.31	8.10	10.41	6.91	11.89	18.66	48	6.17	10.59	16.63
6.88	8.85	11.37	49	6.14	7.88	10.13	6.23	11.02	17.54	49	5.56	9.81	15.63
6.70	8.61	11.07	50	5.98	7.67	9.86	5.57	10.17	16.45	50	4.97	9.06	14.66
6.52	8.38	10.77	51	5.82	7.46	9.60	4.93	9.34	15.39	51	4.40	8.32	13.71
6.34	8.16	10.48	52	5.66	7.26	9.34	4.30	8.54	14.35	52	3.84	7.60	12.79
6.17	7.94	10.20	53	5.51	7.07	9.09	3.69	7.76	13.35	53	3.30	6.91	11.89
6.01	7.73	9.93	54	5.37	6.88	8.85	3.10	6.99	12.37	54	2.77	6.23	11.02
5.85	7.52	9.66	55	5.22	6.70	8.61	2.52	6.25	11.41	55	2.25	5.57	10.17
	7.32	9.41	56		6.52	8.38		5.53	10.49	56		4.93	9.34
	7.12	9.15	57		6.34	8.16		4.83	9.58	57		4.30	8.54
	6.93	8.91	58		6.17	7.94		4.15	8.70	58		3.69	7.76
	6.75	8.67	59		6.01	7.73		3.48	7.85	59		3.10	6.99
	6.57	8.44	60		5.85	7.52		2.83	7.02	60		2.52	6.25
		8.21	61			7.32			6.21	61			5.53
		7.99	62			7.12			5.42	62			4.83
		7.57	63			6.93			4.65	63			4.15
		7.37	64			6.75			3.91	64			3.48
			65			6.57			3.18	65			2.83

ILLUSTRATION 1: When George Turner was 23, he made a $6,000 payment on a single-premium annuity from which he would begin to receive a monthly income starting at 65. How large will these benefits be?

EXPLANATION: Use the Single-Premium Annuity Table on page 421. Run your finger down the "Age" column until you reach the numeral 23. Place the edge of a piece of paper along this row and then run your finger to the left into that part of the table headed by the word "Male." Stop at the column headed by the numeral 65. Your finger should be pointing at $17.92. This is the amount that George will receive monthly, starting at 65, for each $1,000 in the lump-sum payment he made at 23. Since the total payment was $6,000, he will receive 6 times $17.92, or $107.52 monthly.

SOLUTION:

Monthly payment at age 65 per $1,000 = $17.92
Monthly payment at age 65 for $6,000 = 6 × $17.92
= $107.52

ILLUSTRATION 2: At 33, Grace Becker purchased an annual premium annuity by agreeing to pay $500 each year until she reached 60. How large will the monthly payments be that she will receive from the insurance company beginning at 60?

EXPLANATION: In this illustration, use the Annual-Premium Annuity Table and look at the "Female" section. For an entrance age of 33, a woman will receive $17.54 each month when she reaches the age of 60. This $17.54 is for each $100 that Grace paid annually. Since her total annual payment is $500, she will be sent 5 times $17.54, or $87.70 monthly.

SOLUTION:

Monthly payment at age 60 per $100 premium = $17.54
Monthly payment at age 60 for $500 premium = 5 × $17.54
= $87.70

EXERCISES A

1. Determine the monthly income that can be purchased for $1,000 on each of the following single-premium annuities.

	Entrance Age	Age At Maturity	Sex	Monthly Income
a.	25	60	Male	$________
b.	27	60	Female	________

	Entrance Age	Age At Maturity	Sex	Monthly Income
c.	34	65	Female	$______
d.	41	65	Male	______
e.	23	70	Male	______
f.	48	60	Female	______
g.	54	65	Female	______
h.	49	65	Male	______
i.	36	70	Female	______
j.	58	65	Male	______
k.	21	60	Female	______

2. Determine the monthly income that can be purchased for $100 annually on each of the following annual-premium annuities.

	Entrance Age	Age At Maturity	Sex	Monthly Income
a.	22	60	Male	$______
b.	32	60	Female	______
c.	27	65	Male	______
d.	31	70	Male	______
e.	29	65	Female	______
f.	43	70	Female	______
g.	48	65	Female	______
h.	57	70	Male	______

3. Determine the monthly income that can be purchased on each of the following single-premium annuities.

	Lump-Sum Payment	Entrance Age	Age At Maturity	Sex	Monthly Income Per $1,000	Monthly Income
a.	$ 5,000	27	60	Male	$______	$______
b.	4,000	21	65	Male	______	______
c.	6,000	34	65	Male	______	______
d.	12,000	36	60	Female	______	______
e.	10,000	48	70	Female	______	______
f.	15,000	50	65	Male	______	______
g.	18,000	31	60	Female	______	______
h.	25,000	35	70	Male	______	______

4. Determine the monthly income that can be purchased on each of the following annual-premium annuities.

	Annual Premium	Entrance Age	Age At Maturity	Sex	Monthly Income Per $100	Monthly Income
a.	$200	20	60	Male	$______	$______
b.	300	29	60	Male	______	______
c.	300	29	60	Female	______	______
d.	200	45	65	Male	______	______
e.	400	32	65	Female	______	______
f.	400	47	70	Male	______	______
g.	600	30	65	Male	______	______
h.	800	34	60	Female	______	______

5. As in the case of the life-insurance premiums, semiannual payments can be made instead of yearly payments on annual-premium annuities. When this is done, the semiannual premium is 52% of the annual premium. Determine the semiannual premium that will have to be paid for each of the following annual premiums.

	Annual Premium	Semiannual Premium		Annual Premium	Semiannual Premium
a.	$100	$______	d.	$250	$______
b.	200	______	e.	450	______
c.	500	______	f.	750	______

6. If quarterly premiums are paid on an annuity, they are 26.5% of the annual premium. Determine the quarterly premiums that would have to be paid for each of the following annual premiums.

	Annual Premium	Quarterly Premium		Annual Premium	Quarterly Premium
a.	$100	$______	d.	$350	$______
b.	300	______	e.	550	______
c.	800	______	f.	850	______

B

1. Charles Samuels purchased a single-premium annuity for $15,000. He is to begin receiving payments at 60.
   a. How large will the payments be if Mr. Samuels purchased the annuity at 20? ______
   b. How large will the payments be if Mr. Samuels purchased the annuity at 40? ______
   c. How much more will he receive each month if the purchase is made at 20 rather than at 40? ______
2. Evelyn Noyes purchased a $20,000 single-premium annuity at 36.
   a. How much will she receive monthly if the payments are to start at 60? ______
   b. How much will she receive monthly if the payments are to start at 70? ______
   c. How much more will she receive monthly if the payments are to begin at 70 rather than at 60? ______
3. John Blanchard purchased a $10,000 single-premium annuity at 34. He is to begin receiving monthly payments at 60.
   a. How large will each monthly payment be? ______
   b. How much will he receive over the period of 1 year? ______
   c. According to the Mortality Table for the years 1959–1961 on page 357, how many years, to the nearest year, can a man of 60 expect to live? ______

d. If Mr. Blanchard lives exactly the expected number of years shown in the table, how much money will he receive on his annuity? ________

e. How much more—or less—will he receive from the insurance company than he gave in his lump-sum payment? ________

4. Mr. Hawkins purchased a $600 annual-premium annuity at 30 for which payments are to begin at 65.

a. How large will each of his monthly benefits be? ________

b. If Mrs. Hawkins had purchased the same annuity at the same age, how large would her monthly benefits be, beginning at 65? ________

c. How much more would Mr. Hawkins receive during a year than Mrs. Hawkins? ________

d. How much more would Mr. Hawkins receive over a 15-year period than Mrs. Hawkins? ________

Unit 4: Chapter Review and Test

Refer to the tables in this chapter when doing the computation for the following problems.

1. Determine the social security primary insurance amount on each of the following average yearly earnings.

a. $3,850 ________	c. $5,800 ________	e. $4,400 ________
b. $5,250 ________	d. $7,800 ________	f. $9,000 ________

2. Determine the maximum social security benefit a family can receive on each of the following average yearly earnings.

a. $3,550 ________	c. $10,800 ________	e. $6,600 ________
b. $5,150 ________	d. $ 7,400 ________	f. $5,250 ________

3. A husband's average yearly earnings are computed by the social security agency to be $6,800.

a. What will his monthly benefit be if he begins to receive it at 65? ________

b. If his wife is also 65 at the time she begins receiving her monthly allotment, how much will she receive? ________

4. Mr. Campbell's average yearly income under social security was $6,950. How much will his monthly benefit be if he begins to receive it at 62? ________

5. Mr. Perkins was 66 at the time he began to collect his monthly social security benefits on an average yearly earning of $5,600. His wife was 59 at the time, and they have no children.

a. How much did Mr. Perkins receive? ________
b. How much did Mrs. Perkins receive? ________

6. On her 61st birthday, Mrs. Bethea began to collect social security payments based on her deceased husband's average yearly earnings of $7,550. How large was each monthly check? ________
7. Mr. Alkorn died, leaving a wife, 27, and a daughter, 5. His average yearly earnings under social security were $9,000.
   a. How much did Mrs. Alkorn receive each month in social security benefits? ________
   b. How much did the daughter receive each month in social security benefits? ________
   c. If there had been a second young child in the family, how much would the family have received each month in social security benefits? ________
8. The following persons are covered by medicare. How much will their hospital stay cost them if they are there the following number of days?

   a. 48 days ________ b. 72 days ________

9. The following persons are covered by medicare. How much will their nursing-home stay cost them if they are there the following number of days?

   a. 18 days ________ b. 64 days ________

10. Mr. Merkin spent 105 days in the hospital as a result of a serious operation. He was covered by medicare and had never used any of his lifetime-reserve days. The total hospital bill for this stay was $6,615.
    a. How much of this bill did Mr. Merkin have to pay? ________
    b. How much of this bill did the insurance company have to pay? ________
11. During the past year, Mrs. Chester had medical bills amounting to $570. If she was covered for medical costs under the medicare program, how much of this bill did she, herself, have to pay? ________
12. Under the Price-Davis Corporation retirement plan described in this chapter, how much will Robert Riley have to contribute during a year in which he earned $11,460? He started to work for the company at 26. ________
13. Frank Daley had been working for the Price-Davis Corporation for 28 years at the time he retired. His average annual earnings during the last five years of this period were $12,720. How much did Mr. Daley receive from the company each year in retirement benefits? ________

14. When Bruce Johnson was 27, he purchased a single-premium annuity for $8,000. If he begins to collect monthly payments at 65, how large will these payments be? ________

15. Hazel Jorgeson purchased an annuity by electing to make annual payments of $700. Her first payment was made at 35, and her last at 60. How large were the monthly benefits sent to her from age 60 on? ________

COLONIAL AVE
FAIRFAX AVE.

CHAPTER 12

THE COST OF HOUSING

It is quite likely that sometime in your life you will purchase a home or rent an apartment. Both of these ways of living have their advantages and disadvantages. Which way of living you select depends largely on your way of life, or, perhaps, the area in which you want to live.

The person who rents an apartment often does so because it frees him from mortgage payments, real estate taxes, lawn problems, unsatisfactory plumbing, faulty electric wiring, water seepage in the cellar, a leaking roof, peeling paint inside and out, and so on. To him, there is something satisfying about being able to leave his apartment for a vacation and simply close the door with no worries about what will happen to the house or garden.

The homeowner, on the other hand, looks at things quite differently. Usually he has a very definite pride in both his home and the condition in which it is kept. He knows that he can look forward to the day—even though it may be twenty years off—when the property will be his. The payments that he makes over the years do not lead to a pile of rent receipts, but rather to the ownership of a home for him and his family.

In this chapter, you will consider the expenses—other than rent—of a person renting an apartment. In addition, you will also examine the major bills of a homeowner.

Unit 1: Renting an Apartment

Section 1: The Cost of Electricity

PART 1

No doubt you, along with other teen-agers, have had your parents speak to you about leaving the lights on in one room while you went off to study in another. Or you fall asleep late at night while the radio continues to blare. The cause for your parents' concern is the money you are wasting, for the electricity used by these appliances costs money.

The company from which electricity is bought charges for its services in terms of the number of kilowatt-hours of electricity used during a monthly period. Perhaps the simplest way of explaining the meaning of a kilowatt-hour is in terms of the electric light bulbs in your home. These bulbs can be purchased in various sizes, depending on the intensity of light that you want. Usually, for household needs the size will range from small night lights that are labeled 6 watts to the 300-watt bulbs for three-way lights. Should a 100-watt bulb burn 1 hour, then you have used 100 watt-hours of electricity. This is found by multiplying the 100 watts by the 1 hour to get a product that is called 100 watt-hours. Similarly, if a 300-watt bulb burns for 2 hours, then the consumption of electricity is 600 watt-hours. Here, again, the 600 represents the product of 300 and 2.

If you were asked to give the distance from Chicago to London, you would certainly not state the answer in terms of inches, for this is far too small a unit for measuring long distances. Similarly, the watt-hour is also far too small a unit for measuring the cost of electricity. For this reason, the *kilowatt-hour* was devised. The kilowatt-hour is the equivalent of 1,000 watt-hours. Thus, 3,000 watt-hours is the same as 3 kilowatt-hours and 8,000 watt-hours is the same as 8 kilowatt-hours.

> If the number of watt-hours of electricity is divided by 1,000, you will find the number of kilowatt-hours of electricity.

ILLUSTRATION 1: How many kilowatt-hours of electricity are there in 8,350 watt-hours of electricity?

EXPLANATION: Since there are 1,000 watt-hours in each kilowatt-hour, dividing 8,350 watt-hours by 1,000 will determine the number of kilowatt-hours. The quickest way to divide 8,350 by 1,000 is simply to move the decimal point 3 places to the left of its present position in 8,350. Can you show that this is so?

SOLUTION:

$$\text{Number of kilowatt-hours} = 8{,}350 \div 1{,}000 = 8.35$$

If you look at the bottom—or, possibly, the back—of any household appliance, you will find that each one has marked on it the number of watts of electricity needed to operate it. Examples of this are the steam iron at one extreme, which may use as many as 1,100 watts of electricity. At the other extreme is the electric clock, which uses as few as 2 watts.

ILLUSTRATION 2: Lillian Turner spent $3\frac{1}{2}$ hours ironing her clothes last Tuesday. If her iron operates on 1,050 watts of electricity, how many kilowatt-hours of electricity did she consume during this period of ironing?

EXPLANATION: By finding the product of 1,050 and $3\frac{1}{2}$, you will determine the number of watt-hours of electricity consumed. Dividing this answer by 1,000 will give you the number of kilowatt-hours consumed.

SOLUTION:

$$\text{Number of watt-hours} = 1{,}050 \times 3\tfrac{1}{2} = 3{,}675$$

$$\text{Number of kilowatt-hours} = 3{,}675 \div 1{,}000 = 3.675$$

EXERCISES A

1. How many kilowatt-hours are there in each of the following number of watt-hours?

	Watt-Hours	Kilowatt-Hours		Watt-Hours	Kilowatt-Hours
a.	4,000	________	f.	6,750	________
b.	7,000	________	g.	29,324	________
c.	12,000	________	h.	346,815	________
d.	56,000	________	i.	700	________
e.	124,000	________	j.	225	________

2. Each of the following appliances is used for the number of hours indicated. How many watt-hours of electricity are consumed?

	Number Of Watts	Number Of Hours	Watt-Hours		Number Of Watts	Number Of Hours	Watt-Hours
a.	2	24	________	c.	1,100	4	________
b.	345	3	________	d.	240	5	________

	Number Of Watts	Number Of Hours	Watt-Hours		Number Of Watts	Number Of Hours	Watt-Hours
e.	180	7	______	h.	40	$2\frac{1}{4}$	______
f.	2,500	$5\frac{1}{2}$	______	i.	200	$3\frac{3}{4}$	______
g.	645	$4\frac{1}{3}$	______	j.	225	$6\frac{2}{3}$	______

3. How many kilowatt-hours of electricity are consumed by each of the following appliances?

	Number Of Watts	Number Of Hours	Watt-Hours	Kilowatt-Hours
a.	400	15	______	______
b.	800	9	______	______
c.	350	6	______	______
d.	190	4	______	______
e.	2,400	7	______	______
f.	6	24	______	______

B

1. The markings on the motor of Fred Evans' electric table saw show that it operates on 1,150 watts of electricity. When Fred remodeled his home, he used the saw for a period of 75 hours. How many kilowatt-hours of electricity were consumed by the operation of the saw? ______

2. To cool off his bedroom during the summer evenings before going to bed, William Carlton ran a portable fan for a period of $2\frac{1}{2}$ hours. The fan operates on 395 watts of electricity. If William found it necessary to operate the fan for 60 days, how many kilowatt-hours of electricity did he use? ______

3. Doris Templer's electric coffeepot runs for approximately 40 minutes each time she makes coffee. If the information on the appliance shows that it uses 600 watts of electricity, how many kilowatt-hours are used each time Doris brews coffee? ______

4. During a recent evening, Mr. Speer watched television for $4\frac{1}{2}$ hours. During the same evening, Mrs. Speer ironed for 2 hours and 20 minutes and listened to their stereo set at the same time. Each used light bulbs of 30 and 150 watts respectively. In addition, the TV set operated on 180 watts, the stereo on 150 watts, and the iron on 1,200 watts. What was the total number of kilowatt-hours of electricity used that evening? ______

PART 2

As mentioned earlier, the company that supplies the electric current to your home charges for it in accordance with the number of kilowatt-hours used. Each month a company representative will read a meter such as the one below and record the information in a book. From the meter reading for this month, he subtracts the amount shown on the meter last month to find out how many kilowatt-hours of electricity were used during the month.

ILLUSTRATION 1: The electric meter reading on June 28 was 34,726. The previous reading, taken on May 27, was 34,631. How many kilowatt-hours of electricity were used during the month?

EXPLANATION: The numeral 34,726 represents the number of kilowatt-hours of electricity that had been used in this house from the time the meter was installed until June 28. Similarly, the numeral 34,631 gives the number of kilowatt-hours of electricity used from the time the meter was installed until May 27 of the preceding month. Hence, the difference between these numbers will tell you how many kilowatt-hours of electricity were used during the month.

SOLUTION:

$$\begin{aligned} \text{Number of kilowatt-hours used} &= 34{,}726 - 34{,}631 \\ &= 95 \end{aligned}$$

Here is how the meter, shown above, is read. Notice that the numerals on each dial appear in the reverse direction from those on the dial following it. Thus, for the one farthest to the right, the numerals are written in a clockwise direction, while for the one immediately to its left, the numerals are written in a counterclockwise direction. For the next dial, they are clockwise again, and so on. This is done deliberately, for the turning of the hand on the dial farthest to the right activates a wheel that starts the hand on the second dial turning in the opposite direction. And the same is true for each of the other clock hands.

When reading an electric meter, look first at the dial farthest to the left. In this case, notice that the hand is between the numerals 2 and 3. Since there are four numerals yet to follow, this would imply that the number of kilowatt-hours had to be between 20,000 and 30,000. Therefore, you know that the first numeral in the reading must be a 2, making the reading a number such as, perhaps, 27,394. Were you to make the first numeral a 3, then the reading would be a number such as 37,394. This you know cannot be, for the reading must be between 20,000 and 30,000. In the same way, whenever the arrow points between two numerals, always write down the smaller of the two. Of course, if it points directly at a numeral, then it will be that numeral that must be written down.

In examining the second dial from the left, notice that the arrow falls between 6 and 7. Hence the numeral 6 will appear as the second digit. For the third dial, the arrow, being between 4 and 5, makes the third digit a 4. When all five dials are recorded, the reading will be 26,453. This means that 26,453 kilowatt-hours of electricity were used in this house since the meter was installed.

A rate table used by the Cape Electric and Gas Company is shown below. It is on the basis of tables such as this that a monthly electric bill is computed.

CAPE ELECTRIC AND GAS COMPANY	
Residential Rate per Month — Electric	
For the first 8 kilowatt-hours or less	$1.85
For the next 62 kilowatt-hours, per kilowatt-hour	7.3¢
For the next 70 kilowatt-hours, per kilowatt-hour	5.1¢
For all over 140 kilowatt-hours, per kilowatt-hour	3.4¢

ILLUSTRATION 2: On August 25, Joe Muir's electric meter was read and recorded at 35,682. On September 24, when it was read again, it registered 35,796. If Joe's apartment was in the area serviced by the Cape Electric and Gas Company, how large was his electric bill for this month?

SOLUTION:

Number of KWH * used = 35,796 − 35,682 =	114
Cost for first 8 KWH = $1.85	− 8
	106
Cost for next 62 KWH = 62 × $.073 = $4.526	− 62
	44
Cost for next 44 KWH = 44 × $.051 = $2.244	− 44
Cost for 114 KWH = $8.62	0

* The abbreviation KWH means kilowatt-hours

EXPLANATION: On the left is the total number of KWH used. On the far right, beyond the vertical line, is a running tally of how many KWH remained to be paid for. Thus, after paying for the first 8, there were still 106 KWH to be paid for. Then, after paying for the next 62 KWH, this number was subtracted from 106 to leave a balance of 44 KWH to be paid for.

EXERCISES A

1. Record the readings on each of the following electric meters.

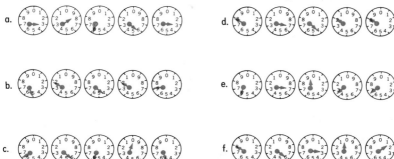

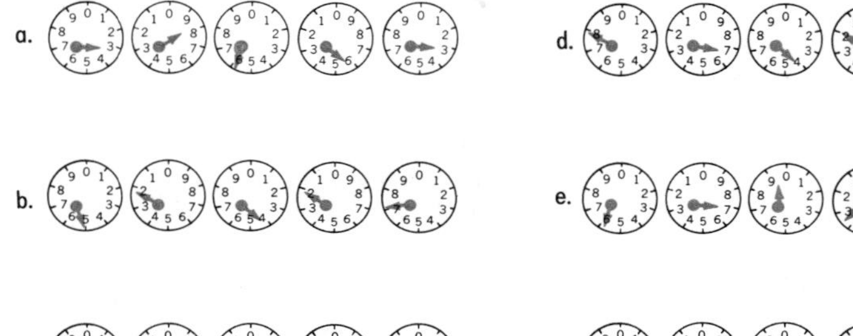

2. For each of the following, determine the number of kilowatt-hours of electricity used during the month.

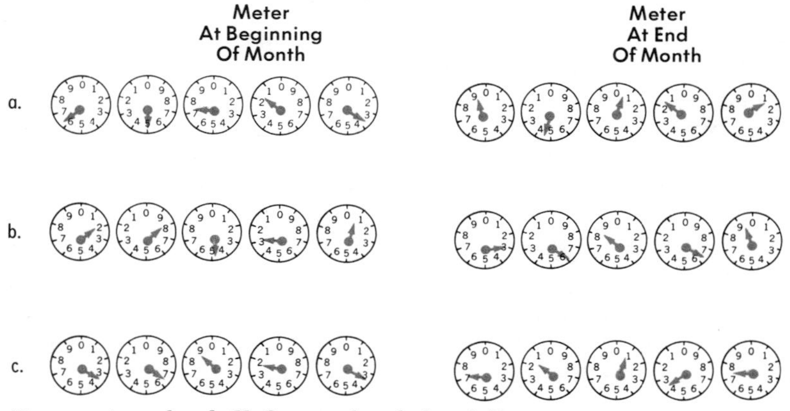

3. Determine the bill for each of the following customers. Use the rate table of the Cape Electric and Gas Company.

	Number of KWH Used During Month	Cost		Number of KWH Used During Month	Cost
a.	20	$______	d.	137	$______
b.	75	______	e.	156	______
c.	6	______	f.	384	______

4. Determine the bill for each of the following customers. Use the rate table of the Cape Electric and Gas Company.

	Reading At Beginning Of Month	Reading At End Of Month	Number Of KWH	Cost
a.	25,674	25,680	______	$______
b.	37,065	37,113	______	______
c.	46,381	46,493	______	______
d.	21,576	21,725	______	______
e.	16,974	17,341	______	______
f.	60,284	60,952	______	______

B

1. The information on the back of an electric clock shows that it operates on 2 watts of electricity. What is the total cost of operating this clock for an entire month of 31 days if the cost of each kilowatt-hour is 6.5¢? ______
2. A 65-gallon hot-water heater requires 2,500 watts of electricity to operate. In order to heat the water, electric current must flow through the appliance approximately 6 hours per day. During a 30-day month, what will be the cost of heating water for this home if the price of each kilowatt-hour is 1.6¢? ______
3. An electric clothes drier operates on 4,200 watts of electricity. Mrs. Armond uses the drier for approximately 2 hours and 30 minutes every Monday. How much will it cost Mrs. Armond to dry her clothes during a month in which there are four Mondays if the cost of each kilowatt-hour is 2.75¢? ______
4. Each weekday evening after dinner, Milton and Ruth Riker sit down to a routine of 4½ hours with their TV set. Their son George goes to his room to study and to listen to the radio for approximately 3 hours before going to bed. The lamp he uses requires a 150-watt bulb, while the light burning in the room where his parents sit is only 50 watts. The TV set operates on 210 watts, and the radio on 32 watts. During a month of 22 weekdays, what will the cost of electricity be for just this use alone? Use the Cape Electric and Gas Company rate table. ______

Section 2: The Cost of Gas

The major need that an apartment dweller would have for gas would be for his gas range and oven. The meters that register the flow of gas are very much the same in appearance as electric meters. But there is one major difference—electric meters measure the quantity of electricity used in kilowatt-hours, while gas is measured in cubic feet.

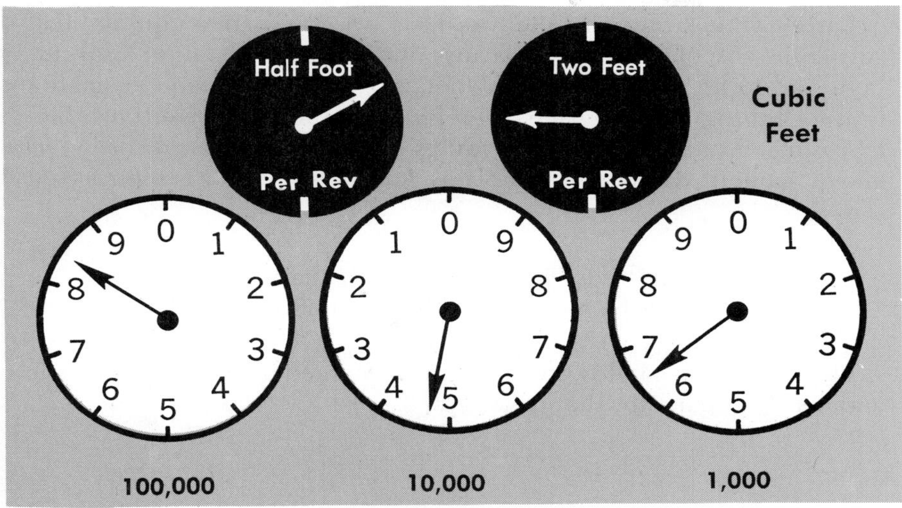

One way of picturing the flow of gas is to think of a box that is 1 foot long, 1 foot wide, and 1 foot deep. Were this box filled with water, then you would say that the amount of water it held was 1 cubic foot. You could pour this same amount of water into a long plastic hose and then close off both ends. Although the water would not have the same shape that it did when it was in the box, the quantity of water—which was 1 cubic foot—would be the same.

Similarly, you can think of this same box as containing gas rather than water and that, in some way, you are able to pour the cubic foot of gas from the box into the hose. This is about what takes place in the purchase of gas. The company that services your apartment pumps the gas out of large storage tanks through pipes into your apartment. In this process, it passes through a gas meter which registers the number of cubic feet of gas used.

In getting a reading from the meter, the two small dials are completely ignored. Now, if the hand on the dial farthest to the right is rotated completely around and returned to the 0, then 1,000 cubic feet of gas would have flowed through the meter. Since the arrow points between the 6 and the 7, this implies that somewhat more than 600 cubic feet of gas have been consumed. Notice that, as in the case of the electric meter, when the arrow falls between two numerals, it is always the smaller one that is recorded. Hence, when the 8 and the 4, which are the readings of the first two dials, are written in front of the 600, then the entire reading becomes 84,600. Thus, 84,600 cubic feet of gas have passed through the meter since it was installed in this apartment.

Earlier you learned that the watt-hour was too small a unit for measuring the cost of electricity. Because of this, the much larger kilowatt-hour had to be used. The cubic foot, too, is much, much too small a unit for billing purposes and, therefore, gas is sold by the 100 cubic-foot units. As a result, meter readings are rarely, if ever, recorded as above, namely, 84,600, but simply as 846. This number is interpreted as follows:

> 846 hundreds of cubic feet of gas have passed through the meter since its installation.

The table shown below gives the rates charged by the Cape Electric and Gas Company for the use of gas.

CAPE ELECTRIC AND GAS COMPANY

Residential Rate per Month — Gas

For the first 2 hundred cubic feet or less	$1.24
For the next 7 hundred cubic feet, per hundred cubic feet	25.3¢
For the next 17 hundred cubic feet, per hundred cubic feet	21.8¢
For the next 24 hundred cubic feet, per hundred cubic feet	17.1¢
For all over 50 hundred cubic feet, per hundred cubic feet	13.5¢

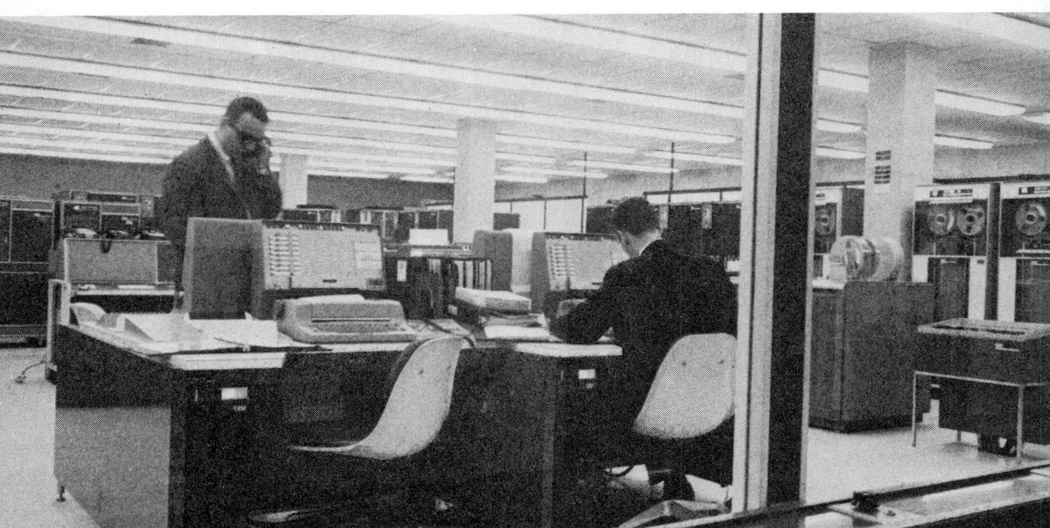

Modern utility companies have adopted computers and other automated equipment in order to keep pace with rapid expansion. The machines can keep company records, calculate rates and charges, and help give better service to millions of regular customers.

ILLUSTRATION: On March 17, the gas meter for Marta Bates' apartment was read as 628. On April 18, when it was again checked, it showed a reading of 732. If Marta lives in the area serviced by the Cape Electric and Gas Company, determine her gas bill for this period.

EXPLANATION: Neither the meter readings nor the rate table include the two zeros that should be at the end of each number. Therefore, to simplify computation, you do not need to use them. Notice, also, that in the following computation, a running account is kept at the far right of the number of hundreds of cubic feet of gas that has been paid for at each step of the work.

SOLUTION:

Number of hundreds of cubic ft. used = 732 − 628	=	104
Cost of first 2 hundred cubic ft.	= \$1.24	− 2
		102
Cost of next 7 hundred cubic ft. = 7 × \$.253 =	1.771	− 7
		95
Cost of next 17 hundred cubic ft. = 17 × \$.218 =	3.706	− 17
		78
Cost of next 24 hundred cubic ft. = 24 × \$.171 =	4.104	− 24
		54
Cost of next 54 hundred cubic ft. = 54 × \$.135 =	7.29	− 54
Cost for 104 hundred cubic ft. =	\$18.111 or \$18.11	0

Incidentally, if the reading for one month was 986, while the reading the following month turned out to be 017, it would merely indicate that, at some time during the month, the dials on the meter had recorded 1,000 hundred cubic feet, which is the largest number the meter can record. When this occurs, the meter begins to register the number of cubic feet from 0 again. Thus, for the readings just described, you would first subtract 986 from 1,000, for a difference of 14. This number is then added to 17 for a total of 31 hundred cubic feet of gas used during that month.

EXERCISES

1. Record the readings on each of the following gas meters in terms of the actual number of cubic feet—not hundreds of cubic feet.

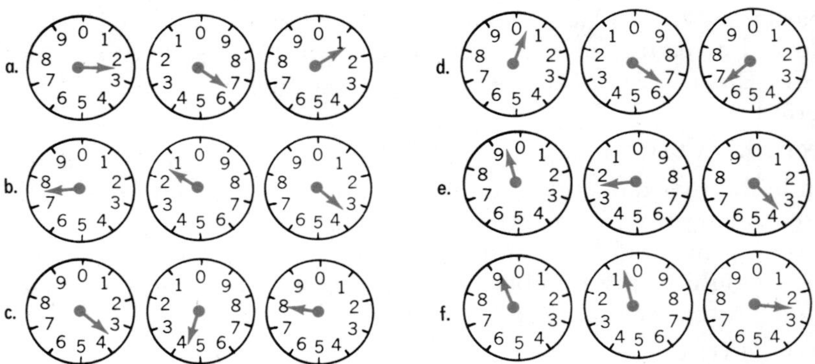

2. For each of the following, determine the number of hundreds of cubic feet of gas used during the month.

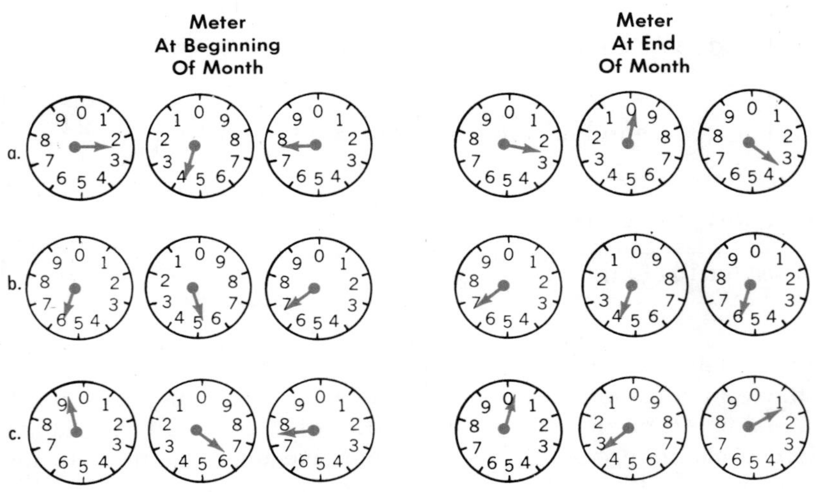

3. Determine the cost of gas for each of the following customers. Use the rate table of the Cape Electric and Gas Company.

	Number of Hundreds Of Cubic Feet Used During Month	Cost		Number of Hundreds Of Cubic Feet Used During Month	Cost
a.	6	$______	d.	57	$______
b.	18	______	e.	98	______
c.	35	______	f.	134	______

4. Determine the cost of gas for each of the following customers. Use the rate table of the Cape Electric and Gas Company.

	Reading At Beginning Of Month	Reading At End Of Month	Number Of Hundreds Of Cubic Feet	Cost
a.	385	398	________	$________
b.	714	740	________	________
c.	888	957	________	________
d.	643	801	________	________
e.	993	014	________	________
f.	954	131	________	________

5. The Great Western Electric and Gas Company charges for gas consumption in accordance with the following monthly rate table.

$1.42 for the first	300 cubic feet or less
27.4¢ per 100 cubic feet for the next	2400 cubic feet
22.3¢ per 100 cubic feet for the next	5300 cubic feet
15.5¢ per 100 cubic feet in excess of	8000 cubic feet

Determine the cost of gas for each of the following customers of the Great Western Electric and Gas Company.

	Reading At Beginning Of Month	Reading At End Of Month	Number Of Hundreds Of Cubic Feet	Cost
a.	257	271	________	$________
b.	193	235	________	________
c.	814	843	________	________
d.	873	942	________	________
e.	961	094	________	________
f.	879	021	________	________

6. The bills of the Cape Electric and Gas Company resemble the following form. Use the rate tables of this company to compute the total cost for electricity and gas for each of the following customers.

a.

CAPE ELECTRIC AND GAS COMPANY

Servant of a Great State

	Service Period			Next Meter Reading Date	
	July 7	August 5		September 6	
	Meter Readings				Amount
Service	From	To			
Electricity	6842	6878	________	KWH	$________
Gas	165	193	________	Hundred cubic feet	$________
				Total	$________

b.

Service	Service Period			Next Meter Reading Date
	May 15	June 16		July 15
	Meter Readings			
	From	To		Amount
Electricity	3591	3725	______	$______
Gas	847	889	______	$______
			Total	$______

c.

Service	Service Period			Next Meter Reading Date
	October 22	November 24		December 21
	Meter Readings			
	From	To		Amount
Electricity	23684	23859	______	$______
Gas	913	024	______	$______
			Total	$______

d.

Service	Service Period			Next Meter Reading Date
	February 16	March 15		April 16
	Meter Readings			
	From	To		Amount
Electricity	61652	61982	______	$______
Gas	416	604	______	$______
			Total	$______

Section 3: The Telephone Bill

One of the major monthly bills of every apartment dweller is the telephone bill. The basic rate he has to pay depends entirely on the area in which he lives. In one state the monthly charges range from a low of $3.44 for a 4-party line to a high of $7.03 for a private line. For this fee the person can make as many calls as he wants at no cost so long as these calls are to certain neighboring towns. However, should he call someone outside of this "free-call" zone, there is an additional charge he must pay. These charges are similar to those given in the table on page 443.

The cost of a phone call depends upon four factors:

1. The distance from the point where you are making the call to the point where the person is who is receiving the call.
2. The number of minutes you talk to the person.
3. The hour of the day and the day itself during which you make the call.
4. Whether you dial the number yourself or ask the operator to assist you in placing the call.

RATES FOR CALLS WITHIN THE STATE (OUTSIDE THE FREE-CALL ZONE)

		Dialed Directly						Operator-Assisted Calls			
Distance (in rate airline miles)		Day 8 A.M.-5 P.M. Mon.-Fri.		Evening & Weekend 5 P.M.-11 P.M. Mon.-Fri. 8 A.M.-11 P.M. Sat.-Sun.		Every Night 11 P.M.-8 A.M.		Day 8 A.M.-5 P.M. Mon.-Fri.		Evening All other hours	
from	through	Initial 2 min.	Additional 1 min.	Initial 2 min.	Additional 1 min.	Initial 1 min.	Additional 1 min.	Initial 3 min.	Additional 1 min.	Initial 3 min.	Additional 1 min.
0	10	$.10	$.02	$.10	$.02	$.10	$.02	$.10	$.02	$.10	$.02
11	15	$.15	$.04	$.15	$.04	$.10	$.03	$.20	$.04	$.20	$.04
16	20	$.20	$.06	$.20	$.06	$.10	$.05	$.30	$.06	$.25	$.06
21	25	$.25	$.08	$.25	$.07	$.15	$.06	$.40	$.08	$.35	$.07
26	32	$.30	$.10	$.25	$.08	$.15	$.07	$.45	$.10	$.35	$.08
33	48	$.35	$.11	$.25	$.08	$.15	$.07	$.55	$.11	$.35	$.08
49	64	$.40	$.13	$.25	$.09	$.15	$.08	$.60	$.13	$.35	$.09
65	80	$.45	$.15	$.25	$.10	$.15	$.09	$.65	$.15	$.35	$.10
81	96	$.50	$.16	$.25	$.10	$.15	$.09	$.75	$.16	$.35	$.10
97	112	$.55	$.17	$.25	$.10	$.15	$.09	$.80	$.17	$.35	$.10
113	Up	$.60	$.18	$.25	$.10	$.15	$.09	$.85	$.18	$.35	$.10

Add 30¢ to day rate for a "Collect" call.

Add 50¢ to day rate for a "Person-to-Person" call.

All of these points have to be considered when examining the table to determine the cost of a phone call. Notice that the "day" rates are much higher than the "evening" rates and that these, in turn, are higher than the "night" rates. Further, if you can dial the number yourself, you can save a good deal of money over what it would cost you by having to ask the operator for help.

There are two words at the very bottom of the table that should be clarified:

1. Collect Call: In this type of call the person who receives the call agrees to pay for it. The charge for a collect call when made to a point within this state is 30¢ more than the normal operator-assisted day call.
2. Person-to-Person Call: In this call you tell the operator that you wish to speak only to a certain person. If that person is not available, even if someone else picks up the phone, you are not charged for the call. However, if the person you are calling does come to the phone, then the charge is 50¢ more than the normal operator-assisted day call.

ILLUSTRATION 1: A phone call was made on Thursday at 7:05 P.M. over a distance of 84 miles. If the conversation lasted 15 minutes, what was the charge for this call? The call was dialed directly.

SOLUTION:

Cost for first 2 minutes	= $ .25
Cost for remaining 13 minutes = 13 × $.10 =	1.30
Total cost	= $1.55

EXPLANATION: The call was made at 7:05 P.M. on Thursday. Hence, the evening rates applied. Since 84 miles is between 81 and 96 miles, you place a piece of paper along this row in the table and run your finger to the section headed by the word "Evening." There are two columns in this section. The left one tells you the cost for the initial, or first, 2 minutes—$.25. From the right column, you learn that each additional minute costs $.10. Since there were 13 additional minutes, the charge for this was 13 × $.10, or $1.30. Hence, the phone call cost $1.55.

ILLUSTRATION 2: Barbara Ervin has a private line for which there is a basic charge of $5.20 per month. During the past month, in addition to the calls made within the free-call zone, she made the following calls:

One 12-minute call over a distance of 14 miles
One 18-minute call over a distance of 17 miles
Two 7-minute calls over a distance of 8 miles

All the calls were dialed directly during the daytime hours. What was Barbara's bill for the month?

SOLUTION:

(a) One 12-minute call,		
First 2 minutes:		$ .15
Remaining 10 minutes:	10 × $.04 =	.40
(b) One 18-minute call,		
First 2 minutes:		.20
Remaining 16 minutes:	16 × $.06 =	.96
(c) One 7-minute call,		
First 2 minutes:		.10
Remaining 5 minutes:	5 × $.02 =	.10
(d) One 7-minute call:		.20
(e) Basic Charge:		+5.20
	Total:	$7.31
	Federal Tax (8%):	+ .58
	Total Charge:	$7.89

EXPLANATION: The solution to this problem involves nothing more than four separate situations similar to that examined in Illustration 1. The total of the four calls outside the free-call zone added to the monthly charge should be Barbara's bill. However, the federal government charges an 8%-tax on all phone bills. Hence, it is necessary to determine 8% of the basic bill of $7.31. This comes to $.58 and when added to the $7.31 the total phone cost for that month turns out to be $7.89.

EXERCISES A

1. Find the cost of each of the following daytime calls made out of the free-call zone. All the calls were dialed directly during a weekday.

	Miles	Minutes	Cost		Miles	Minutes	Cost
a.	7	2	$______	f.	85	4	$______
b.	12	2	______	g.	15	5	______
c.	18	2	______	h.	26	5	______
d.	28	3	______	i.	16	12	______
e.	53	3	______	j.	97	16	______

2. Find the cost of each of the following "person-to-person" calls made out of the free-call zone during daytime hours.

	Miles	Minutes	Cost		Miles	Minutes	Cost
a.	12	13	$______	d.	50	12	$______
b.	7	8	______	e.	31	15	______
c.	29	19	______	f.	24	16	______

3. Find the cost of each of the following "collect" calls made out of the free-call zone during a weekday.

	Miles	Minutes	Time of Day	Cost
a.	18	4	Day	$______
b.	14	10	Evening	______
c.	28	12	Evening	______
d.	61	9	Day	______
e.	43	17	Evening	______
f.	43	17	Day	______

4. Find the cost of each of the following calls made out of the free-call zone. The calls were dialed directly during a weekday.

	Miles	Minutes	Time of Day	Cost
a.	46	2	Day	$______
b.	58	2	Evening	______
c.	137	7	Night	______
d.	49	9	Evening	______
e.	20	10	Day	______
f.	32	15	Night	______

5. Find the cost of each of the following calls made out of the free-call zone. The calls were dialed directly.

	Miles	Minutes	Hour When Call Was Made	Cost
a.	29	7	Monday—2:00 P.M.	$______
b.	52	9	Thursday—10:00 P.M.	______
c.	106	6	Tuesday—8:10 P.M.	______
d.	89	14	Friday—8:00 A.M.	______
e.	68	23	Wednesday—4:30 P.M.	______
f.	151	12	Monday—6:30 P.M.	______
g.	98	17	Sunday—1:30 P.M.	______
h.	74	8	Saturday—9:20 A.M.	______

B

1. The Princess phone is a special small telephone that is offered at an additional charge of 72¢ per month—that is, if there is no other phone in the house. The basic charge in Ben Alden's area is $6.83 for a private line or $5.39 for a two-party line.

a. How much extra will Ben have to pay each month if he chooses to have a private line and a Princess phone rather than the two-party line and the regular phone? ________

b. How much extra will he have to pay over the period of a year? ________

2. Dorothy dialed her mother directly when she called her from college. The college is located 145 miles from her home. The call lasted five minutes and was made at 2:30 on a Wednesday afternoon.

   a. What was the cost of the call? ________

   b. What would the cost have been had it been made at 9:00 P.M. that evening? ________

   c. How much would Dorothy have saved had she made the call in the evening? ________

3. Judy Carlton is now married and lives in a town that is 125 miles from her parents' home. Each week she phones them. The calls are dialed directly and usually last about 15 minutes.

   a. How much would Judy save by making these calls on Saturday at 2:00 P.M. rather than on Friday at 2:00 P.M.? ________

   b. Would there be any saving if the calls were made on Saturday at 9:00 P.M. rather than on Saturday at 2:00 P.M.? ________

4. What additional total charge over the basic fee will Roger Denton have to pay for the following calls that were made out of the free-call zone? All of the calls were dialed directly on a weekday during daytime hours. ________

   12 7-mile calls for less than 2 minutes each
   9 15-mile calls for less than 2 minutes each
   3 23-mile calls for 9 minutes each

5. The basic charge for Sally Clemen's private line is $5.85 per month. She has two extra phones in the house for which she pays $1.00 per month for each. During the past month she made the following daytime calls during weekdays to points that were not within her free-call zone.

   6 9-mile calls for less than 2 minutes each
   14 17-mile calls for less than 2 minutes each
   1 28-mile call for 26 minutes
   1 50-mile call for 15 minutes
   1 112-mile call for 17 minutes

   All calls were dialed directly. Including federal tax of 8%, how large was Sally's telephone bill that month? ________

Unit 2: Home Ownership

Section 1: The Mortgage

PART 1

The homeowner, like the apartment dweller, must pay gas, electric, and telephone bills. He must also meet monthly mortgage payments. There is little likelihood that many people would, or could, buy a house if it were necessary to pay the entire cost at the time of purchase. The price of the average house in this country is somewhere between $15,000 and $45,000. It is a rare family, indeed, that has that much cash to lay out for a house. Normally, the purchaser gives a down payment that may be as small as 10% of the selling price of the house. The rest of the money if often borrowed from either a bank or a savings and loan association.

When a person borrows money, he signs a piece of paper called a *note* to show that at some specified date in the future he intends to pay back that money. In the present situation, where money is borrowed to pay for a home, the piece of paper that is signed is called a *mortgage*. Payments are made on the debt in monthly installments and may extend over a period of 20, 25, 30 or, even, in some rare instances, 40 years. Should the borrower fail to meet these payments, then, by an agreement written in the mortgage, the bank—or whoever may be the lender—is permitted to sell the house to get back the money still owed to it.

To determine what the monthly payments will be, the banker examines a table such as the following. This table is based on each $1,000 in the loan.

MORTGAGE LOAN SCHEDULE

(Monthly cost per $1,000)

Years	8%	8½%	9%	9½%	10%	11%	12%
15	$9.56	$9.85	$10.14	$10.44	$10.75	$11.37	$12.00
20	8.36	8.68	9.00	9.32	9.65	10.32	11.01
25	7.72	8.05	8.39	8.74	9.09	9.80	10.53
30	7.34	7.69	8.05	8.41	8.78	9.52	10.29
35	7.10	7.47	7.84	8.22	8.60	9.37	10.16
40	6.95	7.33	7.71	8.10	8.49	9.28	10.09

ILLUSTRATION 1: Clifford Temple was granted a 9½% mortgage of $18,500 on his home. If the debt is to be paid off over a 20-year period, what will the monthly payments have to be?

EXPLANATION: The numeral at the point where the "20-year" row meets the "9½%" column is \$9.32. This is the amount that Clifford will have to pay monthly for each \$1,000 in the \$18,500 he borrowed. Since there are 18.5 thousands in 18,500, then the total monthly payment will be 18.5 times \$9.32, or \$172.42.

SOLUTION:

Number of thousands in 18,500 = 18,500 ÷ 1,000
= 18.5
Monthly payment per \$1,000 at 9½% = \$9.32
Monthly payment for \$18,500 at 9½% = 18.5 × \$9.32
= \$172.42

There are some states in which the legal maximum interest rate that can be charged is 8%. To get around this law, many lending agencies have begun to charge the mortgage borrower *points* just for the privilege of borrowing money from them. A point is another name for *1 percent*. As an example, if a person is charged 2 points for being granted a mortgage, this simply means that he has to pay a fee of 2% of the amount borrowed merely for having been granted the loan.

There is some justification for charging these points, for there are times when the interest rate that a bank pays its depositors may be very close to the legal limit that it can charge its borrowers. When this is so, there would be no way in which this institution could pay the salaries of its employees, or make a profit, unless it used this point system. Many institutions, however, employ this as a device for getting around the law.

ILLUSTRATION 2: Julius Spencer purchased a \$34,000 home by making a down payment of 20%. For the balance of the debt, he took out a mortgage for which the bank charged him 4 points. To help him with the legal problems involved in buying the home, Mr. Spencer hired a lawyer who charged him \$325. What was the total amount of money that Mr. Spencer had to have in cash on the day he took over possession of the house?

SOLUTION:

Down payment = \$34,000 × 20%
= \$6,800
Size of mortgage = \$34,000 − \$6,800
= \$27,200
Charge for receiving mortgage = \$27,200 × 4%
= \$1,088
Legal expenses = \$325
Total cash needed = \$6,800 + \$1,088 + \$325
= \$8,213

EXPLANATION: Since the points are charged only on the size of the mortgage, the down payment of $6,800 is subtracted from the cost of the house. Therefore, the mortgage is for $27,200. The 4 points are rewritten as 4% and 4% of $27,200 is $1088.

EXERCISES

A

1. Points were charged in obtaining each of the following mortgages. How much extra did the purchaser have to pay?

	Size of Mortgage	Number of Points	Cost For Obtaining Mortgage
a.	$16,000	1	$________
b.	12,000	3	________
c.	9,400	2	________
d.	23,500	4½	________

2. After making the down payment shown, each of the following purchasers had to pay points for being granted a mortgage for the remainder of the money he needed. How much was this charge in each case?

	Price Of Property	Down Payment (Percent)	Down Payment	Mortgage	Points	Additional Charge
a.	$28,000	10%	$________	$________	2	$________
b.	36,000	5%	________	________	4	________
c.	29,000	40%	________	________	1	________
d.	41,800	60%	________	________	3	________
e.	44,500	50%	________	________	3½	________

3. How large will the monthly payments be on each of the following mortgages?

	Size of Mortgage	Interest Rate	Period of Debt	Monthly Payment
a.	$12,000	9%	20 Years	$________
b.	14,000	8½%	25 Years	________
c.	9,200	11%	30 Years	________
d.	16,400	9½%	25 Years	________
e.	15,900	10%	20 Years	________
f.	23,600	8%	15 Years	________

B

1. A mortgage company requires that the borrower purchase *title insurance* to the extent of the mortgage at the time he receives the

money. The purpose of this insurance is to make certain that the mortgage company gets its money from the insurance firm in case someone, at some future time, can legally show that the person who sold the property really had no right to do so. If the cost of title insurance is at the rate of $5.00 per $1,000, how much will a person have to pay for this if the size of his mortgage is $12,000? ________

2. Henry Stevens purchased a house for $48,700. He made a down payment of 45% and was granted a mortgage for the remainder. The title insurance he purchased at $5.50 per $1,000 covered only the amount of the mortgage. How much did this cost him? ________

3. Doris Clarke received a 9% mortgage for $10,500 when she purchased her house. She agreed to pay off this debt over a 20-year period.
   a. What were her monthly payments? ________
   b. How much did this amount to annually? ________
   c. What was the total amount that she paid back over the 20-year period? ________

4. When purchasing his house, Carl Denton put down a 20% deposit on the $34,000 he had to pay. The remainder he borrowed at 10%, to be paid off over a period of 25 years.
   a. What were his monthly payments? ________
   b. What was the total he paid back over the 25-year period? ________
   c. How much more did he pay back than he borrowed? ________

5. At the time that Charles Martin purchased his house, he obtained an $18,000 mortgage from his bank at a 9½% interest rate.
   a. If he agrees to amortize—that is, to pay off—the debt in monthly payments over 20 years, what will be the total amount that he will return to the bank? ________
   b. If he agrees to amortize the debt over a 30-year period, what will be the total amount he will return to the bank? ________
   c. How much will Mr. Martin save by amortizing the mortgage over a 20-year period rather than a 30-year period? ________

6. Miguel Botta was granted a mortgage of $14,000 for his house. He arranged to amortize the loan over a 25-year period.
   a. What will be the total amount he will return if the interest rate is 9%? ________
   b. What will be the total amount he will return if the interest rate is 11%? ________
   c. How much will Mr. Botta save by being able to borrow the money at 9% rather than 11%? ________

7. Gloria Kempton purchased a house for \$38,300 for which she planned to give a 40% down payment. The rest of the money she borrowed from a savings and loan association, which charged her 2 points for obtaining the mortgage.

a. How much did she have to pay just for the privilege of borrowing the money? ________

b. The savings and loan association charged her \$35 for expenses it incurred in checking to see if she should receive the mortgage. In addition, she had to pay George Stacey, her lawyer, \$285 for legal fees connected with his work relative to the purchase of this house. What was the total of these fees? ________

c. Gloria was required to take out title insurance to the extent of the mortgage. How much did this cost her if the rate was \$5.25 per \$1,000? ________

d. What was the total amount of money that she had to have in cash on the day she took possession of the house? Exclude the down payment. ________

PART 2

Each monthly payment on a mortgage consists of two parts. One of these is interest for one month on the debt, while the remaining part is an installment payment used to decrease the debt. As an example, consider a mortgage of \$15,000 that is to be paid off monthly over a 15-year period. By applying the table on page 448, you will find the monthly payments to be \$152.10 on an interest rate of 9%. When the very first payment is made, the debt is still \$15,000, for nothing has been paid prior to that point. Hence, the interest for that month is,

$$I = \$15{,}000 \times 9\% \times 1 \text{ month}$$

or, $$I = \$15{,}000 \times .09 \times {}^{1}/_{12}$$

therefore $$I = \$112.50$$

The monthly payment of \$152.10 includes this \$112.50 in interest. Hence, the amount that remains after the \$112.50 is subtracted from the \$152.10 goes toward reducing the debt. That difference is \$39.60. During the second month, the debt will be \$15,000 less the \$39.60, or \$14,960.40. In the same way, the interest for the second month is,

$$I = \$14{,}960.40 \times .09 \times {}^{1}/_{12}$$

or, $$I = \$112.20$$

Since the monthly payment is still \$152.10 and \$112.20 of this is used for the interest payment, then the balance of \$39.90 is again used to reduce the debt still further.

ORIGINAL DEBT: $15,000 (9%)				
Payment Number	Monthly Payment	Amount For Interest	Amount Toward Decreasing Debt	Balance Of Debt
1	$152.10	$112.50	$39.60	$14,960.40
2	152.10	112.20	39.90	14,920.50

When we arrange this in the form of a table, it becomes apparent that, although the monthly payments remain the same, the interest charge decreases each month, while the amount that goes toward paying off the debt increases. In fact, in this problem, the amount will increase by approximately 30¢ each month. For the very last payment of $152.10 almost all of it will go toward paying off the debt and very little will be used for interest.

ILLUSTRATION 1: Alvin Jenkins had reduced his 8% mortgage to the point where he owed the bank only $5,775.93. His monthly payments were $109.39. How much of the very next payment would be interest and how much would be used to reduce the balance of his debt?

SOLUTION:

$$\begin{aligned} \text{Interest} &= P \times R \times T \\ &= \$5{,}775.93 \times 8\% \times 1 \text{ month} \\ &= \$5{,}775.93 \times .08 \times 1/12 \\ &= \$38.51 \end{aligned}$$

$$\begin{aligned} \text{Amount used to reduce debt} &= \$109.39 - \$38.51 \\ &= \$70.88 \end{aligned}$$

EXPLANATION: Since the debt at this point was only $5,775.93, you compute the interest for the one month on that amount. By subtracting the interest from the monthly payment of $109.39, you find that the amount used toward reducing the debt is $70.88. Had you wished, you could have gone one step farther and found the balance of the debt by subtracting the $70.88 from $5,775.93.

Banks and savings and loan associations, just as other business enterprises, operate for the purpose of making money. For this reason, they do not like to have the person who borrowed money on a mortgage pay off his debt before it is due. When this happens, they lose the interest they had planned on receiving. To discourage an early repayment of the mortgage, a penalty is charged. The rate charged by a number of banks is similar to the one in the table on page 455.

Buying a condominium, or renting an apartment in a co-operative building, usually relieves the tenant of responsibility for outdoor maintenance or for utility charges.

ILLUSTRATION 2: After making payments on his $11,500 mortgage for 5 years and 2 months, Mr. Thorn found that he was in a financial position to pay off the balance of his debt. How much would The Gibralter Savings Bank charge him if he did this?

SOLUTION:

$$\begin{aligned}\text{Penalty} &= \$11{,}500 \times 1\tfrac{1}{4}\% \\ &= \$11{,}500 \times .0125 \\ &= \$143.75\end{aligned}$$

EXPLANATION: The penalty is determined on the original mortgage of $11,500.

THE GIBRALTER SAVINGS BANK			
If Debt Is Paid Off During	**Penalty Charged**	**If Debt Is Paid Off During**	**Penalty Charged**
1st Year	Not Permitted	6th Year	1¼% of Original Debt
2nd Year	Not Permitted	7th Year	1% of Original Debt
3rd Year	2% of Original Debt	8th Year	¾% of Original Debt
4th Year	1¾% of Original Debt	9th Year	½% of Original Debt
5th Year	1½% of Original Debt	10th Year	¼% of Original Debt

EXERCISES A

1. How much would each of the following people be charged if they paid off their mortgages held by The Gibralter Savings Bank during the year shown?

	Original Mortgage	Paid Off During	Penalty Charge
a.	$ 7,000	3rd Year	$________
b.	8,500	7th Year	________
c.	12,400	5th Year	________
d.	15,300	4th Year	________
e.	21,600	6th Year	________
f.	25,750	8th Year	________
g.	26,250	10th Year	________

2. The balance of the debt still owed on their mortgages and the monthly payments for each of the following borrowers are given below. Determine what part of the next payment represents the interest and what part will be used to pay off the balance of the debt of each.

	Unpaid Balance Of Mortgage	Monthly Payment	Interest Rate	Interest	Payment On Debt
a.	$12,000	$107.47	6%	$______	$______
b.	9,200	128.25	9%	______	______
c.	6,450	83.70	8%	______	______
d.	4,600	77.75	7%	______	______
e.	7,846	83.96	10%	______	______
f.	14,351	123.09	9%	______	______
g.	2,424	77.20	8%	______	______
h.	5,946	120.18	7%	______	______
i.	8,000	93.20	11%	______	______
j.	16,000	204.85	12%	______	______

3. To make certain that the real estate tax is paid, the mortgage company requires that the borrower pay the company each month 1/12 of the annual tax bill. This is in addition to the monthly payment on the mortgage. The mortgage company then pays the real estate tax. How much will the monthly tax payments be for each of the following?

	Annual Tax Bill	Monthly Payment		Annual Tax Bill	Monthly Payment
a.	$300	$______	d.	$ 996	$______
b.	420	______	e.	1,488	______
c.	552	______	f.	1,872	______

4. A mortgage company frequently requires that the borrower pay monthly 1/36 of the insurance premium on the house. This money is then sent to the insurance company. The mortgage company does this to make certain that in the event the house is destroyed, it will be paid the balance of its debt by the insurance company. The numeral 1/36 comes from the fact that the insurance is purchased for a three-year period, that is, 36 months. How much will the monthly insurance payment be for each of the following?

	Three-Year Insurance Cost	Monthly Payment
a.	$180	$______
b.	252	______
c.	468	______
d.	972	______

B

1. Paul Tracey currently has a balance of $4,374.24 on his mortgage, for which he is making monthly payments of $114.63. The interest rate on the debt is 8%.
   a. How much of the next payment will be interest? ________
   b. How much of the next payment will be used to reduce the mortgage? ________
   c. What will be the balance of his debt after the next payment? ________

2. After having made her monthly payment of $136.35 on her 10% mortgage for a number of years, Cheryl Dorman found that she still had a balance of $6,200. How much will the balance be after the next payment? ________

3. Arthur Jefferson was given a $12,000 mortgage for a period of 25 years at an interest rate of 9½%.
   a. Determine his monthly payments. Use the table on page 448. ________
   b. Set up a table similar to the one on page 453, which shows the monthly payment, the interest paid each month, the amount of the monthly payment that goes toward decreasing the debt, and the balance of the debt for the first two payments on his mortgage. ________

4. Karen Corbley's mortgage on her house was for $14,000 at 10% for a 20-year period.
   a. Determine the monthly payments on the mortgage. Use the table on page 448. ________
   b. The estimated real estate tax on the house for the year was $608. How large were the monthly tax payments to the mortgage company? ________
   c. The cost of insurance on the house for the three-year period was $756. How large were the monthly insurance payments to the mortgage company? ________
   d. What was the total amount of money that she paid the mortgage company each month? ________

Section 2: Real Estate Tax

PART 1

It is the local government that takes care of the schools, the roads, the police and fire departments, the library, the sanitation department, and many other services in a city or town. The burden of paying for these operations falls on the property owner for the money is raised through a *real estate tax*.

Everyone does not, and should not, pay the same amount of tax. Consider as a very simple example a community in which there are only two residents—Roy Evans and Tom Harper. The value of Roy Evans' property is $1,000, while that of Tom Harper's is $2,000. In the course of a conversation between them they decide that they would like to have a service for which the cost is $600. They soon realize that Tom Harper should pay more than Roy Evans, because his property is the more valuable of the two. Since the Harper property is twice as valuable, Tom Harper agrees to pay twice as much as Roy Evans. Hence, Tom Harper will pay $400, while Roy Evans will pay only $200.

If the two men had had any trouble in deciding what each one has to contribute, they could have solved their problem by finding the total value of both their properties—$3,000. Thus, the cost of the service is $600 for the $3,000 in the total value of the properties. This can be expressed as,

$$\$600 \text{ per } \$3{,}000 \qquad (1)$$

which is the same as saying,

$$\$6 \text{ per } \$30 \qquad (2)$$

and this, in turn, is the same as,

$$\$1 \text{ per } \$5 \qquad (3)$$

Notice that in each situation above, each pair of numbers is divided by exactly the same number. In going from (1) to (2), both numbers were divided by 100, while in going from (2) to (3), both were divided by 6. The interpretation of statement (3) is that for each $5 in the total value of the two properties, $1 will have to be spent for the service needed. However, for computational purposes it would be far easier if the cost of the service was given in terms of each $1 of the total value rather than in terms of each $5. Therefore, to determine this it is simply necessary to divide both numbers in (3) by 5. Hence, (3) becomes,

$.20 per $1   (4)

This now implies that for each $1 in the total value of the two properties, $.20 will have to spent for the service. Since the value of Roy Evans' property is $1,000, then he will have to pay:

1,000 × $.20, or $200

Similarly, the value of Tom Harper's property is $2,000. Hence, he will have to pay:

2,000 × $.20, or $400

These, of course, are the numbers arrived at earlier.

Before leaving this illustration it should be pointed out that it is possible to go directly from

$600 per $3,000
to
$.20 per $1

by simply dividing both $600 and $3,000 by 3,000. Similarly, if the cost of the service had been $750, the comparison would have been,

$750 per $3,000

And by dividing both numbers by 3,000, the comparison becomes,

$.25 per $1

Notice that in both situations the cost per $1 is found by dividing the cost of the service by the total value of the properties. Hence, in general it can be said,

Cost per $1 of property value = Cost of Service ÷ Total Value of Properties

The real estate tax that each property owner must pay is computed in exactly the same way as that just described. At the outset, the sum of all the expenses that a town will have for the year is found. This number is then divided by the total value of all the property of the entire town. The quotient represents the amount of money that will be needed for each dollar in the value of the property.

ILLUSTRATION 1: The town of Triton needs $840,000 to meet expenses for the coming year. If the total value of all the property in the town is $24,000,000, how much money will have to be received for each dollar in the value of the property?

EXPLANATION: As in the case of Tom Harper and Roy Evans, you divide the total amount of money needed by the total value of the property. In this way you will determine the amount of money needed per dollar of the total value. In the following solution, it is found that 3.5¢ per dollar of property value is needed.

SOLUTION:

$$\text{Cost per \$1 of property value} = \$840{,}000 \div 24{,}000{,}000 = \$.035, \text{ or } 3.5¢$$

It was not quite correct to say that the total value of the property in Triton was $24,000,000. What normally happens is that a person, called an *assessor*, is employed by the governing body of a community to visit every piece of property in that community and record what he believes the value of it should be. The price that he attaches to it is called the *assessed value* of the property. This amount varies widely from town to town and from state to state. In fact, the assessed value ranges from as low as 10% of the actual value of the property in some communities to as high as 100% of the actual value in others.

In Illustration 1, the $24,000,000 should have been properly called the total assessed value of the property in Triton rather than merely the total value of the property. One other point has to be made concerning this problem—the 3.5¢ per $1 in the solution is called the *tax rate*. Although there are many towns that quote the rate in this form, there are many, many more that prefer to quote the rate either as a percent value, or in dollars per $100, or in dollars per $1,000, or even in mills per $1.

ILLUSTRATION 2: Change the tax rate of 3.5¢ per $1 to one quoted in dollars per $100.

EXPLANATION: It would be best if at the outset the numeral 3.5¢ was written with a dollar sign. This, of course, is done by moving the decimal point two places to the left and rewriting the numeral as $.035. To change the $1 in the rate to $100, it is necessary to multiply $1 by 100. Hence, the same must be done to the $.035, making it $3.50. Recall that the fastest way to multiply a number by 100 is to move the decimal point two places to the right in the number.

SOLUTION:

3.5¢ per $1 is rewritten as $.035 per $1.

Then both $.035 and $1 are multiplied by 100, giving

$3.50 per $100

ILLUSTRATION 3: Change the tax rate of $4.76 per $100 to one quoted in mills per $1.

EXPLANATION: The first objective should be to change the $4.76 to mills. Although there is no coin in the United States that represents a mill, there are many towns that quote their tax rate in terms of mills per $1. The value of a cent is one hundredth of a dollar. The value of a mill is one thousandth of a dollar. It would be best to reverse this and think in terms of the fact that each dollar is the equivalent of 1,000 mills. Hence, $2 is the equivalent of 2,000 mills, and $8 is the equivalent of 8,000 mills. Or, in general, dollars can be changed to mills simply by multiplying the number of dollars by 1,000. Thus, $4.76 is the equivalent of 4,760 mills, for when 4.76 is multiplied by 1,000, the decimal point is moved 3 places to the right. Therefore, the rate of

$4.76 per $100

can be written as

4,760 mills per $100

Then, if both the 4,760 mills and the $100 are divided by 100, the rate will be quoted in terms of mills per $1: 47.60 mills per $1.

SOLUTION:

$4.76 per $100 is rewritten as 4,760 mills per $100.

Then both 4,760 mills and $100 are divided by 100, giving

47.60 mills per $1

ILLUSTRATION 4: Change the tax rate of $54.20 per $1,000 to one quoted in dollars per $100.

SOLUTION:

$54.20 per $1,000

When both $54.20 and $1,000 are divided by 10, you obtain

$5.42 per $100

EXERCISES A

1. Change each of the tax rates below from its present form to the one quoted at its right.

a. $2.50 per $100 = $________ per $1,000
b. $5.46 per $100 = $________ per $1,000
c. $43.80 per $1,000 = $________ per $100
d. $36 per $1,000 = $________ per $100
e. 4¢ per $1 = $________ per $100
f. 6.1¢ per $1 = $________ per $100
g. $3.40 per $100 = ________¢ per $1
h. $6.27 per $100 = ________¢ per $1
i. 5.2¢ per $1 = $________ per $1,000
j. 3.95¢ per $1 = $________ per $1,000
k. $72.20 per $1,000 = ________¢ per $1
l. $12.46 per $1,000 = ________¢ per $1
m. $3.72 per $100 = ________ mills per $1
n. $6.30 per $100 = ________ mills per $1
o. $35.40 per $1,000 = ________ mills per $1
p. $29.81 per $1,000 = ________ mills per $1

2. For each of the following problems, find the tax rate in the form quoted in the last column. Carry out the division until the remainder is zero.

	Total Expenses For the Year	Total Assessed Value	Tax Rate
a.	$ 450,000	$ 9,000,000	$______ per $1
b.	1,380,000	23,000,000	______¢ per $1
c.	1,035,000	45,000,000	$______ per $100
d.	2,315,500	84,200,000	$______ per $100
e.	1,938,000	57,000,000	______ mills per $1
f.	5,803,976	125,600,000	$______ per $1,000

B

1. Brighton Township is one of four communities that contribute to the support of a regional high school. Brighton's share of this cost amounted to $492,000 last year. If the total assessed value of the property in the township was $41,000,000, what was the tax rate in dollars per $100 that was needed for the high school alone? ________

2. In its budget for the coming year, the town of Lakeside listed its contribution to the cost of maintaining the county government as $801,920. What is the tax rate per $1,000 that is needed for this expenditure if the total assessed valuation in Lakeside is $64,000,000? ________

3. In order to meet its expenses for the coming year, the town of West Camden will have to raise $1,040,000 in taxes. Through fines collected for traffic and building violations, the town will collect $20,100. If the assessed valuation of property in the town is $16,450,000, what will the tax rate have to be in mills per $1? ________

4. During the present year, Lansing Township paid $430,000 to support its school system. For the coming year, it will have to pay $483,749.99 to meet this cost. The total assessment of property in the town is $38,392,850. How much more will the school tax rate be in dollars per $100 for the coming year than it was for the past year? ________

PART 2

Although there are some homeowners who are concerned with the cost of running their local government, the majority are much more interested in what their share of this cost will be. All too frequently their attention seems to be centered on the tax rate, for they wrongly consider a high tax rate to mean high taxes and a low tax rate to mean low taxes. They have overlooked the fact that the tax they pay depends not only on the tax rate, but, also, on the assessed value of their property. The following illustration should help clear up this point.

ILLUSTRATION 1: In the town of West Millford, the tax rate is \$4.12 per \$100, while property is assessed at approximately 80% of its actual value. In the adjacent town of East Millford, the tax rate is \$6.18 per \$100, while the property here is assessed for only 50% of its actual value. How much more tax will Stanley Thompson have to pay if he decides to purchase a \$42,000 home in one of these communities rather than the other?

SOLUTION:

Assessed value in West Millford = \$42,000 × 80%
= \$33,600

Number of 100's in 33,600 = 33,600 ÷ 100
= 336

Tax in West Millford = 336 × \$4.12
= \$1,384.32

Assessed value in East Millford = \$42,000 × 50%
= \$21,000

Number of 100's in 21,000 = 21,000 ÷ 100
= 210

Tax in East Millford = 210 × \$6.18
= \$1,297.80

Amount of tax more in West Millford than in East Millford
= \$1,384.32 − \$1,297.80
= \$86.52

EXPLANATION: Although the tax rate in East Millford is more than \$2 per \$100 greater than in West Millford, Stanley Thompson's tax for a \$42,000 home will be \$86.52 less if he purchases it in East Millford. The cause for this is the fact that property in East Millford is assessed at a smaller percent of the actual value than it is in West Millford. Before deciding whether the taxes in a community are high or low, the homeowner should compute the actual tax he will have to pay. His decision should not be made by examining only the assessed value, or only the tax rate.

Notice that in computing the tax to be paid in the town of West Millford you first had to divide the assessed value of \$33,600 by 100 to find the number of 100's in 33,600. This was necessary since, for each $100 in the assessed value, the owner of the property had to pay $4.12. As there are 336 100's in 33,600, the tax was computed by finding the product of 336 and $4.12. The same method was used for finding the tax in East Millford. If the tax rate had been quoted in dollars per $1,000, then it would have been necessary to find the number of thousands in 33,600. This is done by dividing 33,600 by 1,000, that is, by moving the decimal point 3 places to the left in 33,600. This results in a quotient of 33.6, so there are 33.6 thousands.

ILLUSTRATION 2: The assessed value of Doris Sanford's home and land is $21,600. If the tax rate is 37.2 mills per $1, how much tax will she have to pay?

EXPLANATION: The first objective is to rewrite the 37.2 mills in terms of dollars. Since 1 mill is 1 thousandth of 1 dollar, then 37.2 mills are 37.2 thousandths of 1 dollar. When 37.2 thousandths is expressed as a numeral, it becomes 37.2/1000. After dividing by 1,000, it will be .0372. Thus, the tax rate of 37.2 mills per dollar equals $.0372 per dollar. Hence, for each dollar in the assessed value, the taxpayer will have to pay $.0372.

SOLUTION:

Tax rate = 37.2 mills per $1
= $.0372 per $1

Number of dollars in $21,600 = 21,600 ÷ 1
= 21,600

Tax = 21,600 × $.0372
= $803.52

EXERCISES A

1. Compute the tax for each of the following properties.

	Assessed Value	Tax Rate	Tax
a.	$12,400	$2.30 per $100	$________
b.	18,200	$4.56 per $100	________
c.	23,000	$34.27 per $1,000	________
d.	19,600	$42.85 per $1,000	________
e.	21,300	$.041 per $1	________
f.	29,800	$.067 per $1	________
g.	27,500	5.3¢ per $1	________
h.	12,900	3.94¢ per $1	________
i.	26,800	48 mills per $1	________
j.	35,200	39.4 mills per $1	________

2. Each of the following properties is assessed at the percent of its actual value that is shown. Compute the tax that will have to be paid.

	Actual Value	Assessed At the Following Percent	Assessed Value	Tax Rate	Tax
a.	$28,400	50%	$________	$2.59 per $100	$________
b.	29,600	75%	________	$7.82 per $100	________
c.	25,000	60%	________	$43.76 per $1,000	________
d.	41,400	20%	________	$12.93 per $1,000	________
e.	27,300	90%	________	3.6¢ per $1	________
f.	32,100	80%	________	5.92¢ per $1	________
g.	37,600	70%	________	53 mills per $1	________
h.	68,200	55%	________	64.2 mills per $1	________

B

1. Last year, the borough of Moorestown had a tax rate of 2.57%. How much tax did the owner of a property assessed at $8,400 have to pay? ________
2. The tax rate in Orangeburg is 89¢ per $10. How much tax will have to be paid on a property whose actual value is $38,000 but is assessed at 40% of this value? ________
3. Which of the following tax rates is the greater?
   a. $5.37 per $100 or $48.26 per $1,000 ________
   b. 5.4¢ per $1 or $6.27 per $100 ________
   c. 46 mills per $1 or 6¢ per $1 ________
4. The budget for Elmsport showed that its tax rate of $3.52 per $100 was to be spent as follows:

Borough Tax	$ .19
School Tax	1.18
Regional School Tax	1.20
County Tax	.95
Total	$3.52

   Ronald DeFalco owns a home in Elmsport that is valued at $40,000 but is assessed at 9/10 of its value.
   a. What is the total tax that Mr. DeFalco will have to pay? ________
   b. How much of Mr. DeFalco's tax will go to each of the expenses listed in the budget? ________
5. When Mildred Cramer built an addition to her home, her assessed value was increased from $26,400 to $28,600. If the tax rate last year was $4.81 per $100, how much more tax did she have to pay because of the enlargement of her home? ________

6. Eugene Donnelly owns a house worth $41,000 in Great Meadow and another one valued at $36,000 in Cedarville. In the first town, property is assessed at 100% of its value, while in the second, it is assessed at only 65% of its value. The tax rate in Great Meadow is $4.23 per $100, and in Cedarville it is $38.64 per $1,000. What is the total real estate tax that he has to pay for these two houses?

____

Section 3: The Cost of Water

One of the public utility costs that the person who rents an apartment does not have to pay for is water. There are some cities where water is provided at no charge. The number of these cities, though, is

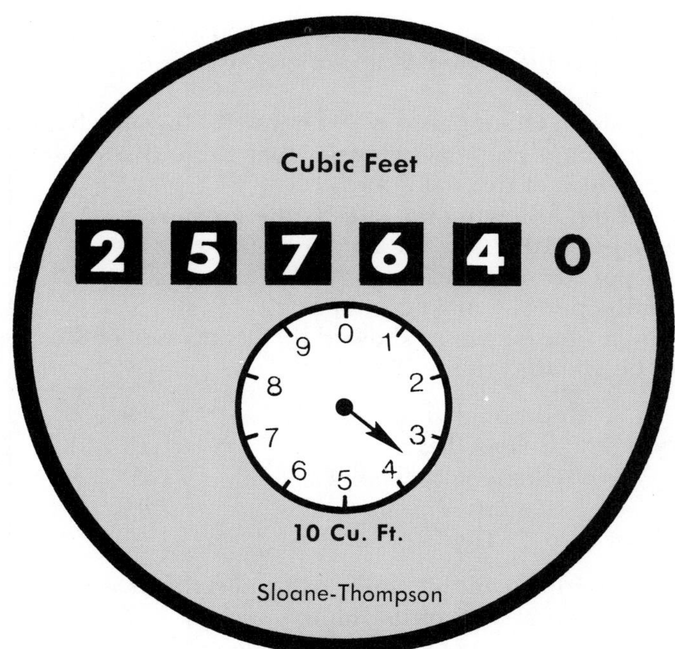

extremely small. Hence, in addition to paying for gas and electricity, the homeowner must also pay for the water that is piped into his house.

Although water meters vary in appearance, most look like the one above. This meter is far easier to read than the gas and electric meters, for here the numerals in the small squares record the reading. The reading of 257,640 indicates the number of cubic feet of water that have passed through the meter since it was installed. To be exact, the last digit should have been a 3 rather than a 0. (The numeral 3 comes from the dial in the center.) However, the cost of 3 cubic feet of water is so small that it will not affect the total bill. Further, although it is dropped off now, it will be included as part of the total water consumption at the next reading.

It is evident from the meter that water is purchased by the cubic foot. The rates, though, are quoted per 1,000 cubic feet, for they would be far too small and too clumsy to use if they were quoted per cubic foot. Some communities prefer to sell water by the gallon rather than the cubic foot. Their meters are the same as the one on page 466. The only difference is that these meters are geared to record consumption in gallons instead of cubic feet.

The way in which the water rates are quoted by the town of Bloomington, Rhode Island, is very much the way you would find it for most communities. Notice that the homeowner is billed for water quarterly. Every three months an inspector from the water department records the reading on the meter. By computing the difference between this reading and the previous reading, the number of cubic feet of water consumed is determined.

BLOOMINGTON, RHODE ISLAND

Water Rates—Quarterly

For the first 700 cubic feet or less	$2.00 minimum charge
For the next 2,000 cubic feet	$2.60 per 1,000 cubic feet
For the next 17,000 cubic feet	$2.40 per 1,000 cubic feet
For the next 20,300 cubic feet	$2.10 per 1,000 cubic feet
For in excess of 40,000 cubic feet	$1.30 per 1,000 cubic feet

ILLUSTRATION: On March 27, the reading on the water meter at Mr. Taylor's home was 136,240. When it was read again on June 29, it was recorded as 142,670. If Mr. Taylor lived in Bloomington, how large was his water bill for this 3-month period?

SOLUTION:

Number of cubic feet used = 142,670 − 136,240	=	6,430
Cost of first 700 cubic feet	= $2.00	− 700
		5,730
Cost of next 2,000 cubic feet = 2 × $2.60	= 5.20	− 2,000
		3,730
Cost of next 3,730 cubic feet = 3.73 × $2.40	= 8.95	− 3,730
Cost for 6,430 cubic feet	= $16.15	0

EXPLANATION: The method for finding the cost of water is exactly the same as that used for finding the cost of either gas or electricity. Care, however, must be taken when determining the cost of the 2,000 cubic feet, for the rate is in terms of $2.60 per 1,000 cubic feet. Hence, 2,000 is divided by 1,000 in order to determine the number of thousands in 2,000. The same is true when finding the cost of 3,730 cubic feet of water. The quotient of 3,730 with 1,000 is 3.73, which is the number of thousands in 3,730.

EXERCISES A

1. Determine the quarterly charge for each of the following customers. Use the water-rate table of the town of Bloomington, Rhode Island.

	Number Of Cubic Feet Used During Quarter	Cost		Number Of Cubic Feet Used During Quarter	Cost
a.	340	$______	e.	14,390	$______
b.	1,460	______	f.	18,150	______
c.	5,670	______	g.	26,940	______
d.	8,280	______	h.	43,510	______

2. Determine the quarterly charge for each of the following customers. Use the water-rate table of the town of Bloomington, Rhode Island.

	Reading At Beginning Of Quarter	Reading At End Of Quarter	Number Of Cubic Feet	Cost
a.	005820	007510	______	$______
b.	024370	024980	______	______
c.	069510	074370	______	______
d.	023840	031620	______	______
e.	369570	382430	______	______
f.	997650	016790	______	______

3. In Livingston Township, water is sold by the gallon, and its rates are quoted as follows:

LIVINGSTON TOWNSHIP

Quarterly Water Rates

Minimum Charge $4.20

60¢ per 1,000 gallons for first 4,000 gallons
45¢ per 1,000 gallons for next 6,000 gallons
40¢ per 1,000 gallons for next 20,000 gallons
33¢ per 1,000 gallons in excess of 30,000 gallons

Determine the quarterly charge to each of the following customers.

	Reading in Gallons At Beginning of Quarter	Reading in Gallons At End of Quarter	Number Of Gallons	Cost
a.	036750	049360	________	$________
b.	058470	064230	________	________
c.	249360	268410	________	________
d.	573540	596290	________	________
e.	628480	671360	________	________
f.	998640	014280	________	________
g.	981370	024830	________	________

B

1. How many gallons of water will have to be consumed by a resident of Livingston Township in order to cover his minimum charge? (See the table for Problem 3 of Group A.) ________
2. Rose Clark has a water softener that requires regenerating twice a week. During each of these periods, 90 gallons of water are used at a cost of 65¢ per 1,000 gallons. How much will she have to pay for water during one year for regenerating the water softener? ________
3. During a particularly dry summer, Maria Kern had to water her lawn an average of 6 hours per day for 47 days. If water flowed through her garden hose at the rate of $2\frac{1}{2}$ gallons per minute, how much did she have to pay to keep the lawn green? The cost of water is 75¢ per 1,000 gallons. ________
4. A cubic foot of water is the equivalent of approximately 7.5 gallons of water. Approximately how many gallons of water are there in 7,000 cubic feet of water? ________
5. Donald Bates has a home in Bloomington, Rhode Island. During a quarterly period he used 6,000 cubic feet of water.
   - **a.** Determine the cost of the water. Use the table on page 467. ________
   - **b.** How many gallons of water were consumed during this quarterly period? ________
   - **c.** If Mr. Bates had lived in Livingston Township, whose water-rate table appears on page 468, what would the water bill have been? ________
   - **d.** How much more, or less, did he have to pay for water by living in Bloomington rather than in Livingston Township? ________

Section 4: The Cost of Repairs and Maintenance

The apartment dweller out for a Sunday drive rarely is aware of the hidden costs that account for the beauty he sees. He may know vaguely of the taxes and mortgage payments of a homeowner, but somehow he thinks such small things as the grass and shrubs have been there forever. Little does he realize that the grass that resembles the putting green of a golf course may have cost the homeowner $3,000 to plant, while the shrubs that look as if they were there long before the house was built were probably brought in at the cost of another $1,800. But this is only the beginning—for someone must fertilize the grass, cut the lawn, trim the shrubs, cut dead branches from trees and so on.

It is these small things that build up to a large part of the expense of owning and maintaining a house. The problems in this section are designed to present an overall picture of the financial obligations that the homeowner will have to face, other than those discussed earlier in this chapter.

Model homes give future residents an excellent idea of how their new homes will look, yet no idea of how much it will cost to keep that home looking like new.

ILLUSTRATION: Ronald Sheldon designed a free-form patio that was surfaced with bricks laid flat side up in a bed of soft sand. For this he needed 4,480 bricks at 12¢ per brick and 11 tons of sand at $5.46 per ton. Since his son volunteered to do the work, there was no charge for labor. How much did the material for the patio cost?

SOLUTION:

Cost for bricks = 4,480 × $.12	=	$537.60
Cost for sand = 11 × $5.46	=	60.06
Total		$597.66

EXERCISES

1. Elena Pollard lives in a community where the water is very hard. For this reason, she rents a water softener that requires servicing once every 4 weeks at a cost of $5.85. How much does she pay over the period of a year in order to have soft water in her home? ________

2. Gary Norton lives in the same community as Elena Pollard of Problem 1. However, Gary preferred to purchase a water softener. The cost and installation for this device was $374. To service the water softener himself, Gary uses salt which he purchases in a 100-pound bag four times each year. The cost of the salt is $2.75 per bag.
   a. How much does the salt cost Gary each year? ________
   b. How much less does Gary pay each year for servicing his water softener than does Elena? ________
   c. In terms of saving alone, to the nearest year, how many years will it take Gary to pay off the cost of his investment in the water softener? ________
3. The driveway of the Moreland home is 60 feet long. Along one edge of the driveway Rona Moreland planted small spruce trees 3 feet apart at a cost of $3.75 for each tree. How much did she have to pay for the trees? (Be careful in counting the trees, for one is needed at both the beginning and end of the driveway.) ________
4. After walking 5 miles while mowing his lawn on a hot summer day, Ray Leach decided that this exercise was no longer to his liking. The following day he bought a riding mower for $510. His neighbor, whose property is approximately the same size as the Leachs', employs a gardener who charges $12 each time he mows the lawn.
   a. If the lawn needs to be cut an average of 16 times during the spring, summer, and fall, how much does Mr. Leach save by not using his neighbor's gardener? ________

b. As the mower is very sturdy, Mr. Leach attaches a plow to the front of it during the winter and uses to it push the snow from his driveway. His neighbor, on the other hand, hires someone to do this at a cost of $8 for each snowplowing. During a normal winter, the driveway needs plowing five times. How much does Mr. Leach save by plowing his driveway himself? ________

c. In terms of Mr. Leach's annual saving, how many years will it take him to pay for the cost of the mower? (The upkeep of the machine has been disregarded in this problem.) ________

5. Mr. Ryan's lawn covers 15,000 square feet. Insects have been chewing the roots of his grass.
   a. He can buy a liquid insecticide—insect killer—at $18.90 a gallon, that will cover 30,000 square feet. How much will this cost him for one application? ________
   b. If he prefers, he can buy a powder insecticide at $5.75 that will cover 5,000 square feet. How much will this cost him for one application? ________
   c. How much will he save by using the liquid rather than the powder? ________

6. The lawn around the Walters' home covers 14,000 square feet. Twice each year Mr. Walter fertilizes the lawn with a fertilizer that costs him $3.85 a 50-pound bag. Each bag will cover 2,000 square feet. What is the cost of fertilizing this lawn each year? ________

7. Both Mr. and Mrs. Skinner love roses. Hence they have set aside a large area of their garden, where they have planted more than 250 bushes. Each year they find it necessary to replace approximately 6 dozen bushes that have either died or are diseased. This year they made the following purchase of roses:

   1 dozen Betty Uprichard at $1.75 per bush
   2 dozen Good News at $2.25 per bush
   2 dozen Saratoga at $2.85 per bush
   1 dozen Summer Rainbow at $3.45 per bush

   What was the total cost? ________

8. Along both sides of his driveway, Mr. Nash laid curved cement blocks at a cost of 37¢ per block. The driveway is 60 feet long, while each block is 15 inches long.
   a. How many cement blocks did Mr. Nash need? (Do not consider the space between the blocks.) ________
   b. What was the total cost of the cement blocks? ________
   c. Had Mr. Nash purchased Belgium blocks, each of which is 9 inches long, how many would he have needed? ________

d. If each Belgium block costs 42¢, what would have been the cost to edge the driveway with these blocks? ________

e. How much did Mr. Nash save by using cement blocks rather than Belgium blocks? ________

9. Mr. Merkle built a paneled family room in the basement of his home with 4- by 8-foot sheets of finished plywood that cost $5.35 per sheet. The dimensions of the room are 18 feet long, 12 feet wide, and 7 feet, 8 inches high. In determining how many plywood sheets he would need, Mr. Merkle disregarded the two small windows and the door, for it is impossible to buy a fraction of a sheet.

a. How many sheets of plywood did he have to purchase? ________

b. What was the total cost of the plywood? ________

10. Being somewhat short of money and having plenty of time on his hands, Mr. Libby decided to paint the outside of his house himself. His estimate of the number of square feet that would have to be covered by paint was 4,800. He planned to buy a latex paint at $6.35 per gallon. Each gallon was said to cover 450 square feet.

a. How many full gallons of paint will he need? ________

b. What will the cost of the paint be? ________

11. The Forsyth home is heated by oil at a cost of 33.4¢ per gallon. From November through May inclusive, Mr. Forsyth finds that he averages about 365 gallons per month. During the remaining months, he uses only 350 gallons.

a. How many gallons of oil does Mr. Forsyth purchase during the year? ________

b. What is the total annual cost for oil to heat the Forsyth home? ________

c. What is the average monthly cost for oil? ________

12. Mrs. Lodge wanted the open porch of her home to be enclosed with louvered windows and knotty pine paneling. The lowest estimate of the cost of this project came to $1,850. Feeling that this price was too high, Mr. Lodge decided to do the work himself. After completing the room, he found that his expenses had been as follows:

8 louvered windows at $32.50 each
1 louvered door at $84.75
Cost of lumber – $67.54
286 vinyl floor tiles at 48¢ each
172 asbestos ceiling tiles at 17¢ each
Incidental supplies – $40

a. What was the total of all of his expenses? ________
b. How much did Mr. Lodge save by doing the work himself? ________
c. Mr. Lodge kept a tally of the number of hours he spent working on the porch. If the record shows that he required 204 hours to complete the job, how much can Mr. Lodge consider his hourly earnings to be? ________

Unit 3: Chapter Review and Test

1. How many kilowatt-hours are there in each of the following number of watt-hours?

a. 6,000 ________ b. 19,000 ________ c. 4,650 ________

2. How many kilowatt-hours of electricity are consumed by the use of each of the following appliances?

	Number Of Watts	Number Of Hours	Watt-Hours	Kilowatt-Hours
a.	500	14	________	________
b.	2,100	$2\frac{1}{2}$	________	________

3. How many kilowatt-hours of electricity were used during a month in which the meter readings at the beginning and end of the month appeared as below?

Meter At Beginning Of Month

Meter At End Of Month

____

4. Determine the cost of electricity for a month in which 142 kilowatt-hours of electricity were used. Use the electric rate table of the Cape Electric and Gas Company on page 434. ________
5. Nora Shanley roasted a turkey in an electric oven for 4 hours and 15 minutes. The oven operated on 2,200 watts of power. If the cost of each kilowatt-hour is 5.8¢, what was the total cost for roasting the turkey? ________
6. Determine the cost of consuming 89 hundred cubic feet of gas during the period of one month. Use the rate table of the Cape Electric and Gas Company. ________

7. The gas meter readings on two successive months were 623 and 691 respectively. How much would the Great Western Electric and Gas Company, whose rates appear in Problem 5, page 441, charge this customer? ________
8. Use the telephone company table on page 443 to determine the cost of each of the following calls that were made out of the free-call zone. The calls were dialed directly.

	Miles	Time In Minutes	Hour Of Call	Cost
a.	16	8	Wednesday—3 P.M.	$________
b.	75	14	Monday—11:04 P.M.	________
c.	8	9	Saturday—9 A.M.	________
d.	93	17	Sunday—4 P.M.	________
e.	158	12	Saturday—4 P.M.	________

9. Allan Green was granted a $14,300 mortgage by his savings and loan association, but he had to pay 3½ points to obtain the loan. How much money did this amount to? ________
10. When the Rymers purchased their home, they were granted a $17,400 mortgage at 9% to be paid off over a period of 20 years in monthly installments.
    a. How large was each payment? ________
    b. How much money did the Rymers pay to the mortgage company over the 20-year period? ________
    c. How much more did they have to pay back than they had borrowed? ________
11. After having made payments on their 6% mortgage for some time, the Engels still owed $8,320. Their monthly payments were $107.02. How much of the next payment was interest and how much would be used to decrease the debt? ________
12. Change each of the following tax rates from its present form to the one quoted at its right.
    a. $4.75 per $100 = $________ per $1,000
    b. $5.40 per $100 = ________ mills per $1
    c. $35.20 per $1,000 = $________ per $100
13. The Durkees' property is worth $40,000, but it is assessed at 80% of its value. If the tax rate in this community is $2.95 per $100, how much real estate tax will they have to pay? ________
14. Compute the cost of water to the consumer whose meter read 468,470 at the beginning of the quarterly period and 471,630 at the end of the period. Use the Bloomington Water Rate Table on page 467. ________

APPENDIX

THE FUNDAMENTAL OPERATIONS AND PERCENT

This appendix is designed as a review of the fundamental operations of arithmetic on whole numbers, decimals, and fractions. You will find that everything included in this appendix has been taught to you at one time or another during your first six or seven years of school. The purpose of including it here is to help refresh your memory in the event that the mechanics of some of the operations may have slipped your mind. In view of this, the explanations that are included are designed primarily to tell you how to perform the necessary steps in arriving at your answer rather than why these steps are necessary.

Unit 1: Addition

Section 1: Addition of Whole Numbers

EXERCISES A

Find the sum in each of the following exercises.

1. 4 1	**2.** 0 1	**3.** 2 3	**4.** 1 2	**5.** 3 3
6. 5 5	**7.** 1 1	**8.** 0 2	**9.** 5 1	**10.** 3 2
11. 3 4	**12.** 0 4	**13.** 2 2	**14.** 2 1	**15.** 4 4
16. 4 2	**17.** 2 4	**18.** 1 3	**19.** 5 4	**20.** 0 3
21. 5 6	**22.** 3 1	**23.** 6 4	**24.** 9 0	**25.** 9 9
26. 1 5	**27.** 7 2	**28.** 4 0	**29.** 5 2	**30.** 4 3
31. 2 5	**32.** 4 5	**33.** 8 0	**34.** 1 4	**35.** 3 5
36. 6 6	**37.** 1 0	**38.** 5 3	**39.** 2 6	**40.** 7 4
41. 1 9	**42.** 5 7	**43.** 0 5	**44.** 7 7	**45.** 4 6
46. 2 7	**47.** 1 6	**48.** 8 4	**49.** 3 6	**50.** 6 7

51. 6 3	**52.** 0 8	**53.** 7 1	**54.** 8 7	**55.** 6 2
56. 2 8	**57.** 5 8	**58.** 1 7	**59.** 6 8	**60.** 0 6
61. 6 5	**62.** 3 7	**63.** 9 4	**64.** 8 6	**65.** 4 7
66. 0 9	**67.** 9 3	**68.** 6 1	**69.** 9 2	**70.** 7 6
71. 7 5	**72.** 2 0	**73.** 5 9	**74.** 7 3	**75.** 4 8
76. 8 2	**77.** 1 8	**78.** 0 7	**79.** 8 5	**80.** 7 1
81. 8 3	**82.** 2 9	**83.** 9 6	**84.** 3 8	**85.** 3 0
86. 9 8	**87.** 7 8	**88.** 9 5	**89.** 7 0	**90.** 8 1
91. 6 0	**92.** 3 9	**93.** 8 8	**94.** 4 9	**95.** 7 9
96. 9 1	**97.** 9 7	**98.** 5 0	**99.** 6 9	**100.** 8 9

B

Find the sum in each of the following exercises.

1. 2 3 7	**2.** 1 5 8	**3.** 4 7 1	**4.** 3 9 2	**5.** 1 6 4

6.	7.	8.	9.	10.
2	3	1	4	9
9	5	8	6	1
4	9	6	7	5

11.	12.	13.	14.	15.
4	2	6	1	4
8	7	5	7	4
5	6	6	8	9

16.	17.	18.	19.	20.
7	3	5	8	9
4	7	9	1	3
8	7	6	8	6

21.	22.	23.	24.	25.
6	8	7	6	9
5	7	9	8	5
8	7	4	7	8

26.	27.	28.	29.	30.
8	6	9	9	9
8	8	7	8	9
7	9	8	8	7

C

Find the sum in each of the following exercises.

1.	2.	3.	4.
13	17	46	62
34	10	12	27

5.	6.	7.	8.
53	21	72	68
46	58	16	21

9.	10.	11.	12.
65	34	46	58
27	44	27	63

13.	14.	15.	16.
64	45	96	47
57	76	24	65

17.	18.	19.	20.
65	78	87	98
66	74	75	56

D

Find the sum in each of the following exercises.

1. 23 46 10	**2.** 31 46 21	**3.** 31 18 11	**4.** 41 25 32
5. 26 18 30	**6.** 43 27 15	**7.** 16 42 38	**8.** 33 18 44
9. 56 23 35	**10.** 62 27 57	**11.** 19 84 36	**12.** 28 63 16
13. 85 39 41	**14.** 76 27 32	**15.** 19 86 54	**16.** 36 45 87
17. 72 43 88	**18.** 57 65 98	**19.** 76 59 87	**20.** 98 69 87

E

Find the sum in each of the following exercises.

1. 123 231 113	**2.** 205 314 260	**3.** 421 307 271	**4.** 533 243 112
5. 237 436 521	**6.** 134 625 246	**7.** 515 372 468	**8.** 239 426 874
9. 624 372 246	**10.** 175 653 365	**11.** 319 584 623	**12.** 581 367 419

13. 657	**14.** 585	**15.** 908	**16.** 488
743	693	675	874
917	778	247	565
17. 675	**18.** 897	**19.** 986	**20.** 876
788	689	869	987
696	758	788	969

Section 2: Addition of Decimals

The mechanics of adding decimal numbers is no different than that of adding whole numbers. Care, however, must be taken to make certain that when the numbers are arranged vertically, the decimal points are placed directly below one another.

ILLUSTRATION 1: Find the sum of the following set of numbers.

$4.26, $3, $8.04, $27

EXPLANATION: If the numbers to be added include some that are given in terms of dollars only, while others are given in terms of dollars and cents, then it would be best to change all numbers to the dollars and cents form. Thus, in the numbers in the illustration, the $3 and $27 are both written in terms of dollars only. Rewrite them so that the $3 appears as $3.00, that is, 3 dollars and no cents and the $27 appears as $27.00, that is, 27 dollars and no cents.

SOLUTION:

$$\begin{array}{r} \$4.26 \\ 3.00 \\ 8.04 \\ \underline{27.00} \\ \$42.30 \end{array}$$

EXPLANATION (continued): Notice that the addition above is done exactly as the addition of whole numbers, with the single exception that it is necessary to place the decimal point in the answer directly in line with the decimal points in the numbers being added.

ILLUSTRATION 2: Find the sum of the following set of numbers.

$3.45, $2.58, 76¢, 18¢

EXPLANATION: In those cases where some of the numbers are expressed with the dollar symbol ($), while others are expressed with the cent symbol (¢), rewrite the latter in terms of dollars. Thus, the 76¢ and 18¢ should be written as \$.76 and \$.18 before the numbers are added.

SOLUTION:

\$3.45
2.58
.76
.18
\$6.97

EXERCISES

A

Find the sum in each of the following exercises.

1.	\$2.15	**2.**	\$4.06	**3.**	\$5.13	**4.**	\$1.65
	3.04		3.12		2.64		4.23
5.	\$8.22	**6.**	\$7.90	**7.**	\$6.78	**8.**	\$9.27
	4.69		5.36		8.45		6.99
9.	\$14.67	**10.**	\$27.42	**11.**	\$49.75	**12.**	\$16.49
	37.09		53.65		13.86		27.19
13.	\$159.95	**14.**	\$105.50	**15.**	\$299.98	**16.**	\$697.19
	42.05		96.49		68.75		489.95

B

Find the sum in each of the following exercises.

1.	\$2.41	**2.**	\$4.50	**3.**	\$1.22	**4.**	\$5.03
	3.27		2.31		3.43		2.61
	1.30		5.15		2.03		2.15
5.	\$6.37	**6.**	\$1.85	**7.**	\$9.42	**8.**	\$7.29
	2.41		4.23		3.27		8.56
	1.16		6.70		5.86		3.35
9.	\$24.09	**10.**	\$11.41	**11.**	\$54.23	**12.**	\$41.75
	32.16		13.28		8.64		29.25
	65.42		7.64		10.17		12.19

13.	14.	15.	16.
\$247.65	\$352.29	\$679.95	\$937.49
109.16	847.63	325.09	895.78
693.27	285.07	437.65	876.88

C

In each of the following exercises, rearrange the numerals vertically before adding.

1. \$2.41 + \$3.76 + \$4.45 = ________
2. \$2.56 + \$4.07 + \$3.98 = ________
3. \$5.48 + \$6.29 + \$8.05 = ________
4. \$3.75 + \$7.34 + \$9.70 = ________
5. \$12.03 + \$6.74 + \$14.39 + \$2.49 = ________
6. \$36.24 + \$18.56 + \$2.27 + \$12.50 = ________
7. \$4.36 + \$43.17 + \$29.25 + \$3.45 = ________
8. \$17.95 + \$15 + \$42.50 + \$8 = ________
9. \$54.80 + \$21.55 + \$39 + \$2.04 = ________
10. \$123.60 + \$43 + \$15 + \$2.73 = ________
11. \$144.75 + \$5.65 + \$86 + \$7 + \$14.36 = ________
12. \$46.30 + 54¢ + 85¢ + \$3.95 + \$8.50 = ________
13. 67¢ + \$12.85 + 14¢ + \$58 + \$16.20 = ________
14. \$125 + 75¢ + \$40 + \$18.12 + 56¢ = ________
15. \$57 + 98¢ + 64¢ + \$176.58 + \$39 = ________
16. \$258.42 + \$43 + \$125 + 72¢ + 134¢ = ________

Section 3: Addition of Fractions

If the denominators of the fractions are alike, then the addition of fractions becomes the simple matter of merely adding the numerators and writing their sum over the denominator of the fraction. For example:

$$3/8 + 4/8 = 7/8 \text{ (Just add 3 and 4)}$$

The reasoning for this is shown below.

$3/8 + 4/8$	
$= 3 \times 1/8 + 4 \times 1/8$	Meaning of Division
$= 1/8 \times 3 + 1/8 \times 4$	Commutative Law of Multiplication
$= 1/8 \times (3 + 4)$	Distributive Law of Multiplication
$= 1/8 \times 7$	Uniqueness of Addition
$= 7 \times 1/8$	Commutative Law of Multiplication
$= 7/8$	Meaning of Division

Or, if you prefer, you can think of $3/8$ as meaning 3 eighths, while $4/8$ means 4 eighths. And just as you add 3 apples and 4 apples and get 7 apples as their sum, so, too, you can add 3 eighths and 4 eighths and get 7 eighths. Since 7 eighths can be rewritten as 7/8, the explanation here leads to the same answer as was obtained on the preceding page.

ILLUSTRATION 1: Add 5/8 and 7/8.

EXPLANATION: It is usually best to rewrite the problem in vertical form before adding the numbers.

SOLUTION:

$$\begin{array}{r} \frac{5}{8} \\ +\ \frac{7}{8} \\ \hline \frac{12}{8} = 1\frac{4}{8} = 1\frac{1}{2} \end{array}$$

EXPLANATION (continued): The numeral 12/8 was changed to its equivalent form of $1\frac{4}{8}$ by dividing 8 into 12. The $\frac{4}{8}$ was then reduced to lowest terms by writing it as 1/2.

ILLUSTRATION 2: Add 2/3 and 3/4.

EXPLANATION: Since the two fractions do not have the same denominator, it is necessary to rewrite them as fractions equivalent to those which do have a common denominator. This can be done by multiplying the first fraction by 4/4, which is one form of the identity element of multiplication. The second fraction is multiplied by the identity element 3/3. Hence, both new fractions will have 12 as their denominator. Incidentally, the 12 is selected as the common denominator of the two fractions, for it is the smallest number for which both 3 and 4 are exact divisors. If the denominators had been 6 and 9, then the common denominator for these numbers would have been 18, for 18 is the smallest number for which both 6 and 9 are exact divisors. What would the common denominator have been had the denominators been 6 and 8?

SOLUTION:

$$\begin{array}{rcl} \frac{2}{3} = \frac{2}{3} \times \frac{4}{4} &=& \frac{8}{12} \\ +\ \frac{3}{4} = \frac{3}{4} \times \frac{3}{3} &=& \frac{9}{12} \\ \hline && \frac{17}{12} = 1\frac{5}{12} \end{array}$$

ILLUSTRATION 3: Add $2\frac{3}{4}$ and $15\frac{5}{6}$.

SOLUTION:

$$\begin{array}{rcl} 2\frac{3}{4} = 2\frac{3}{4} \times \frac{3}{3} &=& 2\frac{9}{12} \\ +\ 15\frac{5}{6} = 15\frac{5}{6} \times \frac{2}{2} &=& 15\frac{10}{12} \\ \hline && 17\frac{19}{12} = 17 + 1\frac{7}{12} = 18\frac{7}{12} \end{array}$$

EXPLANATION: The sum of two mixed numbers is found by adding the whole numbers and then adding the fractions. In this case, it is necessary to add 2 and 15, after which you add $\frac{9}{12}$ and $\frac{10}{12}$. The sum of $17\frac{19}{12}$ can be expressed as $17 + \frac{19}{12}$, and this, in turn, can be rewritten as $17 + 1\frac{7}{12}$, which is what is done.

EXERCISES A

Find the sum in each of the following exercises.

1. $\frac{3}{5}$ $\frac{1}{5}$	2. $\frac{2}{7}$ $\frac{3}{7}$	3. $\frac{1}{3}$ $\frac{1}{3}$	4. $\frac{3}{8}$ $\frac{2}{8}$	5. $\frac{4}{9}$ $\frac{3}{9}$
6. $\frac{2}{11}$ $\frac{3}{11}$	7. $\frac{5}{12}$ $\frac{6}{12}$	8. $\frac{5}{14}$ $\frac{4}{14}$	9. $\frac{2}{6}$ $\frac{3}{6}$	10. $\frac{3}{16}$ $\frac{7}{16}$
11. $\frac{3}{4}$ $\frac{3}{4}$	12. $\frac{1}{2}$ $\frac{1}{2}$	13. $\frac{1}{4}$ $\frac{3}{4}$	14. $\frac{5}{6}$ $\frac{1}{6}$	15. $\frac{4}{6}$ $\frac{5}{6}$
16. $\frac{1}{8}$ $\frac{7}{8}$	17. $\frac{3}{8}$ $\frac{5}{8}$	18. $\frac{3}{8}$ $\frac{7}{8}$	19. $\frac{5}{8}$ $\frac{7}{8}$	20. $\frac{7}{8}$ $\frac{2}{8}$
21. $\frac{3}{10}$ $\frac{5}{10}$	22. $\frac{7}{10}$ $\frac{3}{10}$	23. $\frac{1}{10}$ $\frac{9}{10}$	24. $\frac{9}{10}$ $\frac{3}{10}$	25. $\frac{7}{10}$ $\frac{8}{10}$
26. $\frac{5}{12}$ $\frac{7}{12}$	27. $\frac{7}{12}$ $\frac{7}{12}$	28. $\frac{11}{12}$ $\frac{5}{12}$	29. $\frac{11}{12}$ $\frac{10}{12}$	30. $\frac{8}{12}$ $\frac{10}{12}$
31. $\frac{11}{16}$ $\frac{5}{16}$	32. $\frac{15}{16}$ $\frac{5}{16}$	33. $\frac{5}{16}$ $\frac{13}{16}$	34. $\frac{7}{16}$ $\frac{11}{16}$	35. $\frac{10}{16}$ $\frac{15}{16}$
36. $\frac{1}{3}$ $\frac{1}{3}$ $\frac{2}{3}$	37. $\frac{3}{4}$ $\frac{1}{4}$ $\frac{1}{4}$	38. $\frac{1}{6}$ $\frac{5}{6}$ $\frac{3}{6}$	39. $\frac{1}{8}$ $\frac{3}{8}$ $\frac{5}{8}$	40. $\frac{7}{8}$ $\frac{5}{8}$ $\frac{4}{8}$
41. $\frac{6}{8}$ $\frac{7}{8}$ $\frac{5}{8}$	42. $\frac{3}{8}$ $\frac{6}{8}$ $\frac{5}{8}$	43. $\frac{7}{10}$ $\frac{9}{10}$ $\frac{1}{10}$	44. $\frac{3}{10}$ $\frac{7}{10}$ $\frac{4}{10}$	45. $\frac{1}{10}$ $\frac{8}{10}$ $\frac{6}{10}$

46. $\frac{5}{12}$ $\frac{7}{12}$ $\frac{1}{12}$
47. $\frac{9}{12}$ $\frac{7}{12}$ $\frac{11}{12}$
48. $\frac{5}{16}$ $\frac{7}{16}$ $\frac{10}{16}$
49. $\frac{3}{16}$ $\frac{15}{16}$ $\frac{8}{16}$
50. $\frac{9}{16}$ $\frac{11}{16}$ $\frac{12}{16}$

B

Find the sum in each of the following exercises.

1. $\frac{1}{2}$ $\frac{1}{4}$
2. $\frac{1}{2}$ $\frac{1}{6}$
3. $\frac{1}{3}$ $\frac{1}{6}$
4. $\frac{2}{3}$ $\frac{1}{9}$
5. $\frac{1}{2}$ $\frac{5}{6}$
6. $\frac{1}{2}$ $\frac{3}{8}$
7. $\frac{2}{3}$ $\frac{5}{6}$
8. $\frac{1}{4}$ $\frac{1}{8}$
9. $\frac{3}{4}$ $\frac{3}{8}$
10. $\frac{5}{6}$ $\frac{1}{12}$
11. $\frac{5}{12}$ $\frac{1}{6}$
12. $\frac{5}{8}$ $\frac{1}{2}$
13. $\frac{7}{8}$ $\frac{3}{4}$
14. $\frac{5}{16}$ $\frac{1}{4}$
15. $\frac{1}{6}$ $\frac{2}{3}$
16. $\frac{7}{12}$ $\frac{2}{3}$
17. $\frac{11}{12}$ $\frac{3}{4}$
18. $\frac{3}{16}$ $\frac{1}{2}$
19. $\frac{7}{16}$ $\frac{1}{4}$
20. $\frac{3}{4}$ $\frac{9}{16}$
21. $\frac{1}{2}$ $\frac{1}{3}$
22. $\frac{2}{3}$ $\frac{1}{2}$
23. $\frac{3}{4}$ $\frac{1}{3}$
24. $\frac{1}{4}$ $\frac{2}{3}$
25. $\frac{1}{6}$ $\frac{1}{4}$
26. $\frac{5}{6}$ $\frac{1}{4}$
27. $\frac{3}{4}$ $\frac{5}{6}$
28. $\frac{2}{5}$ $\frac{1}{2}$
29. $\frac{1}{2}$ $\frac{4}{5}$
30. $\frac{1}{3}$ $\frac{4}{5}$
31. $\frac{3}{5}$ $\frac{2}{3}$
32. $\frac{1}{2}$ $\frac{3}{5}$
33. $\frac{5}{8}$ $\frac{3}{16}$
34. $\frac{7}{16}$ $\frac{7}{8}$
35. $\frac{3}{8}$ $\frac{9}{16}$
36. $\frac{3}{4}$ $\frac{7}{16}$
37. $\frac{1}{4}$ $\frac{15}{16}$
38. $\frac{5}{6}$ $\frac{4}{9}$
39. $\frac{5}{9}$ $\frac{5}{6}$
40. $\frac{7}{9}$ $\frac{1}{6}$
41. $\frac{1}{2}$ $\frac{1}{3}$ $\frac{2}{3}$
42. $\frac{2}{3}$ $\frac{2}{3}$ $\frac{1}{2}$
43. $\frac{3}{4}$ $\frac{1}{2}$ $\frac{1}{2}$
44. $\frac{3}{4}$ $\frac{2}{3}$ $\frac{1}{3}$
45. $\frac{1}{2}$ $\frac{1}{3}$ $\frac{1}{4}$
46. $\frac{1}{2}$ $\frac{2}{3}$ $\frac{3}{4}$
47. $\frac{3}{4}$ $\frac{5}{12}$ $\frac{1}{6}$
48. $\frac{1}{4}$ $\frac{2}{3}$ $\frac{7}{12}$
49. $\frac{11}{12}$ $\frac{5}{6}$ $\frac{2}{3}$
50. $\frac{7}{12}$ $\frac{5}{6}$ $\frac{3}{4}$

C

Find the sum in each of the following exercises.

1. $6\frac{1}{5}$ $7\frac{2}{5}$	**2.** $8\frac{1}{3}$ $9\frac{1}{3}$	**3.** $5\frac{1}{8}$ $6\frac{3}{8}$	**4.** $9\frac{5}{8}$ $7\frac{1}{8}$	**5.** $2\frac{3}{10}$ $7\frac{7}{10}$
6. $2\frac{1}{2}$ $3\frac{1}{4}$	**7.** $5\frac{1}{6}$ $4\frac{1}{6}$	**8.** $6\frac{5}{8}$ $2\frac{1}{4}$	**9.** $9\frac{1}{3}$ $7\frac{1}{6}$	**10.** $8\frac{3}{4}$ $3\frac{1}{8}$
11. $7\frac{5}{12}$ $9\frac{1}{4}$	**12.** $8\frac{7}{12}$ $4\frac{1}{3}$	**13.** $6\frac{2}{3}$ $3\frac{1}{12}$	**14.** $1\frac{3}{10}$ $2\frac{3}{5}$	**15.** $4\frac{1}{10}$ $6\frac{1}{5}$
16. $3\frac{1}{2}$ $4\frac{2}{3}$	**17.** $7\frac{1}{2}$ $6\frac{3}{4}$	**18.** $6\frac{5}{6}$ $9\frac{1}{2}$	**19.** $8\frac{5}{8}$ $7\frac{3}{4}$	**20.** $12\frac{3}{8}$ $9\frac{3}{4}$
21. $8\frac{9}{10}$ $7\frac{3}{5}$	**22.** $10\frac{5}{12}$ $9\frac{3}{4}$	**23.** $12\frac{1}{2}$ $7\frac{11}{12}$	**24.** $14\frac{2}{3}$ $11\frac{7}{12}$	**25.** $16\frac{5}{12}$ $9\frac{2}{3}$
26. $11\frac{5}{6}$ $12\frac{11}{12}$	**27.** $16\frac{3}{4}$ $14\frac{5}{6}$	**28.** $14\frac{15}{16}$ $16\frac{3}{4}$	**29.** $14\frac{3}{8}$ $9\frac{11}{16}$	**30.** $21\frac{5}{8}$ $20\frac{2}{3}$
31. $6\frac{1}{2}$ $5\frac{1}{3}$ $2\frac{1}{2}$	**32.** $5\frac{1}{2}$ $6\frac{1}{4}$ $3\frac{1}{4}$	**33.** $7\frac{1}{2}$ $9\frac{3}{4}$ $10\frac{1}{4}$	**34.** $1\frac{3}{4}$ $4\frac{1}{2}$ $7\frac{3}{4}$	**35.** $10\frac{2}{3}$ $5\frac{1}{2}$ $6\frac{1}{2}$
36. $2\frac{3}{4}$ $5\frac{1}{2}$ $4\frac{1}{2}$	**37.** $10\frac{1}{3}$ $7\frac{2}{3}$ $9\frac{1}{6}$	**38.** $5\frac{3}{8}$ $7\frac{1}{2}$ $2\frac{1}{4}$	**39.** $6\frac{7}{8}$ $4\frac{3}{4}$ $9\frac{1}{4}$	**40.** $1\frac{5}{6}$ $7\frac{1}{2}$ $8\frac{2}{3}$
41. $16\frac{3}{4}$ $10\frac{1}{2}$ $15\frac{1}{3}$	**42.** $7\frac{3}{8}$ $9\frac{3}{4}$ $6\frac{1}{2}$	**43.** $14\frac{1}{4}$ $2\frac{3}{4}$ $8\frac{1}{8}$	**44.** $11\frac{5}{6}$ $12\frac{2}{3}$ $7\frac{1}{2}$	**45.** $1\frac{1}{6}$ $2\frac{3}{4}$ $6\frac{1}{2}$
46. $11\frac{1}{4}$ $5\frac{5}{6}$ $12\frac{3}{4}$	**47.** $12\frac{1}{2}$ $6\frac{1}{6}$ $14\frac{3}{4}$	**48.** $17\frac{1}{2}$ $14\frac{3}{16}$ $12\frac{5}{8}$	**49.** $24\frac{2}{3}$ $27\frac{3}{4}$ $16\frac{5}{12}$	**50.** $26\frac{7}{8}$ $31\frac{7}{16}$ $28\frac{1}{2}$

Unit 2: Subtraction

Section 1: Subtraction of Whole Numbers and Decimals

The only time you might run into a bit of difficulty in subtraction of whole numbers is under the following condition:

$$\begin{array}{r} 74 \\ -\ 28 \\ \hline \end{array}$$

Since 8 is larger than 4, you have to employ a special device in determining the answer. The problem is rewritten as:

$$\begin{array}{rcl} 74 = 70 + 4 = 60 + 10 + 4 &=& 60 + 14 \\ \underline{-\ 28} = \underline{20 + 8} = \underline{20 + 8 \qquad\quad} &=& \underline{20 + \ \ 8} \\ && 40 + \ \ 6 = 46 \end{array}$$

That is, the 74 can be thought of as 70 + 4, and this, in turn, as 60 + 10 + 4, and, finally, as 60 + 14. The purpose of this is to rewrite 74 in such a way that the number from which the 8 is subtracted is larger than the 8. Rather than think of the 74 as 70 + 4, where it is not possible to subtract 8 from 4, you now think of it as 60 + 14, where 8 can be subtracted from 14.

ILLUSTRATION 1: Subtract 35 from 83.

SOLUTION:

$$\begin{array}{r} 83 \\ -\ 35 \\ \hline 48 \end{array}$$

EXPLANATION: Rather than rewrite the 83 as above, you think of this number first as 80 + 3; then as 70 + 10 + 3; and, finally, as 70 + 13. From a mechanical standpoint, you can imagine the 8 as having been decreased by 1, and the 3 as increased by 10. Now you can complete the computation in the usual manner.

ILLUSTRATION 2: Subtract \$5.98 from \$10.

SOLUTION:

$$\begin{array}{r} \$10.00 \\ 5.98 \\ \hline \$\ \ 4.02 \end{array}$$

EXPLANATION: As in addition, when subtracting decimals, be careful to place the decimal points directly below one another when writing the numbers vertically. In this case, it is necessary not only to rewrite \$10 by inserting a decimal point after the 10, but also to add two zeros. This is done so that there are numerals above the 9 and the 8 in \$5.98. It is advisable to check your answer by adding the difference of \$4.02 to the subtrahend of \$5.98 to see if the sum is the minuend of \$10.00.

\$10.00	← Minuend
	=
5.98	← Subtrahend
	+
\$ 4.02	← Difference

EXERCISES A

Find the difference in each of the following exercises.

1. 4 1	**2.** 6 0	**3.** 3 2	**4.** 5 3	**5.** 4 4
6. 6 5	**7.** 5 2	**8.** 7 6	**9.** 6 1	**10.** 2 0
11. 5 4	**12.** 6 2	**13.** 8 0	**14.** 5 1	**15.** 6 3
16. 7 7	**17.** 3 1	**18.** 4 3	**19.** 8 4	**20.** 2 1
21. 4 0	**22.** 7 2	**23.** 6 4	**24.** 7 5	**25.** 6 6
26. 8 1	**27.** 6 0	**28.** 9 3	**29.** 8 6	**30.** 9 5
31. 7 4	**32.** 3 0	**33.** 7 1	**34.** 9 4	**35.** 8 8
36. 9 7	**37.** 1 1	**38.** 5 0	**39.** 9 1	**40.** 8 7

41. 8	**42.** 9	**43.** 3	**44.** 9	**45.** 5
5	0	3	8	5
46. 9	**47.** 8	**48.** 2	**49.** 7	**50.** 9
9	2	2	0	6
51. 1	**52.** 4	**53.** 8	**54.** 9	**55.** 7
0	2	3	2	3

B

Find the difference in each of the following exercises.

1. 10	**2.** 11	**3.** 10	**4.** 12	**5.** 14
1	3	8	9	7
6. 11	**7.** 14	**8.** 11	**9.** 10	**10.** 16
2	6	7	5	8
11. 12	**12.** 11	**13.** 10	**14.** 13	**15.** 10
6	6	3	4	9
16. 12	**17.** 14	**18.** 11	**19.** 10	**20.** 11
8	5	4	2	9
21. 18	**22.** 14	**23.** 13	**24.** 11	**25.** 12
9	8	4	8	7
26. 13	**27.** 11	**28.** 10	**29.** 12	**30.** 15
6	5	4	3	7
31. 16	**32.** 10	**33.** 12	**34.** 13	**35.** 14
9	6	5	7	9
36. 15	**37.** 13	**38.** 10	**39.** 12	**40.** 15
8	5	7	4	6

41. 13	**42.** 17	**43.** 16	**44.** 15	**45.** 17
8	9	7	9	8

C

Find the difference in each of the following exercises.

1. 27	**2.** 35	**3.** 48	**4.** 37	**5.** 49
12	14	25	23	42
6. 58	**7.** 46	**8.** 69	**9.** 84	**10.** 97
43	14	27	52	64
11. 76	**12.** 68	**13.** 89	**14.** 76	**15.** 47
26	51	74	25	32
16. 32	**17.** 41	**18.** 53	**19.** 22	**20.** 64
24	15	44	16	26
21. 50	**22.** 54	**23.** 61	**24.** 73	**25.** 62
23	35	19	48	56
26. 87	**27.** 92	**28.** 83	**29.** 67	**30.** 58
78	37	29	48	39
31. 76	**32.** 42	**33.** 64	**34.** 52	**35.** 91
57	25	37	39	78
36. 148	**37.** 354	**38.** 758	**39.** 691	**40.** 574
27	143	203	130	312
41. 315	**42.** 428	**43.** 507	**44.** 346	**45.** 219
194	256	321	182	96
46. 538	**47.** 604	**48.** 657	**49.** 774	**50.** 856
168	293	482	492	364

51. 293 124	**52.** 572 314	**53.** 381 139	**54.** 474 255	**55.** 563 319
56. 624 407	**57.** 737 418	**58.** 856 429	**59.** 583 247	**60.** 954 318
61. 524 367	**62.** 401 269	**63.** 500 127	**64.** 652 467	**65.** 741 582
66. 306 209	**67.** 534 148	**68.** 763 468	**69.** 873 585	**70.** 695 587
71. 478 299	**72.** 657 378	**73.** 504 278	**74.** 710 395	**75.** 683 486

D

Find the difference in each of the following exercises.

1. $2.46 .35	**2.** $4.39 1.26	**3.** $5.88 2.65	**4.** $3.69 1.27
5. $8.27 3.04	**6.** $5.75 2.35	**7.** $6.58 4.17	**8.** $7.31 2.10
9. $5.14 3.91	**10.** $2.26 1.84	**11.** $9.57 4.62	**12.** $8.39 1.43
13. $6.44 3.72	**14.** $7.06 2.46	**15.** $9.23 5.71	**16.** $7.54 6.83
17. $5.45 1.27	**18.** $6.83 2.27	**19.** $2.31 1.19	**20.** $5.64 1.28
21. $9.72 5.25	**22.** $8.45 6.39	**23.** $7.17 4.08	**24.** $6.36 4.18

25. $4.00 2.98	**26.** $6.00 2.27	**27.** $5.00 3.91	**28.** $8.00 5.49
29. $7.00 3.58	**30.** $2.00 .69	**31.** $3.00 2.63	**32.** $9.00 6.34
33. $8.43 3.66	**34.** $7.12 2.58	**35.** $4.67 3.88	**36.** $5.24 2.98
37. $6.04 3.95	**38.** $5.07 2.89	**39.** $7.18 5.99	**40.** $9.65 7.96

Section 2: Subtraction of Fractions

The method used for subtracting one fraction from another is much the same as the method for adding one fraction to another. As before, the denominators must be the same before it is possible to subtract the numerator of the subtrahend from the numerator of the minuend. If the denominators are not the same, then the process for changing them into the same number is identical to the approach used in addition of fractions.

ILLUSTRATION 1: Subtract 1/3 from 3/4.

SOLUTION:

$$\begin{array}{rcccl} ① & & ② & & ③ \\ \frac{3}{4} & = & \frac{3}{4} \times \frac{3}{3} & = & \frac{9}{12} \\ -\frac{1}{3} & = & \frac{1}{3} \times \frac{4}{4} & = & \frac{4}{12} \\ \hline & & & & \frac{5}{12} \end{array}$$

EXPLANATION: Quite frequently, students will perform Step ② mentally and go directly from Step ① to Step ③. There is no reason why you should not do this if you care to.

The only difficulty that might arise in subtracting one fraction from another is if, after converting the fractions to equivalent fractions having a common denominator, you find that the numerator of the minuend is smaller than the numerator of the subtrahend. The method for overcoming this difficulty will be explained in the following illustration.

ILLUSTRATION 2: Subtract $5\frac{3}{4}$ from $7\frac{3}{8}$.

SOLUTION:

$$\begin{array}{r} 7\frac{3}{8} = 7\frac{3}{8} = 7 + \frac{3}{8} = 6 + 1 + \frac{3}{8} = 6 + \frac{8}{8} + \frac{3}{8} = 6\frac{11}{8} \\ \underline{-\ 5\frac{3}{4}} = \underline{5\frac{6}{8}} = \underline{5 + \frac{6}{8}} = \underline{5 + \frac{6}{8} \qquad} = \underline{5 + \frac{6}{8} \qquad} = \underline{5\frac{6}{8}} \\ 1\frac{5}{8} \end{array}$$

EXPLANATION: After changing the mixed numeral $5\frac{3}{4}$ to its equivalent form of $5\frac{6}{8}$, you find that it is not possible to subtract $\frac{6}{8}$ from the $\frac{3}{8}$ in $7\frac{3}{8}$. Hence, it is necessary to rewrite the 7 as 6 + 1, and then to change the form of 1 to the form $\frac{8}{8}$ so that it can be added to the $\frac{3}{8}$ to make the fraction $\frac{11}{8}$. Had it been necessary to add the 1 to a fraction, such as $\frac{4}{5}$, you would have changed the form of the 1 to $\frac{5}{5}$ to give you a total of $\frac{9}{5}$. What form will you change the 1 to if it has to be added to a fraction such as $\frac{2}{3}$? If it has to be added to $\frac{7}{12}$?

ILLUSTRATION 3: Subtract $5\frac{1}{2}$ from $8\frac{1}{3}$.

SOLUTION:

$$\begin{array}{r} \textcircled{1} \quad \textcircled{2} \quad \textcircled{3} \\ 8\frac{1}{3} = 8\frac{2}{6} = 7\frac{8}{6} \\ \underline{-\ 5\frac{1}{2}} = \underline{5\frac{3}{6}} = \underline{5\frac{3}{6}} \\ 2\frac{5}{6} \end{array}$$

EXPLANATION: In going from Step ② to Step ③, you do a number of steps mentally. Thus, you change the 8 into the form 7 + 1; change the 1 to the numeral $\frac{6}{6}$, and then add the $\frac{6}{6}$ to the $\frac{2}{6}$ for a total of $\frac{8}{6}$. Hence, changing the numeral from the form $8\frac{2}{6}$ to the form $7\frac{8}{6}$ can all be done mentally.

EXERCISES A

Find the difference in each of the following exercises.

1. $\frac{3}{5}$ $\underline{\frac{1}{5}}$	2. $\frac{5}{7}$ $\underline{\frac{2}{7}}$	3. $\frac{3}{4}$ $\underline{\frac{2}{4}}$	4. $\frac{9}{10}$ $\underline{\frac{6}{10}}$	5. $\frac{11}{12}$ $\underline{\frac{10}{12}}$
6. $\frac{3}{4}$ $\underline{\frac{1}{4}}$	7. $\frac{7}{8}$ $\underline{\frac{3}{8}}$	8. $\frac{1}{2}$ $\underline{\frac{1}{2}}$	9. $\frac{5}{8}$ $\underline{\frac{1}{8}}$	10. $\frac{7}{10}$ $\underline{\frac{3}{10}}$
11. $\frac{7}{16}$ $\underline{\frac{5}{16}}$	12. $\frac{13}{16}$ $\underline{\frac{1}{16}}$	13. $\frac{11}{12}$ $\underline{\frac{5}{12}}$	14. $\frac{11}{12}$ $\underline{\frac{7}{12}}$	15. $\frac{15}{16}$ $\underline{\frac{7}{16}}$
16. $\frac{9}{10}$ $\underline{\frac{7}{10}}$	17. $\frac{9}{10}$ $\underline{\frac{4}{10}}$	18. $\frac{11}{16}$ $\underline{\frac{9}{16}}$	19. $\frac{17}{20}$ $\underline{\frac{7}{20}}$	20. $\frac{19}{20}$ $\underline{\frac{4}{20}}$

B

Find the difference in each of the following exercises.

1. $\begin{array}{r}\frac{1}{2}\\ \underline{\frac{1}{4}}\end{array}$	**2.** $\begin{array}{r}\frac{1}{2}\\ \underline{\frac{1}{6}}\end{array}$	**3.** $\begin{array}{r}\frac{1}{3}\\ \underline{\frac{1}{6}}\end{array}$	**4.** $\begin{array}{r}\frac{1}{2}\\ \underline{\frac{1}{8}}\end{array}$	**5.** $\begin{array}{r}\frac{1}{4}\\ \underline{\frac{1}{8}}\end{array}$
6. $\begin{array}{r}\frac{1}{3}\\ \underline{\frac{1}{9}}\end{array}$	**7.** $\begin{array}{r}\frac{2}{3}\\ \underline{\frac{1}{9}}\end{array}$	**8.** $\begin{array}{r}\frac{3}{4}\\ \underline{\frac{5}{8}}\end{array}$	**9.** $\begin{array}{r}\frac{7}{8}\\ \underline{\frac{3}{4}}\end{array}$	**10.** $\begin{array}{r}\frac{3}{4}\\ \underline{\frac{1}{2}}\end{array}$
11. $\begin{array}{r}\frac{5}{6}\\ \underline{\frac{1}{3}}\end{array}$	**12.** $\begin{array}{r}\frac{5}{8}\\ \underline{\frac{1}{2}}\end{array}$	**13.** $\begin{array}{r}\frac{11}{12}\\ \underline{\frac{1}{6}}\end{array}$	**14.** $\begin{array}{r}\frac{7}{8}\\ \underline{\frac{1}{2}}\end{array}$	**15.** $\begin{array}{r}\frac{5}{8}\\ \underline{\frac{3}{16}}\end{array}$
16. $\begin{array}{r}\frac{1}{4}\\ \underline{\frac{3}{16}}\end{array}$	**17.** $\begin{array}{r}\frac{9}{16}\\ \underline{\frac{1}{2}}\end{array}$	**18.** $\begin{array}{r}\frac{5}{6}\\ \underline{\frac{2}{3}}\end{array}$	**19.** $\begin{array}{r}\frac{3}{5}\\ \underline{\frac{1}{10}}\end{array}$	**20.** $\begin{array}{r}\frac{9}{10}\\ \underline{\frac{4}{5}}\end{array}$
21. $\begin{array}{r}\frac{3}{4}\\ \underline{\frac{2}{3}}\end{array}$	**22.** $\begin{array}{r}\frac{2}{3}\\ \underline{\frac{1}{2}}\end{array}$	**23.** $\begin{array}{r}\frac{3}{4}\\ \underline{\frac{1}{6}}\end{array}$	**24.** $\begin{array}{r}\frac{5}{6}\\ \underline{\frac{3}{4}}\end{array}$	**25.** $\begin{array}{r}\frac{1}{2}\\ \underline{\frac{1}{5}}\end{array}$
26. $\begin{array}{r}\frac{3}{5}\\ \underline{\frac{1}{2}}\end{array}$	**27.** $\begin{array}{r}\frac{3}{4}\\ \underline{\frac{2}{5}}\end{array}$	**28.** $\begin{array}{r}\frac{4}{5}\\ \underline{\frac{3}{4}}\end{array}$	**29.** $\begin{array}{r}\frac{3}{4}\\ \underline{\frac{7}{10}}\end{array}$	**30.** $\begin{array}{r}\frac{9}{10}\\ \underline{\frac{1}{4}}\end{array}$

C

Find the difference in each of the following exercises.

1. $\begin{array}{r}6\frac{1}{2}\\ \underline{4\frac{1}{2}}\end{array}$	**2.** $\begin{array}{r}8\frac{1}{4}\\ \underline{5\frac{1}{4}}\end{array}$	**3.** $\begin{array}{r}9\frac{4}{5}\\ \underline{6\frac{1}{5}}\end{array}$	**4.** $\begin{array}{r}7\frac{5}{6}\\ \underline{4\frac{1}{6}}\end{array}$	**5.** $\begin{array}{r}5\frac{7}{8}\\ \underline{3\frac{3}{8}}\end{array}$
6. $\begin{array}{r}7\frac{1}{2}\\ \underline{2\frac{1}{4}}\end{array}$	**7.** $\begin{array}{r}9\frac{3}{4}\\ \underline{4\frac{1}{2}}\end{array}$	**8.** $\begin{array}{r}6\frac{1}{3}\\ \underline{5\frac{1}{6}}\end{array}$	**9.** $\begin{array}{r}8\frac{5}{6}\\ \underline{2\frac{2}{3}}\end{array}$	**10.** $\begin{array}{r}7\frac{11}{12}\\ \underline{3\frac{5}{6}}\end{array}$
11. $\begin{array}{r}5\frac{2}{3}\\ \underline{1\frac{1}{2}}\end{array}$	**12.** $\begin{array}{r}8\frac{3}{5}\\ \underline{3\frac{1}{2}}\end{array}$	**13.** $\begin{array}{r}7\frac{4}{5}\\ \underline{2\frac{3}{4}}\end{array}$	**14.** $\begin{array}{r}6\frac{5}{12}\\ \underline{3\frac{1}{4}}\end{array}$	**15.** $\begin{array}{r}9\frac{2}{3}\\ \underline{5\frac{1}{4}}\end{array}$
16. $\begin{array}{r}18\frac{1}{2}\\ \underline{3\frac{1}{5}}\end{array}$	**17.** $\begin{array}{r}16\frac{5}{16}\\ \underline{4\frac{1}{4}}\end{array}$	**18.** $\begin{array}{r}17\frac{1}{4}\\ \underline{6\frac{3}{16}}\end{array}$	**19.** $\begin{array}{r}15\frac{7}{8}\\ \underline{2\frac{3}{4}}\end{array}$	**20.** $\begin{array}{r}12\frac{5}{6}\\ \underline{9\frac{2}{3}}\end{array}$
21. $\begin{array}{r}13\frac{15}{16}\\ \underline{7\frac{5}{8}}\end{array}$	**22.** $\begin{array}{r}11\frac{7}{8}\\ \underline{2\frac{1}{4}}\end{array}$	**23.** $\begin{array}{r}15\frac{3}{4}\\ \underline{6\frac{3}{5}}\end{array}$	**24.** $\begin{array}{r}12\frac{5}{8}\\ \underline{8\frac{5}{16}}\end{array}$	**25.** $\begin{array}{r}14\frac{9}{16}\\ \underline{6\frac{1}{2}}\end{array}$

D

Find the difference in each of the following exercises.

1. $7 - 5\frac{1}{2}$
2. $9 - 4\frac{1}{4}$
3. $6 - 5\frac{3}{8}$
4. $8 - 6\frac{2}{5}$
5. $7 - 6\frac{1}{3}$
6. $9 - 2\frac{3}{4}$
7. $12 - 5\frac{7}{8}$
8. $14 - 2\frac{5}{8}$
9. $23 - 1\frac{4}{5}$
10. $17 - 2\frac{1}{6}$
11. $18 - 5\frac{2}{3}$
12. $16 - 2\frac{5}{12}$
13. $14 - 8\frac{7}{16}$
14. $11 - 7\frac{9}{16}$
15. $10 - 2\frac{11}{12}$

E

Find the difference in each of the following exercises.

1. $8\frac{1}{4} - 3\frac{3}{4}$
2. $6\frac{1}{3} - 2\frac{2}{3}$
3. $7\frac{1}{6} - 2\frac{5}{6}$
4. $9\frac{5}{8} - 2\frac{7}{8}$
5. $8\frac{3}{8} - 7\frac{5}{8}$
6. $7\frac{1}{5} - 4\frac{2}{5}$
7. $9\frac{2}{5} - 6\frac{4}{5}$
8. $5\frac{1}{5} - 1\frac{2}{5}$
9. $9\frac{1}{8} - 6\frac{7}{8}$
10. $6\frac{1}{16} - 1\frac{15}{16}$
11. $9\frac{3}{10} - 2\frac{7}{10}$
12. $9\frac{1}{10} - 8\frac{9}{10}$
13. $6\frac{5}{12} - 2\frac{7}{12}$
14. $7\frac{1}{12} - 3\frac{11}{12}$
15. $8\frac{5}{16} - 5\frac{7}{16}$
16. $8\frac{1}{4} - 5\frac{1}{2}$
17. $9\frac{1}{2} - 4\frac{3}{4}$
18. $12\frac{3}{8} - 1\frac{3}{4}$
19. $16\frac{2}{3} - 2\frac{5}{6}$
20. $12\frac{1}{2} - 1\frac{2}{3}$
21. $17\frac{2}{3} - 5\frac{3}{4}$
22. $18\frac{1}{5} - 4\frac{7}{10}$
23. $16\frac{2}{5} - 3\frac{1}{2}$
24. $19\frac{1}{4} - 6\frac{2}{3}$
25. $15\frac{1}{6} - 4\frac{1}{3}$
26. $11\frac{5}{12} - 7\frac{1}{2}$
27. $12\frac{5}{8} - 5\frac{3}{4}$
28. $14\frac{7}{8} - 6\frac{15}{16}$
29. $13\frac{5}{12} - 7\frac{5}{6}$
30. $10\frac{3}{4} - 7\frac{5}{6}$
31. $21\frac{2}{3} - 12\frac{5}{6}$
32. $20\frac{1}{3} - 16\frac{3}{4}$
33. $24\frac{3}{10} - 9\frac{4}{5}$
34. $25\frac{1}{4} - 17\frac{5}{16}$
35. $28\frac{1}{8} - 19\frac{3}{16}$

Unit 3: Multiplication

Section 1: Multiplication of Whole Numbers and Decimals

If you have any trouble in multiplication, it is usually in the placement of the decimal point in the answer when finding the product of two decimals. Take a moment to recall just what a decimal is. The numeral .7 is but an equivalent form of the numeral 7/10. Similarly, .07 can be written as 7/100, and .007 as 7/1,000. Should you write this information in vertical form, you begin to get a picture of the relation between the fraction numeral and the decimal numeral.

$$7/10 = .7$$
$$7/100 = .07$$
$$7/1{,}000 = .007$$

Thus, you can see that the number of zeros in the denominator of the fraction will tell us exactly how many digits there will be to the right of the decimal point in the decimal numeral.

In the case of 7/10, there is 1 zero in the denominator; therefore, there will be 1 digit to the right of the decimal point, and this is the digit 7. For the fraction numeral 7/100, there are 2 zeros in the denominator, and hence there will be 2 digits to the right of the decimal point. Since 7 is the only digit in the numerator, it is necessary to supply a 0 to act as the first digit. Lastly, in the case of 7/1,000, you would know that there have to be 3 digits to the right of the decimal point. With 7 being only 1 of these digits, 2 zeros will have to be supplied for a total of 3 digits (.007). How would you write 7/100,000 in decimal notation?

If the fraction were 253/100, then to write this as a decimal numeral you would have to have 2 digits to the right of the decimal point. In view of this, the decimal numeral would be 2.53, where the 2 digits to the right of the decimal point are the 5 and the 3. How would you write 253/10,000 as a decimal numeral?

Now you are in a position where you can determine the product of two decimals. For example, consider the following exercise:

$$30.6 \times .231$$

This exercise can be rewritten in the fractional form as:

$$306/10 \times 231/1{,}000$$

Why should there be 1 zero in the denominator of the first fraction and 3 zeros in the denominator of the second fraction? The product of these two fractions will be:

$$70{,}686/10{,}000$$

From the fact that there are 4 zeros in the denominator, you know that there will have to be 4 digits to the right of the decimal point when the number is rewritten in decimal notation. Hence, the answer will have to be 7.0686.

When you write the given problem with its answer immediately next to it,

$$30.6 \times .231 = 7.0686$$

you discover that the total number of digits to the right of the decimal points in the numerals in the problem is the same as the total number of digits to the right of the decimal point in the product. The 6, the 2, the 3, and the 1 make up four digits to the right of the decimal points in the numerals in the exercise (30.6 and .231). In the product, the four digits to the right of the decimal point are 0, 6, 8, and 6. Hence, in general you can say:

> The number of digits to the right of the decimal point in the product of two decimals is exactly the same as the total number of digits to the right of the decimal points in the two decimals.

ILLUSTRATION: Find the product of 2.35 and .6.

SOLUTION:

$$\begin{array}{r} 2.35 \\ \times \quad .6 \\ \hline 1.410 \end{array}$$

EXPLANATION: There are three digits to the right of the decimal point in the two decimals in the exercise (the 3, the 5, and the 6). Therefore, there will have to be three digits to the right of the decimal point in the product (the 4, the 1, and the 0).

EXERCISES A

Find the product in each of the following exercises.

1. $\begin{array}{r} 3 \\ \underline{4} \end{array}$	**2.** $\begin{array}{r} 0 \\ \underline{2} \end{array}$	**3.** $\begin{array}{r} 4 \\ \underline{2} \end{array}$	**4.** $\begin{array}{r} 1 \\ \underline{5} \end{array}$	**5.** $\begin{array}{r} 6 \\ \underline{2} \end{array}$
6. $\begin{array}{r} 1 \\ \underline{3} \end{array}$	**7.** $\begin{array}{r} 2 \\ \underline{5} \end{array}$	**8.** $\begin{array}{r} 3 \\ \underline{1} \end{array}$	**9.** $\begin{array}{r} 6 \\ \underline{0} \end{array}$	**10.** $\begin{array}{r} 3 \\ \underline{3} \end{array}$

11. 2 6	**12.** 3 2	**13.** 1 7	**14.** 5 2	**15.** 0 6
16. 4 1	**17.** 0 8	**18.** 3 5	**19.** 4 4	**20.** 7 1
21. 0 7	**22.** 2 4	**23.** 3 7	**24.** 6 5	**25.** 8 2
26. 2 2	**27.** 1 8	**28.** 5 5	**29.** 6 3	**30.** 9 0
31. 4 0	**32.** 3 6	**33.** 5 1	**34.** 8 4	**35.** 4 5
36. 1 6	**37.** 5 4	**38.** 3 8	**39.** 6 6	**40.** 7 2
41. 5 3	**42.** 0 4	**43.** 6 1	**44.** 7 5	**45.** 4 6
46. 0 0	**47.** 2 8	**48.** 9 3	**49.** 6 7	**50.** 5 9
51. 1 4	**52.** 4 7	**53.** 0 1	**54.** 3 9	**55.** 7 3
56. 2 9	**57.** 5 6	**58.** 7 4	**59.** 8 3	**60.** 9 1
61. 4 8	**62.** 2 7	**63.** 1 1	**64.** 4 3	**65.** 6 4
66. 1 2	**67.** 0 9	**68.** 7 6	**69.** 8 5	**70.** 9 3
71. 2 3	**72.** 7 8	**73.** 0 5	**74.** 9 5	**75.** 3 0

76. 6 8	**77.** 0 3	**78.** 4 9	**79.** 8 7	**80.** 9 9
81. 8 9	**82.** 8 0	**83.** 7 7	**84.** 9 4	**85.** 2 1
86. 9 7	**87.** 5 0	**88.** 8 6	**89.** 5 8	**90.** 9 6
91. 6 9	**92.** 9 8	**93.** 2 0	**94.** 8 1	**95.** 7 9
96. 7 0	**97.** 1 9	**98.** 9 6	**99.** 1 0	**100.** 5 7

B

Find the product in each of the following exercises.

1. 23 2	**2.** 41 3	**3.** 15 4	**4.** 24 5	**5.** 16 3
6. 18 4	**7.** 39 2	**8.** 47 3	**9.** 53 6	**10.** 42 4
11. 45 2	**12.** 36 4	**13.** 25 6	**14.** 28 3	**15.** 39 5
16. 43 6	**17.** 50 7	**18.** 40 9	**19.** 60 8	**20.** 51 7
21. 52 8	**22.** 43 5	**23.** 54 6	**24.** 43 8	**25.** 48 9
26. 64 7	**27.** 65 4	**28.** 72 8	**29.** 68 7	**30.** 74 6

31. 76	**32.** 78	**33.** 77	**34.** 79	**35.** 80
3	5	8	9	8
36. 82	**37.** 81	**38.** 85	**39.** 87	**40.** 89
7	8	6	9	5
41. 93	**42.** 95	**43.** 96	**44.** 94	**45.** 98
4	6	7	8	9

C

Find the product in each of the following exercises.

1. 14	**2.** 16	**3.** 18	**4.** 17	**5.** 18
12	10	12	14	20
6. 23	**7.** 25	**8.** 27	**9.** 29	**10.** 32
16	15	20	23	25
11. 36	**12.** 39	**13.** 40	**14.** 40	**15.** 44
27	26	29	32	35
16. 47	**17.** 53	**18.** 58	**19.** 61	**20.** 64
38	39	46	48	51
21. 69	**22.** 70	**23.** 72	**24.** 75	**25.** 78
56	58	64	65	67
26. 79	**27.** 76	**28.** 83	**29.** 88	**30.** 89
69	72	73	76	78
31. 92	**32.** 94	**33.** 96	**34.** 97	**35.** 99
80	83	85	87	98

D

Find the product in each of the following exercises.

1. 203	**2.** 104	**3.** 406	**4.** 507	**5.** 201
4	5	3	6	8

6. 905	**7.** 703	**8.** 802	**9.** 809	**10.** 907
2	4	8	7	6
11. 430	**12.** 560	**13.** 920	**14.** 740	**15.** 670
5	4	6	8	9
16. 231	**17.** 542	**18.** 968	**19.** 673	**20.** 845
40	50	20	60	70
21. 291	**22.** 403	**23.** 509	**24.** 870	**25.** 706
60	80	70	60	20
26. 902	**27.** 804	**28.** 840	**29.** 760	**30.** 908
30	50	80	60	90

E

Find the product in each of the following exercises.

1.	24	**2.**	32	**3.**	47	**4.**	85	**5.**	68
	.06		.04		.05		.03		.07
6.	57	**7.**	95	**8.**	76	**9.**	83	**10.**	96
	.02		.01		.08		.09		.06
11.	1.05	**12.**	1.06	**13.**	1.08	**14.**	1.09	**15.**	1.02
	23		41		34		17		25
16.	1.03	**17.**	1.04	**18.**	1.01	**19.**	1.06	**20.**	1.08
	62		48		93		85		97
21.	250	**22.**	470	**23.**	640	**24.**	800	**25.**	750
	.035		.045		.055		.065		.025
26.	125	**27.**	275	**28.**	576	**29.**	845	**30.**	955
	.048		.056		.063		.082		.078

31.	24.50 .02	**32.**	56.20 .03	**33.**	48.40 .04	**34.**	75.30 .01	**35.**	86.70 .05
36.	63.50 .06	**37.**	74.60 .07	**38.**	85.40 .08	**39.**	96.80 .09	**40.**	53.70 .10
41.	123.50 .03	**42.**	145.70 .04	**43.**	171.20 .05	**44.**	250.70 .06	**45.**	275.60 .07
46.	340.50 .08	**47.**	458.30 .06	**48.**	627.10 .05	**49.**	734.60 .08	**50.**	857.90 .09
51.	2.04 3.1	**52.**	32.5 4.3	**53.**	.064 .21	**54.**	51.7 .035	**55.**	7.23 .046
56.	29.8 37	**57.**	841 5.8	**58.**	706 .083	**59.**	5.98 24	**60.**	7.69 79

Section 2: Multiplication of Fractions and Mixed Numbers

The method for determining the product of two fractions consists in finding the product of the numerators and then dividing this product by the product of the denominators.

ILLUSTRATION 1: Find the product of $\frac{2}{3}$ and $\frac{5}{7}$.

SOLUTION:

$$\frac{2}{3} \times \frac{5}{7} = \frac{2 \times 5}{3 \times 7} = \frac{10}{21}$$

EXPLANATION: The product of the numerators can be written as 2×5, while that of the denominators can be written as 3×7. These can be replaced by 10 and 21 respectively. Frequently, it is preferable to eliminate the middle step and go directly from the first step ($\frac{2}{3} \times \frac{5}{7}$) to the product (10/21).

ILLUSTRATION 2: Find the product of $\frac{2}{3}$ and $\frac{3}{4}$.

SOLUTION:

$$\frac{2}{3} \times \frac{3}{4} = \frac{6}{12} = \frac{1 \times 6}{2 \times 6} = \frac{1}{2} \times \frac{6}{6} = \frac{1}{2}$$

EXPLANATION: After finding the product of the two fractions, you will notice that 6 is an exact divisor of both the numerator and the denominator. When this occurs, rewrite the numerator as 1×6 and the denominator as 2×6. The fraction $\frac{1 \times 6}{2 \times 6}$ can be expressed in the form of the product of the two fractions $1/2$ and $6/6$. Since $6/6$ is simply another form of the number 1, then the product of $1/2$ and 1 is $1/2$.

ILLUSTRATION 3: Find the product of 6 and $2\frac{1}{4}$.

SOLUTION:

$$6 \times 2\tfrac{1}{4} = \frac{6}{1} \times \frac{9}{4} = \frac{54}{4} = \frac{27 \times 2}{2 \times 2} = \frac{27}{2} = 13\tfrac{1}{2}$$

EXPLANATION: When multiplying a whole number by a mixed number, or when multiplying two mixed numbers together, it is usually best to express each of them as fractions. In this illustration, the 6 is written as 6/1, while the $2\frac{1}{4}$ is written as 9/4. The product is then found and reduced to lowest terms as in Illustration 2. The 9/4 is obtained from $2\frac{1}{4}$ by realizing that $2\frac{1}{4}$ means $2 + 1/4$. The sum of these two numbers is then obtained by using the method for finding the sum of two fractions by obtaining a common denominator. An easier method, however, is to multiply the 2 by the 4 and add the numerator of 1 to that product for a sum of 9. The 9 is then written over the denominator of 4. How would you change $5\frac{2}{3}$ to a fraction?

EXERCISES A

Find the product in each of the following exercises.

1. $1/2 \times 3/5$ = ________	2. $1/2 \times 5/7$ = ________
3. $1/3 \times 4/5$ = ________	4. $2/3 \times 4/5$ = ________
5. $2/3 \times 5/7$ = ________	6. $3/4 \times 1/2$ = ________
7. $1/4 \times 3/5$ = ________	8. $1/4 \times 1/5$ = ________
9. $3/4 \times 3/5$ = ________	10. $4/5 \times 2/5$ = ________
11. $1/6 \times 1/3$ = ________	12. $5/7 \times 2/3$ = ________
13. $1/8 \times 5/6$ = ________	14. $3/8 \times 3/5$ = ________
15. $5/8 \times 1/6$ = ________	16. $5/6 \times 5/8$ = ________
17. $1/6 \times 7/8$ = ________	18. $1/8 \times 1/10$ = ________
19. $3/8 \times 7/10$ = ________	20. $7/8 \times 9/10$ = ________
21. $1/5 \times 1/12$ = ________	22. $1/7 \times 5/12$ = ________
23. $5/7 \times 11/12$ = ________	24. $3/8 \times 9/16$ = ________

B

Find the product in each of the following exercises and reduce each answer to its lowest terms.

1. $1/2 \times 2/5 =$ ________
2. $1/3 \times 3/5 =$ ________
3. $2/3 \times 6/7 =$ ________
4. $2/3 \times 5/8 =$ ________
5. $3/4 \times 1/6 =$ ________
6. $3/4 \times 2/9 =$ ________
7. $1/4 \times 2/5 =$ ________
8. $4/5 \times 1/2 =$ ________
9. $1/5 \times 5/6 =$ ________
10. $4/5 \times 7/10 =$ ________
11. $2/5 \times 5/8 =$ ________
12. $2/3 \times 9/10 =$ ________
13. $5/6 \times 2/5 =$ ________
14. $5/8 \times 4/5 =$ ________
15. $3/10 \times 5/9 =$ ________
16. $5/12 \times 2/5 =$ ________
17. $5/12 \times 3/10 =$ ________
18. $7/8 \times 2/5 =$ ________
19. $3/8 \times 5/12 =$ ________
20. $3/16 \times 2/3 =$ ________
21. $5/16 \times 4/5 =$ ________
22. $2/3 \times 15/16 =$ ________
23. $4/5 \times 5/12 =$ ________
24. $9/16 \times 8/9 =$ ________

C

Find the product in each of the following exercises and reduce each answer to its lowest terms.

1. $4 \times 1\,1/2 =$ ________
2. $6 \times 2\,1/2 =$ ________
3. $10 \times 5\,1/2 =$ ________
4. $3\,1/2 \times 6 =$ ________
5. $4\,1/2 \times 8 =$ ________
6. $7\,1/2 \times 12 =$ ________
7. $6 \times 1\,1/3 =$ ________
8. $12 \times 2\,2/3 =$ ________
9. $9 \times 3\,1/3 =$ ________
10. $3 \times 6\,2/3 =$ ________
11. $15 \times 1\,2/3 =$ ________
12. $21 \times 1\,1/7 =$ ________
13. $2\,2/5 \times 10 =$ ________
14. $3\,4/5 \times 5 =$ ________
15. $5\,1/4 \times 8 =$ ________
16. $3\,1/4 \times 12 =$ ________
17. $2\,1/4 \times 16 =$ ________
18. $3\,1/6 \times 12 =$ ________
19. $2\,5/6 \times 3 =$ ________
20. $2\,3/8 \times 4 =$ ________
21. $4\,5/8 \times 6 =$ ________
22. $10 \times 3\,3/10 =$ ________
23. $5 \times 4\,7/10 =$ ________
24. $15 \times 6\,9/10 =$ ________

D

Find the product in each of the following exercises and reduce each answer to its lowest terms.

1. $1\,1/2 \times 2\,1/2 =$ ________
2. $1\,1/4 \times 2\,1/2 =$ ________
3. $1\,1/3 \times 2\,1/4 =$ ________
4. $2\,1/2 \times 2\,1/4 =$ ________
5. $2\,1/3 \times 2\,1/2 =$ ________
6. $2\,2/3 \times 1\,1/4 =$ ________
7. $3\,1/2 \times 1\,1/3 =$ ________
8. $3\,1/3 \times 1\,1/5 =$ ________
9. $2\,3/4 \times 1\,1/3 =$ ________
10. $2\,3/4 \times 3\,1/2 =$ ________
11. $2\,3/4 \times 3\,3/4 =$ ________
12. $4\,1/2 \times 2\,1/2 =$ ________

13. $3\frac{1}{4} \times 4\frac{1}{2} =$ ________ 14. $3\frac{3}{4} \times 4\frac{1}{2} =$ ________
15. $5\frac{1}{4} \times 5\frac{1}{3} =$ ________ 16. $6\frac{1}{4} \times 3\frac{1}{3} =$ ________

Section 3: Multiplication of a Whole Number and a Mixed Number

When finding the product of a whole number and a mixed number, if either number is relatively large, it is frequently easier to change the mixed number to a decimal instead of to a fraction.

ILLUSTRATION: Find the product of 148 and $12\frac{1}{2}$.

SOLUTION:

```
    148
 × 12.5
 ------
    740
   296
  148
 ------
 1850.0
```

EXPLANATION: The $\frac{1}{2}$ in the mixed number $12\frac{1}{2}$ is changed to the decimal .5, and the $12\frac{1}{2}$ is rewritten as 12.5. The computation is then completed in the same manner as when finding the product of two decimals.

EXERCISES

Find the product in each of the following problems.

1. $48 \times 5\frac{1}{2} =$ ________ 2. $76 \times 9\frac{1}{2} =$ ________
3. $120 \times 6\frac{1}{2} =$ ________ 4. $85 \times 4\frac{1}{2} =$ ________
5. $59 \times 7\frac{1}{2} =$ ________ 6. $157 \times 3\frac{1}{2} =$ ________
7. $24\frac{1}{2} \times 12 =$ ________ 8. $68\frac{1}{2} \times 10 =$ ________
9. $35\frac{1}{2} \times 16 =$ ________ 10. $125\frac{1}{2} \times 46 =$ ________
11. $137\frac{1}{2} \times 23 =$ ________ 12. $168\frac{1}{2} \times 31 =$ ________
13. $24 \times 6\frac{1}{4} =$ ________ 14. $36 \times 5\frac{1}{4} =$ ________
15. $64 \times 10\frac{1}{4} =$ ________ 16. $76 \times 18\frac{1}{4} =$ ________
17. $129 \times 20\frac{1}{4} =$ ________ 18. $158 \times 25\frac{1}{4} =$ ________
19. $58\frac{1}{4} \times 12 =$ ________ 20. $71\frac{1}{4} \times 40 =$ ________
21. $85\frac{1}{4} \times 28 =$ ________ 22. $116\frac{1}{4} \times 20 =$ ________
23. $243\frac{1}{4} \times 22 =$ ________ 24. $250\frac{1}{4} \times 37 =$ ________
25. $56 \times 7\frac{3}{4} =$ ________ 26. $92 \times 6\frac{3}{4} =$ ________
27. $104 \times 8\frac{3}{4} =$ ________ 28. $84\frac{3}{4} \times 16 =$ ________
29. $114\frac{3}{4} \times 32 =$ ________ 30. $156\frac{3}{4} \times 45 =$ ________

Unit 4: Division

Section 1: Division of Whole Numbers and Decimals

If you have difficulty at any time in division, you will usually find it at the time you are dividing one decimal by another. The trouble involves the placement of the decimal point in the answer. Since you are usually able to divide when the divisor is a whole number, it seems apparent that if the divisor is a decimal, it would be best to change it into a whole number. For instance, consider the division of 6.853 by 42.71:

$$6.853 \div 42.71$$

This exercise can be written in the fractional form,

$$6.853/42.71$$

Changing the denominator (or divisor) 42.71 into a whole number would require multiplying that number by 100. If you do this, though, you would change the problem from:

$$6.853/42.71 \text{ to } 6.853/4271.$$

However, these two fraction numerals are not equivalent. Were you also to multiply the numerator by 100, then the new numeral would be equivalent to the old one.

$$\frac{6.853}{42.71} = \frac{6.853}{42.71} \times \frac{100}{100} = \frac{685.3}{4271}$$

The first fraction is equivalent to the last one, for to obtain the last one you multiplied the first by 100/100, which is but another form of the number 1. The number 1, as you recall, is the identity element of multiplication. The product of any number with this one will leave the number unchanged. Hence, in this case, the numeral is changed from the form 6.853/42.71 to the form 685.3/4271, but both fraction numerals represent the same number.

Notice that in the illustration above, the decimal point is moved two places to the right in the denominator to make that number a whole number. The decimal point is also moved two places to the right in the numerator. Hence, in general, you can say:

> If it is necessary to change the divisor to a whole number by moving the decimal point, then move the decimal point in the dividend exactly the same number of places and in the same direction.

How many places will the decimal point have to be moved in the following divisor?

$$1.025\overline{)6.35}$$

How many places will it have to be moved in the number 6.35? What will the new divisor be? What will the new dividend be?

ILLUSTRATION: Divide 2.028 by 2.6.

SOLUTION:

```
          .78
  2.6‸)2.0‸28
        1 8 2
          2 08
          2 08
             0
```

EXPLANATION: To change the divisor 2.6 to a whole number, it is necessary to move the decimal point one place to the right. Hence, the same thing has to be done with the decimal point in the dividend 2.028. The carets indicate where the new decimal points should be placed. Before beginning to divide, place the decimal point in the answer directly above its new position in the dividend.

EXERCISES A

Find the quotient mentally in each of the following exercises.

1. $5 \div 1 =$ ________
2. $12 \div 2 =$ ________
3. $20 \div 4 =$ ________
4. $15 \div 5 =$ ________
5. $6 \div 3 =$ ________
6. $10 \div 2 =$ ________
7. $21 \div 3 =$ ________
8. $4 \div 2 =$ ________
9. $8 \div 4 =$ ________
10. $18 \div 3 =$ ________
11. $16 \div 2 =$ ________
12. $8 \div 1 =$ ________
13. $20 \div 5 =$ ________
14. $18 \div 6 =$ ________
15. $14 \div 7 =$ ________
16. $15 \div 3 =$ ________
17. $32 \div 4 =$ ________
18. $24 \div 3 =$ ________
19. $9 \div 1 =$ ________
20. $45 \div 5 =$ ________
21. $24 \div 4 =$ ________
22. $14 \div 2 =$ ________
23. $3 \div 1 =$ ________
24. $25 \div 5 =$ ________
25. $12 \div 6 =$ ________
26. $21 \div 7 =$ ________
27. $12 \div 3 =$ ________
28. $16 \div 4 =$ ________
29. $7 \div 1 =$ ________
30. $18 \div 2 =$ ________

31. $9 \div 3 =$ ________
32. $4 \div 1 =$ ________
33. $42 \div 6 =$ ________
34. $30 \div 5 =$ ________
35. $4 \div 4 =$ ________
36. $30 \div 6 =$ ________
37. $24 \div 8 =$ ________
38. $6 \div 6 =$ ________
39. $6 \div 1 =$ ________
40. $35 \div 5 =$ ________
41. $28 \div 4 =$ ________
42. $42 \div 7 =$ ________
43. $40 \div 8 =$ ________
44. $24 \div 6 =$ ________
45. $3 \div 3 =$ ________
46. $10 \div 5 =$ ________
47. $36 \div 6 =$ ________
48. $56 \div 7 =$ ________
49. $40 \div 5 =$ ________
50. $28 \div 7 =$ ________
51. $2 \div 1 =$ ________
52. $12 \div 4 =$ ________
53. $48 \div 6 =$ ________
54. $32 \div 8 =$ ________
55. $27 \div 9 =$ ________
56. $5 \div 5 =$ ________
57. $35 \div 7 =$ ________
58. $16 \div 8 =$ ________
59. $1 \div 1 =$ ________
60. $63 \div 9 =$ ________
61. $48 \div 8 =$ ________
62. $7 \div 1 =$ ________
63. $56 \div 8 =$ ________
64. $36 \div 9 =$ ________
65. $7 \div 7 =$ ________
66. $64 \div 8 =$ ________
67. $63 \div 7 =$ ________
68. $72 \div 8 =$ ________
69. $49 \div 7 =$ ________
70. $45 \div 9 =$ ________
71. $54 \div 9 =$ ________
72. $8 \div 8 =$ ________
73. $27 \div 3 =$ ________
74. $18 \div 9 =$ ________
75. $2 \div 2 =$ ________
76. $72 \div 9 =$ ________
77. $36 \div 4 =$ ________
78. $54 \div 6 =$ ________
79. $8 \div 2 =$ ________
80. $81 \div 9 =$ ________

B

Find the quotient in each of the following exercises.

1. $48 \div 3 =$ ________
2. $52 \div 2 =$ ________
3. $81 \div 3 =$ ________
4. $86 \div 2 =$ ________
5. $75 \div 5 =$ ________
6. $85 \div 5 =$ ________
7. $64 \div 4 =$ ________
8. $76 \div 4 =$ ________
9. $92 \div 4 =$ ________
10. $84 \div 6 =$ ________
11. $96 \div 6 =$ ________
12. $98 \div 7 =$ ________
13. $135 \div 3 =$ ________
14. $192 \div 3 =$ ________
15. $207 \div 3 =$ ________
16. $184 \div 4 =$ ________
17. $256 \div 4 =$ ________
18. $384 \div 4 =$ ________
19. $512 \div 4 =$ ________
20. $628 \div 4 =$ ________
21. $235 \div 5 =$ ________
22. $430 \div 5 =$ ________
23. $675 \div 5 =$ ________
24. $590 \div 5 =$ ________
25. $324 \div 6 =$ ________
26. $504 \div 6 =$ ________
27. $744 \div 6 =$ ________
28. $828 \div 6 =$ ________
29. $161 \div 7 =$ ________
30. $245 \div 7 =$ ________

31. 336 ÷ 7 = ________ **32.** 469 ÷ 7 = ________
33. 256 ÷ 8 = ________ **34.** 360 ÷ 8 = ________
35. 504 ÷ 8 = ________ **36.** 768 ÷ 8 = ________
37. 198 ÷ 9 = ________ **38.** 387 ÷ 9 = ________
39. 666 ÷ 9 = ________ **40.** 954 ÷ 9 = ________

C

Find the quotient in each of the following exercises.

1. 384 ÷ 24 = ________ **2.** 480 ÷ 32 = ________
3. 525 ÷ 25 = ________ **4.** 414 ÷ 23 = ________
5. 351 ÷ 27 = ________ **6.** 805 ÷ 35 = ________
7. 608 ÷ 38 = ________ **8.** 943 ÷ 41 = ________
9. 1,058 ÷ 46 = ________ **10.** 1,813 ÷ 49 = ________
11. 1,508 ÷ 52 = ________ **12.** 1,512 ÷ 54 = ________
13. 322 ÷ 14 = ________ **14.** 592 ÷ 16 = ________
15. 846 ÷ 18 = ________ **16.** 663 ÷ 17 = ________
17. 3,712 ÷ 64 = ________ **18.** 2,275 ÷ 65 = ________
19. 5,628 ÷ 67 = ________ **20.** 3,456 ÷ 72 = ________
21. 4,056 ÷ 78 = ________ **22.** 5,644 ÷ 83 = ________
23. 6,192 ÷ 86 = ________ **24.** 7,644 ÷ 91 = ________

D

Find the quotient in each of the following exercises.

1. 4,500 ÷ 125 = ________ **2.** 3,289 ÷ 137 = ________
3. 7,290 ÷ 162 = ________ **4.** 10,672 ÷ 184 = ________
5. 4,738 ÷ 103 = ________ **6.** 7,004 ÷ 206 = ________
7. 34,036 ÷ 508 = ________ **8.** 58,546 ÷ 802 = ________
9. 9,933 ÷ 231 = ________ **10.** 9,288 ÷ 258 = ________
11. 8,424 ÷ 324 = ________ **12.** 32,376 ÷ 568 = ________
13. 48,766 ÷ 659 = ________ **14.** 62,264 ÷ 724 = ________
15. 61,539 ÷ 843 = ________ **16.** 54,834 ÷ 962 = ________
17. 25,235 ÷ 245 = ________ **18.** 75,235 ÷ 367 = ________
19. 267,208 ÷ 526 = ________ **20.** 447,811 ÷ 637 = ________

E

Find the quotient in each of the following exercises.

1. .54 ÷ .6 = ________ **2.** 4.2 ÷ .7 = ________
3. 56 ÷ .8 = ________ **4.** .24 ÷ .3 = ________
5. .02 ÷ .2 = ________ **6.** .2 ÷ .02 = ________
7. 8.4 ÷ .06 = ________ **8.** .85 ÷ .5 = ________

9. $81 \div .09$	= ________	**10.** $.72 \div .08$	= ________
11. $3.5 \div .1$	= ________	**12.** $.64 \div .04$	= ________
13. $156 \div 1.2$	= ________	**14.** $18.2 \div .13$	= ________
15. $.675 \div .25$	= ________	**16.** $1.116 \div 3.6$	= ________
17. $1.458 \div .54$	= ________	**18.** $.2294 \div .062$	= ________
19. $45.75 \div 7.5$	= ________	**20.** $1.29 \div .86$	= ________
21. $6.448 \div 1.04$	= ________	**22.** $826.8 \div 1.06$	= ________
23. $89.64 \div 1.08$	= ________	**24.** $1.0355 \div 1.09$	= ________

Section 2: Division of Fractions and Mixed Numbers

Division of fractions is performed by changing the operation to multiplication. To do this, you simply invert the divisor. The inverse of a fraction—sometimes called the *multiplicative inverse*—is a second fraction in which the numerator of the first fraction is the denominator of the second fraction and the denominator of the first fraction is the numerator of the second fraction. Thus:

$$\text{the inverse of } \frac{2}{5} \text{ is } \frac{5}{2}$$

Similarly, the inverse of $3/4$ is $4/3$. What is the inverse of $2/7$? Of $5/8$? Of $1/6$? Of $7/1$? Of 8?

ILLUSTRATION 1: Divide $2/3$ by $5/6$.

SOLUTION:

$$\frac{2}{3} \div \frac{5}{6} = \frac{2}{3} \times \frac{6}{5} = \frac{12}{15} = \frac{4 \times 3}{5 \times 3} = \frac{4}{5}$$

EXPLANATION: The operation is changed from division to multiplication by inverting the divisor. Thus, the exercise is changed from the form:

$$2/3 \div 5/6$$

to the form:

$$2/3 \times 6/5$$

and the computation is completed as in the case of the product of two fractions.

ILLUSTRATION 2: Divide $4/5$ by 8.

SOLUTION:

$$\frac{4}{5} \div 8 = \frac{4}{5} \div \frac{8}{1} = \frac{4}{5} \times \frac{1}{8} = \frac{4}{40} = \frac{1 \times 4}{10 \times 4} = \frac{1}{10}$$

EXPLANATION: Once you realize that the numeral 8 can be written in the form 8/1, the computation becomes identical with that of the previous illustration.

ILLUSTRATION 3: Divide $3\frac{1}{2}$ by $2\frac{1}{4}$.

SOLUTION:

$$3\tfrac{1}{2} \div 2\tfrac{1}{4} = \frac{7}{2} \div \frac{9}{4} = \frac{7}{2} \times \frac{4}{9} = \frac{28}{18} = \frac{14 \times 2}{9 \times 2}$$
$$= \frac{14}{9} = 1\tfrac{5}{9}$$

EXPLANATION: Each of the mixed numbers is changed to an improper fraction, and the solution is completed in the same manner as the two previous illustrations. If the mixed numbers are relatively large, change them to decimals and divide as was done in the illustration on page 509.

EXERCISES A

Find the quotient in each of the following exercises.

1. $3/5 \div 1/2 =$ ________ **2.** $1/2 \div 3/7 =$ ________
3. $5/4 \div 1/3 =$ ________ **4.** $1/4 \div 3/5 =$ ________
5. $2/3 \div 5/7 =$ ________ **6.** $3/4 \div 1/5 =$ ________
7. $4/5 \div 2/5 =$ ________ **8.** $1/6 \div 2/3 =$ ________
9. $5/6 \div 1/3 =$ ________ **10.** $3/8 \div 5/6 =$ ________
11. $5/8 \div 5/6 =$ ________ **12.** $1/6 \div 7/10 =$ ________
13. $7/8 \div 3/10 =$ ________ **14.** $3/8 \div 9/16 =$ ________
15. $2/3 \div 5/6 =$ ________ **16.** $3/5 \div 9/10 =$ ________
17. $3/8 \div 15/16 =$ ________ **18.** $5/8 \div 7/16 =$ ________
19. $3/10 \div 4/15 =$ ________ **20.** $8/9 \div 8/15 =$ ________
21. $7/10 \div 21/25 =$ ________ **22.** $5/9 \div 20/21 =$ ________

B

Find the quotient in each of the following exercises.

1. $8 \div 1/2 =$ ________ **2.** $10 \div 1/3 =$ ________
3. $6 \div 1/4 =$ ________ **4.** $12 \div 3/4 =$ ________
5. $16 \div 4/5 =$ ________ **6.** $10 \div 2/5 =$ ________
7. $4/5 \div 2 =$ ________ **8.** $3/5 \div 6 =$ ________
9. $1/2 \div 2 =$ ________ **10.** $5/9 \div 10 =$ ________
11. $5/8 \div 15 =$ ________ **12.** $3/8 \div 24 =$ ________

C

Find the quotient in each of the following exercises.

1. $1\frac{1}{2} \div 2 =$ ______	2. $3\frac{3}{4} \div 3 =$ ______
3. $4\frac{1}{2} \div 3 =$ ______	4. $3\frac{1}{5} \div 8 =$ ______
5. $4\frac{2}{3} \div 7 =$ ______	6. $5\frac{1}{4} \div 7 =$ ______
7. $6 \div 1\frac{1}{2} =$ ______	8. $10 \div 2\frac{1}{2} =$ ______
9. $3 \div 3\frac{1}{5} =$ ______	10. $24 \div 5\frac{1}{3} =$ ______
11. $18 \div 4\frac{1}{2} =$ ______	12. $14 \div 2\frac{5}{8} =$ ______

D

Find the quotient in each of the following exercises.

1. $2\frac{1}{2} \div 1\frac{1}{2} =$ ______	2. $2\frac{3}{4} \div 1\frac{1}{4} =$ ______
3. $3\frac{1}{2} \div 2\frac{1}{2} =$ ______	4. $1\frac{3}{4} \div 1\frac{1}{4} =$ ______
5. $2\frac{1}{3} \div 3\frac{1}{2} =$ ______	6. $3\frac{1}{4} \div 1\frac{1}{4} =$ ______
7. $4\frac{3}{4} \div 2\frac{3}{8} =$ ______	8. $1\frac{3}{4} \div 3\frac{1}{2} =$ ______
9. $5\frac{1}{4} \div 2\frac{1}{2} =$ ______	10. $6\frac{1}{2} \div 2\frac{1}{4} =$ ______
11. $5\frac{1}{4} \div 3\frac{1}{2} =$ ______	12. $7\frac{1}{2} \div 1\frac{7}{8} =$ ______

Unit 5: Percents

Section 1: Expressing Percent Numerals as Decimal Numerals and Decimal Numerals as Percent Numerals

A percent numeral is simply another way of expressing a fraction numeral where the denominator of that fraction is 100. For instance, the percent numeral 23% is but an equivalent form of the fraction 23/100. Similarly, 56% and 56/100 are equivalent; so are 3.5% and 3.5/100; and 125% and 125/100. Hence, each time you see the percent symbol, you should immediately think in terms of a fraction where the denominator of that fraction is 100.

ILLUSTRATION 1: Write the percent numeral 15% in its equivalent fractional form.

SOLUTION:

$$15\% = \frac{15}{100} = \frac{3 \times 5}{20 \times 5} = \frac{3}{20}$$

EXPLANATION: As noted above, the numerals 15% and 15/100 are equivalent. After writing 15% as 15/100, the fraction is reduced to lowest terms.

ILLUSTRATION 2: Write the percent numeral 6% in its equivalent decimal form.

SOLUTION:

$$6\% = \frac{6}{100} = .06$$

EXPLANATION: The numeral 6%, as you learned above, can be written in the fractional form of 6/100. But on page 498 you learned that the fraction numeral 6/100 can be expressed as the decimal .06. Hence, the percent numeral 6% and the decimal numeral .06 are equivalent.

You now know that each percent numeral can be expressed as a fraction numeral with 100 as its denominator. You also know that each fraction numeral having a denominator of 100 can be expressed as a decimal with two digits to the right of the decimal point. Therefore, you can say that a percent numeral can be expressed as a decimal numeral with two digits to the right of the decimal point. Thus:

$$\begin{aligned} 23\% &= .23 \\ 58\% &= .58 \\ 115\% &= 1.15 \end{aligned}$$

How would you express 46% as a decimal numeral? 65%? 96%? 127%? 8%?

Another way of examining the above is to realize that each of the numerals 23, 58, and 115 has a decimal point which, although it does not now appear in the numerals, can be written to the right of the last digit without in any way affecting the numerals. Thus, 23% is the same as 23.%, while 58% is the equivalent of 58.%. How can you write 115% with a decimal point and yet retain the percent symbol? Hence, if you rewrite each of the three equalities above and insert the missing decimal points, they become:

$$\begin{aligned} 23.\% &= .23_{\uparrow} \\ 58.\% &= .58_{\uparrow} \\ 115.\% &= 1.15_{\uparrow} \end{aligned}$$

We deliberately placed the arrows in the numerals at the right to show where the decimal points had been when the numbers were written in percent form. In each case, when the number was changed from its percent form to its decimal form, the decimal point was moved two places to the left of where it had been. This condition will always be true whenever a percent numeral is changed to a decimal numeral.

ILLUSTRATION 3: Write the percent numeral $4\frac{1}{2}\%$ in its equivalent decimal form.

SOLUTION:

$$4\tfrac{1}{2}\% = 4.5\% = .04_{\uparrow}5$$

EXPLANATION: Before trying to change the mixed numeral percent value $4\frac{1}{2}\%$ to a decimal, it is best first to write it as 4.5%. Now the problem reduces to the simple situation of merely moving the decimal point two places to the left of where it appears in its percent form. The arrow points to where it had been. It also shows that the decimal point is now two places to the left of where the arrow is.

To change a number from its decimal form to its equivalent percent form involves nothing more than reversing the process just learned. Since you move the decimal point two places to the left in changing from a percent to a decimal, you will now move the decimal point two places to the right to change from a decimal to a percent form.

ILLUSTRATION 4: Write the decimal numeral .085 in its equivalent percent form.

SOLUTION:

$$.085 = {}_{\uparrow}08.5\%, \text{ or } 8.5\%$$

EXPLANATION: The arrow shows where the decimal point had been when the number was written as a decimal. In the percent form, it is two places farther to the right.

EXERCISES A

Write each of the following percent numerals as equivalent decimal numerals.

1. 15%	________	**2.** 26%	________	**3.** 53%	________
4. 72%	________	**5.** 93%	________	**6.** 31%	________
7. 49%	________	**8.** 67%	________	**9.** 85%	________
10. 14%	________	**11.** 60%	________	**12.** 70%	________
13. 80%	________	**14.** 90%	________	**15.** 10%	________
16. 2%	________	**17.** 8%	________	**18.** 3%	________
19. 5%	________	**20.** 7%	________	**21.** 124%	________
22. 136%	________	**23.** 158%	________	**24.** 235%	________
25. 375%	________	**26.** 150%	________	**27.** 250%	________
28. 140%	________	**29.** 320%	________	**30.** 460%	________
31. 100%	________	**32.** 200%	________	**33.** 300%	________
34. 400%	________	**35.** 500%	________	**36.** 26.5%	________
37. 47.8%	________	**38.** 52.3%	________	**39.** 34.6%	________

40. 367% ________ **41.** 3.5% ________ **42.** 6.5% ________
43. 4.2% ________ **44.** 5.7% ________ **45.** 9.3% ________
46. 105.4% ________ **47.** 207.8% ________ **48.** 184.7% ________
49. 169.1% ________ **50.** 300.2% ________ **51.** 14.65% ________
52. 29.37% ________ **53.** 51.04% ________ **54.** 62.71% ________
55. 84.39% ________ **56.** 2.54% ________ **57.** 4.65% ________
58. 3.75% ________ **59.** 5.25% ________ **60.** 6.35% ________
61. .045% ________ **62.** .058% ________ **63.** .074% ________
64. .0956% ________ **65.** .0682% ________ **66.** .0904% ________

B

Write each of the following percent numerals as equivalent decimal numerals.

1. $14\frac{1}{2}\%$ ________ **2.** $16\frac{1}{2}\%$ ________ **3.** $21\frac{1}{2}\%$ ________
4. $53\frac{1}{2}\%$ ________ **5.** $67\frac{1}{2}\%$ ________ **6.** $8\frac{1}{2}\%$ ________
7. $4\frac{1}{2}\%$ ________ **8.** $3\frac{1}{2}\%$ ________ **9.** $6\frac{1}{2}\%$ ________
10. $1\frac{1}{2}\%$ ________ **11.** $128\frac{1}{2}\%$ ________ **12.** $157\frac{1}{2}\%$ ________
13. $220\frac{1}{2}\%$ ________ **14.** $325\frac{1}{2}\%$ ________ **15.** $450\frac{1}{2}\%$ ________
16. $27\frac{1}{4}\%$ ________ **17.** $86\frac{1}{4}\%$ ________ **18.** $37\frac{1}{4}\%$ ________
19. $72\frac{1}{4}\%$ ________ **20.** $93\frac{1}{4}\%$ ________ **21.** $5\frac{1}{4}\%$ ________
22. $7\frac{1}{4}\%$ ________ **23.** $8\frac{1}{4}\%$ ________ **24.** $1\frac{1}{4}\%$ ________
25. $3\frac{1}{4}\%$ ________ **26.** $158\frac{1}{4}\%$ ________ **27.** $194\frac{1}{4}\%$ ________
28. $237\frac{1}{4}\%$ ________ **29.** $205\frac{1}{4}\%$ ________ **30.** $370\frac{1}{4}\%$ ________
31. $32\frac{3}{4}\%$ ________ **32.** $47\frac{3}{4}\%$ ________ **33.** $61\frac{3}{4}\%$ ________
34. $80\frac{3}{4}\%$ ________ **35.** $76\frac{3}{4}\%$ ________ **36.** $6\frac{3}{4}\%$ ________
37. $9\frac{3}{4}\%$ ________ **38.** $3\frac{3}{4}\%$ ________ **39.** $7\frac{3}{4}\%$ ________
40. $2\frac{3}{4}\%$ ________ **41.** $116\frac{3}{4}\%$ ________ **42.** $100\frac{3}{4}\%$ ________
43. $200\frac{3}{4}\%$ ________ **44.** $150\frac{3}{4}\%$ ________ **45.** $250\frac{3}{4}\%$ ________

C

Write each of the following decimal numerals as equivalent percent numerals.

1. .54 ________ **2.** .76 ________ **3.** .42 ________
4. .85 ________ **5.** .93 ________ **6.** .27 ________
7. .19 ________ **8.** .30 ________ **9.** .40 ________
10. .67 ________ **11.** .04 ________ **12.** .05 ________
13. .06 ________ **14.** .09 ________ **15.** .01 ________
16. .07 ________ **17.** .02 ________ **18.** .08 ________
19. .03 ________ **20.** .10 ________ **21.** 1.25 ________
22. 2.50 ________ **23.** 1.75 ________ **24.** 1.50 ________

25. 1.46 ________	**26.** 3.47 ________	**27.** 3.10 ________
28. 2.05 ________	**29.** 1.07 ________	**30.** 1.01 ________
31. .145 ________	**32.** .267 ________	**33.** .394 ________
34. .876 ________	**35.** .105 ________	**36.** .283 ________
37. .504 ________	**38.** .309 ________	**39.** .324 ________
40. .207 ________	**41.** .065 ________	**42.** .073 ________
43. .058 ________	**44.** .061 ________	**45.** .027 ________

D

Write each of the following percent numerals as fraction numerals.

1. 27% ________	**2.** 53% ________	**3.** 89% ________
4. 19% ________	**5.** 47% ________	**6.** 13% ________
7. 49% ________	**8.** 23% ________	**9.** 97% ________
10. 31% ________	**11.** 7% ________	**12.** 3% ________
13. 9% ________	**14.** 1% ________	**15.** 17% ________
16. 119% ________	**17.** 137% ________	**18.** 143% ________
19. 151% ________	**20.** 169% ________	**21.** 203% ________
22. 207% ________	**23.** 229% ________	**24.** 247% ________
25. 281% ________	**26.** 10% ________	**27.** 20% ________
28. 30% ________	**29.** 40% ________	**30.** 50% ________
31. 60% ________	**32.** 70% ________	**33.** 80% ________
34. 90% ________	**35.** 25% ________	**36.** 75% ________
37. 5% ________	**38.** 15% ________	**39.** 35% ________
40. 45% ________	**41.** 100% ________	**42.** 200% ________
43. 300% ________	**44.** 400% ________	**45.** 500% ________
46. 150% ________	**47.** 250% ________	**48.** 350% ________
49. 125% ________	**50.** 175% ________	**51.** 225% ________
52. 120% ________	**53.** 140% ________	**54.** 260% ________

Section 2: Practical Applications of Percent

The practical applications of percent depend on an understanding of the following principle.

> The Product of Two Numbers Principle: If the product of two numbers is divided by one of these numbers, the quotient will be the other of the numbers.

As an example of this principle, consider the situation where the product of 7 and 5 is 35, that is,

$$35 = 7 \times 5$$

Now, should the 35 be divided by either the 7 or the 5, the quotient will be the other of these two numbers. Thus,

$$35 \div 7 = 5$$
or
$$35 \div 5 = 7$$

The illustration below is designed to show you how this principle is applied.

ILLUSTRATION 1: Find the replacement for n in the sentence

$$5 \times n = 85$$

that will make this sentence true.

EXPLANATION: The sentence above states that 85 is the product of two numbers, where one of these numbers is 5. Hence, by the Product of Two Numbers Principle, you know that if the product, 85, is divided by 5, the quotient will have to be the replacement for n.

SOLUTION:

$$5 \times n = 85$$
Therefore, $n = 85 \div 5$
or, $n = 17$

There are just two other simple ideas that have to be clarified and one of these is the interpretation of the word "of." For instance, consider the situation where you had been fishing with a group of people and were told that you could keep "3/4 of the 8" fish that were caught. Quite apparently, the number of fish you would take home would be 6. This number is arrived at by finding the product of 3/4 and 8. Thus,

3/4 of 8

is the same as,

$$3/4 \times 8$$

And in general it is true that whenever the word "of" appears in connection with computation in arithmetic, it will imply the operation of multiplication.

ILLUSTRATION 2: Find 40% of 148.

EXPLANATION: The solution here simply involves replacing the word "of" with the multiplication sign and then finding the product of 40% and 148. However, before this can be done it is necessary to rewrite the numeral 40% in its equivalent decimal form of .40.

SOLUTION:

$$
\begin{aligned}
40\% \text{ of } 148 &= 40\% \times 148 \\
&= .40 \times 148 \\
&= 59.20
\end{aligned}
$$

The other simple but important idea that is needed at this time is the understanding that the word "is" implies the word "equals" in any mathematical situation. Thus, in the statement,

"The number 12 is 3 times the number 4."

the word "is" can be replaced by the equality sign and this statement then becomes,

12 = 3 times the number 4

And, of course, the word "times" can be replaced by the multiplication sign thus changing this statement to,

$$12 = 3 \times 4$$

Similarly, the question, "15 is what percent of 60?" can be rewritten with symbols as, $15 = P \times 60$.

Notice that the word "is" is replaced by the equality sign and the word "of" is replaced by the multiplication sign. In addition, rather than write the words "what percent," we have merely written the letter "P." Finding the value of "P" involves nothing more than an application of The Product of Two Numbers Principle, that is,

$$
\begin{aligned}
& & P &= 15 \div 60 \\
&\text{or} & P &= .25 \\
&\text{therefore} & P &= 25\%
\end{aligned}
$$

Although "P" was originally found as the decimal .25, it had to be changed to the percent numeral 25% since the problem asked "what percent" and not "what decimal."

ILLUSTRATION 3: A shirt that normally sells for $7.95 was reduced 35% during a sale. By how much was the shirt reduced?

EXPLANATION: At the very outset it is best to reword the question so that it is similar to the question in the illustration above. In this situation the question can be stated as,

"What number is 35% of $7.95?"

At this point you simply replace each of the words with a symbol. Rather than "what number," you write the letter "N"; in place of "is" the equality sign appears; and finally, the word "of" is replaced with the multiplication sign. Hence, the question above becomes,

$$N = 35\% \times \$7.95$$

The computation is completed by finding the product of 35% and $7.95.

SOLUTION:

What number is 35% of $7.95?

$$N = 35\% \times \$7.95$$
$$N = .35 \times \$7.95$$
$$N = \$2.78 \text{ (amount reduced)}$$

ILLUSTRATION 4: Last year Artco Products employed 80 people. This year it employs only 65 people. By what percent did its employment drop over the past year?

EXPLANATION: Before it is possible to determine the "percent of increase," or the "percent of gain," or the "percent of decrease," or the "percent of loss," it is always necessary to first know the *amount of increase*, or the *amount of gain*, or *the amount of decrease*, or the *amount of loss*. This would hold true for all situations involving "percent more" or "percent less." In this illustration the question is reworded as,

"The decrease in the number of employees is what percent of the original number employed?"

In place of "the decrease in the number of employees," the number "15" is written; replacing "is" is the equality sign; replacing "what percent" is the letter "P"; and finally, replacing "original number employed" is the number 80. Hence, the question above becomes,

$$15 = P \times 80$$

The value of "P" is now found by using The Product of Two Numbers Principle. It should be noted that the *percent of increase* or the *percent of decrease* is always based on the *earlier* of the two numbers that are involved. In this situation the percent of decrease is based on the 80 people who were originally employed.

SOLUTION:

The decrease in the number of employees is what percent of the original number employed?

$$15 = P \times 80$$
$$P = 15 \div 80$$
$$P = .1875$$
$$P = 18.75\%$$

EXERCISES

A

Find the product in each of the following.

1. 500 × 2% = ________
2. 350 × 4% = ________
3. 740 × 5% = ________
4. 960 × 6% = ________
5. 2,300 × 8% = ________
6. 4,500 × 9% = ________
7. 400 × 5.5% = ________
8. 700 × 6.5% = ________
9. 3,700 × 8.5% = ________
10. 4,000 × 10.5% = ________
11. 2,000 × 6.25% = ________
12. 5,000 × 6.75% = ________

B

Find the product in each of the following.

1. 400 × 5% × 2 = ________
2. 300 × 4% × 3 = ________
3. 600 × 7% × 5 = ________
4. 800 × 5% × 3/4 = ________
5. 900 × 8% × 1/2 = ________
6. 1,200 × 9% × 1/3 = ________
7. 1,600 × 10% × 3/4 = ________
8. 2,000 × 8% × 2/5 = ________
9. 500 × .325% × 20 = ________
10. 900 × .461% × 40 = ________
11. 6,000 × .0356% × 100 = ________
12. 8,000 × .0541% × 80 = ________

C

Find the number requested in each of the following.

1. 25% of 40 = ________
2. 50% of 70 = ________
3. 10% of 150 = ________
4. 30% of 200 = ________
5. 80% of 400 = ________
6. 75% of 12 = ________
7. 2% of 600 = ________
8. 5% of 300 = ________
9. 9% of 800 = ________
10. 16% of 700 = ________
11. 125% of 80 = ________
12. 150% of 38 = ________
13. 100% of 92 = ________
14. 200% of 85 = ________
15. 400% of 67 = ________
16. 900% of 146 = ________
17. 250% of 64 = ________
18. 325% of 24 = ________
19. 16.5% of 38 = ________
20. 14.4% of 170 = ________
21. 23.7% of 310 = ________
22. 46.1% of 430 = ________
23. 2.3% of 75 = ________
24. 5.8% of 560 = ________
25. 4.9% of 148 = ________
26. 6.4% of 212 = ________

27. 7.61% of 500 = ______		**28.** 3.47% of 2,000 = ______	
29. 3½% of 50 = ______		**30.** 4½% of 160 = ______	
31. 7½% of 240 = ______		**32.** 14½% of 96 = ______	
33. 5¼% of 500 = ______		**34.** 6¼% of 1,200 = ______	
35. 1¼% of 180 = ______		**36.** 10¼% of 230 = ______	
37. 6¾% of 2,100 = ______		**38.** 3¾% of 3,600 = ______	
39. 15¾% of 4,500 = ______		**40.** 20¾% of 5,800 = ______	

D

Find the number requested in each of the following problems.

1. 10 is what percent of 40? ______
2. 30 is what percent of 150? ______
3. 50 is what percent of 40? ______
4. 60 is what percent of 80? ______
5. 50 is what percent of 25? ______
6. 75 is what percent of 50? ______
7. 72 is what percent of 60? ______
8. 126 is what percent of 90? ______
9. 18 is what percent of 30? ______
10. 96 is what percent of 128? ______
11. $3 is what percent of $30? ______
12. $15 is what percent of $300? ______
13. $36 is what percent of $450? ______
14. $123 is what percent of $2,050? ______
15. $252 is what percent of $3,150? ______
16. $51 is what percent of $340? ______
17. $117 is what percent of $180? ______
18. $26 is what percent of $208? ______
19. $123 is what percent of $328? ______
20. $371 is what percent of $424? ______
21. $3.12 is what percent of $39? ______
22. $10.92 is what percent of $84? ______
23. $66.42 is what percent of $54? ______
24. $4.56 is what percent of $28.50? ______
25. $2.50 is what percent of $12.50? ______
26. $13.16 is what percent of $23.50? ______
27. $30.24 is what percent of $47.25? ______
28. $23.52 is what percent of $24.50? ______
29. $94.83 is what percent of $65.40? ______
30. $276.42 is what percent of $135.50? ______

E

Find the number requested in each of the following problems.

1. 15 is what percent more than 10? ________
2. 20 is what percent more than 16? ________
3. 35 is what percent more than 20? ________
4. 33 is what percent more than 30? ________
5. 70 is what percent more than 50? ________
6. 18 is what percent less than 24? ________
7. 63 is what percent less than 140? ________
8. 108 is what percent less than 150? ________
9. 231 is what percent less than 275? ________
10. 61 is what percent less than 244? ________

F

Solve each of the following problems.

1. In a basket of 80 peaches, 5% of them were spotted. How many of the peaches were spotted? ________
2. Tires that normally sell for $32 were reduced 25% during a sale. By how much was each tire reduced in price? ________
3. During one year, the price of gasoline rose 20¢ per gallon. If it had sold for 38¢ a gallon, what was the percent of increase? ________
4. The state tax is 4½% of the selling price of an article. How much tax will have to be paid on a suit that sells for $98.80? ________
5. Two years ago, a certain brand shirt could be purchased for $4.50. This same shirt now costs $5.22. What was the percent of increase over the two-year period? ________
6. Mr. Burke has a take-home pay of $150 per week. If $42 of this amount is budgeted for food, what percent of his take-home pay is needed for this item? ________
7. Jim's car was giving him 14 miles to the gallon of gasoline. By replacing the spark plugs and the points, he found that his gasoline mileage is now 125% of what it had been. How many miles to the gallon is Jim now getting from his car? ________
8. Ed has a part-time after-school job. When he first started working, he earned $2.20 an hour. At present, his hourly salary is $2.75. What percent of increase in hourly pay has he received? ________
9. Mrs. Riley has a charge account on which she has to pay a charge of 1½% per month on the unpaid monthly balance. How much will the charge be during a month in which she had a balance of $46? ________

10. Mr. Jacobs purchased stock in a company at $75 a share. When he recently sold the stock, he received only $61.50 for each share. By what percent did the value of the stock decrease? ________

Unit 6: Rounding Off Numbers

Although rounding off numbers is relatively simple, the difficulty arises over the many different ways various individuals prefer to do it. Thus, some businessmen will round off the cost of a sale to the nearest penny, while others will always round off the cost to the next higher penny. Social security computation is rounded off to the next higher dime, while the internal revenue department wants you to complete your income tax form by rounding off each amount to the nearest dollar. In some computation, it is best to round off an answer to the nearest whole number, while in others, the nearest tenth, or nearest hundredth, or even the nearest thousandth is best.

Here are a few of the ways numbers can be rounded off. Consider the following number:

		tenth	hundredth	thousandth	ten thousandth
7	6.	2	8	3	5

If you want to round off this number to the nearest tenth, you will examine the digit immediately to the right of the tenth's digit. If that number is a 5 or greater, you will add 1 to the tenth's digit and drop all other digits to its right. On the other hand, if that digit is less than 5, that is, a 4, 3, 2, 1, or 0, you will add nothing to the tenth's digit, but merely drop all digits to its right. Thus, in the number above, the digit to the right of the tenth's digit is an 8. Since this is greater than 5, you add 1 to the tenth's digit, thus making it a 3, and drop the digits to its right. Hence, 76.2835, when rounded off to the nearest tenth, becomes 76.3.

To round off the number above to the nearest hundredth, again examine the digit immediately to its right. In this case, the digit to the right is a 3. Since 3 is less than 5, simply drop all digits to the right of the hundredth's digit and leave the answer as 76.28. What will the above number be when rounded off to the nearest thousandth?

When a number is to be rounded off to the nearest whole number, it implies that no digits are to appear to the right of the decimal point. In such cases, you examine the first digit to the right of the decimal point and, as before, if it is 5 or greater, you increase the digit to the left of the decimal point by 1; if it is less than 5, the digit to the left of the decimal point remains the same. In either event, all digits to the right of the decimal point are dropped. In rounding off the number 76.2835 to the nearest whole number, you examine the digit 2, which is the first digit to the right of the decimal point. Since this digit is less than 5, you do not increase the 6, which is the first digit to the left of the decimal point. After dropping all digits to the right of the decimal point, you find that the number 76.2835, when rounded off to the nearest whole number, becomes 76.

ILLUSTRATION 1: Round off 376.8054 to the nearest hundredth.

EXPLANATION: To round off this number to the nearest hundredth, examine the first digit to the right of the hundredth's digit. Since this is a 5, you must add 1 to the hundredth's digit and drop all digits to its right.

376.8054
↑

SOLUTION:

The number 376.8054, when rounded off to the nearest hundredth, will be 376.81

ILLUSTRATION 2: Round off the number $45.632 to the nearest cent.

EXPLANATION: Since the 2, which is the first digit to the right of 3 cents, is less than 5, it is dropped. The procedure here is the same as in the previous illustration.

SOLUTION:

The number $45.632, when rounded off to the nearest cent, will be $45.63.

ILLUSTRATION 3: Round off the number $45.632 to the next higher cent.

EXPLANATION: When reading a number in dollars and cents, you need but two digits to the right of the decimal point for the cents amount. For the moment, ignore the third digit to the right of the decimal point. By doing this, the amount becomes 45 dollars and 63 cents. Since the third digit of 2 does represent some small amount of money (2 tenths of a cent), and since you are asked to round off the number to the next higher cent, the amount will be 45 dollars and 64 cents.

SOLUTION:

The number $45.632, when rounded off to the next higher cent, will be $45.64.

ILLUSTRATION 4: Round off the number $45.63 to the nearest dime.

EXPLANATION: The dime amount less than $45.63 is $45.60, while the dime amount greater than $45.63 is $45.70. Since 63¢ is closer to 60¢ than to 70¢, the answer is $45.60.

SOLUTION:

The number $45.63, when rounded off to the nearest dime, is $45.60

Had you been asked in Illustration 4 to round off the number to the next 10¢ or dime amount, the answer would have been $45.70. A difficulty arises when you round off a number, such as $54.92, to the next dime amount. When this is done, the next dime amount will be 100 cents. Hence, you change 54 dollars to 55 dollars, and your answer becomes $55.00. How would you round off $29.94 to the next higher dime?

ILLUSTRATION 5: Round off the number $39.63 to the nearest dollar.

EXPLANATION: This problem is the same as one in which you are asked to round off a number to the nearest whole number. In this case, you look at the first digit to the right of the decimal point. Since it is a 6 and, therefore, greater than 5, the number to the left of the decimal point is increased by 1. Increasing 9 by 1 makes it a 10, which, in turn, makes the number 39 a 40.

SOLUTION:

The number $39.63, when rounded off to the nearest dollar, is $40.

EXERCISES A

Round off each of the following numbers to the nearest tenth.

1. 23.41 ________	**2.** 35.82 ________	**3.** 47.68 ________
4. 64.17 ________	**5.** 58.05 ________	**6.** 42.96 ________
7. 87.98 ________	**8.** 79.97 ________	**9.** 69.05 ________

B

Round off each of the following numbers to the nearest hundredth.

1. 41.672 ________	2. 58.593 ________	3. 34.876 ________
4. 42.935 ________	5. 60.197 ________	6. 21.399 ________
7. 72.998 ________	8. 89.996 ________	9. 49.095 ________

C

Round off each of the following numbers to the nearest whole number.

1. 67.21 ________	2. 84.73 ________	3. 95.04 ________
4. 68.54 ________	5. 123.75 ________	6. 146.49 ________
7. 181.39 ________	8. 117.92 ________	9. 329.82 ________
10. 439.59 ________	11. 619.49 ________	12. 499.61 ________

D

Round off each of the following numbers to the nearest cent.

1. \$4.672 ________	2. \$5.837 ________	3. \$2.835 ________
4. \$6.027 ________	5. \$12.291 ________	6. \$16.396 ________
7. \$27.898 ________	8. \$35.993 ________	9. \$46.996 ________
10. \$59.991 ________	11. \$59.998 ________	12. \$99.999 ________

E

Round off each of the following numbers to the next higher cent.

1. \$6.341 ________	2. \$1.542 ________	3. \$.623 ________
4. \$.836 ________	5. \$27.752 ________	6. \$35.849 ________
7. \$62.291 ________	8. \$49.992 ________	9. \$29.905 ________

F

Round off each of the following numbers to the nearest dime.

1. \$2.34 ________	2. \$4.61 ________	3. \$5.86 ________
4. \$9.12 ________	5. \$16.43 ________	6. \$27.02 ________
7. \$84.07 ________	8. \$53.55 ________	9. \$67.93 ________
10. \$85.96 ________	11. \$39.91 ________	12. \$89.97 ________

G

Round off each of the following numbers to the next higher dime.

1. \$3.21 ________	2. \$4.57 ________	3. \$6.03 ________
4. \$8.15 ________	5. \$35.89 ________	6. \$43.01 ________
7. \$51.45 ________	8. \$69.91 ________	9. \$39.96 ________

H

Round off each of the following numbers to the nearest dollar.

1. $7.23 ________	**2.** $5.48 ________	**3.** $6.87 ________
4. $2.16 ________	**5.** $32.59 ________	**6.** $44.80 ________
7. $53.49 ________	**8.** $68.50 ________	**9.** $157.08 ________
10. $126.46 ________	**11.** $109.63 ________	**12.** $129.40 ________
13. $349.75 ________	**14.** $299.20 ________	**15.** $399.50 ________

I

Round off each of the following numbers as indicated.

1. 12.347 to the nearest tenth ________
2. 16.482 to the nearest hundredth ________
3. 11.271 to the nearest tenth ________
4. 24.693 to the nearest whole number ________
5. 58.529 to the nearest hundredth ________
6. 69.891 to the nearest tenth ________
7. 40.497 to the nearest whole number ________
8. 39.952 to the nearest tenth ________
9. 49.967 to the nearest hundredth ________
10. 69.991 to the nearest hundredth ________
11. 79.992 to the nearest tenth ________
12. 99.593 to the nearest whole number ________

J

Round off each of the following numbers as indicated.

1. $14.673 to the nearest cent ________
2. $18.226 to the nearest cent ________
3. $24.61 to the nearest dime ________
4. $34.52 to the next higher dime ________
5. $41.273 to the next higher penny ________
6. $67.41 to the nearest dollar ________
7. $59.236 to the nearest cent ________
8. $29.92 to the nearest dime ________
9. $29.92 to the next higher dime ________
10. $59.50 to the nearest dollar ________
11. $31.295 to the nearest penny ________
12. $31.295 to the next higher penny ________
13. $49.63 to the nearest dollar ________
14. $99.91 to the next higher dime ________
15. $99.91 to the nearest dollar ________

INDEX